Advanced Level MATHEMATICS

4th Edition

R C Solomon M.A., Ph.D.

Bob Solomon has spent many years teaching and writing for mathematics at this level. In addition to this book, he has also written a series for Key Stage 4.

Letts Educational
Schools and Colleges
9–15 Aldine Street
London W12 8AW

1997

To:

HOULDSWORTH HOUSE

From: Bev. 2005

Acknowledgements

I am very grateful to the following examination authorities for their permission to reproduce past examination questions.

The source of the questions is denoted by the letters in square brackets; questions from Additional Mathematics papers are indicated by *add* after the letters of the board.

The Associated Examining Board	[AEB]
University of Cambridge Local Examinations Syndicate	[C]
The Joint Matriculation Board	[JMB]
London Examinations, A division of Edexcel Foundation	[EDEXCEL]
Northern Ireland Schools Examinations Council	[NI]
University of Oxford Delegacy of Local Examinations	[O]
Oxford and Cambridge Schools Examination Board	[O&C]
The School Mathematics Project	[SMP]
The Mathematics in Education and Industry Project	[MEI]
Southern Universities Joint Board	[SUJB]
Welsh Joint Education Committee	[W]

The solutions at the back of the book are the responsibility of the author, and have neither been provided nor approved by the boards.

A CIP catalogue record for this book is available from the British Library

ISBN 1 84085 000 0

Copyright R C Solomon © 1997

First Edition 1988
Reprinted 1990
Second Edition 1992
Third Edition 1995
Fourth Edition 1997

Printed in Great Britain by Hillman Printers (Frome) Ltd

Preface

Aim

The aim of this book is to provide all the support needed for a course in Advanced Level Mathematics. The book covers, in one volume, the Pure Mathematics, Mechanics and Statistics that are included in the syllabuses for single subject Mathematics at Advanced Level.

It is assumed that the principles of the subject have been taught, and the book contains all the extra material needed, such as course notes, examples, exercises, examination questions and answers.

Need

Many Advanced Level examination questions cover at least two topics. In the author's experience candidates have difficulty tackling these questions, both through a lack of a full understanding of the topics in the syllabus, and from inability to recognise combinations of topics.

The need was seen for a book which helped to achieve the required full understanding by:

(a) assuming the teacher to have explained the principles etc.,

(b) reminding candidates of the principles/formulae involved,

(c) giving graded examples and graded drill exercises in each of the syllabus topics, as well as examination level questions involving combinations of topics,

(d) pointing out common errors made by candidates.

Approach

The main body of the text consists of 44 chapters, divided into three sections as follows:

(a) Pure Mathematics (including the Mathematics of Uncertainty)

(b) Mechanics

(c) Statistics.

Each chapter is divided into topics, each of which includes a statement of principles and formulae, worked examples and graded routine exercises.

At the end of each chapter there is a list of common errors in each topic, and several questions taken from examination papers of the examination boards.

Candidates for AS-level Mathematics should find that the questions from Additional Mathematics papers are at a suitable level of difficulty. Hints for the solution of some of these questions appear in the answer section of the book.

Information to show which topics are required for the various examining boards will be provided in a chart at the start of the book.

At the end of the book there are test papers in the style and syllabuses of four examining boards.

Complete answers are provided.

Preface to Second Edition

I am very grateful for the suggestions provided by users of this book. One suggestion, for a section on algebra, has been incorporated as an appendix.

Several boards now offer modular A and AS level syllabuses, and four exam papers in the modular style have been included.

May 1992

Preface to Third Edition

This book has been thoroughly revised in accordance with the changed syllabus which will be examined from 1996 onwards. Some topics have been removed and others inserted. In particular, elements of probability and statistics now form part of the Pure syllabus.

The section on GCSE algebra has been expanded into a Consolidation and Revision Section for GCSE.

An increasing number of examination boards now offer a modular syllabus for A level. Candidates can acquire an AS level by taking a number of the A level modules. The exam papers at the end of the book have been written to take account of this.

R C Solomon
1997

Contents

Pure Mathematics

Mechanics

Statistics

Exam papers

Solutions

Study and examination hints

1 Study hints

This book has been written to help you pass A-level or AS-level in Mathematics. Of course it must be used in an efficient way. The following hints will help you to make good use of your study time.

A good rule to follow is: *Little but often*. An hour a day for seven days is more useful than seven hours of work on a single day.

Make sure you get a full 60 minutes out of every hour. Do your study in as quiet a room as possible, with all your equipment to hand, and with as few distractions as possible. Do not try to combine study with watching television or eating.

Write as well as read. There is little to be gained from simply reading Mathematics. Read the topic outlines and the worked examples, and then try the exercises. Write down the solutions, do not try to convince yourself that you can do them in your head.

Do not give in too soon. There are answers at the back of the book, but use them for checking that you are right, rather than for finding out how to do a problem.

The test papers at the back of the book should be done under test conditions, with a time limit and no reference books. In all exams you are allowed to use a calculator - make sure that you are confident in its use.

In A-level work it is assumed that you are familiar with GCSE work. In particular, you must be confident and accurate with algebraic operations. Questions are not set directly on this, but fairly complicated algebra is used in all parts of A-level Mathematics.

2 Examination hints

How well you do in an examination depends mainly on how well you have prepared for it. But many candidates do poorly because of bad examination technique. The following hints will help you make the most out of your examination time.

Read the question carefully. Very many marks are lost by candidates who have misunderstood a question. Not only do they lose the marks for that question, but they also lose time because the question is often made more complicated by their mistake.

Do not spend too much time on any one question. There is no point in spending a third of the time on a question which carries a twentieth of the marks. Leave that question, and come back to it later if you have time at the end of the exam.

Show your working. If you obtain the wrong answer just because of a slight slip, then you will not lose many marks provided that you show all your working. If you put down the wrong answer without any explanation then you will get no marks at all.

Try to make your solutions neat. Use enough paper to ensure that your answer can be read easily. But do not spend too much time on this - there is no point in spending five minutes on a beautiful diagram for a question which is only worth two marks.

Recognise what each question is about. Many candidates find that they can answer a question when they are doing an exercise consisting of several similar problems, but cannot answer the same question when it occurs in a test paper surrounded by different questions. Read each question carefully, and identify the topic or topics of the question. The examiner is not trying to "catch you out", but he is trying to test that you have studied each part of the syllabus and are able to answer questions on it.

Recognise combinations of topics. Many questions start with a problem in one area of Mathematics, and then require you to apply your answer to another, but related, area. Make sure that you appreciate what the examiner is looking for.

Above all: *Make good use of your time!* During the months that you are preparing yourself for the examination make sure that each hour of learning or revision is well spent. During the actual examination make sure that you do not waste the precious minutes!

Syllabus analysis

This book covers the syllabus for single subject Mathematics for the large majority of candidates.

The examining authorities describe the contents of their syllabuses in different ways. The following tables are therefore not an exact guide.

Key for boards

A = Associated Examining Board. (AEB)

Modular scheme.

A1 (Pure Mathematics)

A2 (Statistics)

A3 (Mechanics)

A-level: two modules. AS-level: one module.

C = Cambridge Examination Syndicate. (UCLES)

Linear Scheme

C1 (Pure)

C2 (Pure + Mechanics + Statistics)

C3 (Pure + Mechanics)

C4 (Pure + Statistics).

A-level: C1 and one of C2, C3 or C4.

Modular Scheme

CP1, CP2, CP3 (Pure)

CM1, CM2, CM3 (Mechanics)

CS1, CS2 (Statistics)

A-level: six modules, e.g. CP1, CP2, CP3, CM1, CM2, CM3.

AS-level: three modules, e.g. CP1, CP2, CS1

L = London Examinations Council. (ULEAC)

Modular Scheme

LP1, LP2 (Pure)

LM1, LM2 (Mechanics)

LS1, LS2 (Statistics)

A-Level: four modules, e.g. LP1, LP2, LM1, LM2

AS-level: two modules, e.g. LP1, LS1

N = Northern Examining Board. (NEAB).

Modular scheme

N1 (Methods and Applied I)

N2 (Methods and Applied II)

N3 (Methods and Mechanics)

N4 (Methods and Statistics)

A-level: two modules, e.g. N1 and N3

AS-level: one module, e.g. N1.

MEI = Mathematics in Education and Industry.

Modular scheme

MP1, MP2, MP3 (Pure)

MM1, MM2, MM3 (Mechanics)

MS1, MS2, MS3 (Statistics)

A-level: six modules, e.g. MP1, MP2, MP3, MM1, MM2, MM3.

AS-level: three modules, e.g. MP1, MP2, MS1

Pure syllabus

| | *Syllabuses* | | | | | |
	A	*C* *Lin*	*C* *Mod*	*L*	*N*	*MEI*
Chapter 1 Polynomials						
Algebra of Polynomials	A1	C1	CP1	LP1	N1	MP1
Remainder and Factor Theorems	A1	C1	CP1	LP2	N2	MP1
Partial Fractions	A1	C1		LP2	N2	MP3
Chapter 2 APs and GPs						
Arithmetic Progressions	A1	C1	CP2	LP1	N1	MP2
Geometric Progs., sum to ∞	A1	C1	CP2	LP1	N1	MP2

Chapter 3 Binomial Theorem

Binomial for +ve integer n	A1	C1	CP3	LP2	N1	MP1
Binomial for other n		C1	CP3		N2	MP3

Chapter 4 Quadratics

Solution of quadratics	A1	C1	CP1	LP1	N1	MP1
Completing the square	A1	C1	CP1	LP1	N1	MP1
Discriminant		C1	CP1			

Chapter 5 Inequalities

Inequalities in 1 variable	A1	C1	CP1	LP1	N1	MP1
Modulus function	A1	C1	CP2	LP1	N1	MP1
Inequalities in 2 variables						

Chapter 6 Indices and Logs

Indices and Logarithms	A1	C1	CP2	LP1	N1	MP2

Chapter 7 Coord. Geom.

Coordinates of Points	A1	C1	CP1	LP1	N1	MP1
Straight Lines	A1	C1	CP1	LP1	N1	MP1
Circles	A1	C1			N1	MP3
Parameters	A1	C1	CP3	LP2	N1	MP3

Chapter 8 Functs. and Graphs

Composition of Functions	A1	C1	CP1	LP1	N1	MP2
Graphs	A1	C1	CP1	LP1	N1	MP2

Chapter 9 Sine and Cos Rules

Sin and Cos Rules		C1	CP1	LP2	N2	MP1
Angles between Lines and Planes				LP2		MP1

Chapter 10 Trig Equations

The Six Ratios	A1	C1	CP3	LP2	N1	MP1
Other Angles	A1	C1	CP3	LP1	N1	MP1
Compound Angles	A1	C1	CP3	LP2	N2	MP3
The Form $a \sin \theta + b \cos \theta$		C1	CP3			MP3

Chapter 11 Radians

Radians	A1	C1	CP1	LP1	N1	MP1
Small Angles			M3			MP3

Chapter 12 Vectors

Vector Geometry	A3	C1			N2	MP3
Scalar Product	A3	C1			N2	MP3
Lines and Planes in 3 dimensions					N2	MP3

Chapter 13 Differentiation

Derivatives of Powers of x	A1	C1	CP2	LP1	N1	MP1
Tangents and Normals	A1	C1	CP2	LP1	N1	MP1
Maxima and Minima	A1	C1	CP2	LP1	N1	MP1

Chapter 14 Further Differentiation

Product and Quotient Rules	A1	C1	CP3	LP2	N1	MP2
Chain Rule	A1	C1	CP3	LP2	N1	MP2
Trig and Exponential Fns.	A1	C1	CP3	LP2	N1	MP2

Chapter 15 Integration

Integration of Powers of x	A1	C1	CP2	LP1	N1	MP1
Areas	A1	C1	CP2	LP1	N1	MP1
Volumes		C1	CP3	LP2		MM3

Chapter 16 Methods of Integration

Trig and Exponential Fns.	A1	C1	CP3	LP2	N2	MP2
Substitution	A1	C1	CP3	LP2	N2	MP2
Integration by Parts	A1	C1	CP3	LP2	N2	MP3

Chapter 17 Numerical Methods

Numerical Solutions	A1	C1	CP3	LP2	N2	MP2
Trapezium Rule		C1			N1	MP1

Chapter 18 Series

Trig and Exponential Series	C1	CP3
Maclaurin Series	C1	CP3

Chapter 19 Differential Equations

Separable Variables	A1	C1	CP3	LP2	N2 MP3
Modelling	A1	C1	CP3	LP2	N2 MP3
Numerical solution					N1

Chapter 20 Probability

Simple and Conditional Probability	A1	C1	CP1	LP2	N1 MS1

Chapter 21 Representation of Data

Mean, Variance etc	A1	C1	CP2	LP2	N1 MS1
Frequency and Cumulative Frequency	A1	C1	CP2	LP2	N1 MS1

Mechanics syllabus

Chapter 22 Displ. Vel. Acc.

Constant Acceleration	A3	C2	CM1 LM1 N1 MM1
Non-Constant Acceleration	A3	C2	CM1 LM1 N2 MM1
Vector Quantities	A3	C2	CM1 LM1 N2 MM1

Chapter 23 Force and Acceleration

Newton's First and Second Laws	A3	C2	CM1 LM1 N2 MM1
Action and Reaction	A3	C2	CM1 LM1 N2 MM1

Chapter 24 Resolving Forces

Forces at an angle	A3	C2	CM1 LM1 N2 MM1
Problems involving weight	A3	C2	CM1 LM1 N2 MM1

Chapter 25 Friction

Friction	A3	C2	CM1 LM1 N1 MM1

Chapter 26 Moments

Perpendicular Forces	A3	C3	CM2 LM1 MM2
Moments of Forces at an Angle	A3	C3	CM2 LM1 MM2

Chapter 27 Centre of Gravity

One Dimensional Problems	A3	C3	CM2LM1	MM2
Two and Three Dimensional Problems	A3	C3	CM2LM1	MM2
Calculus Problems			LM2	MM3
Statics Problems	A3	C3	CM2LM1	MM3

Chapter 28 Miscellaneous Statics

Couples	A3	C3	CM2	MM2
Equivalent Systems		C3	CM2	MM2
Three Forces on a Body		C3	CM2	MM2
Frameworks	A3			MM2

Chapter 29 Work, Energy, Power

Work and Energy	A3	C3	CM2LM2	MM2
Power	A3	C3	CM2LM2	MM2

Chapter 30 Relative Velocity

Relative Velocity	CM3

Chapter 31 Projectiles

Projectiles	A3	C2	CM1LM1N3MM1

Chapter 32 Momentum

Momentum and Impulse	A3	C2	CM2LM1N1MM2
Coefficient of Restitution			CM3LM2 MM2
Oblique impact			CM3

Chapter 33 Variable Acceleration

Force as Function of Distance or Velocity	A3	C3	CM3LM2N2

Chapter 34 Circular Motion

Circular Motion with Constant Speed	A3	C3	CM2LM2N3MM3
Motion in a Vertical Circle			CM3 MM3

Chapter 35 Elasticity and Oscillations

Elasticity	A3	C3	CM2LM2	MM3
S H M and Oscillating Systems	A3		CM3LM2	MM3

Statistics syllabus

Chapter 36 Perms. and Combs.

Perms. and Combs.	LS1	N1	MS1

Chapter 37 Discrete Random Variables

Distributions	A2	C2	CS1	LS1	N2	MS2
Mean	A2	C2	CS1	LS1	N2	MS2
Variance	A2	C2	CS1	LS1	N2	MS2

Chapter 38 Binomial and Poisson

Binomial Distribution	A2	C2	CS1	LS1	N2	MS1
Poisson Distribution	A2	C4	CS2	LS1	N3	MS2

Chapter 39 Continuous Variables

P.D.F, mean and variance	A2	CS4	LS1	N2	MS3
C.D.F.	A2	CS4	LS1	N2	MS3

Chapter 40 Sampling and Estimation

Sums of RVs	A2	C4	CS2	LS1	N3	MS3
Estimation of μ	A2	C2	CS2	LS2	N3	MS3
Estimation of σ^2		C2	CS2	LS2	N3	MS3

Chapter 41 The Normal Distribution

Normal Calculations	A2	C2	CS1	LS1	N2	MS2
Central Limit Theorem	A2	C2	CS1	LS2	N3	MS3

Chapter 42 Hypothesis Tests

Hypothesis Tests	A2	C4	CS2	LS2	N3	MS1
Confidence Intervals		C2	CS2	LS2	N3	MS3

Chapter 43 Sign, t and χ^2 tests

Sign test			CS3		
The t-test		C4	CS3		MS3
Goodness of Fit		C4	CS3	LS2	MS3
Testing Association	A2	C4	CS3	LS2	

Chapter 44 Regression and Correlation

1 Polynomials

The function $P(x)$ below is an example of a *polynomial*:

$$P(x) = 3x^4 - 2x^2 + 2.5x - 8.$$

In general, polynomial functions of x are made up only of positive whole number powers of x, such as x^3 or x^2, multiplied by constants and added together.

Examples of functions which are not polynomials are:

$$x^{\frac{1}{2}}, \quad \frac{1}{x+3}, \quad \cos x \text{ and } \log_{10} x$$

cannot be a polynomial

The order of a polynomial is the highest power of x. So the order of the polynomial $P(x)$ above is 4.

If the variable x in $P(x)$ is replaced by a number α, the result is written $P(\alpha)$. In the example above:

$$P(2) = 3 \times 2^4 - 2 \times 2^2 + 2.5 \times 2 - 8 = 37.$$

Algebra of polynomials

Polynomials can be added, subtracted and multiplied by using ordinary algebraic methods. The results can be simplified by the collection of terms with the same power of x.

$$(3x^2 - 2x + 1) + (x^3 - 4x + 0.5) = x^3 + 3x^2 - 6x + 1.5$$

$$(3x^2 - 2x + 1) \times (x - 3) = 3x^3 - 11x^2 + 7x - 3$$

When one polynomial is divided by another, long division is used. To divide $(3x^2 - 2x + 1)$ by $(x - 3)$:

$$
\begin{array}{r}
3x + 7 \\
x - 3 \overline{)\, 3x^2 - 2x + 1} \\
\underline{3x^2 - 9x} \\
7x + 1 \\
\underline{7x - 21} \\
22
\end{array}
$$

So the quotient when $3x^2 - 2x + 1$ is divided by $x - 3$ is $3x + 7$, and the remainder is 22.

1.1 Remainder and factor theorems

The *Remainder Theorem* states:

The remainder when P(x) is divided by $x - \alpha$ is P(α).

So the remainder when $3x^2 - 2x + 1$ is divided by $x - 3$ is $3 \times 3^2 - 2 \times 3 + 1 = 22$. This confirms the result above.

A particular case of the Remainder Theorem is the Factor Theorem:

$x - \alpha$ divides P(x) if and only if P(α) = 0

When trying to find factors of P(x), the first values of α to try are the divisors of the constant term in P(x).

1.1.1 Examples

1. Find the remainder when $x^5 + x^3 - 2x + 2$ is divided by $x + 2$.

   Solution

   Use the Remainder Theorem above, putting $\alpha = -2$.

   The remainder is $(-2)^5 + (-2)^3 - 2\times(-2) + 2$

   The remainder is -34

2. $x^3 - 2x^2 + ax - b$ is divisible by $(x - 1)(x + 2)$. Find the values of a and b.

   Solution

   Use the Factor Theorem twice, putting $\alpha = 1$ and $\alpha = -2$.

   $\alpha = 1$: $1 - 2 + a - b = 0$

   $\therefore$ $a - b = 1$

   $\alpha = -2$: $-8 - 8 - 2a - b = 0$

   $\therefore$ $2a + b = -16$

   Solve these simultaneously to obtain:

   $a = -5$ and $b = -6$

3. Factorise $x^3 - 4x^2 + x + 6$.

   Solution

   Use the Factor Theorem, trying first the divisors of 6.

   For $\alpha = 1$, P(α) = 4. For $\alpha = -1$, P(α) = 0

   So we know that $(x + 1)$ is a factor. Use the division process to find the other factor.

   $x^3 - 4x^2 + x + 6 \equiv (x + 1)(x^2 - 5x + 6)$

   This quadratic factor factorises to $(x - 2)(x - 3)$. Hence:

   $x^3 - 4x^2 + x + 6 \equiv (x + 1)(x - 2)(x - 3)$

1.1.2 Exercises

1. Which of the following are polynomials? Write down the order of those which are.

(a) $3x^2 + \dfrac{7}{x}$

(b) $2x^3 + 5$

(c) $2 \sin x - 4 \cos x$

(d) $(x + 3)(x^2 - 7x^3 + 1)$

2. Evaluate the following polynomial sums and products:

(a) $(2x^3 - 3x + 1) + (2x^3 + 4x - 4)$

(b) $(2x^2 + 3x) \times (x^3 - 1)$

(c) $(x^3 + 2x) - (x^2 - 5)$

(d) $(x^4 + x^2 + 1) \times (x^3 - x)$

3. Find the quotient and remainder in each of the following division problems.

(a) $\dfrac{x^3 + 2x^2 + x - 3}{x - 4}$

(b) $\dfrac{x^3 + x^2 - 3x + 1}{x^2 + 5x - 1}$

(c) $\dfrac{x^3 + 2x - 1}{x + 4}$

(d) $\dfrac{4x^4 - 3x^2 + 1}{2x - 3}$

4. Find the remainder in each of the following divisions.

(a) $\dfrac{x^2 + 3x - 2}{x - 5}$

(b) $\dfrac{3x^3 + x^2 + x - 1}{x - 2}$

(c) $\dfrac{x^3 + 7x^2 - 2x - 1}{x + 1}$

(d) $\dfrac{x^4 + 2}{x + 2}$

5. The remainder when $x^3 - 3x^2 + ax - 1$ is divided by $x - 2$ is 5. Find the value of a.

6. The remainder when $ax^3 + 3x^2 + 3x + 5$ is divided by $x + 3$ is 8. Find the value of a.

7. When $x^3 + 2x^2 + ax + b$ is divided by $x - 1$ the remainder is 3, and when it is divided by $x + 2$ the remainder is –1. Find a and b.

8. When $ax^3 - 2x^2 - 3x + b$ is divided by $x + 1$ the remainder is 3, and when it is divided by $x + 2$ the remainder is 1. Find a and b.

9. $x - 3$ divides $x^3 - 2x^2 + x - a$. Find a.

10. Find k, given that $x + 2$ is a factor of $x^3 + 2x^2 - kx - 1$.

11. $x^3 - 3x^2 + ax + b$ is divisible by both $x - 2$ and $x + 3$. Find a and b.

12. $ax^3 + bx^2 - 2x + 5$ is divisible by $(x + 1)(x - 2)$. Find a and b.

13. $x^2 - 4$ divides $x^3 + ax^2 + bx + 20$. Find a and b, and find the third factor.

14. Factorise the following:

(a) $x^3 - 2x^2 - x + 2$

(b) $x^3 + 3x^2 - 4x - 12$

(c) $x^3 - 2x^2 - 5x + 6$

(d) $2x^3 + 11x^2 + 17x + 6$

(e) $2x^3 - 9x^2 + 7x + 6$

(f) $x^4 - x^2 + 4x - 4$

(g) $x^3 - x^2 - x + 1$

(h) $x^3 + 5x^2 + 8x + 4$

15. Solve the following equations:

(a) $x^3 + 4x^2 + x - 6 = 0$

(b) $x - 4x^2 + x + 6 = 0$

(c) $2x^3 + 5x^2 + x - 2 = 0$

(d) $6x^3 - 11x^2 + 6x - 1 = 0$

1.2 Partial Fractions

A Rational Function is a function obtained by dividing one polynomial by another.

$$R(x) \equiv \frac{Q(x)}{P(x)}$$

The following simple rational functions are known as *Partial Fractions*.

$$\frac{A}{(x - \alpha)} \qquad \frac{Bx + C}{(ax^2 + bx + c)} \qquad \frac{D}{(x - \alpha)^n}$$

Here A, B, C, D are constants, and $ax^2 + bx + c$ is a quadratic which cannot be factorised.

Any rational function $Q(x)/P(x)$ can be written as the sum of a polynomial and partial fractions. The polynomial is the quotient when $Q(x)$ is divided by $P(x)$. The partial fractions are found as follows:

For each linear factor $(x - \alpha)$ of $P(x)$, include $\dfrac{A}{(x - \alpha)}$.

For each quadratic factor $(ax^2 + bx + c)$ of $P(x)$, include $\dfrac{Bx + C}{(ax^2 + bx + c)}$.

For each repeated linear factor $(x - \alpha)^2$, include $\dfrac{D}{(x - \alpha)^2} + \dfrac{E}{(x - \alpha)}$

The constants A, B, C, D, E are found by putting in values for x, or by equating coefficients of powers of x.

1.2.1 Example

Express in partial fractions:

(a) $\dfrac{3}{(x - 1)(x + 2)}$

(b) $\dfrac{x + 4}{x(x^2 + 4)}$

(c) $\dfrac{3x + 1}{(x + 1)(x - 1)^2}$

(d) $\dfrac{3x^2 + 11x - 9}{(x - 2)(x + 3)}$

Solution

(a) Write $\dfrac{3}{(x - 1)(x + 2)} \equiv \dfrac{A}{(x - 1)} + \dfrac{B}{(x + 2)}$

Multiply across by $(x - 1)(x + 2)$

$$3 \equiv A(x + 2) + B(x - 1)$$

Put $x = 1$, to obtain $3 = 3A$. Put $x = -2$, to obtain $3 = -3B$.

$$\frac{3}{(x - 1)(x + 2)} \equiv \frac{1}{(x - 1)} - \frac{1}{(x + 2)}$$

(b) Write $\dfrac{x + 4}{x(x^2 + 4)} \equiv \dfrac{A}{x} + \dfrac{Bx + C}{x^2 + 4}$

$$x + 4 \equiv A(x^2 + 4) + (Bx + C)x$$

Put $x = 0$, to obtain $A = 1$.

Equate the x^2 coefficients, to obtain $0 = A + B$. Hence $B = -1$.

Equate the x coefficient, to obtain $1 = C$.

$$\frac{x+4}{x(x^2+4)} \equiv \frac{1}{x} + \frac{1-x}{x^2+4}$$

(c) Write $\dfrac{3x+1}{(x+1)(x-1)^2} \equiv \dfrac{A}{x+1} + \dfrac{B}{x-1} + \dfrac{C}{(x-1)^2}$

$$3x+1 \equiv A(x-1)^2 + B(x+1)(x-1) + C(x+1)$$

Put $x = 1$, to obtain $C = 2$. Put $x = -1$, to obtain $A = -0.5$.

Equate the x^2 coefficient, to obtain $B = -A = 0.5$

$$\frac{3x+1}{(x+1)(x-1)^2} \equiv \frac{-0.5}{x+1} + \frac{0.5}{x-1} + \frac{2}{(x-1)^2}$$

(d) Before putting this into partial fractions, divide through so that the order of the top is less than the order of the bottom.

$$
\begin{array}{r}
3 \\
x^2+x-6 \overline{)\,3x^2+11x-9} \\
3x^2+3x-18 \\
\hline
8x+9
\end{array}
$$

It follows that: $\dfrac{3x^2+11x-9}{(x-2)(x+3)} \equiv 3 + \dfrac{8x+9}{(x-2)(x+3)}$

Now proceed as in part (a).

$$\frac{3x^2+11x-9}{(x-2)(x+3)} \equiv 3 + \frac{5}{x-2} + \frac{3}{x+3}$$

1.2.2 Exercises

1. Express the following as single fractions:

(a) $\dfrac{1}{x+1} + \dfrac{1}{x-1}$ 　　　　　(b) $\dfrac{1}{x} - \dfrac{2}{x+3}$

(c) $\dfrac{1}{x^2} + \dfrac{2}{2-x}$ 　　　　　(d) $\dfrac{2}{x} - \dfrac{1}{x^2+1}$

(e) $\dfrac{4}{x+1} + 1$ 　　　　　(f) $x + \dfrac{3}{5-x}$

Express the following rational functions in terms of partial fractions:

2. $\dfrac{4}{(x+1)(x-1)}$ 　　　　　3. $\dfrac{8}{(x-1)(x+3)}$

4. $\dfrac{x+3}{(x-1)x}$ 　　　　　5. $\dfrac{2x-1}{(x+1)(x-3)}$

6. $\dfrac{2}{(x+1)(2x-1)}$ 　　　　　7. $\dfrac{3x-2}{(3x+1)(x-2)}$

8. $\dfrac{2x}{(x+1)(x^2+1)}$ 　　　　　9. $\dfrac{3}{x(x^2+x+1)}$

10. $\dfrac{x^2-1}{(x+2)(x^2+1)}$ 　　　　　11. $\dfrac{3-2x}{(2x^2+3)(x+1)}$

12. $\dfrac{2}{(x-1)(x-2)^2}$ 　　　　　13. $\dfrac{3x-1}{x^2(x+1)}$

14. $\dfrac{x^2}{(x+1)^2(2x-1)}$

15. $\dfrac{5}{(2x+1)^2(x-1)}$

16. $\dfrac{x^2-2}{(x-3)(x+4)}$

17. $\dfrac{4x^2}{(x+1)(x-1)}$

18. $\dfrac{x^3+x^2+2x-1}{(x-1)(x+2)}$

19. $\dfrac{x^4}{(x-1)(x+1)}$

20. $\dfrac{6}{(x-1)(x-2)(x-3)}$

21. $\dfrac{4x-3}{x(x-1)(x+2)}$

22. Express $\dfrac{1}{n(n+1)}$ in partial fractions.

    By writing each term in partial fractions find the sum of the series:
    $$\frac{1}{1\times 2}+\frac{1}{2\times 3}+\frac{1}{3\times 4}+\cdots+\frac{1}{n(n+1)}$$

23. Find the sum to infinity of the series in Question 22.

24. By methods similar to those of Question 22, find the sums of the following series:

    (a) $\dfrac{1}{1\times 3}+\dfrac{1}{3\times 5}+\dfrac{1}{5\times 7}+\cdots+\dfrac{1}{(2n-1)(2n+1)}$

    (b) $\dfrac{1}{2\times 4}+\dfrac{1}{4\times 6}+\dfrac{1}{6\times 8}+\cdots+\dfrac{1}{2n(2n+2)}$

1.3 Examination questions

1. (i) Write down one factor of the expression
    $$(x+4)(2x^2+5x+5)-(x+4)(x+1)(x-1)$$
    By factorising, or otherwise, show that $(x+3)$ is also a factor, and find the third factor.

    Find the coefficient of x^2 in the expression.

    (ii) $\dfrac{3x^2-x+5}{x-1}$ may be expressed in the form $ax+b+\dfrac{r}{x-1}$

    Show that $b=2$ and find the values of a and r.

    [SMP ADD]

2. Given the expression $6x^4-23x^3+11x^2+12x$,

    (a) find the remainder when this expression is divided by $(x-1)$

    (b) find the remainder when this expression is divided by $(x-3)$

    (c) factorise this expression completely

    (d) solve the equation $6x^4-23x^3+11x^2+12x=0$.

    [AEB ADD 1987]

3. (a) Find the values of a and b so that $x^4+x^3+x^2+ax+b$ may be exactly divisible by $(x-3)(x+2)$.

(b) If $2u^2 - 9u + 10 = 0$ and $u = x + \dfrac{1}{x}$, prove that:

$$2x^4 - 9x^3 + 14x^2 - 9x + 2 = 0.$$

Solve the equation $2x^4 - 9x^3 + 14x^2 - 9x + 2 = 0$.

[SUJB]

4.
$$\frac{5x - 1}{(1 + x)(1 + x + 3x^2)} \equiv \frac{Ax + B}{1 + x + 3x^2} + \frac{C}{1 + x}$$

Find the values of the constants A, B and C.

[L]

Common errors

1 Division of Polynomials

(a) When performing long division, be careful of negative signs. When subtracting $-3x$ from $5x$, the result is $8x$. (Not $2x$).

(b) Do not be confused when you are dividing into a polynomial, such as $x^4 - 2x^2 + x$, which misses out some of the powers. Write it as $x^4 + 0x^3 - 2x^2 + x + 0$, and then perform the long division.

2 Remainder and Factor Theorems

(a) When you are finding the remainder after division by $x + 3$, you must put $\alpha = -3$. A common mistake is to put $\alpha = +3$.

(b) These theorems only apply to polynomials. You cannot use them to factorise something like $\sin x - \sin 30°$.

3 Partial Fractions

(a) Before putting a function into partial fractions you must ensure that the top has a lower order than the bottom. If this is not the case then you must divide first.

(b) The partial fraction corresponding to a quadratic factor is of the form

$$\frac{Bx + C}{ax^2 + bx + c}$$

Do not forget to put in either the B term or the C term.

If your partial fractions include say

$$\frac{Bx + C}{x^2 + 4}$$

then you cannot always find the values of B and C by putting in values for x. You may have to find them by equating coefficients.

(c) The partial fractions corresponding to a repeated factor is of the form

$$\frac{D}{x - \alpha} + \frac{E}{(x - \alpha)^2}$$

Both these terms must be put in.

If your partial fractions include

$$\frac{D}{x-\alpha} + \frac{E}{(x-\alpha)^2}$$

then multiply by $(x-\alpha)^2$. There is no need to multiply by $(x-\alpha)^3$.

2 Arithmetic and geometric progressions

A list of numbers is a *sequence* or *progression*.

A sequence can be written as $u_1, u_2, u_3,...$ The nth term of the sequence is u_n.

2.1 Arithmetic progressions

If the differences between successive terms of a sequence are constant, then the sequence is an *arithmetic progression* (AP). The difference is called the *common difference*.

1, 4, 7, 10 is an arithmetic progression with common difference 3.

$1, \frac{1}{2}, 0, -\frac{1}{2}, -1, -1\frac{1}{2}$ is an A.P. with common difference $-\frac{1}{2}$.

If an arithmetic progression has first term a and common difference d, then the nth term is:

$$u_n = a + (n-1)d$$

The sum of the first n terms is:

$$\sum_{i=1}^{n} u_i = u_1 + u_2 + ... + u_n$$

$$= \frac{n}{2}\{2a + (n-1)d\}$$

2.1.1 Examples

1. Find the tenth term and the sum to 40 terms of the sequence 3, 5, 7, 9,...

   Solution

   The first term is 3 and the common difference is 2.

   The tenth term is $3 + (10-1)2 = 21$.

   Put $n = 40$, $a = 3$ and $d = 2$ into the formula for the sum of an AP

   The sum of 40 terms is $\frac{1}{2}40(2\times3 + (40-1)2) = 1680$

2. The first two terms of an AP are 5 and 8. How many terms are less than 1,000?

   Solution

   Here $a = 5$ and $d = 3$. The nth term is $5 + (n - 1)3 = 2 + 3n$.

   If $2 + 3n < 1000$, then $n < \dfrac{998}{3} = 332\frac{2}{3}$.

   332 terms are less than 1,000.

3. The fifth term of an AP is 13 and the eighth term is 19. Find the first term and the nth term.

   Solution

   The nth term is $a + (n - 1)d$. Use the information above:

   $13 = a + 4d$ and $19 = a + 7d$

   Solve these equations to obtain $d = 2$ and $a = 5$.

   The first term is 5 and the nth term is $5 + 2(n-1)$.

2.1.2 Exercises

1. Find the eleventh terms of the following sequences:
   (a) 1, 4, 7, 10   (b) 13, 17, 21, 25
   (c) 4.2, 4.4, 4.6   (d) 11, 8, 5, 2

2. Find the sum of the first 12 terms for the sequences in Question 1.

3. Find expressions for the nth term and the sum of the first n terms for the sequences in Question 1.

4. Find the first term and the nth term for the sequences which have:
   (a) 5th term 12 and common difference 3
   (b) 4th term 14 and 9th term 29
   (c) 6th term 2.1 and 10th term 2.9
   (d) Third term 13 and seventh term –3.

5. The nth term of an Arithmetic Progression is $5 + 3n$. Find the common difference and the first term.

6. Find the common difference and first term for the sequences which have nth term:
   (a) $2 + 5n$ (b) $7n - 3$
   (c) $2 + \dfrac{n}{5}$ (d) $3 - 2n$

7. The sum of the first n terms of an Arithmetic Progression is $2n^2 + n$. Find the first 3 terms, and hence find the common difference.

8. Find the first term and the common difference for the APs for which the sum of the first n terms is:
   (a) $n^2 + n$ (b) $3n - n^2$
   (c) $2n + 3n^2$ (d) $n - \frac{1}{4}n^2$

9. Find the first term of the sequence 1, 7, 13, 19 which is greater than 100.

10. Which is the first negative term of the sequence 98, 93, 88, 83,....? How many terms must be taken before their sum is negative?

11. Find the sum of the first n integers.

12. Find the sum of the first n odd numbers, simplifying your answer as far as possible.

13. Find the sum of the first ten multiples of 7 which are greater than 100.

14. 3, x, 7 form an Arithmetic Progression. Find x.

15. 53, x, y, 25 form an AP. Find x and y.

2.2 Geometric progressions

If the ratio between successive terms of a sequence is constant, then the sequence is a *geometric progression* (GP) The ratio is the *common ratio*.

2, 6, 18, 54, 162 is a geometric progression with common ratio 3.

$1, -\frac{1}{2}, \frac{1}{4}, -\frac{1}{8}$ is a geometric progression with common ratio $-\frac{1}{2}$.

If the first term of a geometric progression is a and the common ratio is r, then the nth term is:

$$u_n = ar^{n-1}$$

The sum of the first n terms of the sequence is:

$$\sum_{i=1}^{n} u_i = u_1 + u_2 + ... + u_n$$

$$= \frac{a(r^n - 1)}{r - 1}$$

If $-1 < r < 1$, then the *sum to infinity* of the sequence is:

$$\sum_{i=1}^{\infty} u_i = u_1 + u_2 + ... + u_n + ...$$

$$= \frac{a}{1 - r}$$

2.2.1 Examples

1. Find the sixth term and the sum of the first 10 terms of the sequence: 3, 6, 12, 24, ...

   Solution

   The first term is 3 and the common ratio is 2.

   Hence the sixth term is: $3 \times 2^{6-1} = 96$

   The sum to 10 terms is: $\dfrac{3 \times (2^{10} - 1)}{2 - 1} = 3069$

2. How many terms of the sequence 1, 3, 9, 27, ... must be taken for the sum to exceed 1,000?

Solution

The sum to n terms is $\dfrac{1 \times (3^n - 1)}{3 - 1}$.

If this is to be greater than 1,000, then: $3^n > 2001$.

By logs or by trial and error find that $n > 6.9$.

7 terms of the sequence must be taken.

3. A ball is thrown upwards, and returns to the ground after 5 seconds. After each bounce the time until it returns to earth is multiplied by a factor of $\frac{2}{3}$. Find the total time which passes before it stops bouncing.

   Solution

   The time of the first bounce is 5 secs. The time for the second bounce is $5 \times \frac{2}{3}$. The time for the third bounce is $5 \times \left(\frac{2}{3}\right)^2$. And so on.

   The total time is the sum to infinity of the GP with first term 5 and common ratio $\frac{2}{3}$.

   $$\text{Total time} = \frac{5}{1 - \frac{2}{3}} = 15 \text{ seconds.}$$

2.2.2 Exercises

1. Find the seventh term and the sum of the first 5 terms for the following geometric progressions:

   (a) 2, 4, 8, 16, ...

   (b) 4, 2, 1, $\frac{1}{2}$, $\frac{1}{4}$, ...

   (c) 2, –6, 18, –54, ...

   (d) –2, $\frac{1}{2}$, –$\frac{1}{8}$, $\frac{1}{32}$

2. Find the nth term for each of the sequences in Question 1.

3. Find expressions for the sum to n terms of each of the sequences in Question 1.

4. Find, where possible, the sum to infinity of the sequences in Question 1.

5. Find the first term and the common ratio for the geometric progressions with:

   (a) Second term 3 and fifth term 24.

   (b) Third term 8 and sixth term 1.

   (c) Third term 5 and sixth term –40

   (d) Second term 4 and sum to infinity 16.

6. The fourth term of a GP is 4 and the sixth is 100. Find two possible values for the common ratio, and hence find two possible values for the first term.

7. A GP has first term 5 and common ratio 4. How many terms of the sequence are less than 9,000?

8. A GP has first term 2 and common ratio 1.5. How many terms of the sequence must be taken before their sum is greater than 100?

9. A GP has first term 6 and common ratio 0.7. Which is the first term of the sequence less than 1?

10. 3, x, 75 are terms of a GP Find the possible values of x.

11. 8, x, y, -1 are terms of a GP Find x and y.

12. Find the common ratio and the first term of the sequence whose sum to n terms is:

    (a) $2 \times 3^n - 2$ (b) $4 - \left(\frac{1}{4}\right)^{n-1}$

2.3 Miscellaneous examples

1. The first, second and fifth terms of an AP form consecutive terms of a GP Find the common ratio.

   Solution

   Let the first term be a, the common difference be d and the common ratio be r.

   Then: $a + d = ar$

   and $a + 4d = ar^2$

   Eliminate d between these equations:

   $$4(ar - a) = ar^2 - a$$
   $$4r - 4 = r^2 - 1$$
   $$0 = r^2 - 4r + 3$$
   $$(r - 3)(r - 1) = 0$$

   The common ratio is 3 or 1

2. The first term of a GP is two thirds of the sum to infinity. Find the common ratio.

   Solution

   Let the first term be a and the common ratio r.

   $$a = \frac{\frac{2}{3}a}{1 - r}$$

   Hence $1 - r = \frac{2}{3}$

   The common ratio is $\frac{1}{3}$

3. At the beginning of each year a man invests £100 at 10% compound interest. How much will he have at the beginning of the 13th year, i.e. just after the 13th investment?

   Solution

   The £100 which was originally invested will have increased to £100x1.1^{12}. The £100 which was invested at the beginning of the second year will have increased to £100x1.1^{11}. And so on. The total sum of money will be the sum of 13 terms of a GP, with first term 100 and common ratio 1.1.

   $$\text{Total} = \frac{100 \times (1.1^{13} - 1)}{1.1 - 1} = £2,452$$

2.4 Miscellaneous exercises

1. The third term of an AP is x, and the seventh term is y. Express the common difference and the first term as functions of x and y.

2. $x-3$, $2x-3$, $6x+1$ are consecutive terms of a GP. Find the possible values of x.

3. Find the sum of all the numbers less than 100 whose last digit is 5.

4. A man invests £50 each year at 9% compound interest. How much will he have in the bank just before his tenth investment?

5. A job is advertised at a starting salary of £12,750 with annual increments of £900. How much will the salary be during the 10th year? How much will be the total sum earned after 10 years?

6. A job is advertised at a starting salary of £12,000 with an annual increase of 5%. What will the salary be during the 10th year? What will the total sum earned after 10 years?

7. A child builds a triangular wall of bricks, with 1 brick on the top row, 2 bricks on the second, 3 on the third and so on. If the wall is 8 bricks high, how many bricks does it contain? If the child has only 70 bricks, what is the tallest wall she can build?

8. A large sheet of paper is 0.04 mm thick. How thick is it after it has been folded ten times? (Assuming that this is possible). How many times must it be folded before it is 1 metre thick?

9. A king was so pleased with the game of chess that he granted its inventor any prize he desired. The inventor asked for one grain of wheat on the first square, two grains on the second square, four grains on the third square and so on for all 64 squares. How many grains is he asking for in total?

10. How many terms of the series $2 + 1 + \frac{1}{2} + \frac{1}{4} + \frac{1}{8} + \dots$ must be taken so that the sum is within 0.001 of its sum to infinity?

11. Let x be the recurring decimal 0.12121212... Show that x can be written as:

$$\frac{12}{100} + \frac{12}{10000} + \frac{12}{1000000} + \dots$$

Write this as the sum of a geometric series and hence find x as a fraction in its simplest form.

12. By the method of Question 11 express the following as fractions in their simplest form:
    (a) 0.72727272...
    (b) 0.545454...
    (c) 0.037037037...
    (d) 0.135135135...
    (e) 0.063636363...
    (f) 0.00027027027...

13. Achilles can run at 10 feet per second, and the Tortoise at 1 foot per second. They have a race, and the Tortoise is given a 10 feet start. After 1 second T is 1 foot ahead. When A has run that extra foot, T is still ahead by 0.1 foot. When A has run that extra 0.1 ft, T is 0.01 ft ahead. Find how long it takes for A to catch up with T.

2.5 Examination questions

1. The first term of a geometric series is 1 and the sum of the first 3 terms is $\frac{7}{9}$. Find the two possible values of the common ratio of this series.

[L ADD]

2. (i) The sum of an arithmetic progression is −600. The first term is 12, and the common difference is −3. How many terms are there in the series?

   (ii) The second and fourth terms of a geometric series are 2 and $\frac{1}{18}$. Calculate the first term and the values of the common ratio. Write down the first four terms of each of the two possible series.

   (iii) Calculate the smallest number of terms of the geometric series $1 + 4 + 16 +...$ that will give a total greater than 2×10^6.

[O ADD]

3. (i) If a salary is increased during each year by 12% of its value at the start of the year, by what factor is it multiplied each year? By what factor will the original salary have been multiplied after five years and by what percentage has it increased in this time?

   (ii) If the cost of repairs to a new car is £20 in the first year and this cost increases thereafter by £25 each year, write down and simplify a formula for the cost of repairs in the nth year. Find also the total amount paid in repair bills up to the end of the nth year.

   The owner decides to keep the car until the end of the year in which the total repair bill passes £1,000. How old will the car be when he sells it?

[MEI ADD]

4. The sum S_n of the first n terms of a series is given by $S_n = \frac{1}{4}(5n^2 + 11n)$.

   Write down an expression for S_{n-1}. Deduce the value of u_n, the nth term of the series. Hence show that the series is an arithmetic series, and state the values of the first term and of the common difference.

[C]

5. The first term of a geometric series is 10 and the second term is $10 - x$. Show that the set of values for which the series is convergent is given by

   $0 < x < 20$.

   Show also that, for these values, the series converges to a sum greater than 5.

   Given that the series converges to sum 100, find the smallest positive integer n such that the sum of the first n terms is greater than 99.

[L]

Common errors

1. Be sure whether you are dealing with an arithmetic or a geometric progression. Some sequences are neither of these.

2. Do not confuse the nth *term* with the *sum* of n terms.

3. Sometimes the term you want to deal with is not the nth but the $(n-1)$th or the $(n+1)$th. Make sure you know the number of the term.

4. Be very careful with problems which involve investment or salaries. Read the question carefully to make sure whether it is the beginning or the end of the year which is being dealt with.

5. Be careful with signs. If an AP is decreasing, then the common difference is negative. If the common ratio of a GP is negative, then the terms are alternately positive and negative.

6. Be careful when taking square roots. Problems involving GPs often require you to solve an equation like $r^2 = 4$. There are two solutions: $r = 2$ or $r = -2$. Often the question will help you by requiring the values (plural) of r.

3 The binomial theorem

3.1 Positive integer powers

Pascal's Triangle is the triangle of numbers shown below, in which each term is obtained by adding the two terms above it.

$$
\begin{array}{ccccccccccccc}
 & & & & & & 1 & & & & & & n=0 \\
 & & & & & 1 & & 1 & & & & & n=1 \\
 & & & & 1 & & 2 & & 1 & & & & n=2 \\
 & & & 1 & & 3 & & 3 & & 1 & & & n=3 \\
 & & 1 & & 4 & & 6 & & 4 & & 1 & & n=4 \\
 & 1 & & 5 & & 10 & & 10 & & 5 & & 1 & n=5 \\
1 & & 6 & & 15 & & 20 & & 15 & & 6 & & 1 \qquad n=6
\end{array}
$$

The *binomial coefficient* ^nC_r is the rth term of the nth row of Pascal's Triangle, (counting from 0 instead of from 1).

So for example: $\qquad ^5C_0 = 1; \qquad ^4C_2 = 6; \qquad ^6C_6 = 1$

These coefficients are also given by the formula:

$$^nC_r = \frac{n!}{r!(n-r)!}$$

The binomial coefficients are sometimes written as $\binom{n}{r}$.

The *binomial theorem* states that:

$$(a + b)^n \equiv a^n + {}^nC_1 a^{n-1}b + ... + {}^nC_r a^{n-r}b^r + ... + b^n.$$

So for example $(a + b)^5 \equiv a^5 + 5a^4b + 10a^3b^2 + 10a^2b^3 + 5ab^4 + b^5.$

The binomial theorem can be used to find approximations for expressions of the form $(1 + x)^n$, where x is small. Continue taking terms until they are so small that they do not affect the answer to the required degree of accuracy.

3.1.1 Examples

1. Expand $(x + 2y)^4$.

   Solution

   Use the binomial theorem, with the fourth row of Pascal's Triangle.
   Put $a = x$ and $b = 2y$.

   $$(x + 2y)^4 \equiv x^4 + 4x^3(2y) + 6x^2(2y)^2 + 4x(2y)^3 + (2y)^4$$

   $$(x + 2y)^4 \equiv x^4 + 8x^3y + 24x^2y^2 + 32xy^3 + 16y^4.$$

2. Use the binomial theorem to find an approximation for $(0.997)^7$, taking the first three terms of the expansion of $(1 + x)^7$.

   Solution

   The first three terms of $(1 + x)^7$ are: $1 + {}^7C_1 x + {}^7C_2 x^2$.

   Put $x = -0.003$ to obtain $1 - 7{\times}0.003 + 21{\times}0.003^2$

   $$(0.997)^7 \approx 0.979189.$$

3.1.2 Exercises

1. Expand the following using the binomial theorem, and simplify as far as possible.

   (a) $(2 + b)^5$ (b) $(1 + 3b)^4$

   (c) $(2x + 3y)^4$ (d) $(1 - 2z)^6$

   (e) $(2a - b)^7$ (f) $(2 - 0.5x)^7$

2. In the following expansions, write down the appropriate terms. Simplify your answers as far as possible.

   (a) $(1 + x)^8$ x^3 term   (b) $(1 - y)^9$ y^5 term

   (c) $(2 + x)^{10}$ x^8 term   (d) $(1 + 2x)^8$ x^3 term

   (e) $(3 + 2y)^5$ y^3 term   (f) $(3x - 5)^5$ x^2 term

   (g) $(x + y)^{16}$ x^5y^{11} term   (h) $(2a - 3b)^7$ a^5b^2 term

   (i) $(x + \dfrac{1}{x})^8$ x^4 term   (j) $(y - \dfrac{2}{y})^7$ y^{-3} term

   (k) $(x^2 + \dfrac{1}{x})^7$ x^8 term   (l) $(y - \dfrac{1}{y^2})^9$ constant term.

3. Find the greatest coefficient of a power of x in the following expansions:

   (a) $(1 + x)^{17}$ (b) $(1 + 2x)^7$

   (c) $(1 - 3x)^8$ (d) $(2 + 3x)^9$

4. Expand and simplify $(1 + \sqrt{3})^6 + (1 - \sqrt{3})^6$, without using a calculator.

5. Expand $(1 + x)^{12}$ up to the term in x^3. Hence find approximations for:

   (a) 1.02^{12} (b) 0.96^{12}

6. Use the binomial expansion up to the x^3 term to find approximations for:

   (a) 1.01^8 (b) 0.95^7

   (c) 2.01^9 (d) 2.96^5

7. The first two terms of the expansion of $(2 + ax)^n$ are $1024 + 15360x$. Find a and n.

8. The constant term in the expansion of $(ax + \dfrac{b}{x})^{10}$ is 8064. Find a in terms of b.

9. There is no x^2 term in the expansion of $(1 + ax)^6 - (2 + bx)^7$. Find the ratio of a to b.

10. Use the expansion of $(1 + y)^{10}$ to find $\{1 + (x + x^2)\}^{10}$, up to the term in x^2.

11. Expand the following, up to the term indicated:

    (a) $(1 - x + x^2)^7$ x^2 term   (b) $(1 + x^2)^8$ x^6 term

    (c) $(1 + 2x + 3x^2)^6$ x^2 term   (d) $(2 - x + 2x^2)^7$ x^2 term

    (e) $(1 + x)^7(1 + x)$ x^2 term   (f) $(1 - 2x)^5(1 + x)$ x^2 term

    (g) $(1 + x)^8(1 + x^2)$ x^3 term   (h) $(1 - x)^{10}(1 - x + x^2)$ x^3 term

3.2 Binomial theorem for other powers

If n is not a positive integer, the binomial theorem is still true, with certain restrictions. Provided that $-1 < x < 1$:

$$(1 + x)^n = 1 + nx + \frac{n(n-1)x^2}{2!} + \frac{n(n-1)(n-2)x^3}{3!} + \dots$$

In general, this series continues to infinity. So if only the first few terms are taken then the result is only an approximation.

3.2.1 Examples

(1) Find an expansion for $\sqrt{(1 + x)}$, up to the term in x^2. Hence find an approximation for $\sqrt{17}$.

Solution

Write $\sqrt{(1 + x)}$ as $(1 + x)^{0.5}$. Putting $n = 0.5$ in the binomial expansion:

$$(1 + x)^{0.5} \approx 1 + 0.5x + \frac{0.5(0.5 - 1)}{2!}x^2$$

$$= 1 + 0.5x - 0.125x^2$$

Write $\sqrt{17}$ as $(16 + 1)^{0.5} = 4(1 + 0.0625)^{0.5}$.

Put $x = 0.0625$ in the expansion above:

$$\sqrt{17} \approx 4[1 + (0.5)(0.0625) - (0.125)(0.0625)^2]$$

$$= 4.1230.$$

2. Expand $\dfrac{1 + 3x}{1 - 2x}$ up to the term in x^2. For which values of x is the expansion valid?

Solution

Write $\dfrac{1 + 3x}{1 - 2x}$ as $(1 + 3x)(1 - 2x)^{-1}$.

$$(1 - 2x)^{-1} \approx 1 + -1x(-2x) + \frac{-1x - 2x(-2x)^2}{2!}$$

$$= 1 + 2x + 4x^2$$

$$\frac{1 + 3x}{1 - 2x} \approx (1 + 3x)(1 + 2x + 4x^2).$$

Expand this, ignoring the term in x^3:

$$\frac{1 + 3x}{1 - 2x} \approx 1 + 5x + 10x^2$$

The expansion is valid if $-1 < 2x < 1$.

The expansion is valid for $-0.5 < x < 0.5$

3.2.2 Exercises

1. Expand the following up to the term in x^2.

    (a) $(1+x)^{\frac{1}{4}}$ (b) $\sqrt{(1 + 3x)}$

    (c) $(1-x)^{\frac{3}{2}}$ (d) $(1-2x)^{\frac{4}{3}}$

    (e) $(1 + x)^{-2}$ (f) $\dfrac{1}{1 + 2x}$

    (g) $\dfrac{1}{1 - x^2}$ (h) $\dfrac{3}{1 + x^2}$

2. For which values of x are the expansions in Question 1 valid?

3. Use the binomial expansion up to x^2 to find approximations for:

    (a) $1.01^{\frac{1}{2}}$ (b) $\sqrt{1.05}$

    (c) $0.98^{\frac{1}{2}}$ (d) $\sqrt{0.96}$

4. Without using a calculator or tables, use the binomial expansion up to x^3 to find an approximation for $\sqrt{1.01} + \sqrt{0.99}$.

5. Using the binomial expansion up to x^3 of $(1+x)^{\frac{1}{2}}$, and writing 50 as 49 + 1, find an approximation for $\sqrt{50}$.

6. Use the method of Question 5 to find approximations for:
    (a) $\sqrt{101}$ (b) $\sqrt{98}$

    (c) $28^{\frac{1}{3}}$ (d) $63^{\frac{1}{3}}$

7. Expand the following up to the term in x^2:
    (a) $\dfrac{1 + x}{1 - x}$ (b) $\dfrac{1 + x^2}{1 + 2x}$

    (c) $\dfrac{1 + 2x - x^2}{1 + 3x}$ (d) $\dfrac{1 + x}{1 + x^2}$

8. Show that the expansion of $\sqrt{(1 + x)} + \sqrt{(1 - x)}$ up to the term in x^3 is of the form $a + bx^2$. Find a and b.

9. $\dfrac{1 + ax + bx^2}{(1 - x)^2}$ has no term in either x or x^2. Find a and b.

10. Find the expansion of $\sqrt[3]{(1 - x)}$, up to the x^2 term. By putting $x = \frac{1}{8}$, show that $\sqrt[3]{7}$ is approximately $\frac{551}{288}$.

11. Find the expansion of $\sqrt{(1 - x)}$ up to the x^2 term. By putting $x = \frac{1}{10}$, show that $\sqrt{10}$ is approximately $\frac{800}{253}$.

3.3 Examination questions

1. Find the first three terms in the expansion, in ascending powers of x, of

   (i) $(1 - 3x)^5$ (ii) $(2 + x)^4$

   Hence find the coefficient of x^2 in the expansion of $(1 - 3x)^5(2 + x)^4$.

   [C ADD]

2. (i) Write down the expansion of $(1 - x)^5$. Deduce that the first three terms in the expansion of $(1 - 3x)(1 - x)^5$ are $1 - 8x + 25x^2$ and find the term in x^3.

   (ii) Find an approximation to $(1 - 3x)(1 - x)^5$ when $x = \frac{1}{100}$ by taking the first three terms of the expansion. Show that the inclusion of the term in x^3 does not affect the approximation when working to 4 decimal places.

   [O&C ADD]

3. Obtain the expansion in ascending powers of x of $(1 - x)^8$. Hence calculate the value of $(0.95)^8$ correct to three decimal places.

   When a ball is dropped on to level ground it always rebounds to a height of 0.95 times the height from which it fell. If it is dropped from a height of 10 metres, calculate, correct to three significant figures, the height to which it rebounds after eight bounces.

   [L ADD]

4. (a) Evaluate the term which is independent of x in the expansion of

   $$\left(x + \frac{1}{x} \right)^8$$

   (b) Expand $(1 - x)^2\sqrt{(1 + 2x)}$ in ascending powers of x as far as the term in x^3. For which values of x is this expansion valid?

   [NI]

5. The first three terms in ascending powers of x of $\dfrac{1 + px}{1 + qx}$ and $(1 + x)^{\frac{1}{10}}$ are identical. Find the values of p and q, assuming that x is sufficiently small for both expansions to be valid.

   Use this result to show that the tenth root of 33 is approximately $\dfrac{651\sqrt{2}}{649}$.

   [C]

6. (a) Express $\dfrac{1}{(1 + x)(2 + x)}$ in partial fractions.

Hence or otherwise, given that x is sufficiently small for powers of x above the second to be neglected, show that

$$\frac{1}{(1+x)(2+x)} = \tfrac{1}{8}(4 - 6x + 7x^2)$$

(b) Show that the first three non–zero terms in the series expansion of

$$\left(1 - \frac{1}{n}\right)^{\frac{1}{n}}$$

in ascending powers of $\frac{1}{n}$ are:

$$1 - \left(\frac{1}{n}\right)^2 - \tfrac{1}{2}\left(\frac{1}{n}\right)^3$$

and find the term in $\left(\frac{1}{n}\right)^4$.

By giving n a suitable value, use the first four non–zero terms of the series to find a value for

$$(0.9)^{\frac{1}{10}}$$

giving your answer to five decimal places.

[C]

7. Use the binomial series to expand $(1-x)^{\frac{1}{4}}$ in ascending powers of x as far as the term in x^3.

By putting $x = \frac{1}{81}$ in the expression and in the series, calculate the value of

$5^{1/4}$ correct to five decimal places, explaining why your working ensures this degree of accuracy.

[AEB 1986]

Common errors

1. **Positive integer powers**

   (a) When writing out the expansion of $(a + b)^n$ do not forget the binomial coefficients.

   (b) When expanding something like $(a + 2b)^5$, then do not forget to take powers of 2 as well as of b. For example, the third term is $10a^3(2b)^2 = 40a^3b^2$, not $10a^3 2b^2 = 20a^3b^2$.

   (c) Similarly, be careful of negative numbers. If you are expanding $(a - 2b)^5$, then the terms will be alternately positive and negative.

2. **Other powers**

   If n is not a positive integer, then the binomial theorem only holds for expressions of the form $(1 + x)^n$, where $-1 < x < 1$. Do not try to expand $\sqrt{5}$ as $(1 + 4)^{1/2}$, using $x = 4$.

   Similarly, the first term inside the bracket must be 1. Do not write $\sqrt{5}$ as $(4\tfrac{1}{2} + \tfrac{1}{2})^{1/2}$ and attempt to expand.

   The correct way to find $\sqrt{5}$ is to write it as $(4 + 1)^{1/2} = 2(1 + \tfrac{1}{4})^{1/2}$. This can now be expanded using the Binomial theorem.

4 Quadratics

A *quadratic function* has the form $y = ax^2 + bx + c$, where a, b, c are constants.

A *quadratic equation* has the form $ax^2 + bx + c = 0$.

4.1 Solving quadratic equations

Quadratic equations can be solved by factorizing or by use of the following formula:

$$x = \frac{-b \pm \sqrt{b^2 - 4ac}}{2a}$$

Simultaneous equations, one linear and the other quadratic, can often be solved by substitution.

4.1.1 Examples

1. The length of a rectangle is 1 m greater than the width. If the area is 150 m², find the length.

    Solution

    If the length is x m, then the width is $(x–1)$. Using the fact that the area is 150:

    $$x(x - 1) = 150$$
    $$x^2 - x - 150 = 0$$
    $$x = \frac{+1 \pm \sqrt{1^2 - 4 \times 1 \times (-150)}}{2 \times 1}$$
    $$x = -11.76 \text{ or } 12.76.$$

    Ignore the negative value

    The length is 12.76 m.

2. Solve the equation $x^4 - 4x^2 + 3 = 0$.

    Solution

    This seems to be a quartic (fourth degree) equation. But it can be regarded as a quadratic in x^2. The expression factorizes.

    $$(x^2 - 3)(x^2 - 1) = 0$$
    $$x^2 = 3 \text{ or } x^2 = 1.$$
    $$x = \pm\sqrt{3} \text{ or } \pm 1$$

3. Find where the line $y = x + 3$ crosses the circle $x^2 + y^2 = 20$.

   Solution

   Substitute the first equation into the second.

   $$x^2 + (x+3)^2 = 20$$
   $$2x^2 + 6x - 11 = 0$$
   $$x = 1.284 \text{ or } -4.284.$$

   Hence: $y = 4.284 \text{ or } -1.284.$

   They cross at $(1.284, 4.284)$ and at $(-4.284, -1.284)$

4.1.2 Exercises

1. Solve the following equations:

   (a) $x^2 + 4x - 77 = 0$

   (b) $2y^2 - 7y - 15 = 0$

   (c) $x^2 + 8x + 3 = 0$

   (d) $5z^2 + 3z - 2 = 0$

   (e) $3x^2 - 8x - 7 = 0$

   (f) $0.1x^2 + 2x - 3 = 0$

2. Solve the following equations:

   (a) $x^4 - 3x^2 + 1 = 0$

   (b) $3y^4 - 2y^2 - 7 = 0$

   (c) $x^6 + 4x^3 + 2 = 0$

   (d) $x^2 = 1 + \dfrac{1}{x^2}$

   (e) $(2x+1)^2 + 3(2x+1) - 9 = 0$

   (f) $\dfrac{3}{y^2} - \dfrac{7}{y}$

3. A rectangle is 3 ft longer than it is broad. If its area is 33 sq. ft. find the width.

4. The area of a circle in cm^2 is 4 greater than its perimeter in cm. Find the radius of the circle.

5. A man rows upstream 5 miles against a current, and then rows back with the current. He can row at 4 mph, and the total time taken is 3 hours. Find the speed of the current.

6. Solve the following pairs of equations:

   (a) $y = x + 1$
       $y = x^2 - 3$

   (b) $y = 2x - 3$
       $x^2 + y^2 = 18$

   (c) $x + y = 3$
       $x^2 - y^2 = 1$

   (d) $2x + 3y = 5$
       $xy = 1$

   (e) $x^2 + 2y^2 = 8$
       $2y + 3x = 1$

   (f) $x^2 + xy + 2y^2 = 4$
       $x + y = 2$

7. The sum of two numbers is 23 and their product is 20. Find the numbers.

8. Find the points where the line $y = x + 2$ crosses the parabola $y = 4x^2$.

9. Find where the line $x + y = 1$ crosses the circle $x^2 + y^2 = 8$.

10. The sum of two numbers is 17, and the sum of their squares is 170. Find the two numbers.

11. By subtracting one equation from the other, find the line which goes through the points of intersection of the circles $x^2 + y^2 = 10$ and $x^2 + y^2 - 9x + y = 0$. Hence find the co-ordinates of the points of intersection.

4.2 Completing the square

A quadratic expression $ax^2 + bx + c$ can be written in the *completed square* form:

$$a(x + k)^2 + l$$

If a is positive, the expression has a least value of l, achieved when $x = -k$. If a is negative, l will be the greatest value.

When completing the square of $x^2 + bx + c$, consider the expansion of

$$\left(x + \frac{b}{2}\right)^2.$$

Examples 4.2.1

1. Complete the square of $f(x) = x^2 + 3x - 1$, and hence find the least value of $f(x)$.

    Solution

    Consider the expansion of $(x + 1.5)^2$.

    $(x + 1.5)^2 = x^2 + 3x + 2.25$

    This is 3.25 greater than $f(x)$.

    $f(x) = (x + 1.5)^2 - 3.25$

    The least value of $f(x)$ occurs when the squared term is zero.

    The least value of $f(x)$ is -3.25

2. Write $2x^2 - 4x - 5$ in the form $a(x + b)^2 + c$, and hence solve the equation $2x^2 - 4x - 5 = 0$, leaving your answer in square root form.

    Solution

    Expanding, $2x^2 - 4x - 5 \equiv ax^2 + 2abx + ab^2 + c$

    Equating coefficients of x^2, $a = 2$

    Equating coefficients of x, $-4 = 2ab$. Hence $b = -1$

    Equating constants, $-5 = ab^2 + c$. Hence $c = -7$

    $2x^2 - 4x - 5 \equiv 2(x - 1)^2 - 7$

    Put $2(x - 1)^2 - 7 = 0$

    $$x = \sqrt{\frac{7}{2}} + 1$$

Exercises 4.2.2

1. Complete the square for the following expressions and hence find their least values.

    (a) $x^2 - 2x + 4$ (b) $x^2 + 4x - 7$

    (c) $x^2 - 5x + 3$ (d) $x^2 + x + 1$

2. For each of the following expressions, complete the square. Hence find the value of x which gives the least or greatest value, stating which it is.

   (a) $2x^2 + 8x - 3$ (b) $-x^2 - 6x + 4$

   (c) $4x^2 - 2x$ (d) $3 - 10x - 2x^2$

3. Complete the square for the following equations by writing the left hand side in the form $a(x + b)^2 + c$, and hence solve the equations.

   (a) $x^2 + 2x - 3 = 0$ (b) $x^2 - 7x + 2 = 0$

   (c) $3x^2 + 6x + 1 = 0$ (d) $2x^2 - 3x - 8 = 0$

4. A stone is thrown up, and after t seconds the amount it has risen is h metres, where $h = 80t - 5t^2$. By completing the square of the expression find the greatest height it reaches.

4.3 Discriminant

The *discriminant* of the equation $ax^2 + bx + c = 0$ is the expression $\Delta = b^2 - 4ac$.

If $\Delta > 0$ then the equation has 2 solutions.

If $\Delta = 0$ then the equation has 1 solution.

If $\Delta < 0$ then the equation has no solutions.

4.3.1 Examples

1. Find the range of values of m for which $mx^2 + 3x + 5 = 0$ can be solved.

   Solution

   The equation can be solved if the discriminant is not negative.

   $3^2 - 4 \times m \times 5 \geq 0$

   $$m \leq \frac{9}{20}$$

2. Find the values of λ if the line $y = \lambda x$ is a tangent to the parabola $y = x^2 + 3$.

   Solution

   Solving the equations simultaneously: $x^2 - \lambda x + 3 = 0$.

   If the line is a tangent, this equation must have exactly one solution. The discriminant is 0.

   $\lambda^2 - 12 = 0$

   $$\lambda = \pm \sqrt{12}$$

4.3.2 Exercises

1. How many solutions do the following equations have?

   (a) $x^2 + x + 3 = 0$ (b) $x^2 - 4x + 4 = 0$

   (c) $2x^2 - 3x - 7 = 0$ (d) $101x^2 + 99x + 24 = 0$

2. For the following equations, find the range of values of λ if there is to be a solution.

   (a) $\lambda x^2 + 2x + 3 = 0$ (b) $x^2 - 3x - \lambda = 0$
   (c) $x^2 + \lambda x + 4 = 0$ (d) $\lambda x^2 + x + 2\lambda = 0$

3. Show that for all values of λ and μ the equation $\lambda x^2 + \mu x - \lambda = 0$ has a solution.

4. Find the value of k which will ensure that $x^2 + kx - k + 1 = 0$ has equal roots.

5. Show that $\lambda x^2 - (\lambda + \mu)x + \mu = 0$ always has solutions, for all values of λ and μ.

6. Find the range of values of λ if the line $y = \lambda x$ meets the circle $x^2 + y^2 + 4y + 1 = 0$.

7. Find the values of λ if $y = \lambda x$ is a tangent to $y = x^2 + 2$.

8. Find the values of μ if $y = \mu x - 3$ is a tangent to $y = x^2$.

9. Find the values of υ if $y = \upsilon x - 4$ is a tangent to $x^2 + y^2 = 1$.

10. Find the values of ρ if $y = \rho x$ is a tangent to $x^2 + y^2 + 8y + 15 = 0$.

Handwritten margin notes:

using the discriminant

$\sqrt{P^2 - 4 \times \lambda \times 2}$
$1^2 - 8\lambda$
$1 - 8\lambda < 0$

4.4 Examination questions

1. Given that $f(x) \equiv 3x^2 + 12x + 17$, find constants a, b, c such that
   $f(x) \equiv a(x + b)^2 + c$.

   (a) Show that $f(x)$ is always positive.

   (b) Find the least value of $f(x)$.

   (c) Solve the equation $f(x) = 7$, giving your answers to one decimal place.

   (d) Sketch the graph of $f(x)$.

   [L ADD]

2. (a) Find the values of p for which the equation $(p + 1)x^2 + 4px + 9 = 0$ has equal roots.

   (b) Find the range of values of m for which the straight line $y = mx - 5$ intersects the curve $y = x^2 - 1$ in two distinct points.

   [C ADD]

3. Given that the roots of the equation $ax^2 + bx + c = 0$ are β and $n\beta$, show that $(n + 1)^2 ac = nb^2$.

   [L]

Common errors

1. **Use of formula**

   When using the formula to solve a quadratic equation, be sure that you do not ignore the signs. For the equation $x^2 - 3x - 4 = 0$ the constants are:

   $a = 1$ (not 0) : $b = -3$ (not 3) : $c = -4$ (not 4)

2. **Completing the square**

Be careful when completing the square of a quadratic. It is often a good idea to expand your result to ensure that you have the correct values. In particular:

$x^2 + 3x + c$ begins $(x + 1.5)^2$, not $(x + 3)^2$.

3. **Simultaneous equations**

When you solve a linear and a quadratic equation, you will usually get two values of x and two values of y. Make sure that the correct value of y goes with the correct value of x.

5 Inequalities

An *inequality* asserts that one expression is less than another.

$x + 1 < 3$, $3x - 2y < 4$, $x^2 + 3x - 7 < 0$ are examples of inequalities.

To *solve* an inequality is to find the range of values for which it is true.

When multiplying or dividing an inequality by a negative number the inequality changes round.

If $x < y$ then $-2x > -2y$.

5.1 Inequalities in one variable

Linear inequalities are solved by the same algebraic operations as linear equations. Quadratic and rational inequalities are solved by factorizing.

5.1.1 Example

Solve the following inequalities:

(a) $2x + 3 < 7$

(b) $x^2 + 3x - 10 < 0$

(c) $\dfrac{1 + x}{3 - x} \geq 1$

Solution

(a) Subtract 3 from both sides, then divide by 2.

$$x < 2$$

(b) Factorize the quadratic.

$$(x + 5)(x - 2) < 0$$

refer to postons notes

The quadratic is zero at –5 and 2. These values divide the number line into three regions. Compile a table to show when the factors are positive and when negative.

	$x < -5$	$-5 < x < 2$	$2 < x$
$x + 5$	$-$	$+$	$+$
$x - 2$	$-$	$-$	$+$
$(x + 5)(x - 2)$	$+$	$-$	$+$

The inequality is satisfied in the middle region: $-5 < x < 2$

(c)   Take the 1 over to the left hand side.

$$\frac{1+x}{3-x} - 1 \geq 0$$

$$\frac{1+x-(3-x)}{3-x} \geq 0$$

$$\frac{2(x-1)}{3-x} \geq 0$$

The method of (a), when expressions are multiplied, applies when they are divided. Proceed as in (a).

The solution is: $1 \leq x < 3$

5.1.2 Exercises

Solve the following inequalities:

1. $3x + 1 > 4$

2. $1 - 2x \geq 2$

3. $1 + x < 6 - 2x$

4. $3(1 + 2x) \leq 2(x - 3)$

5. $x^2 + 8x + 12 < 0$

6. $x^2 - 3x - 18 > 0$

7. $2x^2 - 3x + 2 \geq 0$

8. $x^2 + x - 3 \leq 0$

9. $x^2 + x < 2$

10. $x^2 > 2x + 35$

11. $(x + 1)(x + 2)(x + 3) < 0$

12. $(2x - 1)(x - 3)(3 - 2x) > 0$

13. $(x + 1)^2(x - 1) \leq 0$

14. $x^2(2x + 1) > 0$

15. $\dfrac{(x - 1)(x + 2)}{x + 3} < 0$

16. $\dfrac{(x + 3)(1 - 2x)}{(x + 2)^2} > 0$

17. $x + 3 < \dfrac{10}{x}$

18. $\dfrac{x + 1}{2 - x} > 1$

19. $\dfrac{x}{3} < \dfrac{12}{x}$

20. $\dfrac{x - 2}{x} > \dfrac{x - 1}{x}$

5.2 Modulus inequalities

The *modulus* function $|x|$ gives the positive value of x.

$$|x| = \begin{cases} x & \text{if } x \geq 0 \\ -x & \text{if } x < 0 \end{cases}$$

If $|x| < k$, for k positive, then $-k < x < k$.

If $|x| > k$, for k positive, then $x < -k$ or $x > k$.

The graph of $y = |x|$ is shown in Fig. 5.1

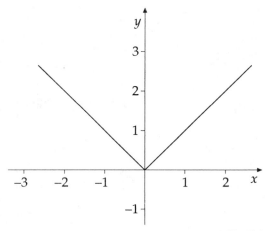

Fig 5.1

Modulus inequalities are often best solved by graphs.

Example 5.2.1

Solve the following inequalities:

(a) $|2x - 1| > 2$

(b) $|x - 3| < 2x$, by drawing graphs

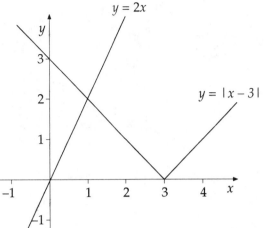

Fig 5.2

Solution

(a) Remove the modulus signs:

$$2x - 1 < -2 \text{ or } 2x - 1 > 2$$

$$x < -\tfrac{1}{2} \text{ or } x > 1\tfrac{1}{2}$$

(b) The graphs of $y = |x - 3|$ and $y = 2x$ are shown. They cross at $x = 1$. The modulus graph is below the linear graph after this value.

$$x > 1$$

Exercises 5.2.2

Solve the following inequalities

1. $|x| < 5$
2. $|x| \geq 4$
3. $|2x| < 1$
4. $|x - 2| < 4$
5. $|x + 3| > 2$

Solve questions 6 to 9 by drawing graphs.

6. $x < |x|$
7. $x > |\tfrac{1}{2}x|$
8. $x + 1 \geq |2x|$
9. $|2x| - |x| \geq 2$

5.3 Inequalities in two variables

Inequalities in two variables correspond to areas on a graph. It is usual to illustrate the required region by shading the areas which are *not* wanted.

5.3.1 Example

Illustrate on a graph the region corresponding to the inequalities:

$$x \geq 0 \; ; y \geq 0 \; ; 3x + 2y \leq 6; 2x + 5y \leq 10.$$

Find the point in the region which gives the greatest value of $x + y$.

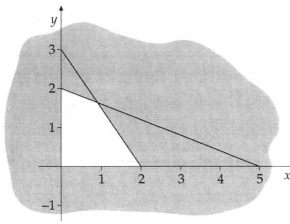

Fig 5.3

Solution

The boundaries of all the regions involved are straight lines. Shade the areas outside the wanted region.

The greatest value of $x + y$ will be at one of the corners of the region. Find the intersection points of the boundary lines. The corners are:

$(0,0)$ (where $x = 0$ meets $y = 0$)

$(0,2)$ (where $x = 0$ meets $2x + 5y = 10$)

$(2,0)$ (where $y = 0$ meets $3x + 2y = 6$)

$(\frac{10}{11}, \frac{18}{11})$ (where $3x + 2y = 6$ meets $2x + 5y = 10$)

The greatest value of $x + y$ is at the fourth of these points.

The greatest value is $2\frac{6}{11}$.

5.3.2 Exercises

1. Illustrate on a graph the region corresponding to the inequalities:
$$x \geq 0 : x + y \leq 3 : y \geq 2x$$

2. Illustrate on a graph the region corresponding to the inequalities:
$$3y + x \geq 2 : 2y + 3x \leq 6 : y \leq 3x + 4$$

3. Illustrate on a graph the region corresponding to the inequalities:
$$y \leq x + 2 : 2x + y \leq 5 : 3y + x + 1 \geq 0$$

4. In the region of Question 1 find the maximum value of
   (a) $x + 2y$ (b) $2x + y$.

5. In the region of Question 2 find the maximum value of
   (a) $x + y$ (b) $2x - y$.

6. In the region of Question 3 find the
   (a) maximum value of $x + y$ (b) the minimum value of $x + y$.

7. Find the ranges of values taken in the region of Question 3 by
   (a) x (b) y.

5.4 Examination questions

1. Find:
   (a) the range of values of x for which $2x^2 + 5x - 12 < 0$

   (b) the range of values of x for which $\dfrac{3}{2 - x} < 1$

   [AEB ADD 1987]

2. (a) Express $x^3 + x^2 - 8x - 12$ as $(x - 3)g(x)$, where $g(x)$ is a polynomial.

   (b) Factorise $g(x)$.   (c) Solve the inequality $x^3 + x^2 - 8x - 12 > 0$.

   [SMP ADD]

3. With the same axes, draw accurately on graph paper the straight lines

$$2x + y = 6, y - x = 3, y + x = 3$$

Indicate clearly the boundary of the region A defined by the three inequalities

$$2x + y \leq 6, y - x \leq 3, y + x \geq 3$$

State the coordinates of the point in the region A at which $2y - 3x$ takes its largest value.

Calculate the area of the region A.

[L ADD]

4. (a) In each of the following cases, find the set of values of x which satisfy the given inequality

    (i) $(x - 2)(4 - x) < 0$ (ii) $\dfrac{3x}{1 - x} \geq 2$

(b) Show, by means of a sketch and shading, that there are values of x and y which satisfy $x + y \geq 7$, $3x - y \leq 13$, and $y^2 = 2x - 1$.

Write down one pair of values of x and y which satisfy all three relationships.

[O ADD]

5. (a) Illustrate the solution set of the simultaneous inequalities

$$9 \leq y + 3x \leq 18, 0 \leq 2y - 3x \leq 18$$

by means of a diagram, and write down the sets of values to which x and y are separately restricted.

(b) Find the solution set of the inequality

$$\frac{2}{x - 3} > \frac{3}{x - 2}$$

where $x \in R$, $x \neq 2$, $x \neq 3$.

[C]

6. Sketch the graph of $y = |2x - 1|$

Determine the set of values of x for which $|2x - 1| > \dfrac{1}{x}$.

[C]

Common errors

1. **Solving inequalities**

    (a) Do not multiply or divide an inequality by a term unless you are sure that the term is positive.

    (b) If the solution to a quadratic inequality consists of two regions, then leave it like that. Write $x < 1$ or $x > 3$, do not write $1 > x > 3$.

2. **Inequalities in two dimensions**

If you are dealing with say the inequality $3x + 2y \leq 6$, then the region is enclosed by the line $3x + 2y = 6$. It is not enclosed by the lines $x = 2$ and $y = 3$.

6 Indices and logarithms

6.1 Laws of indices and logarithms

Indices obey the following laws:

$$a^n \times a^m = a^{n+m}$$

$$a^n \div a^m = a^{n-m}$$

$$(a^n)^m = a^{nm}$$

$$a^{-n} = \frac{1}{a^n}$$

$$a^{m/n} = \sqrt[n]{(a^m)} = (\sqrt[n]{a})^m$$

The *exponential* function is defined as e^x where e is approximately equal to 2.71828.

The *logarithm* function is the inverse of the index function. i.e.: if $a^n = x$, then $n = \log_a x$.

This is read: 'log to the base a of x'. If the base is not mentioned then by convention it is 10.

$$\log x = \log_{10} x.$$

Logarithms to the base e are called *natural logarithms*. They are written as $\ln x$.

$$\ln x = \log_e x$$

Logarithms obey the following laws:

$$\log_a x + \log_a y = \log_a xy$$

$$\log_a x - \log_a y = \log_a x/y$$

$$\log_a x^n = n \log_a x$$

To change the base of logarithms use the following:

$$\log_b x = \frac{\log_a x}{\log_a b}$$

In particular,

$$\log_a x = \frac{\log x}{\log a}$$

To convert to powers of 10 or of e use the following:

$$a^x = 10^{x \log a} = e^{x \ln a}$$

6.1.1 Examples

1. Simplify the expression $2 \log_2 x + \log_2 3$ by writing it as a single log.

   Solution

   First write $2 \log_2 x$ as $\log_2 x^2$. Then use the rule for addition of logs.

   $$2 \log_2 x + \log_2 3 = \log_2 x^2 + \log_2 3$$
   $$= \log_2 (x^2 \times 3)$$
   $$2 \log_2 x + \log_2 3 = \log_2 (3x^2)$$

2. Solve the equation $e^{2x} + 2e^x - 15 = 0$

   Solution

   Note that $e^{2x} = (e^x)^2$. Write the equation as a quadratic in e^x.

   $$(e^x)^2 + 2e^x - 15 = 0$$
   $$(e^x + 5)(e^x - 3) = 0$$
   $$e^x = -5 \text{ or } 3.$$

   $e^x = -5$ has no root.

   The solution for $e^x = 3$ is: $x = \ln 3 = 1.0986$

3. The population of a country is increasing at 3% per annum. At this rate of growth how long will it be before the population doubles?

   Solution

   Every year the population is multiplied by $\frac{103}{100} = 1.03$.

   After x years the population will be multiplied by 1.03^x. If it has doubled after x years, this gives the equation:

   $$2 = 1.03^x$$

   Take logs of both sides: $\quad \log 2 = \log 1.03^x = x \log 1.03$

   $$x = \frac{\log 2}{\log 1.03} = 23.45$$

   The population doubles after 23.45 years

6.1.2 Exercises

1. Without use of a calculator evaluate the following:
   (a) $16^{1/2}$ (b) $100^{3/2}$
   (c) $\left(\frac{1}{4}\right)^{-2}$ (d) $8^{4/3}$
   (e) $5 \times 25^{1/4} \times 125^{1/6}$ (f) $3^{1/2} \div 9^{-1/4}$

2. Simplify the following as far as possible:
   (a) $x^3 \times x^{-2} \div x^5$ (b) $y^{1/2} \times y^{3/2} \div y^{-1}$
   (c) $5^x \times 25^x \times 125^{2x}$ (d) $2^{2n} \times 4^{3n} \div 16^{-3n}$

3. Write the following in logarithmic form:
   (a) $2^4 = 16$ (b) $10^3 = 1000$

(c) $9^{3/2} = 27$

(d) $25^{-1/2} = \dfrac{1}{5}$

(e) $e^2 = 7.34$

(f) $e^{2.0258} = 10$

4. Write the following in index form:

(a) $\log_2 8 = 3$

(b) $\log_9 3 = \dfrac{1}{2}$

(c) $\log 0.1 = -1$

(d) $\log_{16} 8 = \dfrac{3}{4}$

(e) $\ln 6 = 1.792$

(f) $\ln 12.18 = 2.5$

5. Without the use of a calculator evaluate the following:

(a) $\log_2 16$

(b) $\log_5 125$

(c) $\log_9 3$

(d) $\log 0.001$

(e) $\log_2 \dfrac{1}{8}$

(f) $\log_a a$

(g) $\log_a a^2$

(h) $\log_a \dfrac{1}{\sqrt{a}}$

6. Use a calculator to find the following:

(a) $\log_2 3$

(b) $\log_4 9$

(c) $\log_5 2$

(d) $\log_3 0.002$

7. Simplify the following expressions by writing them as single logarithms:

(a) $\log x + \log 2$

(b) $\log_2 x - \log_2 3x$

(c) $\log_2 x + 3 \log_2 x$

(d) $\log x + 2 \log 3x$

(e) $\log x + 1$

(f) $\log_2 x + 2$

8. Solve the following equations:

(a) $2^x = 3$

(b) $10^x = 6$

(c) $3^{x+1} = 4$

(d) $2^{2x-1} = 4^{1-3x}$

(e) $4^x - 5 \times 2^x + 6 = 0$

(f) $3^x = 5^{x-1}$

(g) $2^x \times 3^{x+1} = 10$

(h) $2^x = 5 \div 3^x$

(i) $e^{2x} - 7e^x + 10 = 0$

(j) $e^x + e^{-x} = 4$

9. Write the following equations so that y is the subject.

(a) $\log x + \log y = 3$

(b) $\log_y x = 3$

10. Solve the following equations:

(a) $\log_2 x = 7$

(b) $\log_2 x + \log_2(x+1) = \log_2 6$

(c) $\log x - \log (x-2) = 2$

(d) $2 \log_3 x = 5$

(e) $\log_3 x - \log_9 x = 2$

(f) $\log_x 4 = 5$

(g) $\ln x = 3$

(h) $\ln x + \ln \sqrt{x} = -3$

11. A population is growing at 5% each year. How long will it be before the population has tripled?

12. A man invests £1,200 in a building society at 9% compound interest. When will he have £2,000?

13. A radio-active isotope decays so that each year it loses $\frac{1}{5}$ of its mass. What is its half-life? (The time when it has lost half its mass?)

14. The half-life of an isotope is 8 years. How much is lost after 1 year? How long does it take to lose $\frac{9}{10}$ of its mass?

6.2 Examination Questions

1. (i) Write the cube root of 4 as a power of 2. Hence evaluate $(\sqrt[3]{4})^{4.5}$ without using a calculator or tables, showing the steps of your working.

   (ii) Simplify $\left(\dfrac{x^3 y}{z}\right)^{-2} \times \dfrac{x^4 y^2}{z}$

   (iii) Simplify $\log_b(ab^2) - \log_b a$.

   [MEI ADD]

2. (i) Express as a single logarithm in its simplest form
   $\log_{10} 5 - 3 \log_{10} 25 + 2 \log_{10} 50$.

   (ii) Solve the equation $3 \times 2^{2x} - 7 \times 2^x + 2 = 0$

   [O ADD]

3. (a) Express as powers of 2:

   $\dfrac{1}{16}, \quad 64^a, \quad \dfrac{8^b}{4^c}$

   (b) If $x^x = 30$, without attempting to evaluate x, find the values of $x^{\frac{1}{2}x}$ and x^{3x}.

   (c) Solve the equation $(17.1)^x = 9$

   [O&C ADD]

4. (a) Solve the equation: $2 \log_3 x = 1 + \log_3(18 - x)$

   (b) Given that $3 = a^k$, express in terms of k,

   (i) $\log_a \dfrac{3}{a}$ (ii) $\log_9 3a$

   [AEB 1986]

5. Solve each of the following equations, to find x in terms of a, where $a > 0$ and $a \neq e^2$:

   (i) $a^x = e^{2x+1}$ (ii) $2 \ln(2x) = 1 + \ln a$.

   [C]

6. Evaluate in terms of $\ln 2$

   (i) $\ln 2 + \ln(2^2) + \ldots + \ln(2^n) + \ldots + \ln(2^{100})$

   (ii) $\displaystyle\sum_{n=1}^{\infty} (\ln 2)^n$

   [JMB]

Common errors

1. **Indices**

   Algebraic and arithmetic mistakes are very common when dealing with indices. Pay regard to the following:

   $$a^n \times a^m \neq a^{mn}$$

   $$a^{1/n} \neq \frac{a}{n}$$

   $$a^{-n} \neq -a^n$$

2. **Logarithms**

   Similar mistakes arise when dealing with logarithms. Pay regard to the following:

   $$\log a + \log b \neq \log (a + b)$$

   $$\log a \times \log b \neq \log ab$$

3. **Compound Interest**

   In problems involving compound interest, or percentage growth or decay, remember that the original number is *multiplied* by the same amount each year. Do not *add* a constant amount.

7 Coordinate geometry

7.1 Coordinates of points

Suppose (x_1, y_1) and (x_2, y_2) are points in a plane.

The *distance* between (x_1, y_1) and (x_2, y_2) is

$$\sqrt{(x_1 - x_2)^2 + (y_1 - y_2)^2}$$

The *midpoint* of (x_1, y_1) and (x_2, y_2) is

$$\left(\tfrac{1}{2}(x_1 + x_2), \ \tfrac{1}{2}(y_1 + y_2) \right)$$

Fig 7.1

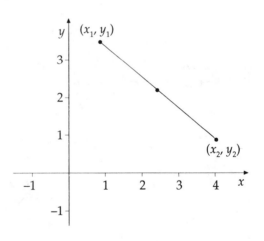

Fig 7.2

7.1.1 Examples

1. Find the distance between (3, 4) and (–1, 8).

   Solution

   Use the formula above, being careful with minus signs.

   $$\text{Distance} = \sqrt{(3 - (-1))^2 + (4 - 8)^2}$$

   $$= \sqrt{32}$$

   $$= 5.66$$

2. Find the midpoint of the line joining (3, 4) and (–1, 8).

   Solution

   Use the formula above

   $$(\tfrac{1}{2}(3 + -1), \tfrac{1}{2}(4 + 8)) = (1, 6)$$

7.1.2 Exercises

1. Find the distances between the following pairs of points:

   (a) (2,1) and (4,7) (b) (0,0) and (2,5)
   (c) (4,6) and (2,9) (d) (2,–3) and (–2,8)
   (e) (–3,–2) and (1,–5) (f) (2,–6) and (–5,–3)

2. By finding the lengths of its sides show that the quadrilateral formed by the points (1,1), (4,5), (4,10) and (1,6) is a rhombus.

3. Show that the points (1,1), (4,3) and (–1,4) form a right-angled triangle. What is its area?

4. Find the midpoints of the pairs of points in Question 1.

5. By showing that its diagonals bisect each other, show that the quadrilateral formed by the points (1,1), (3,5), (9,7) and (7,3) is a parallelogram.

6. Is the quadrilateral of Question 6 a rhombus?

7. Show that the points (0,0), (m,1), (–1,m) form a right-angled triangle.

8. Show that the points (x, y), ($x+\lambda\ y+\mu$), ($x+\mu, y-\lambda$) form a right-angled triangle.

7.2 Equations of straight lines

The *gradient* of a straight line is the ratio of its y-change to its x-change.

The equation of a straight line can be written in the following forms:

❏ $ax + by + c = 0$, where a, b, c are constants.

❏ $y = mx + c$, where m is the gradient and $(0,c)$ the intercept on the y-axis.

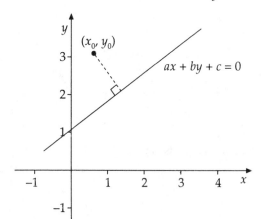

❏ $y - y_0 = m(x - x_0)$, where the gradient is m and the line goes through (x_0, y_0).

❏ $\dfrac{x}{a} + \dfrac{y}{b} = 1$, where $(a,0)$ and $(0,b)$ are the intercepts on

the x and y axes respectively.

$y = mx + c$ and $y = nx + d$ are *parallel* if $m = n$.

$y = mx + c$ and $y = nx + d$ are *perpendicular* if $m \times n = -1$.

Fig 7.3

7.2.1 Examples

1. Find the equation of the line through (1,4) and (2,6).

   Solution

   The ratio of the y–change to the x–change is $6-4 : 2-1 = 2:1$. Use the third form of the equation of a line.

   $$y - 4 = 2 \times (x - 1)$$

   $$y = 2x + 2$$

2. A triangle has its vertices at A(6,1), B(1,6) and C(–3,–2). Find the equations of the perpendicular bisectors of BC and AB. Find the coordinates of the point D where these lines meet, and verify that D is the circumcentre of the triangle, i.e. is the same distance from A, B, and C.

   Solution

   The midpoint of BC is (–1,2). The gradient of BC is 2, hence the gradient of the perpendicular is $-\frac{1}{2}$.

   The equation of the perpendicular is therefore:

   $$y = -\tfrac{1}{2}x + \tfrac{3}{2}.$$

   Similarly, the equation of the perpendicular bisector of AB is:

   $$y = x$$

   Solve these equations simultaneously:

   D is at (1,1)

   Use the definition of distance in 7.1:

   $$AD = BD = CD = 5$$

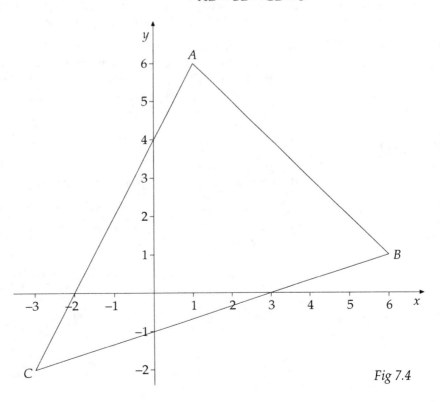

Fig 7.4

7.2.2 Exercises

1. Find the equations of the following straight lines.
   (a) Through (1,1) and (2,5)   (b) Through (2,4) and (5,5)
   (c) Through (2,3) and (3,1)   (d) Through (6,3) and (2,6)
   (e) With gradient 2 and through (3,4)
   (f) With gradient $\frac{1}{2}$ and through (2,1)
   (g) With gradient –3 and through (1,5)
   (h) With gradient $-\frac{3}{4}$ through (1,–3)
   (i) Through (2,3), parallel to $y = 4$
   (j) Through (2,1), parallel to $y = 2 - x$
   (k) Through (5,7), perpendicular to $y = x - 3$
   (l) Through (2,–3), perpendicular to $y = 2x + 1$

2. Find the perpendicular distances between the following points and lines.
   (a) (1,2) and $2y + 3x - 1 = 0$ (b) (3,4) and $y + x + 3 = 0$
   (c) (2,3) and $y = 2x - 4$ (d) (0,0) and $2y = 3x - 1$

3. Show that opposite sides of the quadrilaterals in Questions 2 and 6 of 7.1.2 are parallel.

4. Show that the diagonals of the quadrilateral in Question 2 of 7.1.2 are perpendicular.

5. Show that the quadrilateral formed by the points (1,1), (5,5), (8,2) and (4,–2) is a rectangle. Is it a square?

6. By the method of Question 2 of 7.2.1 find the circumcentre of the triangle formed by (1,4), (0,1) and (4,1). Find the radius of the circumcircle.

7. ABC is the triangle whose vertices are (2,3), (1,–1), (4,3). Find the equations of the sides. Find the equations of the lines through A, B, C perpendicular to BC, AC, AB respectively. Find the point where these three lines intersect. (The *orthocentre* of ΔABC).

7.3 Circles

If a circle has radius r and centre (h,k), then its equation is:

$$(x - h)^2 + (y - k)^2 = r^2$$

7.3.1 Examples

1. Find the centre and radius of the circle with equation:
   $x^2 + y^2 + 2x - 4y - 15 = 0$.

   Find the equation of the tangent at (1,–2).

Solution

Complete the square for x and y.

$(x + 1)^2 + (y - 2)^2 = 1 + 4 + 15 = 20$

The centre is at $(-1,2)$ and the radius is $\sqrt{20}$

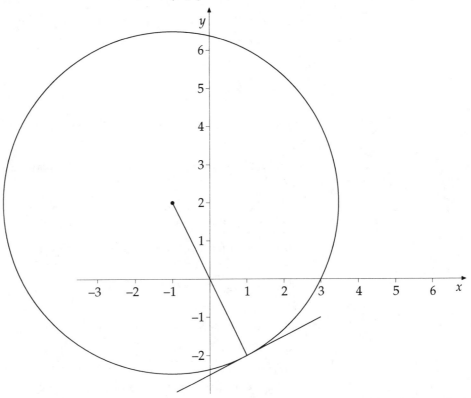

Fig 7.5

The radius from the centre to $(1,-2)$ has gradient -2. Hence the gradient of the tangent is $\frac{1}{2}$.

The tangent has equation $y + 2 = \frac{1}{2}(x - 1)$.

The equation is $y = \frac{1}{2}x - \frac{5}{2}$

2. A is at $(0,3)$ and B is at $(6,0)$. P is such that PA = 2PB. Show that the locus of P is a circle, and find its centre and radius.

Solution

Let P be at (x,y). Use the formula for distance:

$PA = \sqrt{(x^2 + (y - 3)^2)}$ $PB = \sqrt{((x - 6)^2 + y^2)}$

Use the fact that PA = 2PB, and hence $PA^2 = 4PB^2$:

$$x^2 + (y - 3)^2 = 4((x - 6)^2 + y^2)$$

Expand and collect like terms.

$$0 = 3x^2 + 3y^2 - 48x + 6y + 135$$

$$x^2 + y^2 - 16x + 2y + 45 = 0$$

$$(x - 8)^2 + (y + 1)^2 = 20$$

The locus is a circle, with centre $(8,-1)$ and radius $\sqrt{20}$

7.3.2 Exercises

1. Write down the equations of the following circles:
   (a) centre (1,2) and radius 5
   (b) centre (1,–3) and radius 8

2. Find the centres and radii of the following circles:
   (a) $x^2 + y^2 + 4x - 2y - 3 = 0$
   (b) $x^2 + y^2 - 3x - y + 1 = 0$
   (c) $x^2 + y^2 - 6y + 2 = 0$
   (d) $x^2 + y^2 + 3x = 0$

3. Find the equation of the circle with centre (1,3) which goes through the point (2,7).

4. Find the equation of the circle whose diameter is the line between (1,4) and (–3,6).

5. Find the distance from (1,–1) to the line $3x + 4y = 2$. Hence find the equation of the circle with centre (1,–1) which touches $3x + 4y = 2$.

6. Find the equation of the circle which has centre (2,3) and which touches the line $x - 3y + 5 = 0$.

7. Find the equation of the tangent to $x^2 + y^2 + 2x - 6y + 2 = 0$ at the point (1,1).

8. Find where the circle $x^2 + y^2 - 3x + 2y + 2 = 0$ cuts the x-axis. Find the equations of the tangents to the circle at these points.

9. Find the points where the circle $x^2 + y^2 + 3x + 1 = 0$ cuts the line $y = x$. Find the equations of the tangents at these points.

10. P moves so that its distance from the origin is twice its distance from (3,–9). Prove that P moves in a circle, and find its centre and radius.

11. The centre of a circle is on the line $x = 3$, and both the axes are tangents to the circle. Find the equation of the circle.

12. A is at (2,–3) and B is at (4,5). P moves so that PA is perpendicular to PB. Show that P moves in a circle, and find its centre and radius.

13. With A and B as in Question 12, let P move so that $PA^2 + PB^2 = 100$. Show that the locus of P is a circle, and find its centre and radius.

14. Let a circle have centre at C(1,1) and radius 3. Find the distance from P(4,5) to C. Does P lie inside or outside the circle? Find the length of the tangent from P to the circle.

15. Find the values of m so that $y = mx$ is a tangent to the circle $x^2 + y^2 + 3x - 2y + 2 = 0$.

16. Find the values of k so that the line $y + x = k$ is a tangent to the circle $x^2 + y^2 + 4x - 3 = 0$.

7.4 Parameters

If a curve is defined by an equation relating x and y then the equation is the *Cartesian* form of the curve.

If x and y are expressed in terms of a third variable t then t is a *parameter* for the curve. The equations which define x and y in terms of t are the *parametric* equations of the curve.

7.4.1 Examples

1. Let the parametric equations of a curve be $x = t^2 + 1$ and $y = t^3$. Obtain the Cartesian equation of the curve.

    Solution

    Re-write the equations as $t^2 = x - 1$ and $t^3 = y$. Cube the first equation and square the second.

    $$t^6 = (x - 1)^3 = y^2$$

    The equation is $(x - 1)^3 = y^2$

2. Verify that the point $(t^2, 2t)$ lies on the curve $y^2 = 4x$. Find the equation of the chord from $(t^2, 2t)$ to $(1, 2)$. By letting t tend to 1 find the equation of the tangent at $(1, 2)$.

    Solution

    If $y = 2t$, then $y^2 = 4t^2 = 4x$.

    $(t^2, 2t)$ lies on the curve.

    The gradient of the chord is

    $$\frac{2t - 2}{t^2 - 1} = \frac{2(t - 1)}{(t - 1)(t + 1)} = \frac{2}{t + 1}$$

    The equation of the chord is:

    $$y - 2 = \frac{2}{t + 1} (x - 1)$$

    $$(y - 2)(t + 1) = 2(x - 1)$$

    The equation is: $ty + y - 2x = 2t$

    Now put $t = 1$.

    The equation of the tangent is $y - x = 1$

7.4.2 Exercises

1. The parametric equations of curves are given below. Obtain the equations of the curves in a form which does not mention the parameter.

    (a) $x = t^2, y = t^3$

    (b) $x = t, y = \dfrac{5}{t}$

    (c) $x = t + 1, y = 3t - 2$

    (d) $x = 2t, y = t^2 - 1$

    (e) $x = t^3, y = \dfrac{1}{t}$

    (f) $x = t^2, y = \dfrac{1}{1 + t}$

(g) $x = \frac{1}{2}\left(t + \frac{1}{t}\right), y = \frac{1}{2}\left(t - \frac{1}{t}\right)$　　(h) $x = \frac{1}{1 + 2t}, y = \frac{t}{1 + 2t}$

2.　Verify that the point $(t, \frac{3}{t})$ lies on the curve $xy = 3$.

Find the equation of the chord joining the points with parameters p and q.

3.　Verify that the point $(4t, t^2)$ lies on the curve $16y = x^2$. Find the equation of the chord joining the points with parameters 2 and p. By letting p tend to 2 find the equation of the tangent to the curve at $t = 2$.

4.　Show that the point $\left(\frac{1}{1+t^2}, \frac{t}{1+t^2}\right)$ lies on a circle, and find its centre and radius.

7.5 Angles and lines

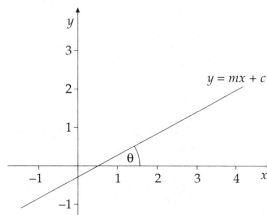

Fig 7.6

If a line has equation $y = mx + c$, then the angle θ it makes with the x-axis is given by $\tan \theta = m$.

The angle between two lines is the difference between the angles they make with the x-axis.

7.5.1 Example

Find the angle that $y = 2x + 3$ makes with the x-axis. Find the angle between this line and the line $2y = x - 4$,

Solution

If the angle is θ then $\tan \theta = 2$.

The angle is 63.4°

Rewrite the equation of the second line as $y = \frac{1}{2}x - 2$. The angle this makes with the x-axis is $\tan^{-1}\frac{1}{2} = 26.6°$. Now subtract.

The angle between the lines is 36.9°

7.5.2 Exercises

1.　Find the angles the following lines make with the x-axis.
   (a)　$y = x + 1$ 　　　　　　　　(b)　$y = 3x - 2$
   (c)　$y = -2x - 1$ 　　　　　　　(d)　$2y = 3x - 1$
   (e)　$4y + 3x = 7$ 　　　　　　　(f)　$\frac{1}{2}y = \frac{1}{3}x + 1$

2.　Find the angles between the following pairs of lines from Question 1:
   (i)　(a) and (b) 　　　　　　　(ii)　(a) and (d)
   (iii)　(b) and (c) 　　　　　　(iv)　(c) and (e)

7.6 Examination questions

1. Find the gradient of the line through A(–4,–1) and C(8,7) and write down the coordinates of E, the middle point of AC.

   Find the equation of the line through E perpendicular to AC and the coordinates of B where this line meets the y–axis.

   Find the equation of the line through C parallel to AB and calculate the coordinates of the point D where this line meets BE produced.

   [MEI ADD]

2. (a) Find an equation of the line l which passes through the points A(1,0) and B(5,6).

      The line m with equation $2x + 3y = 15$ meets l at the point C.

   (b) Determine the coordinates of C.

      The point P lies on m and has x-coordinate –3.

   (c) Show, by calculation, that PA = PB.

   [L]

3. The line L passes through the points A(1,3) and B(–19,–19).

   (a) Calculate the distance between A and B.

   (b) Find an equation of L in the form $ax + by + c = 0$, where a, b and c are integers.

   [L]

4. Find the points of intersection of the circle $x^2 + y^2 – 6x + 2y – 17 = 0$ and the line $x – y + 2 = 0$. Show that an equation of the circle which has these points as the ends of a diameter is $x^2 + y^2 – 4y – 5 = 0$.

   Show also that this circle and the circle $x^2 + y^2 – 8x + 2y + 13 = 0$ touch externally.

   [L]

5. (a) Calculate the coordinates of the centres C_1, C_2 and the radii of the two circles whose equations are $x^2 + y^2 + 2x – 4y – 5 = 0$ and $x^2 + y^2 – 2x – 6y + 5 = 0$.

      Find the coordinates of the points of intersection A, B of the two circles, and show that AB is perpendicular to C_1C_2.

   (b) Show that the point $P(ap^2, 2ap)$ lies on the curve having equation $y^2 = 4ax$ for all values of p.

      The point $Q(aq^2, 2aq)$ is another point on the curve. Show that the equation of PQ is $(p + q)y – 2x = 2apq$.

   If PQ passes through the point S(a,0), show that $q = -\dfrac{1}{p}$, and in this case deduce the coordinates of R, the midpoint of PQ, in terms of p. Hence show that the equation of the locus of R as p varies is $y^2 = 2a(x – a)$.

   [W]

Common errors

1. **Suffices**

    Do not confuse x_3 (the third variable in the series x_1, x_2, x_3) with x^3 (x-cubed).

2. **Arithmetic**

    Throughout coordinate geometry, be very careful of negative signs. The difference between 5 and -3 is 8, not 2.

    When finding distances, do not oversimplify the expression.

    $$\sqrt{(x^2 + y^2)} \neq x + y$$

3. **Gradients**

    The gradient of the line between two points is the *y-change* over the *x-change*. It is not the *y-value* over the *x-value*

    When finding the gradient of a line from its equation, it must first be written in the form $y = mx + c$. The gradient of $2y = 3x + 4$ is $\frac{3}{2}$. It is not 3.

8 Functions

8.1 Composition and inverses of functions

A function $y = f(x)$ can be written in the form $f : x \rightarrow y$. The set of possible x values is called the *domain*, and the set of possible y values is the *range* or *image* or *co-domain*.

The *composition* f°g or fg of two functions f and g is defined by:

$$f°g(x) = f\{g(x)\}$$

The *identity* function i(x) is such that i(x) = x for all x.

The *inverse* of a function f is the function f^{-1} such that:

$$f\{f^{-1}(x)\} = f^{-1}\{f(x)\} = x$$

Equivalently, $f°f^{-1} = f^{-1}°f = i$.

8.1.1 Examples

1. Let f and g be defined by $f : x \rightarrow 3x - 1$, $g : x \rightarrow 2 - 5x$.

    Find   (i) f°g(2)   (ii) g°f(2)   (iii) f°g   (iv) f^{-1}.

    Solution

    (i)   Apply g first and then f. g(2) = –8, f(–8) = –25.

    $$f°g(2) = -25$$

    (ii) Apply f first and then g. f(2) = 5, g(5) = –23.

    $$g°f(2) = -23$$

    (iii) g(x) = 2 – 5x. Apply f; f(2 – 5x) = 3(2 – 5x) – 1.

    $$f°g : x \rightarrow 5 - 15x$$

    (iv) f is obtained by multiplying by 3 and subtracting 1. The inverse is obtained by adding 1 and dividing by 3.

    $$f^{-1} : x \rightarrow \tfrac{1}{3}(x + 1)$$

2. The function h is defined by $h : x \rightarrow 4 - x^2$. Its domain is the set of all real numbers. Find the range of h, and explain why it has no inverse. Restrict the domain of h so that it does have an inverse.

    Solution

    x^2 is always at least 0. Hence $4 - x^2$ is always at most 4.

    The range of h is $\{y: y \leq 4\}$.

h(1) = h(–1) = 3. Hence h^{-1} cannot be defined on 3, for example.

h^{-1}(3) does not exist.

If the domain of h is restricted to positive values of x, then the inverse is

h^{-1} : $x \to \sqrt{(4-x)}$.

Restrict h to the domain $\{x : x \geq 0\}$

8.1.2 Exercises

1. With f and g as in Example 1 above, find:
   (a) g°f(–3)
   (b) f°g(–3)
   (c) g°f
   (d) g^{-1}

2. Let j : $x \to 2x + 3$ and k : $x \to 3x - 4$. Find:
   (a) j°k(–2)
   (b) k°j(–2)
   (c) j°k
   (d) k°j
   (e) j^{-1}
   (f) k^{-1}
   (g) (j°k)$^{-1}$
   (h) (k°j)$^{-1}$
   (i) j^{-1}°k^{-1}
   (j) k^{-1}°j^{-1}

3. For the functions f and g of Example 1 above show that: (f°g)$^{-1}$ = g^{-1}°f^{-1} and (g°f)$^{-1}$ = f^{-1}°g^{-1}

4. The function m is defined by m : $x \to 2 + 5x$, for $x \geq 1$. Find the range of m.

5. Find the inverse of m of Question 4, and find its domain and range.

6. Find the ranges of the following functions:
   (a) $\sin x$
   (b) x^2
   (c) $\cos x + 3$
   (d) 10^x
   (e) $2 \sin x - 1$
   (f) $(x + 1)^2 + 5$
   (g) $x^2 + 4x + 1$
   (h) $(x + 1)^3$

7. For the following functions, state whether or not they have an inverse. Find the inverse if it does exist, and for those functions without an inverse restrict the domain so that an inverse exists.
   (a) $x^2 + 3$
   (b) $3x - 4$
   (c) x^3
   (d) $\sin x$
   (e) $x^2 - 2x - 3$
   (f) $(x + 1)^3$

8.2 Graphs of functions

Standard graphs

Some standard graphs are as shown in Figs 8.1 to 8.7.

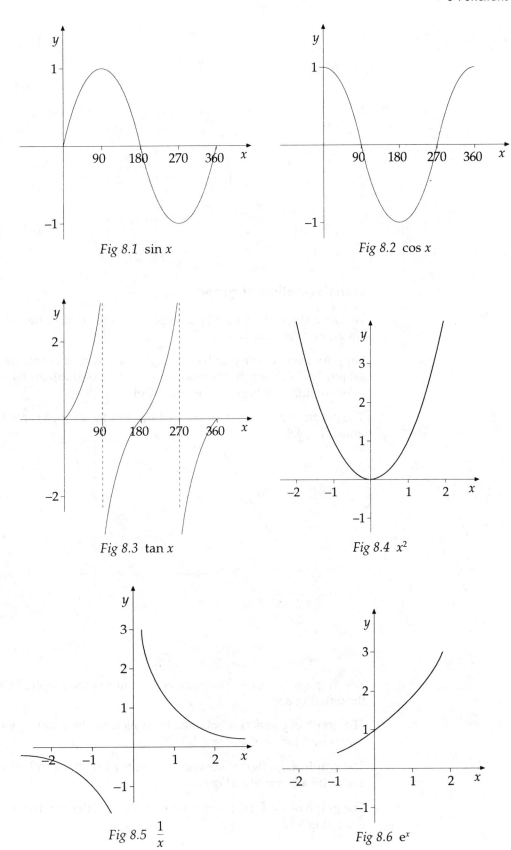

Fig 8.1 sin x

Fig 8.2 cos x

Fig 8.3 tan x

Fig 8.4 x²

Fig 8.5 $\frac{1}{x}$

Fig 8.6 eˣ

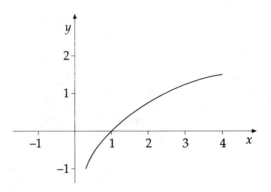

Fig 8.7 ln x

Transformation of graphs

We can convert these standard graphs to more complicated graphs, such as sin $2x$, or 3 cos x, or $(x + 2)^2$.

Suppose we have the graph of $y = f(x)$. The effect of simple transformations on graphs is as follows. In the diagrams the dotted graph is of $y = f(x)$. The filled–in line is of the transformed graph.

The graph of $y = f(x) + a$ is obtained by shifting up the graph of $y = f(x)$ by a units. (Fig 8.8)

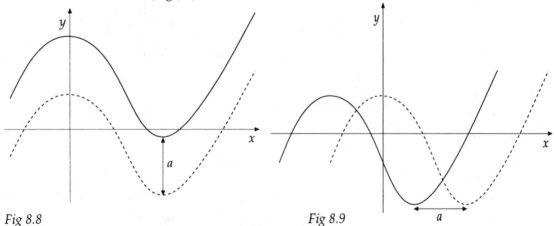

Fig 8.8

Fig 8.9

The graph of $y = f(x + a)$ is obtained by shifting the graph of $y = f(x)$ a units to the left. (Fig 8.9)

The graph of $y = af(x)$ is obtained by stretching the graph of $y = f(x)$, along the y–axis by a factor of a. (Fig 8.10)

The graph of $y = f(ax)$ is obtained by contracting the graph of $y = f(x)$, along the x–axis by a factor of a. (Fig 8.11)

The graph of $y = f^{-1}(x)$ is obtained by reflecting the graph of $y = f(x)$, in the line $y = x$. (Fig 8.12)

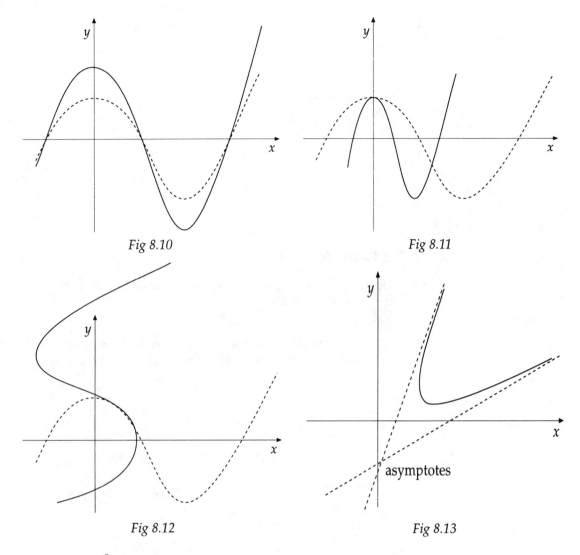

Fig 8.10

Fig 8.11

Fig 8.12

Fig 8.13

Asymptotes

If a graph approaches a straight line, as *y* or *x* tends to infinity, then the straight line is an *asymptote* of the graph. (Fig 8.13)

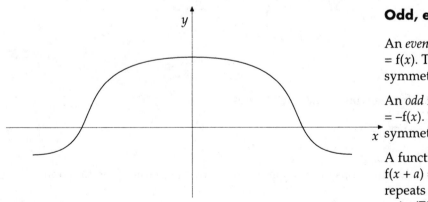

Fig 8.14

Odd, even, periodic functions

An *even* function is one for which f(−*x*) = f(*x*). The graph of an even function is symmetric about the *y*–axis. (Fig 8.14)

An *odd* function is one for which f(−*x*) = −f(*x*). The graph of an odd function is symmetric about the origin. (Fig 8.15)

A function is *periodic* with period *a* if f(*x* + *a*) = f(*x*) for all *x*. The graph repeats itself after *a* units along the *x* axis. (Fig 8.16)

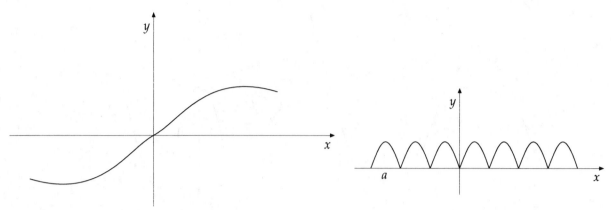

Fig 8.15

Fig 8.16

8.2.1 Examples

1. Using the graph of $y = \sin x$ sketch the graph of $y = \sin 2x - 1$, for x in the range $0° \leq x \leq 360°$.

   Solution

   The graph of $\sin x$ is the dotted line of Fig 8.17. Contract it by 2 in the x direction and shift it down by 1. The result is the filled in line of Fig 8.17.

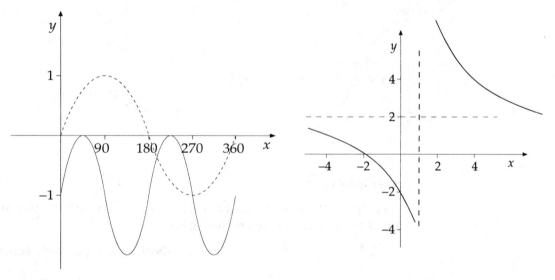

Fig 8.17

Fig 8.18

2. Let a function be defined by

$$y = \frac{2x + 3}{x - 1}$$

   Find the equations of its asymptotes. Draw the graph of the function.

Solution

Use long division, as in Chapter 1, to rewrite y as

$$y = \frac{2x + 3}{x - 1} = 2 + \frac{5}{x - 1}$$

As x tends to infinity, then y tends to 2. As x tends to 1, then y tends to infinity.

The asymptotes are $y = 2$ and $x = 1$

A graph of the curve is shown in Fig 8.18.

8.2.2 Exercises

1. Sketch the graphs of the following functions, for x in the range $0° \leq x \leq 360°$:

    (a) $\cos 2x$

    (b) $2 \sin x$

    (c) $\cos x + 2$

    (d) $3 \sin x - 1$

    (e) $\sin(x - 180°)$

    (f) $2 \cos(x + 45°)$

    (g) $\tan(x + 90°)$

    (h) $3 \sin 2x - 1$

    (i) $\ln (x + 2)$

    (j) e^{2x}

2. Sketch the graphs of the following:

    (a) $\dfrac{2}{x}$

    (b) $\dfrac{3}{x - 1}$

    (c) $\dfrac{1}{1 - x}$

    (d) $3 + \dfrac{1}{x}$

    (e) $2 + \dfrac{1}{x + 3}$

    (f) $1 - \dfrac{3}{x + 2}$

3. Find, where relevant, the equations of the asymptotes of the graphs in Question 2.

4. Sketch, on the same paper, the graphs of e^x and $\ln x$. What is the relationship between the two graphs?

5. Sketch the following graphs:

    (a) $|2x|$

    (b) $|x + 1|$

    (c) $|2x - 1|$

    (d) $|x^2 - 1|$

    (e) $|\sin x|$

    (f) $|x| - 1$

    (g) $|x| - x$

    (h) $|x + 1| - |x|$

6. Sketch the following graphs, and in each case write down the equation of the line of symmetry:

    (a) $x^2 + 3$

    (b) $2x^2 + 4$

    (c) $(x - 2)^2 - 5$

    (d) $x^2 + 4x - 3$

    (e) $x^2 - 3x - 1$

    (f) $3x^2 + x - 4$

7. Each of the following graphs is of the form $y = (x + b)^2 + c$. In each case find the values of b and c.

(a)

(b)

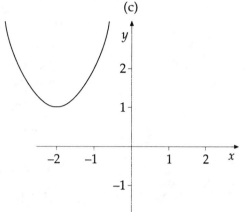
(c)

Fig 8.19

8. Each of the following graphs is of the form $y = x^2 + bx + c$. In each case find the values of b and c.

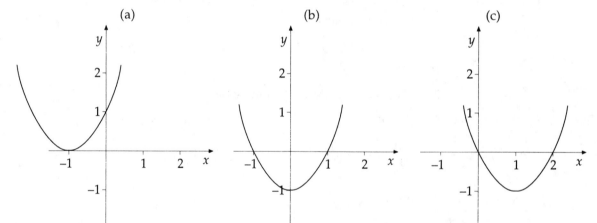

(a)   (b)   (c)

Fig 8.20

9. Each of the following graphs is of the form $y = a + \dfrac{1}{x + b}$. In each case find the values of a and b.

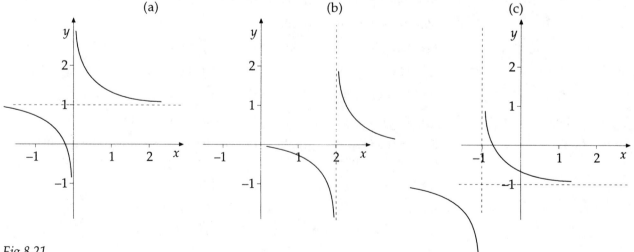

(a)   (b)   (c)

Fig 8.21

10. Sketch the graphs of the following functions:

   (a) $x^3 - x$

   (b) $x + \dfrac{1}{x}$

   (c) $x - \dfrac{2}{x}$

   (d) $x^2 + x - \dfrac{1}{x}$

   (e) $x + \dfrac{3}{x + 3}$

   (f) $1 - \dfrac{1}{x^2}$

   (g) $1 + \dfrac{2}{(x + 1)^2}$

   (h) $x - \dfrac{1}{x^2}$

11. Find the equations of the asymptotes of the graphs in Question 9.

12. Draw the graph of $y = x^3 + 2x^2 - 1$. By drawing a suitable line solve the equation $x^3 + 2x^2 + x - 1 = 0$.

13. Draw the graph of $y = x^2 + \dfrac{1}{x}$. By drawing a suitable line solve the equation $x^3 - x^2 + 2x + 1 = 0$.

14. Draw on the same paper the graphs of $y = \sin 2x$ and $y = \cos x$. Hence solve $\sin 2x = \cos x$, for $0° \leq x \leq 360°$.

15. Draw on the same paper the graphs of $y = \tan x$ and $y = 2 - \sin x$, for $0° \leq x \leq 180°$. Hence solve the equation $\tan x + \sin x = 2$.

16. By drawing suitable graphs solve the following equations. The trigonometric equations are to be solved in the range $0° \leq x \leq 360°$.

   (a) $\cos x = 2 \sin x$

   (b) $e^x = 2 - x$

   (c) $\sin x = \frac{1}{2} + \cos x$

   (d) $\tan x = 2 \sin x$

17. For each of the following functions, state whether they are odd, even or periodic. If they are periodic give the period.

   (a) x^2

   (b) $\dfrac{1}{x}$

   (c) $\sin x$

   (d) $\cos x$

   (e) $x + \sin x$

   (f) $\cos^2 x$

   (g) $x + 1$

   (h) $\tan x$

   (i) e^x

   (j) $\tan 3x$

   (k) $\sin \frac{1}{2}x$

   (l) $\cos(2x - 45°)$

8.3 Examination Questions

1. The functions f and g are defined as follows:

   $f : x \rightarrow x^2$ and $g : x \rightarrow x + 3$

   (i) Show that gf(5) = 28, and write down expressions for the following:
      (a) gf(x)
      (b) fg(x).

   (ii) If the domain is the set of real numbers, state the range of gf.

   (iii) Say whether the inverse of gf is a function, and justify your answer.

   [SMP ADD]

2. (a) A function is defined by $f : x \rightarrow \dfrac{2x - 3}{x + 1}$ for all real values of x except $x = -1$.

      (i) Express f^{-1} and ff in similar form and state the values of x for which these functions are not defined.

      (ii) Express the equation $f(x) = x$ in the form $ax^2 + bx + c = 0$ and hence show that there are no values of x which map on to themselves under the function x.

  (b) The function g is defined by $g : x \rightarrow \dfrac{ax - 4}{x + 1}$ for all real values of x except $x = -1$. Find the positive value of a for which there is only one value of x satisfying $g(x) = x$.

                                             [C ADD]

3. Using the same scales and axes draw the graphs of $y = 2 \sin x$ and $y = \cos(x - 60°)$ between the values $x = 0°$ and $x = 360°$. Take a scale of 2 cm for 30° on the x–axis and 4 cm for 1 unit on the y–axis and plot points corresponding to 30° intervals on the x–axis.

Use your graph to:

(a) solve the equation $2 \sin x = \cos(x - 60°)$, for $0° < x < 360°$,

(b) estimate the range of values of x, between $x = 0°$ and $x = 360°$, for which $2 \sin x < \cos(x - 60°)$.

                                           [AEB ADD 1987]

4. Draw separate sketches of the curves

  (a) $y = x^2 + 1$ (b) $y = (x + 1)^2$ (c) $y^2 = x + 1$.

                                           [AEB ADD 1987]

5. Express $2x^2 - 12x + 9$ in the form $a[(x - r)^2 + s]$, where a, r and s are constants.

The graph of $y = 2x^2 - 12x + 9$ may be obtained from the graph of $y = x^2$ by means of appropriate translations and scalings (stretches). Describe suitable transformations in detail and in the order in which they are to be used.

The function is defined for the domain $x \geq 3$ by $f(x) = 2x^2 - 12x + 9$.

Sketch the graph of $y = f(x)$.

State the domain and range of f^{-1} and determine f^{-1}.

                                                  [JMB]

6.

Fig 8.22

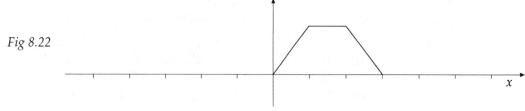

The diagram shows the graph of a function $x \rightarrow f(x)$ over the interval $0 \leq x \leq 3$. You are given that f is an odd, periodic function with period 6. Draw the graph of f over the interval $-6 \leq x \leq 6$.

What is the smallest positive value of *a* for which the function defined by $x \rightarrow f(x - a)$ is an even function?

[SMP]

(7) The figure shows a sketch of the part of the graph of $y = f(x)$ for $0 \le x \le 2a$.

The line $x = 2a$ is a line of symmetry of the graph.

Sketch on separate axes the graphs of:

Fig 8.23

(a) $y = f(x)$ for $0 \le x \le 4a$ (b) $y = -f(2x)$ for $0 \le x \le a$

(c) $y = 3f(\frac{1}{2}x)$ for $0 \le x \le 2a$ (d) $y = f(x - a)$ for $2a \le x \le 4a$.

[AEB 1987]

Common errors

1. **Composition and inverses**

   (a) Do not confuse composition with multiplication, or inverses with dividing.

   $$f°g(x) \neq f(x) \times g(x), \text{ and } f^{-1}(x) \neq \frac{1}{x}.$$

   (b) When finding $f°g(x)$, f must be applied to the *whole* of $g(x)$. If for example $f : x \rightarrow 3x + 1$ and $g : x \rightarrow 2x - 3$, then:

   $$f°g : x \rightarrow 3(2x - 3) + 1 = 6x - 8.$$

   (c) There is nothing special about the letter *x*. Any letter will do to define a function. The function f above could be defined as:

   $$f : y \rightarrow 3y + 1, \text{ or as } f : Z \rightarrow 3Z + 1$$

   (d) $f°g$ means: *do g first and then f*. Do not get this the wrong way round.

2. **Graphs**

   (a) When plotting a curve do not join up the points with straight line segments. Make as smooth a curve as you can between them.

   (b) Changing $y = f(x)$ to $y = f(x + a)$ moves the graph *a* units to the *left*, not to the right.

   (c) Changing $y = f(x)$ to $y = f(ax)$ *shrinks* the graph by a factor of *a*. It does not expand it.

   (d) An asymptote divides the graph into two separate pieces. Do not try to make the graph cross the asymptote.

9 Sine and cosine rules

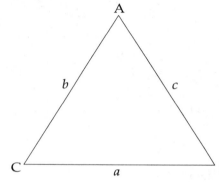

Fig 9.1

9.1 The sine and cosine rules

The *sine rule* and the *cosine rule* extend trigonometry to triangles which are not necessarily right-angled.

When labelling the sides and angles of the triangle ABC, the convention is that each side is labelled with the same letter as the opposite angle. So side c is opposite $\hat{C}$ etc.

The *sine* rule is:

$$\frac{\sin \hat{A}}{a} = \frac{\sin \hat{B}}{b} = \frac{\sin \hat{C}}{c}$$

The rule can be written the other way up:

$$\frac{a}{\sin \hat{A}} = \frac{b}{\sin \hat{B}} = \frac{c}{\sin \hat{C}}$$

The *cosine* rule is:

$$c^2 = a^2 + b^2 - 2ab \cos \hat{C}$$

In this form it gives a side in terms of the other sides and the opposite angle. To find an angle in terms of the sides it can be re-written in the form:

$$\cos \hat{C} = \frac{a^2 + b^2 - c^2}{2ab}$$

A useful formula for the area Δ of a triangle is:

$$\Delta = \tfrac{1}{2} bc \sin \hat{A}$$

9.1.1 Examples

Fig 9.2

1. From the point A, a church spire is on a bearing of 020°. I walk 200 m due North to B, and the spire is now on a bearing of 098°. How far is B from the church?

    Solution

    Fig 9.2 is a diagram of the situation. $c = 200$, $\hat{A} = 20°$, $\hat{B} = 82°$.

    Use of the sine rule gives: $\dfrac{BC}{\sin 20°} = \dfrac{200}{\sin 78°}$ (where $a = BC$)

    BC = 69.9 m.

60

2. In the triangle ABC, $c = 3$, $a = 4$ and $\hat{C} = 43°$. Find the possible values of $\hat{B}$

Solution

Use of the sine rule gives: $\sin \hat{A} = \sin 43° \times \dfrac{4}{3} = 0.909$

$\hat{A}$ could either be acute or obtuse.

$\hat{A} = 65.4°$ or $180° - 65.4° = 114.6°$

$\hat{B} = 71.6°$ or $22.4°$

3. In the triangle ABC, $AB = 5$, $BC = 6$, $CA = 7$. Find $\hat{A}$.

Solution

Use the second form of the cosine rule.

$$\cos \hat{A} = \frac{5^2 + 7^2 - 6^2}{2 \times 5 \times 7} = 0.543$$

$$\hat{A} = 57°$$

4. A tower is 2 miles away on a bearing of 345°, and a spire is 1.4 miles away on a bearing of 036°. How far is the tower from the spire?

Solution

The angle between the two directions is 51°. Use the first form of the cosine rule:

$$TS^2 = 2^2 + 1.4^2 - 2 \times 2 \times 1.4 \times \cos 51°$$

The distance is 1.56 miles

Fig 9.3

9.1.2 Exercises

1. Find the unknown sides in the following triangles.

   (a)   (b)

Fig 9.4

2. Find the unknown angles in the following triangles, given that they are acute.

   (a)   (b)

Fig 9.5

3. Find the unknown angles in the following triangles, given that they are obtuse.

(a)   (b)

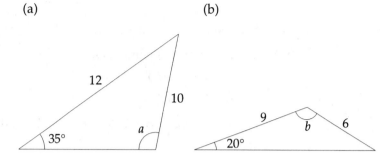

Fig 9.6

4. Find the possible values of the unknown angles in the following triangles.

(a)   (b)

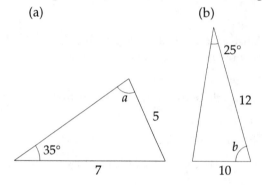

Fig 9.7

5. In the triangle ABC, AB = 5, Â = 45° and B̂ = 56°. Find AC and BC.

6. In the triangle ABC, AB = 12, BC = 14 and Ĉ = 54°. Find the possible values of Â and of B̂.

7. The bearing of a target from a gun is 006°. From an observation point 300 m to the West the bearing is 012°. How far is the target from the gun?

8. Aytown is 20 km from Beetown on a bearing of 080°. The bearing of Ceetown from Aytown is 345°, and from Beetown is 027°. How far is Ceetown from Beetown?

9. A surveyor measures the angle of elevation of a tower as 23°. He walks 50 m towards the tower, yielding elevation 35°. How high is the tower?

10. A mountain is on a bearing of 035°. After walking 2 km due North, I am told that I am now 1.8 km from the mountain. What are the possible bearings of the mountain from my new position? What are the possible distances from my original position to the mountain?

Fig 9.8 (a)   (b)

11. Find the unknown sides in the triangles below left.

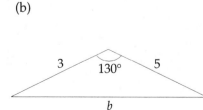

12. Find the unknown angles in the triangles below.

    (a)   (b)

Fig 9.9

13. In the triangle ABC, AB = 12, BC = 14, CA = 13.7. Find the angles of the triangle.

14. In the triangle DEF, DE = 23, DF = 17, $\hat{D} = 76°$. Find EF.

15. I drive 50 miles due North, then turn through 57° and drive a further 43 miles. How far away am I from my starting point?

16. A ship sails 15 km on a bearing of 123°, then for 12 km on a bearing of 284°. How far is it away from its starting point?

17. The hands of a clock are 5 cm and 8 cm long. What is the distance between the tips of the hands at 7 o'clock?

18. The diagonals of a parallelogram are of length 12 cm and 17 cm, and the longer side is 13 cm. Find the angle between the diagonals, and the length of the shorter side.

19. Two guns are 200 m apart, and are 1500 and 1600 m from a target. What is the difference between the bearings of the target from the guns?

20. Find the unknown angles of the triangles below.

    (a)   (b)

Fig 9.10

21. Find the areas of the triangles below.

    (a)   (b)

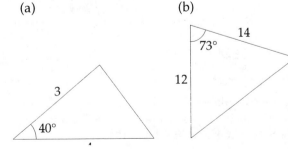

Fig 9.11

22. The triangle ABC has AB = 4, AC = 7, Â = 43°. Find Ĉ.

23. The triangle DEF has DE = 8, DF = 7.3, D̂ = 102°. Find Ê.

24. The triangle ABC has AB = 3, BC = 2.9, AC = 3.7. Find the area of the triangle.

25. The triangle DEF has DE = 7, DF = 8.4, F̂ = 47°. Find the possible values of the area of the triangle.

26. The triangle XYZ has XY = 12, X̂ = 57°, Ẑ = 76°. Find the area of the triangle.

27. The triangle ABC has AB = 12.7, AC = 6.3, BC = 6.2. Find Ĉ. What has gone wrong?

28. Two circles, of radius 12 and 17 cm, are in the same plane with their centres 25 cm apart. Find the length of the chord common to both circles.

9.2 Angles between lines and planes

Straight lines which are not parallel yet which do not cross are *skew* lines. (Fig 9.12)

The angle between two skew lines is found by translating one of the lines until they do cross. (Fig 9.13)

Suppose a line *l* meets a plane *Π* at P. Drop a perpendicular from *l*, meeting the plane at Q. Then the angle between *l* and *Π* is the angle between *l* and PQ. (Fig 9.14)

Fig 9.12   *Fig 9.13*

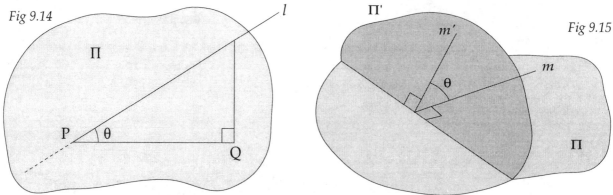

Fig 9.14

Fig 9.15

Suppose two planes *Π* and *Π′* intersect in a line *l*. Take lines *m* and *m′*, in *Π* and *Π′*, which are perpendicular to *l*. Then the angle between *Π* and *Π′* is the angle between *m* and *m′*. (Fig 9.15)

Sometimes it is necessary to use the sine or cosine rules in a 3-dimensional problem.

9.2.1 Examples

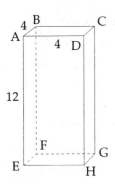

Fig 9.16

1. ABCDEFGH is a cuboid, in which ABCD is a rectangle vertically above EFGH. AB = 4, AD = 4, AE = 12. Find the following angles:

    (a) Between AH and CF.

    (b) Between AG and the plane ABCD.

    (c) Between the planes BDE and BDG.

    Solution

    (a) Translate CF to DE. DE crosses AH at X say. The angle between AH and CF is $A\hat{X}D$.

    The angle between AH and CF is $2 \times \tan^{-1}\frac{2}{6} = 37°$

    (b) First use Pythagoras to find the length of the diagonal of ABCD.

    $AC = \sqrt{(4^2 + 4^2)} = \sqrt{32}$

    The perpendicular projection of AG in the plane ABCD is AC. The angle between AG and ABCD is $C\hat{A}G$.

    The angle between AG and ABCD is $\tan^{-1}\frac{12}{\sqrt{32}} = 65°$.

    (c) The line of intersection of BDE and BDG is BD. If Y is the midpoint of BD, then by symmetry YE and YG are both perpendicular to BD. The angle between the two planes is $E\hat{Y}G$.

    The angle between BDE and BDG is $2 \times \tan^{-1}\frac{\sqrt{8}}{12} = 26.5°$.

2. OA, OB and OC are line segments perpendicular to each other and meeting at O. Their lengths are 5 cm, 8 cm and 7 cm respectively. Find the angle $A\hat{B}C$.

Fig 9.17

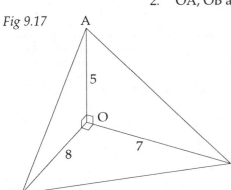

    Solution

    The lengths of AB, BC and CA can be found from Pythagoras.

    $AB = \sqrt{89}$; $BC = \sqrt{113}$; $CA = \sqrt{74}$

    Now use the cosine rule in triangle ABC.

    $$\cos A\hat{B}C = \frac{89 + 113 - 74}{2 \times \sqrt{89} \times \sqrt{113}}$$

    $A\hat{B}C = 50.3°$

9.2.2 Exercises

1. ABCDEFGH is a cube of side 8 units, in which the square ABCD is vertically above EFGH. Find the angles between:

    (a) AC and FH   (b) AD and BE

    (c) AC and BE   (d) AG and BF.

2. In the cube of Question 1, find the angles between the following:

    (a) AH and DCGH   (b) AC and BCGF

    (c) AG and ABCD   (d) AG and ABGH

3. In the cube of Question 1, find the angles between the following:

    (a) ABCD and ABGH   (b) ABCD and BDG

    (c) BDG and BDHF   (d) BDG and CAEG.

4. PQSRWXYZ is a cuboid, in which PQRS is directly above WXYZ. PQ = 6, PS = 5, PW = 7. Find the following angles:

    (a) Between PZ and RX
    (b) Between PY and RQ
    (c) Between PY and QRYX
    (d) Between QRZW and PSYX.

5. VABCD is a pyramid, in which ABCD is a square base of side 8 units. VA = VB = VC = VD = 12 units. Find the following angles:

    (a) Between VA and VD
    (b) Between VA and BC
    (c) Between VA and ABCD
    (d) Between VAB and ABCD.

6. ABCDEF is a wedge, in which ABCD is a horizontal square base of side 10 units, and E and F are 4 units vertically above C and D respectively. Find the following angles:

    (a) Between AC and FE
    (b) Between AE and CD
    (c) Between AE and ABCD
    (d) Between ABEF and ABCD.

7. ABCD is a regular tetrahedron of side 4 units. Find the following angles:

    (a) Between AC and BCD
    (b) Between ABC and ACD.

8. VABCD is a tetrahedron in which VA = 21 cm, VB = 27 cm and VC = 32 cm. VA, VB and VC are at right angles to each other. Find the angle $B\hat{A}C$.

9. ABC is an equilateral triangle of side 80 m on level ground. Vertical poles AD, BE, CF of lengths 11 m, 12 m and 15 m respectively are fixed at A, B and C. The tops of the poles, D, E and F, form the corners of a triangular roof. Find the area of this roof.

10. From the top of a 100 m cliff, Ship A is due North at an angle of depression of 20°. Ship B is on a bearing of 045°, at an angle of depression of 25°. Find the distance of A from B.

11. Three spheres have centres A, B and C and radii 5 cm, 6 cm and 7 cm respectively. They rest on a flat plane touching each other. The spheres meet the plane at D, E and F respectively. Find the angle $D\hat{F}E$.

9.3 Examination questions

1. An observer standing on a cliff 50 m high observes a ship due East at an angle of depression of 5°. Seven minutes later he observes the ship on a bearing of 040° at an angle of depression of 3°. Calculate the speed of the ship in knots and the course which it is taking.

    [1 nautical mile = 1.853 km.]

    [O ADD]

2. The triangle ABC lies in a *horizontal* plane; AB = 3 cm, BC = 8 cm, AC = 7 cm.

    (a) Prove that $A\hat{B}C = 60°$.
    (b) Find, in cm², the area of △ABC.

    The point P is 9 cm *vertically* above A. Calculate, to the nearest 0.5°,

    (c) the acute angle between PB and the horizontal,
    (d) the acute angle between the plane PBC and the horizontal.

    [L ADD]

3. Find the smallest angle and the area of a triangle whose sides are measured as 6.3 m, 7.2 m and 8.1 m.

[MEI]

4. In the triangle ABC, the point D is the foot of the perpendicular from A to BC. Show that:

$$AD = \frac{BC \sin \hat{B} \sin \hat{C}}{\sin \hat{A}}$$

The triangle ABC lies in a horizontal plane. A vertical pole FT stands with its foot F on AD and between A and D. The top T of the pole is at a height 3 m above the plane, and the angle of elevation of T from D is 65°. Given that BC = 7 m, angle B = 62° and angle C = 34°, calculate AF correct to two decimal places.

Find, to the nearest degree, the angle between the planes ATC and ABC.

[JMB]

Common errors

1. **General**

   Make sure that you label the triangle correctly. The formulae are true only if side *a* is opposite angle A etc.

2. **Sine rule**

   When using the sine rule to find an angle, do not forget the ambiguity of the sine function. If $\sin \theta = \frac{1}{2}$, then θ could be either 30° or 150°. Questions are set deliberately to test knowledge of this point.

3. **Cosine rule**

   Arithmetic errors are very common, especially when using the cosine rule to find an angle. After working out the top line of the formula, be sure to press the $\boxed{=}$ button. If you do not do so, then only the c^2 term will be divided by 2*ab*.

   Be sure that you *divide* the top line by 2 and by *a* and by *b*. If your formula is

   $$\cos \hat{C} = \frac{5^2 + 6^2 - 7^2}{2 \times 5 \times 6}$$

   then you should obtain $\cos \hat{C} = 0.2$. If instead you obtain $\cos \hat{C} = 180$, then you have multiplied by 5 and by 6.

4. **Angles between lines and planes**

   Make sure you use the correct lines when finding the angle between a line *L* and a plane *P*. The line within the plane must be the *perpendicular* projection of *L* on *P*.

   Make sure you use the correct lines when finding the angle between two planes *P* and *Q*. The lines must be perpendicular to the line of intersection of *P* and *Q*.

10 Trigonometric equations

10.1 The six trigonometric ratios

The right-angled triangle is labelled as shown. The six ratios between the sides are:

Fig 10.1

$$\sin\theta = \frac{OPP}{HYP}; \; \cos\theta = \frac{ADJ}{HYP}; \; \tan\theta = \frac{OPP}{ADJ}$$

$$\cot\theta = \frac{ADJ}{OPP}; \; \sec\theta = \frac{HYP}{ADJ}; \; \text{cosec}\,\theta = \frac{HYP}{OPP}$$

Some relations between these functions are as follows:

$$\tan\theta = \frac{\sin\theta}{\cos\theta}; \; \cot\theta = \frac{\cos\theta}{\sin\theta}; \; \sec\theta = \frac{1}{\cos\theta}; \; \text{cosec}\,\theta = \frac{1}{\sin\theta}$$

Pythagoras's Theorem gives rise to the three identities:

$$\cos^2\theta + \sin^2\theta \equiv 1$$

$$\sec^2\theta \equiv 1 + \tan^2\theta$$

$$\text{cosec}^2\theta \equiv 1 + \cot^2\theta$$

(Here $\cos^2\theta$ means $(\cos\theta)^2$ etc).

10.1.1 Example

Prove the identity: $\tan\theta + \cot\theta \equiv \dfrac{1}{\sin\theta\cos\theta}$

Solution

Write the left hand side in terms of sin and cos, and add.

$$\tan\theta + \cot\theta \equiv \frac{\sin\theta}{\cos\theta} + \frac{\cos\theta}{\sin\theta} \equiv \frac{\sin^2\theta + \cos^2\theta}{\sin\theta\cos\theta}$$

Use the identity: $\cos^2\theta + \sin^2\theta \equiv 1$

$$\tan\theta + \cot\theta \equiv \frac{1}{\sin\theta\cos\theta}$$

10.1.2 Exercises

1. Prove the following identities.

   (a) $\cos^2\theta - \sin^2\theta \equiv 2\cos^2\theta - 1$

   (b) $\cos^4\theta - \sin^4\theta \equiv \cos^2\theta - \sin^2\theta$

(c) $\sec^4\theta - \tan^4\theta \equiv \sec^2\theta + \tan^2\theta$ (d) $\sec^2\theta + \csc^2\theta \equiv \sec^2\theta \csc^2\theta$

(e) $\dfrac{\tan^2\theta - 1}{\tan^2\theta + 1} \equiv 2\sin^2\theta - 1$ (f) $\dfrac{1}{1 - \sin\theta} + \dfrac{1}{1 + \sin\theta} \equiv 2\sec^2\theta$

(g) $\dfrac{\cos\theta}{1 - \sin\theta} - \tan \equiv \sec\theta$

2. If $\sin x = \frac{3}{5}$ find, without using a calculator, the values of $\csc x$, $\cos x$, $\tan x$.

3. If $\tan x = 2$ find, in square root form, the values of $\sec x$, $\cos x$, $\sin x$.

4. If $\sin x = \dfrac{2t}{1 + t^2}$ find $\cos x$ and $\tan x$ in terms of t.

5. Simplify the following expressions:
    (a) $1 - \cos^2 x$ (b) $2\tan^2 x + 2$
    (c) $\dfrac{1 - \sin^2 x}{\cot x}$ (d) $\dfrac{\cot x}{1 + \cot^2 x}$

6. If $x = 2\cos\theta$ and $y = 2\sin\theta$ show that $x^2 + y^2 = 4$.

7. Find an equation involving x and y, without θ, from the following.
    (a) $x = 3\cos\theta, y = 3\sin\theta$ (b) $x = 2\cos\theta, y = 3\sin\theta$
    (c) $x = \tan\theta, y = \sec\theta$ (d) $x = \frac{1}{2}\cot\theta, y = 2\csc\theta$
    (e) $x = 1 + \cos\theta, y = 2 + \sin\theta$ (f) $x = 3 + 2\cos\theta, y = 2 + 3\sin\theta$
    (g) $x = \cos\theta + \sin\theta, y = \cos\theta - \sin\theta$
    (h) $x = \sec\theta + \tan\theta, y = \sec\theta - \tan\theta$.

10.2 Trigonometric functions for other angles

The definition of the trigonometric functions can be extended to angles other than acute angles.

For $90° \leq \theta \leq 180°$

   $\sin\theta = \sin(180° - \theta), \cos\theta = -\cos(180° - \theta), \tan\theta = -\tan(180° - \theta)$.

For $180° \leq \theta \leq 270°$

   $\sin\theta = -\sin(\theta - 180°), \cos\theta = -\cos(\theta - 180°), \tan\theta = \tan(\theta - 180°)$

For $270° \leq \theta \leq 360°$

   $\sin\theta = -\sin(360° - \theta), \cos\theta = \cos(360° - \theta), \tan\theta = -\tan(360° - \theta)$.

cosec, sec and cot obey the same rules as sin, cos and tan respectively.

For angles greater than 360° or less than 0°, $\sin\theta = \sin(\theta \pm 360°)$. Similar rules hold for all the other functions.

10.2.1 Examples

1. Solve for $0° \leq \theta \leq 180°$, $\cos 2\theta = 0.25$.

Solution

Using the **inv cos** button, $2\theta = 76°$. By the formulae above, there is also a value in the range 270° to 360°.

$2\theta = 76°$ or $360° - 76° = 284°$

$\theta = 38°$ or $142°$

2. Solve for $0° \leq \theta \leq 360°$, $2\cos^2\theta + \sin\theta - 1 = 0$.

Solution

Write $\cos^2\theta$ as $1 - \sin^2\theta$ and rearrange.

$1 + \sin\theta - 2\sin^2\theta = 0$.

This factorizes, giving: $(1 - \sin\theta)(2\sin\theta + 1) = 0$

The first bracket gives $\sin\theta = 1$, so $\theta = 90°$.

The second bracket gives $\sin\theta = -\frac{1}{2}$, which has solutions in the ranges 180° to 270° and 270° to 360°.

$\theta = 90°$ or $210°$ or $330°$

10.2.2 Exercises

1. Express the following in terms of ratios of acute angles.
   (a) $\sin 156°$ (b) $\cos 220°$
   (c) $\tan 325°$ (d) $\cot 130°$
   (e) $\sec 370°$ (f) $\mathrm{cosec}\ 784°$

2. Solve the following equations, giving all the solutions in the range 0° to 360°.
   (a) $\sin\frac{1}{2}x = 0.3$ (b) $\tan 2x = 3$
   (c) $\sin(x + 60°) = 0.3$ (d) $\cos(x - 20°) = 0.4$
   (e) $\sec x = 4$ (f) $\mathrm{cosec}(x - 50°) = 1.5$
   (g) $\cot\frac{1}{2}x = 2.5$ (h) $\cos\frac{1}{2}x = -0.3$
   (i) $\sin(x - 30°) = -0.1$ (j) $\tan(50° - x) = 1.9$

3. Find x in the range $0° \leq x \leq 360°$, if $\sin x = \frac{3}{5}$ and $\cos x = -\frac{4}{5}$.

4. Find x in the range $0° \leq x \leq 360°$, if $\cos x = -\frac{5}{13}$ and $\sin x = -\frac{12}{13}$.

5. If $\sin x = \frac{8}{17}$ find $\cos x$, given that x is between 90° and 180°.

6. If $\tan x = -\frac{7}{24}$ find $\mathrm{cosec}\ x$, given that x is between 90° and 180°.

7. Solve the following equations, giving all the solutions in the range 0° to 180°.
   (a) $\sin^2 x = 0.5$ (b) $\tan^2 x = 3$
   (c) $3\cos x = \sec x$ (d) $\tan x = 2\cot x$
   (e) $5\cos x = \sin x$ (f) $\sin x = \tan x$
   (g) $\tan^2 x - 5\sec x + 7 = 0$ (h) $4\cos x + \sec x = 4$
   (i) $\tan x + \cot x = 2$

10.3 Compound angles

Trigonometric functions of sums and differences of angles can be found by the following formulae.

$$\sin(A + B) = \sin A \cos B + \cos A \sin B$$

$$\sin(A - B) = \sin A \cos B - \cos A \sin B$$

$$\cos(A + B) = \cos A \cos B - \sin A \sin B$$

$$\cos(A - B) = \cos A \cos B + \sin A \sin B$$

$$\tan(A + B) = \frac{\tan A + \tan B}{1 - \tan A \tan B}$$

$$\tan(A - B) = \frac{\tan A - \tan B}{1 + \tan A \tan B}$$

Important cases occur when A = B.

$$\sin 2A = 2 \sin A \cos A$$

$$\cos 2A = \cos^2 A - \sin^2 A$$

$$= 2 \cos^2 A - 1$$

$$= 1 - 2 \sin^2 A$$

$$\tan 2A = \frac{2 \tan A}{1 + \tan^2 A}$$

The following are known as factor formulae:

$$\sin C + \sin D = 2 \sin \tfrac{1}{2}(C + D) \cos \tfrac{1}{2}(C - D)$$

$$\sin C - \sin D = 2 \sin \tfrac{1}{2}(C - D) \cos \tfrac{1}{2}(C + D)$$

$$\cos C + \cos D = 2 \cos \tfrac{1}{2}(C + D) \cos \tfrac{1}{2}(C - D)$$

$$\cos C - \cos D = 2 \sin \tfrac{1}{2}(C + D) \sin \tfrac{1}{2}(D - C)$$

10.3.1 Examples

1. If θ and φ are acute angles, for which $\sin \theta = \frac{3}{5}$ and $\sin \varphi = \frac{5}{13}$, find $\sin(\theta + \varphi)$ without using a calculator.

    Solution

    Using the identity $\cos^2 A + \sin^2 A \equiv 1$, $\cos \theta = \frac{4}{5}$ and $\cos \varphi = \frac{12}{13}$. Apply the formula above:

    $$\sin(\theta + \varphi) = \sin \theta \cos \varphi + \cos \theta \sin \varphi$$

    $$= \tfrac{3}{5} \times \tfrac{12}{13} + \tfrac{4}{5} \times \tfrac{5}{13}$$

    $$\sin(\theta + \varphi) = \tfrac{56}{65}$$

2. Use the fact that $\cos 30° = \frac{1}{2}\sqrt{3}$ to find an expression for $\cos 15°$, without using a calculator.

    Solution

    Let A = 15° in the formula for cos 2A above.

$$\cos 30° = 2\cos^2 15° - 1.$$

Make $\cos 15°$ the subject of this formula.

$$\cos 15° = \sqrt{(\tfrac{1}{2} + \tfrac{1}{4}\sqrt{3})}$$

3. Prove the identity:

$$\frac{\sin 2x + \sin 2y}{\sin 2x - \sin 2y} \equiv \frac{\tan(x + y)}{\tan(x - y)}$$

Solution

Factorize both top and bottom of the left hand side:

$$\frac{\sin 2x + \sin 2y}{\sin 2x - \sin 2y} \equiv \frac{2\sin\tfrac{1}{2}(2x+2y)\cos\tfrac{1}{2}(2x-2y)}{2\cos\tfrac{1}{2}(2x+2y)\sin\tfrac{1}{2}(2x-2y)}$$

$$\equiv \frac{\sin(x + y)\cos(x - y)}{\cos(x + y)\sin(x - y)}$$

Use the fact that $\tan\theta \equiv (\sin\theta)/(\cos\theta)$.

$$\frac{\sin 2x + \sin 2y}{\sin 2x - \sin 2y} \equiv \frac{\tan(x + y)}{\tan(x - y)}$$

10.3.2 Exercises

1. Simplify the following expressions, without using a calculator.
   (a) $\sin 10°\cos 30° + \cos 10°\sin 30°$ (b) $\cos 30°\cos 50° + \sin 30°\sin 50°$
   (c) $\sin A \cos 2A - \cos A \sin 2A$ (d) $\cos^2 2A - \sin^2 2A$

2. Simplify
   (a) $\sin 40° \cos 40°$ (b) $\dfrac{2\tan 20°}{1 - \tan^2 20°}$

3. Letting α be the angle such that $\sin\alpha = \tfrac{3}{5}$, $\cos\alpha = \tfrac{4}{5}$, express in terms of α and θ:
   (a) $\tfrac{4}{5}\sin\theta + \tfrac{3}{5}\cos\theta$ (b) $\tfrac{4}{5}\cos\theta + \tfrac{3}{5}\sin\theta$

4. $\cos 45° = \sin 45° = \tfrac{1}{\sqrt{2}}$, $\sin 30° = \cos 60° = \tfrac{1}{2}$, $\sin 60° = \cos 30° = \tfrac{\sqrt{3}}{2}$.

   Use these values to obtain square root expressions for the following. Do not use a calculator.
   (a) $\sin 75°$ (b) $\sin 15°$
   (c) $\cos 75°$ (d) $\tan 15°$
   (e) $\cos 22.5°$ (f) $\tan 22.5°$

5. Without using a calculator find the value of $\tan x$, given that $\tan(45° + x) = 3$

6. If α and β are acute angles so that $\sin\alpha = \tfrac{3}{5}$ and $\sin\beta = \tfrac{5}{13}$, find the values of the following.
   (a) $\sin(\alpha + \beta)$ (b) $\sin(\alpha - \beta)$
   (c) $\cos(\alpha - \beta)$ (d) $\tan(\alpha + \beta)$

7. Solve the following equations, for values of θ between $0°$ and $180°$.
    (a) $\sin 2\theta = 1.7 \sin \theta$
    (b) $\cos 2\theta + \cos \theta = 1$
    (c) $\sin(\theta + 30°) = \cos(\theta - 60°)$
    (d) $4 \sin(45° - \theta) = \cos(\theta + 45°)$
    (e) $\tan 2\theta = 3 \tan \theta$
    (f) $\tan(\theta + 45°) = 3 \tan \theta$

8. Prove the following identities.
    (a) $\sin(A + B) + \sin(A - B) \equiv 2 \sin A \cos B$
    (b) $\cos(A + B) + \cos(A - B) \equiv 2 \cos A \cos B$

9. Use the factor formulae to prove the following identities:
    (a) $\dfrac{\cos A - \cos B}{\sin A + \sin B} \equiv \tan\frac{1}{2}(B - A)$
    (b) $\dfrac{\sin X + \sin Y}{\cos X + \cos Y} \equiv \tan\frac{1}{2}(X + Y)$
    (c) $\sin x + \sin(x + 120°) + \sin(x + 240°) \equiv 0.$

10. Use the factor formulae to solve the following equations, for $0° \leq x \leq 180°$:
    (a) $\sin x + \sin(x - 60°) = 1$
    (b) $\cos x + \cos 3x = 0$
    (c) $\sin 5x + \sin x = \cos 2x$
    (d) $\cos(x + 10°) + \cos(x - 10°) = \frac{1}{2}$
    (e) $\sin(x + 30°) \sin(x - 30°) = \frac{1}{2}$
    (f) $\cos x + \cos 3x = \sin x + \sin 3x$

11. Writing $3A = 2A + A$, find an expression for $\cos 3A$ in terms of $\cos A$ only.

12. Find an expression for $\sin 3A$ in terms of $\sin A$ only.

10.4 The form $a \sin \theta + b \cos \theta$

$a \sin \theta + b \cos \theta \equiv \sqrt{(a^2 + b^2)} \sin(\theta + \alpha)$, where $\tan \alpha = \dfrac{b}{a}$.

$a \sin \theta + b \cos \theta \equiv \sqrt{(a^2 + b^2)} \cos(\theta - \beta)$, where $\tan \beta = \dfrac{a}{b}$.

10.4.1 Examples

1. Find the range of the function $y = 8 \sin x + 15 \cos x$.
    Solution

    Use the formula above.

    $y = \sqrt{(8^2 + 15^2)} \sin(x + \alpha) = 17 \sin(x + \alpha)$

    Whatever the value of α, $\sin(x + \alpha)$ lies between -1 and 1.

    $$-17 \leq y \leq 17$$

2. Solve the equation $3 \sin x + 4 \cos x = 1$, for $0° \leq x \leq 360°$.
    Solution

    Use the formula above to rewrite the equation.

    $5 \sin(x + \alpha) = 1$, where $\alpha = \tan^{-1}\frac{4}{3} = 53.1°$.

    $$x + \alpha = \sin^{-1}\tfrac{1}{5} = 11.5° \text{ or } 168.5° \text{ or } 371.5°.$$

    When α is subtracted the first value becomes out of range.

    $$x = 115° \text{ or } 318°$$

10.4.2 Exercises

1. Write the following in the form $r \sin(x + \alpha)$, stating the values of r and α.

   (a) $3 \sin x + 4 \cos x$ (b) $4 \sin x - 5 \cos x$

   (c) $6 \cos x - 3 \sin x$ (d) $\sin x - \cos x$

   (e) $\frac{1}{2} \sin x + \frac{1}{4} \cos x$ (f) $\frac{3}{2} \sin x - \frac{1}{8} \cos x$

2. Find the greatest value of each of the functions in Question 1, and the value of x which gives the maximum.

3. Write down the range of values of the functions in Question 1.

4. Solve the following equations, for values of x between $-180°$ and $180°$.

   (a) $2 \sin x + 3 \cos x = 1$ (b) $4 \sin x - 5 \cos x = 3$

   (c) $7 \sin x + 8 \cos x = 9$ (d) $12 \sin x - 11 \cos x = 13$

5. Write $y = 3 \sin x + 4 \cos x$ in the form $r \sin(x + \alpha)$. Show that y can also be written as $s \cos(x - \beta)$, giving the values of s and β. Solve the equation $y = 2.5$ in the range $-180° \leq x \leq 180°$, using both forms of y. Check that your answers are the same.

10.5 Examination questions

1. Prove the identity:
$$\frac{1 + \sin x}{\cos x} + \frac{\cos x}{1 + \sin x} \equiv 2 \sec x$$

   [C ADD]

2. Solve the equations below, giving all the answers in the range $0° \leq x \leq 360°$:

   (i) $\cos 2x = 0.35$,   (ii) $\tan x - 4 \cot x = 3$

   (iii) $8 \sin^2 x - 8 \sin x + 3 \cos^2 x = 0$

   [O&C ADD]

3. (i) On the same diagram, sketch the graphs of $y = 3 \cos x$ and $y = 2 \sin 2x$ in the interval $0° \leq x \leq 360°$.

   (ii) By using the formula for $\sin 2x$, solve by calculation the equation $2 \sin 2x = 3 \cos x$ in the same interval.

   (iii) Solve the inequality $2 \sin 2x \geq 3 \cos x$ in this interval.

   [SMP ADD]

4. (i) *Without the use of tables or a calculator*, find the values of

   (a) $\sin 40° \cos 10° - \cos 40° \sin 10°$

   (b) $\frac{1}{\sqrt{2}} \cos 15° - \frac{1}{\sqrt{2}} \sin 15°$ (c) $\frac{1 - \tan 15°}{1 - \tan 15°}$

   (ii) Find, to one decimal place, the elements of the set $\{x: 0° \leq x \leq 360°\}$ which satisfy the equation $2 \sin x° = \cos(x° - 60°)$

   [L ADD]

5. Show that $\tan A + \tan B = \dfrac{\sin(A + B)}{\cos A \cos B}$ and use it to find all the angles in the range $0 \leq x \leq 180°$ which satisfy the equation $\tan x + \tan 3x = \tan 4x$.

   [O]

6. Determine all of the angles between $0°$ and $180°$ which satisfy the equation

$$\cos 5\theta + \cos 3\theta = \sin 3\theta + \sin \theta$$

[NI]

7. Express $3 \cos x + 4 \sin x$ in the form $R \cos(x - \alpha)$, where R is positive and α lies between $0°$ and $90°$.

What are the maximum and minimum values of $3 \cos x + 4 \sin x$, and for what values of x in the range $0°$ to $360°$ do they occur?

Draw the graph of $y = 3 \cos x + 4 \sin x$ for values of x, at intervals of $30°$, in the range $0°$ to $360°$, taking 1 cm to represent $30°$ on the x axis and 1 cm to represent 1 unit on the y axis.

Using your graph, and giving solutions in the range $0°$ to $360°$:

(i) solve the equation $6 \cos x + 8 \sin x = 7$;

(ii) solve the inequality $6 \cos x + 8 \sin x < 7$.

[SUJB]

Common errors

1. **Identities**

   Do not confuse identities and equations. An identity is true for all values of x. An equation is only true for some values, and we find these values when we solve the equation.

   When proving an identity, do not assume the answer, i.e. do not start with the expression you are asked to show true. Start with one side, and show that it can be reduced to the other side. Alternatively, show that both sides can be reduced to the same expression.

2. **Solving equations**

   When you are solving an equation in the range $0°$ to $360°$, you must give all the solutions. The trig functions take each value twice in that range.

   When solving say $\sin 2x = 0.5$ in the range $0°$ to $360°$, you must consider the values of $\sin^{-1} 0.5$ up to $720°$. When you divide $2x$ by 2 the value will be less than $360°$.

   When solving an equation of the form $\sin(x + \alpha) = 0.5$ in the range $0°$ to $360°$, you may have to consider values of $\sin^{-1} 0.5$ greater than $360°$, for when α is subtracted, the result may be within the correct range.

   When you solve a quadratic in $\cos x$, you might get the answer $\cos x = 2$ or $\frac{1}{2}$. Only the $\frac{1}{2}$ value is relevant here – do not worry about the impossible value of 2.

3. **Compound angles**

   These formulas must be used when finding sin or cos of compound angles. Be aware of the following:

   $$\sin(A + B) \neq \sin A + \sin B$$

11 Radians

11.1 Radians

Often angles are measured in terms of *radians* rather than degrees.

If a sector of a circle with radius r subtends an arc of length α, then the angle of the sector measured in radians is α/r. (Fig 11.1)

There are 2π radians in a circle. A right angle is $\frac{1}{2}\pi$ radians.

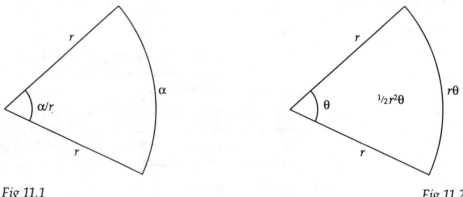

Fig 11.1   Fig 11.2

To convert degrees to radians, multiply by $\pi/180$.

To convert radians to degrees, multiply by $180/\pi$.

Suppose a circle has radius r. Then a sector which subtends θ radians at the centre of the circle has area $\frac{1}{2}r^2\theta$ *(Fig 11.2)*.

The length of an arc which subtends θ radians at the centre of a circle radius r is $r\theta$.

Angular velocity is measured in radians per second.

Inverse trig. functions

The ranges of the inverse trig. functions are as follows.

For sin and cosec. $-\frac{1}{2}\pi \le \theta \le \frac{1}{2}\pi$

For cos and sec. $0 \le \theta \le \pi$

For tan and cot. $-\frac{1}{2}\pi < \theta < \frac{1}{2}\pi$

11.1.1 Examples

1. Solve the equation tan $x = 3$, giving all the solutions in the range 0 to 2π.

   Solution

   If you have a scientific calculator, then it will work directly in radians.

   If your calculator works only in degrees, then multiply tan$^{-1}3$ by $\pi/180$. In both cases the answer is tan$^{-1}3 = 1.25$.

   There is another solution between π and $3\pi/2$.

   $$x = 1.25 \text{ or } \pi + 1.25 = 4.39$$

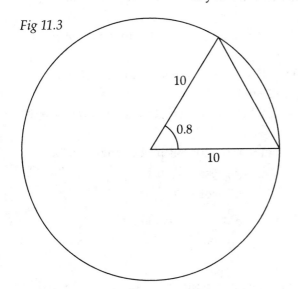

Fig 11.3

2. A circle with radius 10 cm is cut by a chord which subtends 0.8 radians at the centre. (Fig 11.3). Find the area of the smaller segment.

   Solution

   The area of the sector is $\frac{1}{2} \times 10^2 \times 0.8$.

   The area of the triangle is $\frac{1}{2} \times 10^2 \times \sin 0.8$.

   The area of the segment is the difference between these.

   $$\text{Area} = \tfrac{1}{2} \times 10^2 (0.8 - \sin 0.8) = 4.13 \text{ cm}^2$$

11.1.2 Exercises

1. Convert the following to radians, leaving your answers in terms of π.
   (a) 180°   (b) 60°
   (c) 240°   (d) 30°
   (e) 10°

2. Convert the following to degrees.
   (a) $\frac{1}{3}\pi$ (b) 1.3
   (c) 3.7   (d) 4π
   (e) $\frac{1}{4}\pi$

3. A wheel is spinning at 50 revolutions per minute. What is its angular speed?

4. Convert an angular speed of 20 radians per second to revolutions per minute.

5. What are the angular speeds of the minute and hour hands of a clock?

6. A wheel of radius 2 m rolls along the floor at an angular speed of 35. What is the speed of the centre of the wheel in m s^{-1}?

7. The wheel of a cycle is of radius 45 cm. What is the angular speed of the wheel when the cycle is moving at 4 m s^{-1}?

8. What is the angular speed of
   (a) the earth about its axis   (b) the earth about the sun?

9. A sector of a circle radius 5 cm has angle 0.4. Find the arc length of the sector and the area of the sector.

10. An arc of length 3 cm lies on a circle of radius 15 cm. What angle does the arc subtend at the centre?

11. An arc of length 5 cm subtends an angle of 1.1. What is the radius of the circle?

12. A chord subtends 1.05 at the centre of a circle radius 12 cm. Find the areas of the minor and major segments.

13. Two circles, each of radius 10 cm, have their centres 15 cm apart. Find the area which is common to both the circles.

14. A circle of radius r has a sector of which the arc length is a. Find the area of the sector in terms of r and a.

15. Solve the following equations, giving the solutions in the range 0 to 2π.

    (a) $\sin x = 0.2$ (b) $\cos x = -0.4$

    (c) $\tan x = 2$ (d) $\cot x = -\frac{1}{2}$

    (e) $\sec^2 x + \tan x = 1$ (f) $\operatorname{cosec} x = \frac{5}{2}\sin x$

    (g) $\sin(\frac{1}{3}\pi + x) = 0.1$ (h) $\tan(\frac{1}{2}\pi - x) = 1.8$

    (i) $6\sin^2 x - 5\sin x - 1 = 0$

16. Use your calculator to verify that the inverse functions $\sin^{-1}$, $\cos^{-1}$, $\tan^{-1}$ do lie within the ranges given.

17. Without a calculator find the following

    (a) $\sin^{-1}(-\frac{1}{2})$ (b) $\cos^{-1}(-1)$

    (c) $\cot^{-1}(-1)$ (d) $\sin^{-1}(\sin 2\pi)$

    (e) $\cos^{-1}(\cos(-\frac{1}{6}\pi))$ (f) $\tan^{-1}(\tan 2)$

18. Show that for $-1 \le x \le 1$, $\cos^{-1}x + \sin^{-1}x$ is constant, and find its value.

11.2 Small angles

If θ is a small angle measured in radians, then the following approximations hold.

$$\sin\theta \approx \theta,\ \tan\theta \approx \theta,\ \cos\theta \approx 1 - \tfrac{1}{2}\theta^2$$

11.2.1 Example

Find an approximation for $\dfrac{\theta\sin\theta}{1-\cos\theta}$, valid when θ is small.

Solution

Rewrite the function using the approximations above.

$$\frac{\theta\sin\theta}{1-\cos\theta} \approx \frac{\theta\times\theta}{1-(1-\tfrac{1}{2}\theta^2)}$$

$$= \frac{\theta^2}{\tfrac{1}{2}\theta^2}$$

$$\frac{\theta\sin\theta}{1-\cos\theta} \approx 2$$

11.2.2 Exercises

1. Find approximations for the following, valid when θ is small.

    (a) $\dfrac{\sin \theta}{\tan \theta}$

    (b) $\dfrac{\sin 2\theta}{\theta}$

    (c) $\dfrac{1 - \cos \theta}{\theta^2}$

    (d) $\dfrac{\sec \theta - 1}{\theta^2}$

    (e) $\dfrac{\sin \theta \tan 2\theta}{1 - \cos 3\theta}$

    (f) $\tan(\tfrac{1}{4}\pi + \theta)$

    (g) $\cot(\tfrac{1}{4}\pi - 2\theta)$

2. Find an expression for $\dfrac{\tan(\tfrac{1}{4}\pi + \theta) - \tan\tfrac{1}{4}\pi}{\theta}$, valid when θ is small.

3. Use the values $\sin \tfrac{1}{6}\pi = \tfrac{1}{2}$, $\cos \tfrac{1}{6}\pi = \tfrac{1}{2}\sqrt{3}$ to find an approximation for $\sin(\tfrac{1}{6}\pi + \theta)$.

4. Find an approximation for $\dfrac{\cos(\tfrac{1}{3}\pi + \theta) - \cos\tfrac{1}{3}\pi}{\theta}$.

5. Show that $\sin 1° \approx \dfrac{\pi}{180}$. Find a similar approximation for $\cos 2°$.

6. Use the approximation for $\cos x$ to find a solution to $\cos x = 0.9$, valid when x is small.

7. Find a small value of x which is an approximate solution of $\sin x + \cos x = 1.05$.

11.3 Examination questions

Fig 11.4

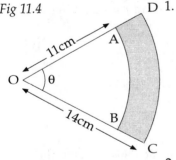

D 1. The diagram shows two arcs, AB and CD, of concentric circles, centre O. The radii OA and OC are 11 cm and 14 cm respectively, and AOB = θ radians. Express in terms of θ the area of

    (i) sector AOB

    (ii) the shaded region ABCD.

    Given that the area of the shaded region ABCD is 30cm^2, calculate

    (iii) the value of θ

    (iv) the perimeter of the shaded region ABCD.

    [C ADD]

2. After t seconds the extension of a piston is given by $x = \sin 3t$ and of its crankshaft by $x = \sin 2t$.

    (a) Sketch these two curves on the same axes for $0 \le t \le 2\pi$.

    (b) Prove that $\sin(t + 2t) = 3 \sin t - 4 \sin^3 t$.

    (c) Hence verify that the extension of the piston is the same as that of the crankshaft when $S(S + 1)(4S - 3) = 0$, where $S = \sin t$.

    (d) Calculate, corrected to 3 significant figures, all the times in the first five seconds when the extensions are the same.

(e) Hence find the percentage of the time in each cycle for which the piston is more extended than the crankshaft.

[SMP ADD]

3. State the exact principal values, in radians, of

   (i) $\sin^{-1}(-1)$ (ii) $\cos^{-1}(\frac{1}{2})$

   (iii) $\sin^{-1}(0.4) + \cos^{-1}(0.4)$.

   [*Warning*. Because your calculator works to a finite number of figures it may not give you the *exact* values.]

   [SMP]

4. (a) (i) Express $7 \sin \theta - 24 \cos \theta$ in the form $R \sin(\theta - \alpha)$, giving the values of R and α, where $0 < \alpha < \frac{1}{2}\pi$.

   (ii) What is the maximum value of $7 \sin \theta - 24 \cos\theta$, and for what value of x between 0 and 2π does it occur?

   (iii) What is the minimum value of $\dfrac{1}{7 \sin \theta - 24 \cos \theta + 5}$ for values of θ between $\pi/2$ and $3\pi/2$, and for what value of θ does it occur?

Fig 11.5

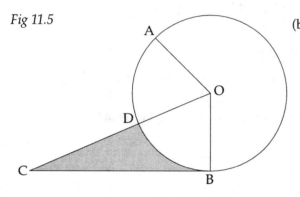

   (b) (i) A sector of a circle, centre O, has radius r and area A. If the length of the arc of the sector is s, prove that $A = \frac{1}{2}rs$.

   (ii) In the diagram, A and B are points on a circle, centre O, such that the length of the arc AB = x. The tangent BC of length x is drawn and OC is joined, meeting the circle at D. Prove that the shaded area is equal to the area of the sector OAD.

   [SUJB]

5. Use the approximations $\sin x \approx x$; $\tan x \approx x$; $\cos x \approx 1 - \frac{1}{2}x^2$ to find the smallest positive root of the equation $\sin x + \cos x + \tan x = 1.5$ giving your answer to 2 decimal places.

   [W]

Common errors

1. **Radians**

   When working with radians, make sure that your calculator is correctly adjusted.

   If a question is about radians, then it will tell you directly, or it will ask you to give the answer in the range 0 to 2π. You will get very few marks if you then give your answers in degrees.

2. **Small angles**

   The approximations for sin, cos and tan of small angles hold only when the angle is measured in radians. They do not apply if the angle is given in degrees.

12 Vectors

A quantity with both direction and magnitude is a *vector*. A quantity with magnitude only is a *scalar*.

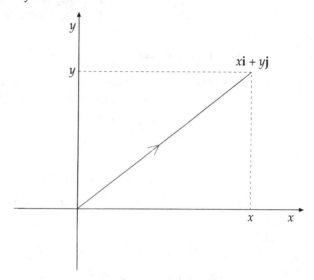

Fig 12.1

A vector with magnitude 1 is a *unit vector*.

A two dimensional vector can be written as $\begin{pmatrix} x \\ y \end{pmatrix}$ or as (x,y) or as $x\mathbf{i} + y\mathbf{j}$,

where $\mathbf{i}$ and $\mathbf{j}$ are unit vectors in the x and y directions respectively.

The *magnitude* or *modulus* of (x,y) is $|(x,y)| = \sqrt{(x^2 + y^2)}$.

Three dimensional vectors can be written as $\begin{pmatrix} x \\ y \\ z \end{pmatrix}$ or as (x,y,z) or as $x\mathbf{i} + y\mathbf{j} + z\mathbf{k}$,

where $\mathbf{i}$, $\mathbf{j}$, $\mathbf{k}$ are unit vectors in the x, y, z directions respectively.

The magnitude of (x,y,z) is $|(x,y,z)| = \sqrt{(x^2 + y^2 + z^2)}$.

12.1 Vector geometry

If A and B are points, the vector from A to B is written $\underline{AB}$.

The vector from the origin to a point is the *position vector* of that point.

If the position vectors of A and B are $\mathbf{a}$ and $\mathbf{b}$, then $\underline{AB} = \mathbf{b} - \mathbf{a}$.

Vectors can be added by a *vector triangle* or a *vector parallelogram*.

Note that if OABC is a parallelogram, with the position vectors of A, B, C relative to O being **a**, **b**, **c** respectively, then **b** = **a** + **c**.

Fig 12.2

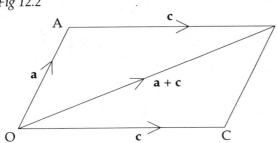

One vector is *parallel* to another if it is a scalar multiple of it. i.e.:

> **a** is parallel to **b** if there is a scalar λ so that **a** = λ**b**.

If w**a** + x**b** = y**a** + z**b**, where **a** and **b** are not parallel to each other, then $w = y$ and $x = z$.

If A has position vector **a**, then a general point on the line through A parallel to **b** has position vector **a** + t**b**, where t is a scalar.

12.1.1 Examples

1. OABC is a parallelogram, X and Y lie on OC and AC respectively, with OX = $\frac{2}{3}$OC, AY = $\frac{3}{4}$AC. Show that X, Y, B lie on a straight line.

Fig 12.3

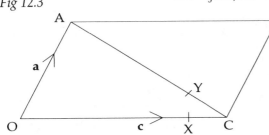

Solution

Let the position vectors relative to O of A and C be **a** and **c**.

The position vector of B is **a** + **c**.

The position vector of X is $\frac{2}{3}$**c**.

> The position vector of Y is **a** + $\frac{3}{4}$(**c** − **a**) = $\frac{1}{4}$**a** + $\frac{3}{4}$**c**.
>
> $\underline{YB}$ = **a** + **c** − ($\frac{1}{4}$**a** + $\frac{3}{4}$**c**) = $\frac{3}{4}$**a** + $\frac{1}{4}$**c**.

$\underline{XB}$ = **a** + **c** − $\frac{2}{3}$**c** = **a** + $\frac{1}{3}$**c**.

$\underline{YB}$ = $\frac{3}{4}$ $\underline{XB}$. It follows that YB is parallel to XB.

X, Y, B lie on a straight line

2. OABC is a parallelogram, with the position vectors of A and C relative to O being **a** and **c**. X is the midpoint of OA, and OB and XC meet at Y. Find the position vector of Y.

Fig 12.4

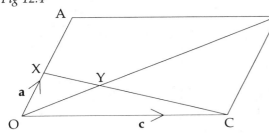

Solution

As above, the position vector of B is **a** + **c**. The position vector of X is $\frac{1}{2}$**a**.

A general point on OB is t(**a** + **c**).

A general point on XC is **c** + s($\frac{1}{2}$**a** − **c**).

Y is on both these lines.

t**a** + t**c** = **c** + $\frac{1}{2}$$s$**a** − s**c**

This gives two equations:

$t = \frac{1}{2}s$ and $t = 1 - s$.

Solve to find that $s = \frac{2}{3}, t = \frac{1}{3}$.

Y has position vector $\frac{1}{3}$(**a** + **c**)

12.1.2 Exercises

1. Which of the following quantities are vectors and which are scalars?
    (a) Velocity   (b) Mass
    (c) Magnetic field   (d) Temperature.

2. Find the magnitudes of the following vectors:
    (a) (3,4)   (b) (2,1,–7)
    (c) $\mathbf{i} + 3\mathbf{j}$ (d) $2\mathbf{i} - 3\mathbf{j} - 2.5\mathbf{k}$

3. Find the vectors <u>AB</u> for the following points A and B:
    (a) A(3,7), B(4,9)   (b) A(2,7,4), B(1,2,3)
    (c) A(x,y), B(p,q)   (d) A($2x, -y, 3z$), B($x+1, y-3, 4z$)

4. OAB is a triangle, and X and Y are the midpoints of OA and OB respectively. Let <u>OA</u> = **a** and <u>OB</u> = **b**. Find <u>XY</u> in terms of **a** and **b**. Show that XY is parallel to AB.

5. OAB is a triangle, with <u>OA</u> = **a** and <u>OB</u> = **b**. X and Y are such that <u>OX</u> = λ**a** and <u>OY</u> = μ**b**. If XY is parallel to AB show that = μ.

6. OABC is a parallelogram, with <u>OA</u> = **a** and <u>OC</u> = **c**. Find <u>OB</u> in terms of **a** and **c**. Find the position vectors of the midpoints of OB and AC in terms of **a** and **c**. What can you deduce?

7. A, B, C, D are four points in space, with position vectors **a**, **b**, **c**, **d** respectively. I, J, K, L are the midpoints of AB, BC, CD, DA respectively. Find the position vectors of I, J, K, L in terms of **a**, **b**, **c**, **d**. Find the vectors <u>IJ</u>, <u>JK</u>, <u>LK</u>, <u>IL</u>. What can you say about the figure IJKL?

8. A, B, C have position vectors **a**, **b**, **c** respectively. Find the position vector of M, the midpoint of BC. G lies on AM with AG = 2GM. Show that the position vector of G is $\frac{1}{3}(\mathbf{a} + \mathbf{b} + \mathbf{c})$. Show that G lies also on the lines from B to the midpoint of AC and from C to the midpoint of AB.

9. The position vectors of A and B relative to O are **a** and **b**. X is the midpoint of OA and Y lies on OB with OY = $\frac{1}{3}$OB. XY meets AB at Z. Find the position vector of Z.

10. **a** and **b** are two non–parallel vectors. The position vectors of X, Y and Z are **a** + 2**b**, $\frac{1}{2}$**a** + $\frac{3}{4}$**b** and λ**a** + **b**. Find the value of λ if X, Y and Z lie on a straight line.

11. ABCDEF is a regular hexagon, with centre at O. <u>OA</u> = **a** and <u>OB</u> = **b**. Express, in terms of **a** and **b**, <u>FA</u>, <u>DE</u>, <u>CD</u>, <u>CF</u>.

12.2 Scalar Product

Fig 12.5

The *scalar*, or *dot* product of two vectors is defined as follows:

$$\mathbf{a}.\mathbf{b} = |\mathbf{a}| |\mathbf{b}| \cos \theta,$$

where θ is the angle between **a** and **b**.

In terms of coordinates the scalar product is as follows:

$$(a,b).(x,y) = ax + by \text{ for two-dimensional vectors}$$

$(a\mathbf{i} + b\mathbf{j} + c\mathbf{k}).(x\mathbf{i} + y\mathbf{j} + z\mathbf{k}) = ax + by + cz$, for three-dimensional vectors.

In particular, $\mathbf{a}.\mathbf{b} = 0$ if and only if $\mathbf{a}$ and $\mathbf{b}$ are perpendicular.

In particular, putting $\mathbf{a} = \mathbf{b}$, $\mathbf{a}.\mathbf{a} = |\mathbf{a}|^2$

The *component* or *projection* of $\mathbf{a}$ in the direction of $\mathbf{b}$ is $\dfrac{\mathbf{a}.\mathbf{b}}{|\mathbf{b}|}$

12.2.1 Examples

1. Find the angle θ between the vectors (1,2,3) and (2,1,−4).

    Solution

    Apply the formula above. $|(1,2,3)| = \sqrt{14}$ and $|(2,1,-4)| = \sqrt{21}$.

    $(1,2,3).(2,1,-4) = 1 \times 2 + 2 \times 1 + 3 \times -4 = -8$.

    $\sqrt{14} \times \sqrt{21} \times \cos\theta = -8$.

    $$\theta = \cos^{-1}\left(\frac{-8}{\sqrt{14} \times \sqrt{21}}\right) = 117.8°$$

2. A, B, C are the vertices of a triangle. Let the perpendiculars from A to BC and from B to AC meet at D. Show that CD is perpendicular to AB. (Note: D is called the *orthocentre* of $\triangle$ABC.)

    Solution

    Let A, B, C, D have position vectors $\mathbf{a}$, $\mathbf{b}$, $\mathbf{c}$, $\mathbf{d}$ respectively. From the information given:

    $(\mathbf{d} - \mathbf{a}).(\mathbf{b} - \mathbf{c}) = 0$ and $(\mathbf{d} - \mathbf{b}).(\mathbf{a} - \mathbf{c}) = 0$ *Fig 12.6*

    Expand these:

    $$\mathbf{d}.\mathbf{b} - \mathbf{d}.\mathbf{c} - \mathbf{a}.\mathbf{b} + \mathbf{a}.\mathbf{c} = 0$$

    $$\mathbf{d}.\mathbf{a} - \mathbf{d}.\mathbf{c} - \mathbf{b}.\mathbf{a} + \mathbf{b}.\mathbf{c} = 0$$

    Subtract these equations:

    $$\mathbf{d}.\mathbf{b} - \mathbf{d}.\mathbf{a} - \mathbf{b}.\mathbf{c} + \mathbf{a}.\mathbf{c} = 0$$

    $$(\mathbf{d} - \mathbf{c}).(\mathbf{b} - \mathbf{a}) = 0$$

    DC is perpendicular to AB.

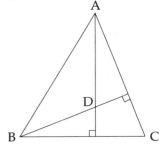

12.2.2 Exercises

1. Evaluate the following:

    (a) (1,2).(3,4)   (b) (2,−4).(7,−1)

    (c) (1,2,5).(2,1,1)   (d) $(3\mathbf{i} + 2\mathbf{j}).(\mathbf{i} - 5\mathbf{j})$

2. Find the angles between the pairs of vectors in Question 1.

3. Find the value of x if $(x,3)$ is perpendicular to (3,1).

4. Find a vector which is perpendicular to (2,7).

5. Find a unit vector which is perpendicular to (7,24)

6. Find the values of x and y if $(x,y,3)$ is perpendicular to both (1,2,4) and (4,−2,−1).

7. Find a vector which is perpendicular to both (1,0,3) and (2,1,2).

8. Find a unit vector which is perpendicular to both (3,3,5) and (1,1,1).

9. Find the component of (2,4) in the direction of (3,1).

10. Find the component of $2\mathbf{i} + 3\mathbf{j} + \mathbf{k}$ in the direction of $3\mathbf{i} - \mathbf{j}$.

11. Verify that the component of (x,y) in the direction of (1,0) is x.

12. Verify that the component of $x\mathbf{i} + y\mathbf{j} + z\mathbf{k}$ in the $\mathbf{j}$ direction is y.

13. Let OAB be a triangle, with $\underline{OA} = \mathbf{a}$ and $\underline{OB} = \mathbf{b}$. Let $\mathbf{c} = \mathbf{a} - \mathbf{b}$ be the third side of the triangle. By expanding $\mathbf{c}.\mathbf{c}$ prove the cosine rule for ΔOAB.

14. OABC is a parallelogram, with $\underline{OA} = \mathbf{a}$ and $\underline{OC} = \mathbf{c}$. By considering $\underline{OB}.\underline{CA}$ show that OABC is a rhombus if and only if its diagonals are perpendicular.

15. Let O be the circumcentre of ΔABC. Let the position vectors of A, B, C relative to O be $\mathbf{a}, \mathbf{b}, \mathbf{c}$. (So that $|\mathbf{a}| = |\mathbf{b}| = |\mathbf{c}|$). Show that $\mathbf{a} + \mathbf{b} + \mathbf{c}$ is the orthocentre of the triangle. (See (2) of 12.2.1).

16. Find the point X on the line $(2,3) + t(4,3)$ such that OX is perpendicular to the line. Hence find the perpendicular distance from the origin to the line.

17. Find the point X on the line of Question 16 such that AX, where A is at $(2,-7)$, is perpendicular to the line. Hence find the perpendicular distance from A to the line.

12.3 Lines and planes in three dimensions

Suppose a line goes through a point with position vector $\mathbf{a}$ and is parallel to the vector $\mathbf{v}$. Then a general point on the line is:

$$\mathbf{r} = \mathbf{a} + \lambda\mathbf{v}$$

where λ is a scalar.

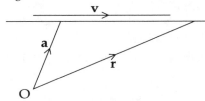

Fig 12.7

If $\mathbf{a} = a\mathbf{i} + b\mathbf{j} + c\mathbf{k}$ and $\mathbf{v} = v\mathbf{i} + u\mathbf{j} + w\mathbf{k}$, then the *Cartesian* equations of the line are:

$$\frac{x-a}{v} = \frac{y-b}{u} = \frac{z-c}{w}$$

Suppose a plane goes through a point with position vector $\mathbf{a}$ and is parallel to vectors $\mathbf{u}$ and $\mathbf{v}$. Then a general point on the plane is:

$$\mathbf{r} = \mathbf{a} + \lambda\mathbf{u} + \mu\mathbf{v}$$

where λ and μ are scalars.

If $\mathbf{n}$ is a vector perpendicular to the plane, then its equation can be written as:

$$\mathbf{r}.\mathbf{n} = \mathbf{a}.\mathbf{n}$$

If $\mathbf{n} = l\mathbf{i} + m\mathbf{j} + n\mathbf{k}$, then the Cartesian equation of the plane is:

$$lx + my + nz = d$$

where $d = \mathbf{a}.\mathbf{n}$ is a constant.

The shortest, i.e. perpendicular, distance from the point (a,b,c) to the plane $lx + my + nz = d$ is:

$$\frac{|la + mb + nc - d|}{\sqrt{l^2 + m^2 + n^2}}$$

The angle between two lines is the angle between their direction vectors. This can be found from the scalar product, defined in 12.2.

To find the angle between a line and a plane, find the angle between the direction of the line and the perpendicular to the plane, and subtract that angle from $90°$.

The angle between two planes is the angle between their perpendiculars.

12.3.1 Examples

1. Two lines are given by:

    $$\mathbf{r} = \mathbf{i} + 2\mathbf{j} - 3\mathbf{k} + \lambda(2\mathbf{i} - \mathbf{j}) \text{ and } \mathbf{r} = t\mathbf{i} + \mathbf{j} - 4\mathbf{k} + \mu(\mathbf{i} - \mathbf{j} + \mathbf{k})$$

    Find the value of t so that the lines intersect. Find the angle between the lines.

    Solution

    Equate the values of r.

    $\mathbf{i} + 2\mathbf{j} - 3\mathbf{k} + \lambda(2\mathbf{i} - \mathbf{j}) = t\mathbf{i} + \mathbf{j} - 4\mathbf{k} + \mu(\mathbf{i} - \mathbf{j} + \mathbf{k})$.

    This gives the following three equations:

    $1 + 2\lambda = t + \mu; \quad 2 - \lambda = 1 - \mu; \quad -3 = -4 + \mu.$

    From the last two equations $\mu = 1$ and $\lambda = 2$. Substitute these values into the first equation to find t.

    $$t = 4$$

    The angle between the lines is the angle between the two direction vectors. Find this by the scalar product.

    $(\sqrt{5})(\sqrt{3})\cos\theta = 3.$

    The angle is $39°$

2. Find the equation of the plane which contains the two lines of example 1.

    Solution

    Let a perpendicular to the plane be $l\mathbf{i} + m\mathbf{j} + n\mathbf{k}$. This vector is at right angles to the direction vectors of the lines.

    $2l - m = 0$ and $l - m + n = 0$.

    These equations are satisfied by $l = 1, m = 2, n = 1$. Hence a perpendicular vector is $\mathbf{i} + 2\mathbf{j} + \mathbf{k}$. The equation of the plane is

    $x + 2y + z = (\mathbf{i} + 2\mathbf{j} + \mathbf{k}).(\mathbf{i} + 2\mathbf{j} - 3\mathbf{k})$

    The equation is $x + 2y + z = 2$

12.3.2 Exercises

1. Find vector equations for the following lines:
    (a) Through $(1,1,2)$, parallel to $2\mathbf{i} + \mathbf{j} + 7\mathbf{k}$
    (b) Through $(1,0,3)$, parallel to $4\mathbf{i} + 2\mathbf{j}$
    (c) Through $(1,3,1)$ and $(2,5,2)$ (d) Through $(1,2,-1)$ and $(1,-2,1)$.

2. Find the Cartesian equations of the lines in Question 1.

3. Find the values of t so that the following pairs of lines intersect:

(a) $\mathbf{r} = (1,3,2) + \lambda(t\mathbf{i} + \mathbf{j})$ and $\mathbf{r} = (1,-4,-1) + \mu(2\mathbf{i} + 3\mathbf{j} + \mathbf{k})$

(b) $\dfrac{x-1}{t} = \dfrac{y-4}{1} = \dfrac{z-5}{2}$ and $\dfrac{x-1}{2} = \dfrac{y}{1} = \dfrac{z+1}{1}$

4. Find the angles between the pairs of lines in Question 3.

5. Find in the form $\mathbf{r} = \mathbf{a} + \lambda\mathbf{u} + \mu\mathbf{v}$ the equations of the following planes:

   (a) Through (1,2,3) parallel to $(\mathbf{i} + \mathbf{j} + \mathbf{k})$ and $(\mathbf{i} + \mathbf{k})$.

   (b) Through (1,2,1), (2,1,3) and (1,-1,1).

6. Find in the form $\mathbf{r}.\mathbf{n} = k$ the equations of the following planes:

   (a) Through (1,2,1), perpendicular to $(2\mathbf{i} + \mathbf{j} - \mathbf{k})$

   (b) Through (2,1,4), perpendicular to the z-axis.

   (c) Through (1,1,2), parallel to $(\mathbf{i} + \mathbf{j})$ and to $\mathbf{k}$.

   (d) Through (2,1,2), (2,3,0) and (0,4,1).

7. Find the angles between the following:

   (a) The line $(0,1,2) + \lambda(\mathbf{i} + \mathbf{j})$ and the plane $\mathbf{r}.(-\mathbf{i} + 3\mathbf{j} - \mathbf{k}) = 1$.

   (b) The line $\dfrac{x-4}{3} = \dfrac{y+3}{-1} = \dfrac{z-2}{1}$ and the plane $x + 2y + z = 0$

   (c) The line $(0,1,1) + \lambda(2\mathbf{i} + \mathbf{j} + \mathbf{k})$ and the plane $(1,1,1) + \mu(\mathbf{i} + \mathbf{j}) + \nu\mathbf{k}$.

8. Find the angles between the following pairs of planes:

   (a) $x + y + 2z = 3$ and $2x - y + z = 1$

   (b) $\mathbf{r}.(\mathbf{i} + 2\mathbf{j} + 3\mathbf{k}) = 0$ and $\mathbf{r}.(-2\mathbf{i} + \mathbf{j} - 3\mathbf{k}) = 3$.

   (c) $\mathbf{r} = (1,1,0) + \lambda(\mathbf{i} + \mathbf{k}) + \mu\mathbf{j}$ and $\mathbf{r} = (2,1,7) + \alpha(\mathbf{i} - \mathbf{j}) + \beta\mathbf{k}$

9. Find the perpendicular distance between the following:

   (a) The point (1,1,1) and the plane $x + 2y - z = 4$

   (b) The point (2,0,-3) and the plane $2x - 3y + 4z = 1$

10. Find the point where the line $\mathbf{r} = (5,7,3) + \lambda(\mathbf{i} + 3\mathbf{j} + 2\mathbf{k})$ meets the plane $x + 2y + z = 4$. Find the angle between the line and the plane.

11. Find the point where the line $\mathbf{r} = (1,0,-1) + \lambda(\mathbf{i} - 2\mathbf{j})$ meets the plane $2x - y - z = 1$. Find the angle between the line and the plane.

12.4 Examination questions

1. Referred to the point O as origin, the position vectors of the points A and B are $3\mathbf{i} + \mathbf{j}$ and $8\mathbf{i} - 4\mathbf{j}$ respectively. The point P lies on the line OB, between O and B, such that $4\underline{OP} = \underline{OB}$. The point Q lies on the line AB, between A and B, such that $5\underline{AQ} = 2\underline{AB}$. Find, in terms of $\mathbf{i}$ and $\mathbf{j}$, the vectors $\underline{OP}$, $\underline{AB}$, $\underline{AQ}$, $\underline{OQ}$ and $\underline{AP}$.

   The lines AP and OQ intersect at the point R. Given that OR:OQ = λ and AR:AP = μ, express the position vector of R in terms of

   (a) λ, $\mathbf{i}$ and $\mathbf{j}$ (b) μ, $\mathbf{i}$ and $\mathbf{j}$.

   Hence find the values of λ and μ.

   Prove that the length of OR is $\frac{5}{11}\sqrt{26}$.

   [L ADD]

2. The position vectors, relative to an origin O, of three points A, B, C are $2\mathbf{i} + 2\mathbf{j}$, $5\mathbf{i} + 11\mathbf{j}$ and $11\mathbf{i} + 9\mathbf{j}$ respectively.

   (i) Given that $\underline{OB} = m\underline{OA} + n\underline{OC}$, where m and n are scalar constants, find the value of m and of n.

   (ii) Evaluate $\underline{AB}.\underline{BC}$ and state the deduction which can be made about $\hat{ABC}$.

   (iii) Evaluate $\underline{AB}.\underline{AC}$ and *hence* find $\hat{BAC}$.

   [C ADD]

3. The position vectors of the points A, B with respect to an origin O are $\mathbf{a}$ and $\mathbf{b}$ respectively, where A, B and O are not collinear. Points L, M, N have position vectors $p\mathbf{a}$, $q\mathbf{b}$ and $2\mathbf{b} - \mathbf{a}$ respectively, where p and q are non–zero constants and LM is not parallel to AB. Show that N lies on the line AB. Prove that L, M, N are collinear if and only if $2p = q(1 + p)$.

   If $p = \frac{1}{3}$ and $q = \frac{1}{2}$, find LM:LN.

   If, further, $\mathbf{a} = 2\mathbf{i} + 3\mathbf{j} + 6\mathbf{k}$ and $\mathbf{b} = 4\mathbf{i} + \mathbf{j} + 4\mathbf{k}$, find the position vector of the foot of the perpendicular from N to OA.

   [O&C ADD]

4. A cartesian frame of reference, having origin O, is defined by the mutually perpendicular unit vectors $\mathbf{i}$, $\mathbf{j}$ and $\mathbf{k}$.

   (i) Find the vector equation of the line which passes through the two points, having position vectors relative to O, $2\mathbf{i} - \frac{1}{3}\mathbf{j} + 2\mathbf{k}$ and $\mathbf{i} + \frac{1}{3}\mathbf{j}$ in the form $\mathbf{r} = \mathbf{a} + t\mathbf{b}$.

   (ii) A second line has vector equation $\mathbf{r} = -3\mathbf{i} - 4\mathbf{j} - \frac{1}{2}\mathbf{k} + s(2\mathbf{i} + \mathbf{j} + \frac{3}{2}\mathbf{k})$.

   Find the point of intersection of the two lines.

   [NI]

5. Relative to an origin O, points A and B have position vectors $2\mathbf{i} + 9\mathbf{j} - 6\mathbf{k}$ and $6\mathbf{i} + 3\mathbf{j} + 6\mathbf{k}$ respectively, $\mathbf{i}$, $\mathbf{j}$ and $\mathbf{k}$ being orthogonal unit vectors. C is the point such that $\underline{OC} = 2\underline{OA}$ and D is the midpoint of AB. Find

   (i) the position vectors of C and D;

   (ii) a vector equation of the line CD;

   (iii) the position vector of the point of intersection of CD and OB;

   (iv) the angle AOB correct to the nearest degree.

   [SUJB]

6. Calculate unit vectors in the directions $\begin{pmatrix} 3 \\ 4 \end{pmatrix}$ and $\begin{pmatrix} 4 \\ -3 \end{pmatrix}$.

   By considering the sum of these two vectors, or otherwise, calculate the equation of one of the bisectors of the angles between the lines

   $$\begin{pmatrix} x \\ y \end{pmatrix} = s\begin{pmatrix} 3 \\ 4 \end{pmatrix} \text{ and } \begin{pmatrix} x \\ y \end{pmatrix} = t\begin{pmatrix} 4 \\ -3 \end{pmatrix}$$

   Deduce the equation of one of the bisectors of the angles between the lines

   $$\begin{pmatrix} x \\ y \end{pmatrix} = \begin{pmatrix} 4 \\ 1 \end{pmatrix} + s\begin{pmatrix} 3 \\ 4 \end{pmatrix} \text{ and } \begin{pmatrix} x \\ y \end{pmatrix} = \begin{pmatrix} 5 \\ 19 \end{pmatrix} + t\begin{pmatrix} 4 \\ -3 \end{pmatrix}, \text{ giving your answer in a}$$

   similar form.

   [O&C]

7. The lines L and M have the equations $\mathbf{r} = \begin{pmatrix} 3 \\ 2 \\ 4 \end{pmatrix} + s \begin{pmatrix} 1 \\ 3 \\ -5 \end{pmatrix}$ and $\mathbf{r} = \begin{pmatrix} -3 \\ 4 \\ 6 \end{pmatrix} + t \begin{pmatrix} 1 \\ -2 \\ 2 \end{pmatrix}$ respectively.

   The plane Π has the equation $\mathbf{r} . \begin{pmatrix} 2 \\ 0 \\ -1 \end{pmatrix} = 16$.

   (i) Verify that the point A with coordinates (1, –4, 14) lies on L and on M but not on Π.

   (ii) Find the position vector of the point of intersection B of L and Π.

   (iii) Show that M and Π have no common point.

   (iv) Find the cosine of the angle between the vectors $\begin{pmatrix} 1 \\ 3 \\ -5 \end{pmatrix}$ and $\begin{pmatrix} 2 \\ 0 \\ -1 \end{pmatrix}$.

   Hence find, to the nearest degree, the angle between L and Π.

   [JMB]

8. With respect to the origin O the points A, B C have position vectors $a(5\mathbf{i} - \mathbf{j} - 3\mathbf{k})$, $a(-4\mathbf{i} + 4\mathbf{j} - \mathbf{k})$, $a(5\mathbf{i} - 2\mathbf{j} + 11\mathbf{k})$ respectively, where a is a non–zero constant. Find

   (a) a vector equation for the line BC,

   (b) a vector equation for the plane OAB,

   (c) the cosine of the acute angle between the lines OA and OB.

   Obtain, in the form $\mathbf{r}.\mathbf{n} = p$, a vector equation for Π, the plane which passes through A and is perpendicular to BC.

   Find cartesian equations for

   (d) the plane Π,   (e) the line BC.

   [L]

9. The line L passes through A(0,–1,1) and is parallel to $\begin{pmatrix} 1 \\ 0 \\ 1 \end{pmatrix}$, and the line M passes through B(2,1,3) and is parallel to $\begin{pmatrix} 1 \\ -1 \\ 2 \end{pmatrix}$.

   Show that L and M do not intersect.

   M' is the line through A parallel to M. The lines M' and L lie in the plane Π.

   (i) Find the direction of the normal to Π.

   (ii) Find the angle between AB and Π.

   (iii) Write the equation to Π in standard Cartesian form.

   (iv) Use the formula for the distance of a point from a plane to show that the shortest distance from B to Π is $\frac{1}{3}$AB. Explain how you could have deduced this result from your answer to (ii).

   [SMP]

Common errors

1. **Points and Vectors**

   (a) The vector from the origin to (3,4) is (3,4). But this vector also goes from say (1,7) to (4,11). Vectors have magnitude and direction, but not position.

   (b) The vector from (2,5) to (1,10) is (–1,5), not (1,–5).

   (c) In general, if A and B have position vectors **a** and **b**, then <u>AB</u> is **b** – **a**. It is not **b**, or **a** + **b**, or **a** – **b**.

2. **Modulus**

   (a) The modulus of (3,4) is $\sqrt{(3^2 + 4^2)} = 5$, not $3 + 4 = 7$.

   (b) Be careful of negative signs. Any number squared is positive, so the modulus of (–3,–4) is the same as the modulus of (3,4).

3. **Scalar Product**

   (a) **a.b** is a scalar, not a vector:

   $(2,3).(3,4) \neq (6,12)$. It should be $6 + 12 = 18$.

   (b) Do not be confused if there are many possible answers to a problem. There are infinitely many vectors perpendicular to (1,2,3), for example. Just give the simplest one you can find.

4. **Lines and Planes**

   (a) Do not confuse the position vector of a point on a line and the direction vector of that line.

   (b) In three dimensions, *two* Cartesian equations are needed to define a line. If you have only one equation then that will describe a plane.

   (c) Do not confuse vectors *perpendicular* to a plane with vectors *parallel* to the plane.

13 Differentiation

If y is a function of x, the rate of change of y with respect to x is called the *derivative* or the *differential coefficient* of y. It represents the gradient of the graph of y against x.

The derivative of y is written $\dfrac{dy}{dx}$.

If the function is of the form $y = f(x)$, then the derivative is sometimes written as

$$\frac{dy}{dx} = f'(x).$$

The process of going from y to $\dfrac{dy}{dx}$ is called *differentiation*.

The result of differentiating twice, i.e. of differentiating the derivative, is the *second derivative*.

$$\frac{d}{dx}\left(\frac{dy}{dx}\right) = \frac{d^2y}{dx^2}$$

13.1 Differentiation of powers of x

Let y be a power of x, (even a negative or a fractional power of x). Differentiate by multiplying by the power and subtracting 1 from the power.

If $y = x^n$, then $\dfrac{dy}{dx} = nx^{n-1}$.

If a function is multiplied by a constant, then the derivative is also multiplied by the constant.

If $y = ax^n$, then $\dfrac{dy}{dx} = anx^{n-1}$

If two functions are added, then their derivatives are also added.

If $y = ax^n + bx^m$, then $\dfrac{dy}{dx} = anx^{n-1} + bmx^{m-1}$

Two special cases are as follows:

If y is a constant, then $\dfrac{dy}{dx} = 0$.

If y is the straight line $y = mx + c$, then $\dfrac{dy}{dx} = m$.

13.1.1 Examples

1. Differentiate $y = 3x^2 - \dfrac{2}{x} + \sqrt{x}$.

   Solution

   Write y in terms of powers of x.

   $$y = 3x^2 - 2x^{-1} + x^{\frac{1}{2}}$$

   Apply the formulae above, using $n = 2$, $n = -1$ and $n = \frac{1}{2}$ respectively.

   $$\frac{dy}{dx} = 3(2)x^{2-1} - 2(-1)x^{-1-1} + \tfrac{1}{2}x^{\frac{1}{2}-1}$$

   $$\frac{dy}{dx} = 6x + 2x^{-2} + \tfrac{1}{2}x^{-\frac{1}{2}}$$

2. Differentiate $y = \dfrac{(x+3)(x-4)}{x^2}$

   Solution

   Before differentiating it is necessary to multiply out the expression and divide by x^2.

   $$y = \frac{x^2 - x - 12}{x^2} = 1 - x^{-1} - 12x^{-2}$$

   Now use the formulae above.

   $$\frac{dy}{dx} = -(-1)x^{-2} - 12 \times (-2) \times x^{-3}$$

   $$= x^{-2} + 24x^{-3}$$

   $$= \frac{1}{x^2} + \frac{24}{x^3}$$

13.1.2 Exercises

1. Differentiate the following:

   (a) $y = x^3$

   (b) $y = 7x^5$

   (c) $y = 3x^2 + 2x$

   (d) $y = 2 - 2x + 4x^5$

   (e) $y = 2x^{-3}$

   (f) $y = 2x - 3x^{-4}$

   (g) $y = 4x^{1/2}$

   (h) $y = 3x^{-3} + 2x^{-1/2} + 17$

   (i) $y = \dfrac{7}{x^3}$

   (j) $y = \dfrac{2}{x} - \dfrac{8}{x^3}$

   (k) $y = \sqrt{x}$

   (l) $y = 3\sqrt{x} - \dfrac{7}{\sqrt{x}}$

   (m) $y = 2x^5 - \dfrac{5}{x^6} + \dfrac{7}{x^{1/4}}$

   (n) $y = 2 + \dfrac{2}{\sqrt{x}} - \dfrac{9}{x}$

2. Differentiate the following:

   (a) $y = x(x - 3)$

   (b) $y = (x + 1)(x - 6)$

   (c) $y = (2 - 3x^2)(4 + x^3)$

   (d) $y = x(1 + \dfrac{1}{x})(2 + \dfrac{3}{x^3})$

   (e) $y = (x + 2)^2$

   (f) $y = (3 + 2x^2)^2$

(g) $y = (2 + \frac{3}{x})^2$ (h) $y = (3x - \frac{4}{x})^2$

(i) $y = x^{1/2}(x - 4)$ (j) $y = (x^{1/2} + 1)(x^{1/2} - 2)$

(k) $y = \frac{x + 17}{x^4}$ (l) $y = \frac{2x^2 - 3x + 1}{x}$

(m) $y = \frac{x + 8}{\sqrt{x}}$ (n) $y = \frac{\sqrt[3]{x} - \sqrt[4]{x} + 3}{\sqrt{x}}$

3. Find the second derivatives of the following:

     (a) $y = x^3$ (b) $y = 2x^2 - 3x + 1$

     (c) $y = (x^3 + 1)(x - 4)$ (d) $y = 3\sqrt{x} - 2x^{-2}$

13.2 Tangents and normals

The derivative of a function at a point is the gradient of the tangent of the function at that point. (Fig 13.1)

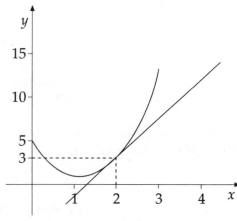

Fig 13.1   *Fig 13.2*

13.2.1 Examples

1. Find the equation of the tangent to the curve $y = 3x^2 - 7x + 5$ at the point (2, 3). (Fig 13.2)

     Solution

     Differentiate to find that $\frac{dy}{dx} = 6x - 7$. When $x = 2$, the gradient of the tangent is $6 \times 2 - 7 = 5$.

     The tangent is of the form $y = 5x + c$. The tangent goes through the point (2, 3), hence $c = 3 - 5 \times 2 = -7$.

           The tangent is $y = 5x - 7$

2. At what points of the curve $y = 4x^3 - 12.5x$ is the normal parallel to $y = 2x + 4$?

     Solution

     The gradient of the line $y = 2x + 4$ is 2.

The gradient of the curve $y = 4x^3 - 12.5x$ is $\dfrac{dy}{dx} = 12x^2 - 12.5$.

If these are at right angles, then:

$$2(12x^2 - 12.5) = -1.$$
$$24x^2 = 24.$$
$$x = 1 \text{ or } -1.$$

The points are $(1, -8.5)$ and $(-1, 8.5)$

13.2.2 Exercises

1. Find the equations of the tangents to the following curves at the points given.

    (a) $y = x^2$ at $(2, 4)$ (b) $y = x^3 - 2x$ at $(1, -1)$

    (c) $y = 3x^2 - 7x + 2$ at $(-1, 12)$ (d) $y = 1 - \dfrac{2}{x}$ at $(4, \frac{1}{2})$

2. Find the normals to the curves in Question 1 at the same points.

3. Where is the tangent to $y = 3x^2 + 7x - 4$ parallel to $y = 3x + 4$?

4. Find the points where the tangents to $y = x^3 - x$ are parallel to the x–axis.

5. Show that the tangents to the curve $y = x^3 + 2x$ are never parallel to the x–axis.

6. The line $y = x + 7$ is a tangent to the curve $y = x^2 + a$, where a is a constant. Find the value of a.

13.3 Maxima and minima

A flat point of a curve is a *stationary point.* At a stationary point, $dy/dx = 0$.

A point of a curve where it changes from convex to concave or vice versa is a *point of inflection.* At a point of inflection, $\dfrac{d^2y}{dx^2} = 0$.

There are three kinds of stationary point.

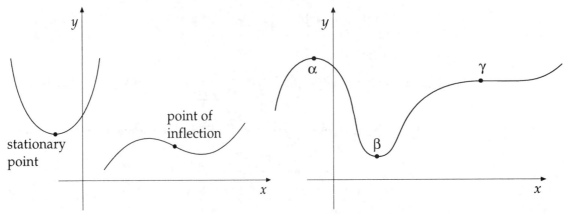

Fig 13.3   *Fig 13.4*

A point where y is at the top of a peak is a *maximum* (α). A point where y is at the bottom of a pit is a *minimum* (β). A point where the curve is flat but continues to go up or down is a *point of inflection* (γ).

There are three ways to distinguish between these three kinds of stationary point.

1. Find the values of y on both sides of the point.

2. Find the values of $\frac{dy}{dx}$ on both sides of the point.

3. Use the second derivative.

    If $\frac{d^2y}{dx^2} > 0$ then it is a minimum.

    If $\frac{d^2y}{dx^2} < 0$ then it is a maximum.

    If the second derivative is 0, then use either 1. or 2.

13.3.1 Examples

1. Find the maxima and minima of $y = 2x^3 + 3x^2 - 12x + 4$, distinguishing between them. Sketch the graph of the function.

    Solution

    Differentiating, $\frac{dy}{dx} = 6x^2 + 6x - 12$. This is zero at a maximum or a minimum.

    $$6x^2 + 6x - 12 = 0$$
    $$6(x - 1)(x + 2) = 0$$
    $$x = 1, y = -3 \text{ and } x = -2, y = 24.$$

    To find out whether $(1, -3)$ is a maximum or a minimum, find the value of y on either side of the point.

    For $x = 0.9$, $y = -2.9$. For $x = 1.1$, $y = -2.91$

    $(1, -3)$ is a minimum. Similarly, $(-2, 24)$ is a maximum.

    Sketch the graph as shown, with a peak at $(-2, 24)$ and a pit at $(1, -3)$.

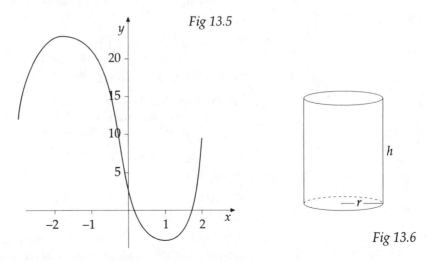

Fig 13.5

Fig 13.6

2. Thin metal is used to make cylindrical cans which are to hold 1,000 cm³ of soup. What should be the radius of the cans if they are to use as little metal as possible? (Fig 13.6)

Solution

Let the height be h cm and the base radius r cm. The volume is 1,000 cm³, hence $\pi r^2 h = 1,000$.

The surface area is A cm², where $A = 2\pi r^2 + 2\pi rh$. Write h in terms of r, so that A is in terms of r only.

$$h = \frac{1,000}{\pi r^2} \text{, so } A = 2\pi r^2 + \frac{2,000}{r}.$$

Differentiate to find where A is a minimum.

$$\frac{dA}{dr} = 4\pi r - \frac{2,000}{r^2}.$$

At a minimum, $\dfrac{dA}{dr} = 0$.

$$4\pi r = \frac{2,000}{r^2}$$

$$r^3 = \frac{2,000}{4\pi}.$$

The best radius is 5.42 cm.

13.3.2 Exercises

1. Find the coordinates of the maxima and minima of the following, distinguishing between them.
   (a) $y = x^2 - 2x$ (b) $y = 2 + 4x - x^2$
   (c) $y = x^3 - 3x$ (d) $y = 2x^3 - 15x^2 + 36x - 4$
   (e) $y = x + \dfrac{1}{x}$ (f) $y = x + \dfrac{4}{x^2}$

2. Find the points of inflection of the functions of Question 1.

3. The function $y = x^2 - 2x + a$ has a minimum of 5. Find the value of a.

4. The function $y = ax^2 + bx$ has a maximum at (2,3). Find the values of a and of b.

5. A metal basket is made in the form of a cylinder with an open top. Its height is h cm and its radius r cm. It is to contain 5,000 cm³. What is the radius, if it is to consist of the smallest possible amount of metal?

6. A cardboard box is to be made in the form of a cuboid with square cross-section. Its volume must be 2,000 cm³. Let x cm be the side of the square, and z cm be the length. What value of x will use the least cardboard?

7. Repeat Question 6, if the squares at the end use a double thickness of cardboard.

8. Repeat Example 2 of 13.3.1, if the top and bottom of the can use a double thickness of metal.

9. A cuboid box is to have a volume of 512 cm³. The length is twice the breadth. Find the height, if the surface area is to be as small as possible.

10. A farmer has 100 m of fencing, with which to make a rectangular sheepfold. One side of the fold is already provided by a stone wall. How should he make his fold if he is to enclose as much area as possible?

11. A 100 cm length of wire is cut in two pieces, which are then made into two squares. Show that the total area enclosed by the squares is least when they have equal sides.

12. 100 cm of wire is cut into two pieces, one of which is made into a square and the other into a circle. Find the radius of the circle if the total area is to be as small as possible.

13. The line through (1,2) with gradient m is $y - 2 = m(x - 1)$. Find where this line crosses the axes. Find the value of m which will make the area enclosed by the line and the two axes as small as possible.

14. If a book is sold for £x, the number of copies sold will be $1000(10 - x)$. What value of x will make the revenue from sales of the book as great as possible?

15. The cost of making a tie is £2. If the tie costs £x, the number sold will be $100(25 - x^2)$. What price will maximise:

    (a) the revenue   (b) the profit?

13.4 Examination questions

1. Find $\dfrac{dy}{dx}$ when:

    (i) $y = x^3 + \dfrac{1}{x^3}$ (ii) $y = x(x - 1)^2$

    (iii) $y = x^{-3/2}$ and $x = 9$ (iv) $y = \dfrac{x^2 + 1}{x}$ and $x = 2$

    [O&C ADD]

2. A curve has equation $y = \frac{1}{3}x^3 - 4x^2 + 13x$.
    (a) Show that the tangent at the point where $x = 2$ has gradient 1 and find its equation.
    (b) Find the x-coordinate of another point where the tangent has gradient 1.
    (c) Show that there is only one tangent with gradient –3.

    [SMP ADD]

3. The point P(0,2) lies on the curve $y = x^3 - 3x + 2$.

    The tangent and normal to the curve at P intersect the x–axis at A and B respectively. Calculate the length of AB.

    [L ADD]

4. In making closed cylindrical tins of height h cm and radius r cm the walls can be made from rectangular sheets of width h cm and length $2\pi r$ cm without waste, but stamping out each circular end of area πr^2 cm² requires an area $4r^2$ cm² and some is wasted.

If the tins are to contain 1000 cm ,

(i)   find h in terms of r to give the correct volume;

(ii)   find the area of tinplate required for each tin in terms of r.

If tinplate costs 0.01 p per cm^2, find by a calculus method the radius, height and cost of the tin which will contain the required volume most cheaply.

[MEI ADD]

5.   At which point (other than the origin) do the parabolas $y^2 = 4ax$ and $x^2 = 4ay$ meet?

Write down the equation of the tangent to each parabola at this point.

If the angles which these tangents make with the positive direction of the x–axis are θ_1 and θ_2, show that $|\tan(\theta_1 - \theta_2)| = \frac{3}{4}$.

[NI]

6.   In the diagram, CDEF is a rectangle with CD = FE = $2x$ and CF = DE = y, and OAB is a triangle with angles at A and B each equal to θ.

Fig 13.7

(a)   Show that the area, Δ, of the triangle OAB is given by

$$\Delta = (x + \frac{y}{t})(y + tx),$$

where $t = \tan \theta$.

Deduce that, as t varies, with x and y remaining fixed, the *least* value of Δ is $4xy$.

(b)   Given further that OA = OB = l, show that $y = l \sin \theta - x \tan \theta$, and that the area, S, of the rectangle CDEF is given by

$$S = 2[lx \sin \theta - x^2\tan \theta].$$

Deduce that, as x varies with l and θ remaining fixed, the *greatest* value of S is $\frac{1}{2} l^2\sin \theta \cos \theta$.

[C]

Common errors

1.   **Differentiation**

There are a number of common mistakes made when differentiating. Be careful of negative powers, of constants, of products and of ratios. Watch out for the following:

If $y = x^{-5}$, $\frac{dy}{dx} \neq -5x^{-4}$. It should be $-5x^{-6}$.

If $y = x^2 + 7$, $\frac{dy}{dx} \neq 2x + 7$. It should be $2x$.

If $y = x^2 \times x^3$, $\frac{dy}{dx} \neq 2x \times 3x^2$. It should be $5x^4$.

If $y = \frac{x^6}{x^2}$, $\frac{dy}{dx} \neq \frac{6x^5}{2x}$. It should be $4x^3$.

2. **Maxima and minima**

When you are asked for the maximum or minimum value, then you must give the y value, not the x value. If you are asked for the point at which it is a maximum, give both the x and the y values.

If $\dfrac{d^2y}{dx^2} = 0$ at a stationary point, then do not conclude that it is a point of inflection. Examine either y or $\dfrac{dy}{dx}$ on both sides of the point.

When you are solving problems about minimum area, make sure that your area is expressed in terms of only one variable. If the area is in terms of both the height and the width then it cannot be differentiated.

14 Further Differentiation

14.1 The product and quotient rules

These rules enable products and quotients of functions to be differentiated.

The *Product Rule*. If $y = uv$, then $\dfrac{dy}{dx} = u\dfrac{dv}{dx} + v\dfrac{du}{dx}$

The *Quotient Rule*. If $y = \dfrac{u}{v}$, then $\dfrac{dy}{dx} = \dfrac{v\dfrac{du}{dx} - u\dfrac{dv}{dx}}{v^2}$

14.1.1 Examples

1. Differentiate $y = (x^2 + 3x - 2)(4 - x^2)$

    Solution

    Here $u = x^2 + 3x - 2$ and $v = 4 - x^2$. Apply the Product Rule:

    $$\frac{dy}{dx} = (x^2 + 3x - 2)(-2x) + (4 - x^2)(2x + 3)$$

    $$\frac{dy}{dx} = -4x^3 - 9x^2 + 12x + 12$$

2. Differentiate $y = \dfrac{x}{2x^2 - 3x + 5}$

    Solution

    Here $u = x$ and $v = 2x^2 - 3x + 5$. Apply the Quotient Rule:

    $$\frac{dy}{dx} = \frac{(2x^2 - 3x + 5) \times 1 - x \times (4x - 3)}{(2x^2 - 3x + 5)^2}$$

    $$\frac{dy}{dx} = \frac{-2x^2 + 5}{(2x^2 - 3x + 5)^2}$$

14.1.2 Exercises

1. Without multiplying out the brackets, differentiate the following:

    (a) $y = x(x^2 + 7x - 3)$ (b) $y = (x + 3)(2x^3 + 6x)$

    (c) $y = x^2(3x^5 - 3x^2 + x)$ (d) $y = (x^2 - 1)(x^2 + 1)$

2. Differentiate the following:

    (a) $y = \dfrac{x}{x + 3}$
                (b) $y = \dfrac{x^2 + 7x - 2}{x^2 + 3}$

    (c) $y = \dfrac{3x^2}{x - 17}$
                (d) $y = \dfrac{1}{x + 3}$

3. Find the equation of the tangent to the curve $y = \dfrac{x^2}{x - 1}$ at the point (2,4).
Find the equation of the normal at (3,4.5).

4. Find the maxima and minima of the following functions

    (a) $y = \dfrac{x^2}{x - 1}$
                (b) $y = \dfrac{x^2 + 1}{x + 1}$

    (c) $y = \dfrac{1}{x^2 + 1}$
                (d) $y = \dfrac{1}{x^2 + 4x + 9}$

14.2 The chain rule

The *Chain Rule* enables functions of functions to be differentiated. If y is a function of z, and z is a function of x, then the derivative of y is found by the following:

$$\frac{dy}{dx} = \frac{dy}{dz} \times \frac{dz}{dx}$$

14.2.1 Examples

1. Differentiate $y = (x^2 + 1)^{1/2}$.

   Solution

   Substitute for the inside function. Let $z = x^2 + 1$. Then $y = z^{\frac{1}{2}}$.

   Use the chain rule above.

$$\frac{dy}{dx} = \frac{dy}{dz} \times \frac{dz}{dx}$$

$$= \tfrac{1}{2} z^{-\frac{1}{2}} \times 2x$$

$$\frac{dy}{dx} = x(x^2 + 1)^{-\frac{1}{2}}$$

2. Differentiate $x(x^2 + 1)^{1/2}$

   Solution

   This is a product. $u = x$ and $v = (x^2 + 1)^{1/2}$. Use the product rule of 14.1, with the derivative of v which was found in Example 1.

$$\frac{dy}{dx} = u \frac{dv}{dx} + v \frac{du}{dx}$$

$$= x \times x(x^2 + 1)^{-1/2} + (x^2 + 1)^{1/2} \times 1$$

$$\frac{dy}{dx} = x^2(x^2 + 1)^{-1/2} + (x^2 + 1)^{1/2}$$

14.2.2 Exercises

1. Differentiate the following:

   (a) $y = (3x + 7)^{1/2}$

   (b) $y = (2 - x^2)^5$

   (c) $y = \sqrt{(1 + 2x^2)}$

   (d) $y = \dfrac{1}{\sqrt{(1 + x)}}$

   (e) $y = \sqrt{(1 + x + x^2)}$

   (f) $y = (1 + x^2)^{100}$

2. Differentiate the following:

   (a) $y = x(1 + 2x)^{1/2}$

   (b) $y = (x + 3)(x - 17)^{21}$

   (c) $y = \dfrac{x + 4}{\sqrt{(x^2 + 1)}}$

   (d) $y = \dfrac{\sqrt{x}}{\sqrt{(x + 1)}}$

3. Let $y = \sqrt{(x^2 + 3)}$. Find the equations of the tangent and normal to the curve at the point (1,2).

14.3 Differentiation of trig and log functions

Provided that the angles are measured in radians, the trigonometric functions are differentiated as follows:

If $y = \sin x$, $\dfrac{dy}{dx} = \cos x$

If $y = \cos x$, $\dfrac{dy}{dx} = -\sin x$

If $y = \tan x$, $\dfrac{dy}{dx} = \sec^2 x$.

e is a number approximately equal to 2.718281828. The exponential function is defined as e^x.

$\ln x$ is defined as $\log_e x$.

e^x and $\ln x$ can be differentiated as follows:

If $y = e^x$, $\dfrac{dy}{dx} = e^x$

If $y = \ln x$, $\dfrac{dy}{dx} = \dfrac{1}{x}$.

14.3.1 Examples

1. Differentiate $y = e^x \cos x$.

   Solution

   This is a product, so the product rule must be used.

   $$\frac{dy}{dx} = e^x \cos x + e^x(-\sin x)$$

   $$\frac{dy}{dx} = e^x(\cos x - \sin x)$$

2. Differentiate $y = \ln (1 + x^2)$

   Solution

This is a function of a function, so the chain rule is used.

$$\frac{dy}{dx} = \frac{1}{1 + x^2} \times 2x$$

$$\frac{dy}{dx} = \frac{2x}{1 + x^2}$$

14.3.2 Exercises

1. Differentiate the following:

   (a) $\sin 3x$ (b) $\cos 4x$

   (c) e^{2x-1} (d) $\tan(5x-3)$

   (e) $5\cos 3x - 2\sin 4x$ (f) $e^{\cos x}$

   (g) $\ln(2x - 3)$ (h) $\ln(\cos x)$

   (i) $x\cos x$ (j) $x^2\sin x$

   (k) $e^x\tan x$ (l) $x\ln x$

   (m) $e^x\ln x$ (n) $e^{-x}\sin 2x$

   (o) $(\cos 3x)(\sin 2x)$ (p) $\cos(1 + x^2)$

   (q) $x\sin(1 + 3x^2)$ (r) $\cos^2 x$

   (s) $\sin^3 3x$ (t) $\dfrac{x}{\cos x}$

   (u) $\dfrac{x^2}{\cos x + \sin x}$ (v) $\dfrac{\cos^2 x}{\ln x}$

   (w) $\cos\sqrt{(x^2 + 3)}$ (x) $e^x(\cos x - \sin x)$

   (y) $\ln 3x - \ln x$ (z) $e^{\ln x}$

2. By considering $\tan x = \dfrac{\sin x}{\cos x}$, use the quotient rule to prove that

$$\frac{d}{dx}(\tan x) = \sec^2 x$$

3. Find the derivatives of $\cot x$, $\sec x$, $\operatorname{cosec} x$.

4. Use the fact that $10^x = e^{x\ln 10}$ to differentiate 10^x.

5. Use the fact that $\log_{10} x = \dfrac{\ln x}{\ln 10}$ to differentiate $\log_{10} x$.

6. Let a be a positive constant. Differentiate a^x and $\log_a x$.

7. Find the maxima and minima of the following:

   (a) $x^2 e^x$ (b) $\ln(1 + x + x^2)$

14.4 Applications of the chain rule

An *explicit* function gives y directly in terms of x. An *implicit* function connects y and x together by an equation.

$y = 3x^2 + 7x - 3$ and $y = \cos 3x - 7e^x$ are explicit.

$x^2 + y^2 = 3$ and $\cos xy + 7y^2 = 8x$ are implicit.

If x and y are both expressed, not in terms of each other, but in terms of a third variable t, then t is a parameter.

A small change in x is often written as δx. (Pronounced delta x). Small changes are connected by the following approximation:

$$\delta y \approx \frac{dy}{dx} \times \delta x$$

14.4.1 Examples

1. Find the gradient of the curve $y^2 + 3xy + 2x^2 = 6$ at the point (1,1).

   Solution

   Here y is an implicit function of x. The y^2 term and the $3xy$ term are differentiated as follows:

   $$\frac{d(y^2)}{dx} = \frac{d(y^2)}{dy} \times \frac{dy}{dx} = 2y\frac{dy}{dx} \quad \text{(Using the Chain Rule)}$$

   $$\frac{d(3xy)}{dx} = y\frac{d(3x)}{dx} + 3x\frac{dy}{dx} = 3y + 3x\frac{dy}{dx} \quad \text{(Using the Product Rule)}$$

   Go through the equation, differentiating each term.

   $$2y\frac{dy}{dx} + 3y + 3x\frac{dy}{dx} + 4x = 0$$

   Substitute the values $x = 1$ and $y = 1$.

   $$2\frac{dy}{dx} + 3 + 3\frac{dy}{dx} + 4 = 0$$

   $$\frac{dy}{dx} = -\frac{7}{5}$$

2. Variables x and y are given by $x = t^2 + 1$, $y = t^3 + 2$. Find $\frac{dy}{dx}$ in terms of t.

   Solution

   Use the chain rule:

   $$\frac{dy}{dx} = \frac{dy}{dt} \times \frac{dt}{dx} = \frac{dy}{dx} \div \frac{dx}{dt} = 3t^2 \div 2t$$

   $$\frac{dy}{dx} = \tfrac{3}{2}t$$

3. The radius of a sphere is 12 cm. What is the approximate change in surface area if the radius increases by 0.01 cm?

   Solution

   The area is given by $A = 4\pi r^2$. Use the small change formula above, with $\delta r = 0.01$.

   $$\delta A \approx \frac{dA}{dr} \times \delta r = 8\pi r \times 0.01 = 8\pi \times 12 \times 0.01$$

   The change is approximately 3 cm^2

4. Air is pumped into a spherical balloon at 10 cm^3 s^{-1}. How fast is the radius increasing when it is 8 cm?

Solution

The rate of change of the volume is $\dfrac{dV}{dt} = 10$.

The rate of change of the radius is $\dfrac{dr}{dt}$.

The volume is given by $V = \dfrac{4\pi r^3}{3}$.

Use the chain rule: $\dfrac{dV}{dt} = \dfrac{dV}{dr} \times \dfrac{dr}{dt} = 4\pi r^2 \times \dfrac{dr}{dt}$

$\dfrac{dr}{dt} = \dfrac{10}{4\pi 8^2}$

The radius is increasing at 0.012 cm per second

14.4.2 Exercises

1. Find the gradients of the following functions at the points shown.
   - (a) $x^2 + y^2 = 5$ at (1,2)
   - (b) $x^2 - y^3 = 1$ at (3,2)
   - (c) $y^2 - 3x + 2y + x^2 = 1$ at (2,1)
   - (d) $x \cos y = 1$ at (1,0)
   - (e) $y^2 - 2xy = -3$ at (2,3)
   - (f) $yx^2 + x^3 + 2y = 2$ at (2,-1)
   - (g) $ye^x + e^y + e^x = 2$ at (0,0)
   - (h) $y^2x^2 + 2x - 3y = 0$ at (1,2)

2. For each of the following functions, express $\dfrac{dy}{dx}$ in terms of x and y.
   - (a) $x^2 + y^2 = 4$
   - (b) $x^2 + y^3 - 3x + y = 5$
   - (c) $x^2 + 4xy - y^2 = 3$
   - (d) $x^2 + 3yx^3 + 4y = 7$

3. Show that the stationary points of the ellipse $2x^2 + xy + y^2 = 1$ occur when $y + 4x = 0$.

4. Find the equation of the tangent to $5x^2 - 4y^2 = 1$ at the point (1,1).

5. Find the maximum and minimum values of y for the curve $x^2 - xy + y^2 = 1$.

6. Find the maximum and minimum values of x for the curve in Question 5.
   (Hint: when x is a maximum or minimum, $\dfrac{dx}{dy} = 0$.)

7. Find $\dfrac{dy}{dx}$ in terms of the parameter t for the following functions:
   - (a) $x = t^2, y = 2t^3 + 1$
   - (b) $x = \dfrac{1}{1+t}, y = t^2$
   - (c) $x = t + 2t^2, y = t^2 - t^3$
   - (d) $x = \dfrac{1}{1+t}, y = \dfrac{1}{1+t^2}$
   - (e) $x = at^2, y = 2at$ (a is constant)
   - (f) $x = ct, y = \dfrac{c}{t}$ (c is constant)
   - (g) $x = \cos t, y = \sin t$
   - (h) $x = 3 \cos t, y = 2 \sin t$
   - (i) $x = e^t + e^{-t}, y = e^t - e^{-t}$
   - (j) $x = 2 \tan t, y = \dfrac{3}{\cos t}$

8. If x and y are given parametrically by $x = 3 \cos t$ and $y = 4 \sin t$, find the equation of the tangent at the point where $t = \frac{1}{4}\pi$.

9. Find the equation of the normal to the curve given by $x = t^2 + 1$, $y = t^3 - 1$, at the point where $t = 2$.

10. Find the approximate increase in the area of a square when its side changes by 0.02 cm, when the side is 10 cm.

11. A cube has side 3 cm. Find the approximate change in its volume if its side changes by 0.01 cm.

12. The radius of a sphere is 5 cm. Find the approximate change in radius if the volume changes by 0.1 cm³.

13. The radius of a sphere is measured as 12.3 cm, with a possible error of 0.05 cm. What is the possible error in the volume?

14. The surface area of a sphere is measured as 67 cm², with a possible error of 0.5 cm². What is the approximate error in the radius? What is the approximate error in the volume?

15. The side of a square is measured, with a possible error of 1%. What is the approximate percentage error in the area?

16. The percentage error when measuring the area of a circle was 4%. What was the approximate percentage error in its radius?

17. The side of a square is increasing at 0.5 cm s⁻¹. At what rate is the area increasing at a time when the side is 15 cm?

18. The radius of a sphere is increasing at 0.02 cm s⁻¹. At what rate is the surface area increasing when the radius is 6 cm? At what rate is the volume increasing?

19. The area of a circle is increasing at 20 cm² s⁻¹. At what rate is the radius increasing, when it is 45 cm?

20. Water is poured into a cone, of semi–vertical angle 45°, at 10 cm³ s⁻¹. When the height of the water is 15 cm, at what rate is it increasing?

21. The volume of a cube is decreasing at 3 cm³ s⁻¹. When the side is 4 cm, what is the rate of decrease of (a) the side (b) the surface area?

22. At the equinox on the equator the angle θ of elevation of the sun changes at 0.000073 radians/sec. A flagpole of height 40 m. throws a shadow of length $40/\tan\theta$. Find the rate of decrease of the shadow when $\theta = 0.1$.

14.5 Examination questions

1. (a) Differentiate with respect to x,

    (i) $\ln(3x + 1)$ (ii) $x \cos 2x$

   (b) Find the equation of the tangent to the curve
   $$y = \frac{3 + x}{1 - 2x}$$
   at the point where the curve crosses the line $y = -1$.

   (c) Given that $x^2y + y^2 = 10$, find $\dfrac{dy}{dx}$ in terms of x and y.

   [C ADD]

2. (a) Sketch the curve $y = \log_e(x + 3)$.

   (b) Find the gradient of this curve at the point where $x = e - 3$. Hence show that the equation of the tangent to the curve at this point is $ey = x + 3$.

   [AEB ADD 1987]

3. The surface area of an expanding spherical balloon is increasing at the rate of 16 cm^2/s. At the instant when the surface area is 144 cm^2, calculate

   (a) the rate, in cm/s to 2 significant figures, at which the radius of the balloon is increasing,

   (b) the rate, in cm^3/s to 2 significant figures, at which the volume of the balloon is increasing.

   Find, in cm^3 to 2 significant figures, the approximate increase in the volume of the balloon when the surface area increases from 144 cm^2 to 146 cm^2.

   [L ADD]

4. Express $\dfrac{3x + 16}{(x - 3)(3x + 2)}$ in partial fractions.

   Hence find the value of $\dfrac{d}{dx}\left[\dfrac{13x + 6}{(x - 3)(3x + 2)}\right]$ when $x = 2$.

   [AEB 1986]

5. (a) A curve has the equation $x^3 - xy + y^3 = k$, where k is a constant.

   Find $\dfrac{dy}{dx}$ in terms of x and y.

   Prove that the curve cannot possess a tangent which is parallel to the y–axis if $k < -\frac{1}{27}$.

   (b) If $y = \dfrac{e^x}{1 + x^2}$, prove that $\dfrac{dy}{dx}$ may be written in the form $\dfrac{(x - 1)^2 e^x}{(1 + x^2)^2}$

   Hence, or otherwise, prove that, for all positive values of x,

   $$\frac{e^x}{1 + x^2} > 1$$

   [SUJB]

6. (a) The parametric equations of a curve are: $x = a\left(1 + \dfrac{1}{t}\right)$, $y = a\left(t - \dfrac{1}{t^2}\right)$, where a is a constant and $t \neq 0$.

   Find the equation of the normal to the curve at the point where $t = 2$.

   (b) The equation of a curve is $(y - x)^2 = 2a(y + x)$, where a is a constant.

   Find an expression for $\dfrac{dy}{dx}$ in terms of x, y and a.

   (c) The velocity v of a point moving in a straight line is given in terms of the time t by $v = e^{-2t} \sin 3t$.

   Find the smallest positive value of t for which the acceleration of the point is zero, giving two significant figures in your answer.

   [C]

7. Apply the small increment formula $f(x + \delta x) - f(x) \approx \delta x\, f'(x)$ to $\tan x$ to find an approximate value of

$$\tan\left(\frac{100\pi + 4}{400}\right) - \tan\frac{\pi}{4}$$

[L]

8. Sketch the curve whose equation is $\dfrac{x^2}{a^2} + \dfrac{y^2}{b^2} = 1$ $(a, b > 0)$

Find the gradient of the curve at the point $P(a\cos\theta, b\sin\theta)$.

Hence show that the equation of the tangent at P is $bx\cos\theta + ay\sin\theta = ab$

and that the equation of the normal at P is

$$ax\sin\theta - by\cos\theta = (a^2 - b^2)\sin\theta\cos\theta.$$

The tangent at P meets the x-axis at T and the y-axis at U; the normal at P meets the x-axis at M and the y-axis at N. Show that NT is perpendicular to MU.

Write down the coordinates of the mid-point Q of UT and hence find the equation of the locus of Q as θ varies.

[W]

Common errors

1. **Products and quotients**

   The derivative of a product is not the product of the derivatives. Similarly the derivative of a quotient is not the quotient of the derivatives. In both cases the rules must be used.

   If $y = uv$, then $\dfrac{dy}{dx} \neq \dfrac{du}{dx} \times \dfrac{dv}{dx}$

   If $y = \dfrac{u}{v}$, then $= \dfrac{dy}{dx} \neq \dfrac{du}{dx} \div \dfrac{dv}{dx}$

2. **Chain rule**

   When using the chain rule

   $$\frac{dy}{dx} = \frac{dy}{dz} \times \frac{dz}{dx}$$

   make sure you put the value of z in the $\dfrac{dy}{dz}$ term. Watch out for the following:

   For $y = \sin x^2$, $\dfrac{dy}{dx} \neq 2x\cos x$. It should be $2x\cos x^2$.

   Once you have found the derivative, substitute back so that the answer is in terms of x. It would be incorrect to leave z in the answer.

3. **Differentiating power functions**

   The function a^x is very different from x^a. Do not differentiate as though they were the same function. In particular:

   If $y = e^x$, then $\dfrac{dy}{dx} \neq xe^{x-1}$. It should be e^x.

4. **Implicit functions**

Many difficulties are found when differentiating implicit functions.

For something like y^2, use $\dfrac{d(y^2)}{dx} = \dfrac{d(y^2)}{dy} \times \dfrac{dy}{dx}$.

For something like $3xy$, use the product rule. And if there is a constant at the right hand side, its derivative is 0. Note the following:

If $x^2 + y^2 = 3$, then $2x + 2y \times \dfrac{dy}{dx} \neq \dfrac{dy}{dx}$.

The right hand side of the last equation should be 0.

15 Integration

Integration is the opposite operation to differentiation.

If $\dfrac{d(F(x))}{dx} = f(x)$, then $\displaystyle\int f(x)\, dx = F(x) + c$.

The constant c is called the *constant of integration*.

15.1 Integration of powers of x

Powers of x are integrated by the rule:

$$\int x^n\, dx = \frac{x^{n+1}}{n+1} + c$$

for all n except $n = -1$.

If functions are added or multiplied by constants, then the integrals are added or multiplied by constants.

$$\int (ax^n + bx^m)\, dx = \frac{ax^{n+1}}{n+1} + \frac{bx^{m+1}}{m+1} + c.$$

In particular, $\displaystyle\int 0\, dx = c$; $\displaystyle\int k\, dx = kx + c$, where k is a constant.

15.1.1 Examples

1. If $\dfrac{dy}{dx} = 6x^2 + 2$, find y given that $y = 7$ when $x = 1$.

    Solution

    Integrate $6x^2 + 2$.

    $$y = \int (6x^2 + 2)\, dx = 2x^3 + 2x + c.$$

    Substitute $x = 1$ and $y = 7$ to find that $c = 3$.

    $$y = 2x^3 + 2x + 3$$

2. Integrate $(\sqrt{x} + 1)(x^2 - 3)$.

    Solution

    The brackets must be multiplied out before integration.

    $$(\sqrt{x} + 1)(x^2 - 3) = x^{\frac{5}{2}} - 3\, x^{\frac{1}{2}} + x^2 - 3.$$

$$\int (\sqrt{x} + 1)(x^2 - 3)\, dx = \frac{x^{\frac{7}{2}}}{\frac{7}{2}} - \frac{3x^{\frac{7}{2}}}{\frac{3}{2}} + \frac{x^3}{3} - 3x + c$$

$$= \frac{2x^{\frac{7}{2}}}{7} - 2x^{\frac{3}{2}} + \frac{x^3}{3} - 3x + c$$

15.1.2 Exercises

1. For each of the following find y as a function of x.

   (a) $\dfrac{dy}{dx} = 2x$, $y = 1$ for $x = 0$

   (b) $\dfrac{dy}{dx} = 3x^2 + x$, $y = 1$ for $x = 1$

   (c) $\dfrac{dy}{dx} = x^2 + x + 1$, $y = 3$ for $x = 1$

   (d) $\dfrac{dy}{dx} = \dfrac{1}{x^2}$, $y = 1$ for $x = 1$

   (e) $\dfrac{dy}{dx} = x^{3/2}$, $y = 1$ for $x = 4$

   (f) $\dfrac{dy}{dx} = \dfrac{3}{\sqrt{x}}$, $y = 4$ for $x = 16$

   (g) $\dfrac{dy}{dx} = x(x^2 + 1)$, $y = 0$ for $x = 1$

   (h) $\dfrac{dy}{dx} = \dfrac{x^2 + 3}{\sqrt{x}}$, $y = 3$ for $x = 4$

2. Evaluate the following integrals:

   (a) $\displaystyle\int 2x\, dx$

   (b) $\displaystyle\int (3x^2 + 2x + 1)\, dx$

   (c) $\displaystyle\int (x^2 + 2x^3 + 5)\, dx$

   (d) $\displaystyle\int (2x^5 - \tfrac{5}{2}x^7)\, dx$

   (e) $\displaystyle\int x^{3/2}\, dx$

   (f) $\displaystyle\int (3 - \sqrt{x})\, dx$

   (g) $\displaystyle\int \dfrac{1}{x^3}\, dx$

   (h) $\displaystyle\int \left(\dfrac{2}{x^2} + \dfrac{7}{x^3} + 2\right) dx$

   (i) $\displaystyle\int x(3x^2 + 7)\, dx$

   (j) $\displaystyle\int (x - 3)(x^2 + 2x)\, dx$

   (k) $\displaystyle\int x(4x^2 - 2x^3)\, dx$

   (l) $\displaystyle\int \left(\sqrt{x} + \dfrac{1}{\sqrt{x}}\right)(x^4 - 3)\, dx$

15.2 Definite integrals and areas

When $f(x)$ is integrated to find $F(x)$, the result is the *indefinite integral* of f.

The difference of $F(x)$ between two values of x is the *definite integral* of f.

If $\displaystyle\int f(x)\, dx = F(x)$, then:

$$\int_a^b f(x)\, dx = \big[F(x)\big]_a^b = F(b) - F(a)$$

The area bounded by a curve $y = f(x)$, the x-axis and the limits $x = a$ and $x = b$ is given by the definite integral of $f(x)$ between a and b.

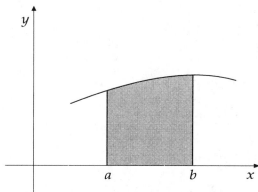

Fig 15.1

$$\text{Area} = \int_a^b f(x)\, dx$$

Negative area corresponds to a region *below* the *x*-axis.

If *x* and *y* are expressed in terms of a parameter *t*, then integrals can be found from the following:

$$\int y\, dx = \int y\, \frac{dx}{dt}\, dt.$$

15.2.1 Examples

1. Evaluate the definite integral $\displaystyle\int_1^2 (x^2 - \frac{3}{x^3})\, dx$.

    Solution

    First find the indefinite integral.

    $$\int (x^2 - \frac{3}{x^3})\, dx = \tfrac{1}{3}x^3 + \tfrac{3}{2}x^{-2} + c.$$

    Evaluate this at the values 1 and 2 and subtract.

    $$\int_1^2 (x^2 - \frac{3}{x^3})\, dx = (\tfrac{1}{3} \times 2^3 + \tfrac{3}{2} \times 2^{-2} + c) - (\tfrac{1}{3} \times 1^3 + \tfrac{3}{2} \times 1^{-2} + c)$$

    $$\int_1^2 (x^2 - \frac{3}{x^3})\, dx = 1.2083$$

2. Find the area enclosed by the curve $y = \sqrt{x}$, the *x*-axis and the line $y = x - 2$.

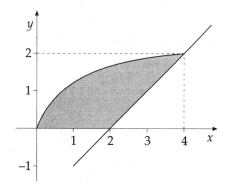

Fig 15.2

    Solution

    A rough sketch of the area is shown. The curve and the line cross at (4,2). The area is the difference between the area under the curve and the area under the line.

    $$\text{Area} = \int_0^4 \sqrt{x}\, dx - \int_2^4 (x - 2)\, dx = \left[\tfrac{2}{3}x^{\frac{3}{2}}\right]_0^4 - \left[\tfrac{1}{2}x^2 - 2x\right]_2^4$$

    $$\text{Area} = 3\tfrac{1}{3}$$

15.2.2 Exercises

1. Evaluate the following definite integrals:

    (a) $\displaystyle\int_0^3 (2x + 3x^2)\, dx$

    (b) $\displaystyle\int_0^1 (x^2 - \tfrac{1}{4}x^4)\, dx$

(c) $\displaystyle\int_1^9 (\sqrt{x} - \frac{3}{x^2})\, dx$

(d) $\displaystyle\int_1^4 x(x+3)\, dx$

(e) $\displaystyle\int_1^4 \frac{x^2-1}{\sqrt{x}}\, dx$

(f) $\displaystyle\int_{-1}^2 (x^3+2)^2\, dx$

2. Find the areas enclosed by the following curves and the x-axis, between the limits shown:

(a) $y = x^2$, $x = 1$ and $x = 3$

(b) $y = \dfrac{1}{x^2}$, $x = 1$ and $x = 20$

(c) $y = x^{-1/2}$, $x = 0$ and $x = 9$

(d) $y = x^3 - x$, $x = 0$ and $x = 1$

3. Sketch the curve $y = 3 - 2x - x^2$. Find the area of the region enclosed by the curve and the x-axis.

4. Sketch the curve $y = x^3 - x$. Find the areas of the regions:

(a) enclosed by the curve above the x-axis

(b) enclosed by the curve below the x-axis. What do you notice?

5. On the same graph sketch the curve $y = 1 - x^2$ and the line $y = 1 - x$. Find the areas

(a) between the curve and the line

(b) enclosed between the curve, the line and the x-axis.

6. Find the area between the y-axis, the curve $y = x^3 - 4$ and the line $y = 4$.

7. Find the areas of the two regions between the x-axis and the curve $y = (x+1)(x-3)(2x+1)$.

8. For each of the following, evaluate the definite integral and sketch the area to which it corresponds.

(a) $\displaystyle\int_0^4 3x^2 dx$

(b) $\displaystyle\int_1^2 \frac{4}{x^3}\, dx$

(c) $\displaystyle\int_0^2 (4 - x^2)\, dx$

(d) $\displaystyle\int_1^9 x^{-1/2} dx$

9. The variables x and y are given in terms of the parameter t by $x = t^2 + 1$, $y = t^3 - t$. Find the area enclosed by the curve between $t = 0$ and $t = 1$ and the x-axis.

10. The variables x and y are given in terms of t by $x = t + \dfrac{1}{t}$, $y = t^2 + \dfrac{1}{t^2}$.

Find the area enclosed by the curve between $t = 1$ and $t = 2$ and the x-axis.

15.3 Volumes of revolution

When a curve $y = f(x)$ is rotated through $360°$ about the x-axis, it passes through a region of space called a *solid of revolution*. The volume of this solid is the *volume of revolution*. The volume is given by:

$$V = \int \pi y^2\, dx$$

Fig 15.3

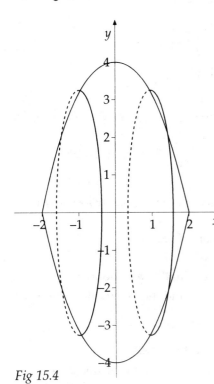

Fig 15.4

15.3.1 Example

The area enclosed by the curve $y = 4 - x^2$ and the x-axis is rotated about the x-axis. Find the volume of revolution. (Fig 15.4)

Solution

The curve crosses the x-axis at $x = -2$ and $x = 2$. The volume is therefore:

$$V = \int_{-2}^{2} \pi(4 - x^2)^2 \, dx = \int_{-2}^{2} \pi(16 - 8x^2 + x^4) \, dx$$

$$V = \pi \left[16x - \frac{8x^3}{3} - \frac{x^5}{5} \right]_{-2}^{2}$$

$$V = 107.2$$

15.3.2 Exercises

1. Find the volumes enclosed when the following curves between the limits shown are rotated about the x-axis.

   (a) $y = 3x^2$, $x = 1$ and $x = 2$ (b) $y = \sqrt{x}$, $x = 0$ and $x = 3$

   (c) $y = \dfrac{1}{x}$, $x = 1$ and $x = 10$ (d) $y = 2x - 3$, $x = 2$ and $x = 4$

   (e) $y = 3x - \dfrac{2}{x}$, $x = 1$ and $x = 4$ (f) $y = \sqrt{(1 + x^2)}$, $x = 0$ and $x = 3$

2. The line $y = 3x$, between $x = 0$ and $x = 4$, is rotated about the x-axis. Show that the solid of revolution is a cone. What is its height and its base radius? Find the volume of revolution, and verify that this agrees with the formula $V = \frac{1}{3}\pi r^2 h$.

3. By rotating the line $y = rx/h$, from $x = 0$ to $x = h$, about the x-axis, prove that the volume of a cone of height h and base radius r is $\frac{1}{3}\pi r^2 h$.

4. The circle with centre at the origin and radius 1 has equation $y = \sqrt{(1 - x^2)}$. What is the solid formed when this curve is rotated about the x-axis? Find the volume of revolution, and verify that it agrees with the formula for the volume of this solid.

5. Find the equation of the straight line through (0,1) and (2,3). When this line is rotated about the x-axis, the solid of revolution is a *frustum*, of height 2 and radii 1 and 3. Find the volume of this frustum.

6. A curve is given parametrically by $x = at^2$, $y = 2at$. Find the area enclosed by the curve and the line $x = a$. Find the volume when this area is rotated about the x-axis.

15.4 Examination questions

1. (a) Integrate with respect to x:

   (i) $x^2 - x^{3/2}$ (ii) $(x^2 - 1)^2$.

(b) A curve passes through the point (9,2) and its gradient at the point (x,y) is given by $\dfrac{dy}{dx} = \sqrt{x} + 3$. Find the equation of the curve and the equation of the tangent at the point (9,2).

[O&C ADD]

2. The finite region contained between the x-axis and the curve whose equation is $y = x(2 - x)$ is completely rotated about the x-axis. Calculate the volume of the solid so formed. (Leave your answer as a multiple of π.)

[L ADD]

3. (a) Using a scale of 2 cm to 1 unit on each axis, sketch the graph of $y = 3 - \dfrac{5}{x^2}$, for $1 \le x \le 5$.

(b) Shade the area represented by I where $I = \displaystyle\int_2^4 (3 - \dfrac{5}{x^2})\, dx$.

(c) The rate of flow of water through a drainpipe t minutes after the beginning of a storm is approximated by $100(3 - \dfrac{5}{t^2})$ m/min for $t \ge 2$.

If the drainpipe remains full and has cross–sectional area 0.2 m², calculate the volume of water flowing through the drain during the time from $t = 2$ to $t = 4$.

[SMP ADD]

4. Sketch the curve $y = 3x^{2/3}$ for values of x from 1 to 8. A vase is made from thin glass in the shape of the surface obtained by rotating this curve, together with the line segment from (0,3) to (1,3), about the y-axis which is vertical. The unit along each axis is 1 cm. Water is poured into the vase at a constant rate of 30 cm³ s⁻¹. Prove by integration that the volume, V cm³, of water in the vase, when its depth is h cm, is given by

$$V = \tfrac{\pi}{108}\, [(h + 3)^4 - 3^4].$$

(a) How long does it take for the depth to increase from 0 to 6 cm?

(b) Find, when $h = 6$, the rate at which

 (i) the water level is rising,

 (ii) the area of the horizontal water surface is increasing.

[AEB 1986]

5. A curve is defined by the equations $x = t^2 - 1$, $y = t^3 - t$, where t is a parameter.

Sketch the curve for all real values of t.

Find the area of the region enclosed by the loop of the curve.

[L]

6. Sketch the graph of the function $f : x \to |3x - 2|$ in the interval $0 \le x \le 1$.

Evaluate $\displaystyle\int_0^1 f(x)\, dx$. [If you wish, you may use a formula for the area of a triangle.]

[SMP]

Common errors

1. **Integration**
    (a) Do not integrate when you are asked to differentiate, or the other way round.
    (b) When integrating a negative power of x, you still add 1 to the power.

    $$\int x^{-3}\, dx = -\tfrac{1}{2}x^{-2} + c, \text{ not } -\tfrac{1}{4}x^{-4} + c.$$

    (c) Do not forget to divide by $(n+1)$ when integrating x^n. And divide by $(n+1)$, not by n.
    (d) If functions are multiplied, you cannot integrate them individually and multiply the results.

    $$\int f(x)g(x)\, dx \neq \int f(x)\, dx \times \int g(x)\, dx.$$

    A similar mistake arises when one function is divided by another.
    (e) Do not forget the constant of integration c.

2. **Definite integrals**

    Make sure that you get the limits of integration the correct way round. Be very careful of negative signs when subtracting the second value from the first.

3. **Areas**

    Questions often ask you to find the area between two curves. You must first find out where they intersect.

4. **Volume**

    (a) When using the formula $\int \pi y^2 dx$, you must square first and then integrate. Watch out for the following:

    $$\int \pi y^2 dx \neq \pi \left(\int y\, dx \right)^2$$

    (b) When using the formula $\int \pi y^2 dx$, you must express y as a function of x. And the other way round: if a curve is rotated about the y-axis, you will use the formula $\int \pi x^2 dy$.

    Write x as a function of y before integrating.

16 Methods of integration

Trigonometric and exponential functions are integrated as follows:

$$\int \cos x \, dx = \sin x + c \qquad\qquad \int \sin x \, dx = -\cos x + c$$

$$\int e^x \, dx = e^x + c \qquad\qquad \int \frac{1}{x} \, dx = \ln x + c.$$

16.1 Integration by substitution

Simple functions can often be integrated by inspection.

More complicated functions which cannot be directly integrated can be reduced to a simpler form by *substitution*.

When an expression involves a 'function of a function', $f(g(x))$, it is often helpful to substitute for the inside function. That is, put $u = g(x)$.

16.1.1 Examples

1. Find the integral $\int \cos 3x \, dx$.

    Solution

    The answer must be of the form $k \sin 3x + c$, where k is a constant. The derivative of $\sin 3x$ is $3 \cos 3x$. This is 3 times too great. Hence to balance out k must be $\frac{1}{3}$.

    $$\int \cos 3x \, dx = \tfrac{1}{3} \sin 3x + c$$

2. Evaluate the integral $\displaystyle\int_0^{\frac{\pi}{4}} \sin^3 x \cos x \, dx$.

    Solution

    $\sin^3 x$ is of the form $f(g(x))$, where $g(x) = \sin x$. Put $u = \sin x$. $\dfrac{du}{dx} = \cos x$, hence $du = \cos x \, dx$. The integral becomes:

    $$\int u^3 \, du = \left[\tfrac{1}{4} u^4 \right]_{x=0}^{x=\frac{\pi}{4}} = \left[\tfrac{1}{4} \sin^4 x \right]_{x=0}^{x=\frac{\pi}{4}}$$

    The integral is $\tfrac{1}{4} \sin^4 \tfrac{\pi}{4} = \tfrac{1}{16}$.

3. Find the indefinite integral $\int x\sqrt{(1 + x)}\, dx$.

    Solution

    Put $u = 1 + x$. Then $x = u - 1$. Also $\dfrac{du}{dx} = 1$, hence $du = dx$.

    The integral becomes:

    $$\int (u - 1)\sqrt{u}\, du = \int (u^{3/2} - u^{1/2})\, du = \frac{u^{5/2}}{5/2} - \frac{u^{3/2}}{3/2} + c$$

    The integral is $\frac{2}{5}(1 + x)^{5/2} - \frac{2}{3}(1 + x)^{3/2} + c$

16.1.2 Exercises

1. Find the following integrals by inspection:

    (a) $\int \sin 2x\, dx$

    (b) $\int \cos \tfrac{1}{2}x\, dx$

    (c) $\int \sin(3x - 1)\, dx$

    (d) $\int 4 \cos(2x + 3)\, dx$

    (e) $\int e^{3x}\, dx$

    (f) $\int e^{2x+1}\, dx$

    (g) $\int \dfrac{1}{x + 3}\, dx$

    (h) $\int \dfrac{1}{2x - 5}\, dx$

    Evaluate the following integrals:

2. $\displaystyle\int_0^{\frac{\pi}{2}} \cos^4 x \sin x\, dx$

3. $\displaystyle\int_0^4 x\sqrt{(1 + x^2)}\, dx$

4. $\displaystyle\int_0^1 e^x\sqrt{(2 + e^x)}\, dx$

5. $\displaystyle\int_1^2 xe^{x^2}\, dx$

6. $\displaystyle\int_0^{\frac{\pi}{6}} \cos x\, e^{\sin x}\, dx$

7. $\displaystyle\int_0^a \dfrac{x}{a + x^2}\, dx$

8. $\displaystyle\int_0^{\frac{\pi}{2}} \dfrac{\cos x}{1 + \sin x}\, dx$

9. $\displaystyle\int_1^2 \dfrac{2x + 1}{x^2 + x + 1}\, dx$

10. $\displaystyle\int x^2\sqrt{(x^3 + 4)}\, dx$

11. $\displaystyle\int \dfrac{\cos \sqrt{x}}{\sqrt{x}}\, dx$

12. $\displaystyle\int \sec^2 x \tan^3 x\, dx$

13. $\displaystyle\int \dfrac{1}{x \ln x}\, dx$

14. $\displaystyle\int x\sqrt{(3 + x)}\, dx$

15. $\displaystyle\int \dfrac{2x}{\sqrt{(1 + 3x)}}\, dx$

16. $\displaystyle\int (x - 1)(x + 1)^{3/2}\, dx$

17. $\displaystyle\int \dfrac{1}{(3x - 1)^3}\, dx$

18. $\displaystyle\int x(1 + 4x)^{14}\, dx$

19. $\displaystyle\int (x - 3)(x + 2)^{12}\, dx$

20. Use the identity $\cos^2 x = 1 - \sin^2 x$ to evaluate $\displaystyle\int \cos^3 x\, dx$

21. $\displaystyle\int \sin^5 x\, dx$

22. $\displaystyle\int \frac{dx}{1 - e^x}$ (Multiply top and bottom by e^{-x})

23. $\displaystyle\int \cos^2 x\, dx$ (Use the identity $\cos 2x \equiv 2\cos^2 x - 1$).

24. $\displaystyle\int \sin^2 3x\, dx$ (Use the identity $\cos 2x \equiv 1 - 2\sin^2 x$).

25. Express $f(x) = \dfrac{1}{(1 + x)(2 + x)}$ in partial fractions. Hence find $\displaystyle\int f(x)\, dx$.

26. By using partial fractions, find the following:

   (a) $\displaystyle\int \frac{1}{(3 + x)(2 + x)}\, dx$

   (b) $\displaystyle\int \frac{x + 4}{(2 + x)(1 + x)^2}\, dx$

   (c) $\displaystyle\int \frac{2 - x}{(1 + 2x)(1 - 3x)}\, dx$

16.2 Integration by parts

A product of two functions can sometimes be integrated by means of *integration by parts*. Suppose that w is the derivative of u, i.e. that $w = \dfrac{du}{dx}$.
Then:

$$\int wv\, dx = uv - \int u\, \frac{dv}{dx}\, dx$$

16.2.1 Examples

1. Find $\displaystyle\int xe^x\, dx$.

   Solution

   Here let v be x and w be e^x. Then $u = e^x$. Apply the formula:

   $$\int x\, e^x\, dx = x\, e^x - \int e^x\, \frac{dx}{dx}\, dx = x\, e^x - \int e^x\, dx$$

   $$\int x\, e^x\, dx = x\, e^x - e^x + c$$

2. Find $\displaystyle\int \ln x\, dx$.

   Solution

   Regard $\ln x$ as $1 \times \ln x$. Take w as 1 and v as $\ln x$. Then $u = x$. Apply the formula:

   $$\int 1 \times \ln x\, dx = x \ln x - \int x\, \frac{d\ln x}{dx}\, dx = x \ln x - \int \frac{x}{x}\, dx$$

   $$\int \ln x\, dx = x \ln x - x + c$$

16.2.2 Exercises

Evaluate the following:

1. $\int x\,e^{-x}\,dx$

2. $\int x\cos x\,dx$

3. $\int x\sin x\,dx$

4. $\int x\ln x\,dx$

5. $\int x^2\ln x\,dx$

6. $\int x^n\ln x\,dx$

7. $\int \sin^{-1}x\,dx$ (Use the fact that $\dfrac{d(\sin^{-1}x)}{dx} = \dfrac{1}{\sqrt{(1-x^2)}}$)

8. $\int \tan^{-1}x\,dx$ (Use the fact that $\dfrac{d(\tan^{-1}x)}{dx} = \dfrac{1}{1+x^2}$)

9. $\int x^2 e^x\,dx$

10. $\int x^2 e^{ax}\,dx$

11. $\int x^2\cos 3x\,dx$

12. $\int e^x(x-3)\,dx$

13. $\int x^2\sin ax\,dx$

14. $\int \dfrac{\ln x}{x^2}\,dx$

16.3 Examination questions

1. (a) Integrate with respect to x
    (i) $\sin 4x$
    (ii) $\frac{1}{2}\cos\left(\frac{1}{2}x + \frac{1}{2}\right)$.
    (b) Evaluate $\displaystyle\int_0^1 (1+9x)^{-1}\,dx$.

    [AEB ADD 1986]

2. Draw a sketch to show the finite region bounded by the curve $y = e^{x/2}$ and the lines $x = 2$, $x = 4$ and $y = 0$.

    Leaving your answer in terms of e, calculate the area of this region.

    [L ADD]

3. (a) (i) Find

    $$\int \frac{1}{x(x+1)}\,dx, \; x > 0$$

    Using the substitution $u = e^x$ and the answer to (i), or otherwise,
    (ii) find

    $$\int \frac{1}{1+e^x}\,dx$$

    (b) Use integration by parts to find

    $$\int x^2\sin x\,dx$$

    [L]

4. (i) Find $\int (3x + 4)\, e^{2x}\, dx.$

    (ii) By using the substitution $x = 2 \tan \theta$, evaluate $\int_0^2 \dfrac{2}{(4 + x^2)^2}\, dx.$

    [L]

5. Using the substitution $x = 3 + \sin \theta$, show that:

    $$\int_2^4 \sqrt{(4 - x)(x - 2)}\, dx = \int_{-\frac{\pi}{2}}^{\frac{\pi}{2}} \cos^2 \theta\, d\theta.$$

    Hence evaluate the integral.

    [W]

6. Sketch the graph of $y = \sin^{-1} \dfrac{x}{a}$, where $a > 0$, stating the domain and the range of the function.

    Using the fact that the derivative of $\sin x$ is $\cos x$, show that

    $$\frac{dy}{dx} = + \frac{1}{\sqrt{(a^2 - x^2)}}.$$

    Hence, or otherwise, show that

    $$\int_0^1 \frac{dx}{\sqrt{(4 - (x + 1)^2)}} = \frac{\pi}{3}.$$

    [SMP]

Common errors

1. **Substitution**

    (a) When substituting u for x, do not forget to change the dx to a du by means of $\dfrac{du}{dx}$. You cannot integrate a function of u with respect to x.

    (b) When finding an indefinite integral by substituting u for x, you must re–substitute back at the end to get the answer in terms of x. Do not give the answer in terms of u.

    (c) When finding a definite integral by substitution, remember that the limits refer to values of x. Do not apply these values to u when working out the final answer.

2. **Integration by parts**

    When integrating something like $x\, e^x$, integrate the e^x term first. If you integrate the x term first, you will obtain $\frac{1}{2}x^2 e^x$, which is harder to integrate than the function you started with.

17 Numerical methods

If a value cannot be found exactly, then an approximate value can often be obtained by *numerical methods*.

17.1 Solution of equations

Suppose we want to solve an equation f(x) = 0. A sequence of numbers x_0, x_1, x_2,..., x_n... which gets closer to the solution *converges* to the solution.

If the sequence does not get closer to a fixed value, then it *diverges*.

Three methods to find a convergent sequence are as follows.

A LINEAR INTERPOLATION METHOD

Linear interpolation estimates the root of the equation f(x) = 0 by drawing a straight line between two known values of the function, and calculating where that straight line crosses the *x*-axis.

If *a* and *b* are near the root α, then draw the straight line between (a,f(a)) and (b,f(b)). If this line crosses the *x*-axis at A, then by similar triangles:

$$\frac{A - a}{-f(a)} = \frac{b - A}{f(b)}$$

where A = $\dfrac{af(b) - bf(a)}{f(b) - f(a)}$ (Fig 17.1)

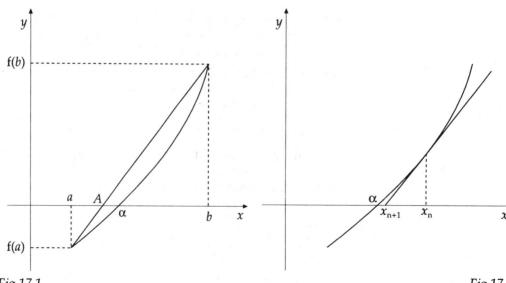

Fig 17.1   *Fig 17.2*

B Newton-Raphson method

The *Newton-Raphson* method obtains approximations to the root of f(x) = 0 by drawing a tangent to the curve of y = f(x), and calculating where that tangent crosses the x-axis.

Pick a first approximation x_0, and successive approximations are given by:

$$x_{n+1} = x_n - \frac{f(x_n)}{f'(x_n)} \quad \text{(Fig 17.2)}$$

C Picard's method

Picard's method rearranges the equation f(x) = 0 in the form x = g(x). It then obtains a sequence of approximations to the root of x = g(x) by the following:

Pick a first approximation x_0. Successive approximations are given by:

$$x_{n+1} = g(x_n)$$

There are often several ways to arrange an equation in the form x = g(x). If the iteration diverges, try another arrangement.

17.1.1 Examples

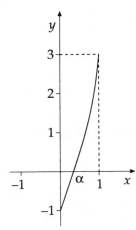

Fig 17.3

1. Show that there is a root of $x^3 + 3x - 1 = 0$ between 0 and 1. Obtain an approximation for this root by linear interpolation.

   Solution

   Let $f(x) = x^3 + 3x - 1$. Then f(0) = –1, and f(1) = 3. Hence the graph of $y = x^3 + 3x - 1$ must cross the x-axis at some point α between 0 and 1.

   To find an approximation for α, apply the formula above, using a = 0 and b = 1.

   $$\alpha \approx \frac{0 \times 3 - 1 \times -1}{3 - (-1)} = \tfrac{1}{4}$$

2. Use the Newton-Raphson formula to find a solution to $x^3 + 3x - 1 = 0$, accurate to 6 decimal places.

   Solution

   Take $x_0 = \tfrac{1}{4}$ as the starting point. The iteration is:

   $$x_{n+1} = x_n - \frac{x_n^3 + 3x_n - 1}{3x_n^2 + 3} \quad \text{giving:}$$

   $x_1 = 0.3235294$

   $x_2 = 0.3221859$

   $x_3 = 0.3221854$

   $x_4 = 0.3221854$

   The last two values agree to 6 decimal places.

   The solution is $\alpha = 0.322185$

3. Show that the equation $x^3 + 3x - 1 = 0$ can be arranged in the following ways:

   (a) $x = \sqrt[3]{(1 - 3x)}$ (b) $x = \tfrac{1}{3}(1 - x^3)$

Apply Picard's method to both these rearrangements, and hence find the solution to 3 decimal places.

Solution

(a) Rewrite the equation as $x^3 = 1 - 3x$. Take the cube root of both sides.

$x = \sqrt[3]{(1 - 3x)}$

(b) Rewrite the equation as $3x = 1 - x^3$. Divide both sides by 3.

$x = \frac{1}{3}(1 - x^3)$

In both cases let $x_0 = \frac{1}{4}$.

For arrangement (a)

the next terms are:

$x_1 = 0.62996, \; x_2 = -0.96186, \; x_3 = 1.57212$
This seems to be diverging.

For the arrangement (b)

the next terms are:

$x_1 = 0.32813, \; x_2 = 0.32156, \; x_3 = 0.32225$
The last two agree to 3 decimal places.

The solution is $\alpha = 0.322$

17.1.2 Exercises

1. Show that there is a root of $x^4 + 6x + 1 = 0$ between -1 and 0, and use linear interpolation to find an approximation to that root.

2. Use Newton-Raphson's iteration to find the solution to the equation in Question 1, accurate to 6 decimal places.

3. Find a pair of integers between which there is a root of $x^3 - 2x^2 - 3 = 0$. Use linear interpolation to find an approximation to that root.

4. Find the solution to the equation of Question 3, accurate to 5 decimal places, by means of Newton-Raphson's iteration.

5. Find the solution to the equation $e^x = 2 - x$, accurate to 6 decimal places.

6. Solve to 6 decimal places the equation $\sin \theta + \theta = 1$. (θ is measured in radians).

7. Solve the equation $\tan \theta = \theta + 1$, accurate to 6 decimal places.

8. Use Picard's iteration to solve the equation $\cos x = x$, to 3 decimal places.

9. Show that the equation $x^3 + x - 1 = 0$ can be written either as

   (a) $x = 1 - x^3$ or as (b) $x = \sqrt[3]{(1 - x)}$.

   Apply Picard's iteration to the equation, using both of the forms (a) and (b). Which one works? Find the solution of the equation, given to 3 decimal places.

10. Show that there is a root of the equation $x^4 + x = 20$ between $x = 2$ and $x = 3$. Show that the equation can be written in the following forms:

    (a) $x = \sqrt[4]{(20 - x)}$ (b) $x = 20 - x^4$ (c) $x = \dfrac{20}{1 + x^3}$

Apply Picard's iteration to each of these. Hence solve the equation to 3 decimal places.

11. Show that there is a root of the equation $e^x + x = 2$ between $x = 0$ and $x = 1$. Show that the equation can be written as

    (a) $x = 2 - e^x$ or as   (b) $x = \ln(2 - x)$.

    Use Picard's iteration to solve the equation to 3 decimal places.

12. Show that there is a root of the equation $x + 3 \sin x = 1.5$ between $x = 0$ and $x = 1$. (Here x is measured in radians.) Rearrange the equation in two forms, and hence use Picard's method to solve the equation to 3 decimal places.

17.2 Numerical integration

In many cases a function cannot be exactly integrated. There is a method for finding the definite integral of f(x) from $x = a$ to $x = b$.

Divide the interval $[a,b]$ into n equal intervals of length h. $(h = \dfrac{b-a}{n})$.

$a = x_0 < x_1 < ... < x_n = b$.

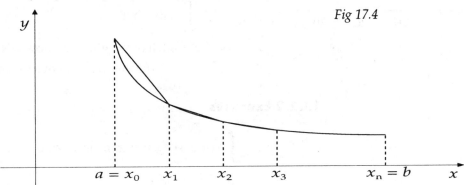

Fig 17.4

TRAPEZIUM RULE

The *trapezium rule* approximates the integral by dividing the area into n trapezia. The formula is:

$$\int_a^b f(x)\, dx \approx \tfrac{1}{2}h\, [\, f(a) + f(b) + 2(f(x_1) + f(x_2) + ... + f(x_{n-1}))\,]$$

If the graph of f(x) is concave, as shown in the figure, then the Trapezium rule will overestimate the true value. If the graph is convex then the rule will underestimate the value.

17.2.1 Examples

1. Evaluate $\displaystyle\int_1^2 \sin \sqrt{x}\, dx$, using the trapezium rule with 4 intervals.

   Solution

   Here $a = 1$, $b = 2$, $h = \tfrac{1}{4}$. Apply the formula:

$$\int_1^2 \sin \sqrt{x}\, dx \approx \tfrac{1}{8}[\, \sin \sqrt{1} + \sin \sqrt{2} + 2(\, \sin \sqrt{(\tfrac{5}{4})} + \sin \sqrt{(\tfrac{3}{2})} + \sin \sqrt{(\tfrac{7}{4})}\,)\,]$$

$$\int_1^2 \sin \sqrt{x}\, dx \approx 0.931$$

2. y is a function of x: the table below gives six values for x and y:

x	0	10	20	30	40	50
y	1.3	1.7	2.3	3.0	3.9	4.9

Use the trapezium rule to find an approximation for

$$\int_0^{50} y\, dx.$$

Is your answer an over or underestimate?

Solution

Apply the trapezium rule with $a = 0$, $b = 50$, $h = 10$.

$$\int_0^{50} y\, dx \approx \tfrac{1}{2} \times 10 \times [\, 1.3 + 4.9 + 2(\, 1.7 + 2.3 + 3.0 + 3.9\,)\,]$$

$$\int_0^{50} y\, dx \approx 140$$

A sketch of the graph is shown. Note that it is concave.
The answer is an overestimate

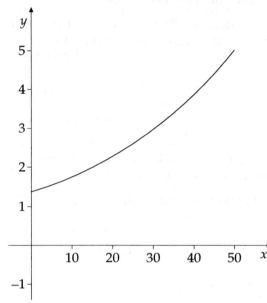

Fig 17.5

17.2.2 Exercises

1. Evaluate $\displaystyle\int_1^2 \sqrt{(x^3 + 1)}\, dx$, using the trapezium rule with four intervals.

2. Evaluate $\displaystyle\int_0^1 \sqrt{(\sin x)}\, dx$, using the trapezium rule with 6 intervals.

3. Evaluate $\displaystyle\int_1^3 (x^2 + 1)\, dx$, using the trapezium rule with 8 intervals.

4. Evaluate $\displaystyle\int_0^{\frac{\pi}{2}} \cos x\, dx$,

    (a) by exact integration,
    (b) by the trapezium rule with 4 intervals.

    What conclusion do you make about the accuracy of the rule?

5. y is a function of x, with values given by the following table:

x	2	3	4	5	6	7
y	85	74	66	59	51	47

Use the trapezium rule to approximate $\displaystyle\int_2^7 y\, dx$.

6. y is given in terms of x by the following table:

x	0	0.2	0.4	0.6	0.8	1.0	1.2
y	0.35	0.47	0.57	0.65	0.79	0.86	1.03

Approximate $\displaystyle\int_0^{1.2} y\,dx$, using the trapezium rule.

7. y is given in terms of x by the table:

x	10	13	16	19	22	25
y	0.3	0.8	1.4	2.1	3.0	4.2

Find an approximation for $\displaystyle\int_{10}^{25} y\,dx$ using the trapezium rule.

Write out an extra row for the values of y^2, and hence find an

approximation for $\displaystyle\int_{10}^{25} y^2\,dx$, using the trapezium rule.

8. By considering the shape of the graph, show that your answer to Question 3 is an overestimate of the true value.

9. By considering the shape of the graph, show that any evaluation of

$\displaystyle\int_0^{\frac{\pi}{2}} \cos x\,dx$ by the trapezium rule will be an underestimate.

Is this confirmed in your answer to Question 4?

17.3 Examination questions

1. The equation of a curve is $y = x^2 - 3x + 5$. A region is bounded by the curve, the axes and the ordinate at $x = 4$.

   (i) By using the trapezium rule with four strips of equal width, find an approximate value of the area of the region.

   (ii) Use a sketch to show why the approximate value of the area of the region is greater than the actual value.

   [JMB ADD]

2. (a) Rearrange the cubic equation $x^3 - 6x - 2 = 0$ into the form

   $$x = \pm\sqrt{a + \frac{b}{x}}$$

   State the values of the constants a and b.

(b) Use the iterative formula

$$x_{n+1} = \sqrt{a + \frac{b}{x_n}}$$

with $x_0 = 2$ and your values of a and b to find the approximate positive solution x_4 of the equation, to an appropriate degree of accuracy. Show all your intermediate answers.

[L]

3. Show that the cubic equation $x^3 + 2x - 11 = 0$ has only one real root and further that the root lies between $x = 1$ and $x = 2$.

Two possible iterative schemes for finding the root are

(i) $x_{n+1} = \frac{1}{2}(11 - x_n^3)$ and $\qquad$ (ii) $x_{n+1} = (11 - 2x_n)^{1/3}$.

Show that only one of these schemes converges from an initial estimate of $x = 2$ and hence find the root correct to 3 d.p., justifying the accuracy of your answer.

[MEI]

4. Draw a diagram to show why, if x_0 is an approximate solution of the equation $f(x) = 0$, then $x_0 - \dfrac{f(x_0)}{f'(x_0)}$ is, in general, a better one.

Prove that the cubic equation $x^3 + 6x - 2 = 0$ has a root lying between 0 and 1, and find it correct to two decimal places.

[O&C]

5. Show that $\displaystyle\int_0^1 x^2 e^x \, dx = e - 2$.

Show that use of the trapezium rule with 5 strips (6 ordinates) gives an estimate that is about 3.8% too high.

Explain why approximate evaluation of this integral using the trapezium rule will always result in an overestimate, however many strips are used.

[MEI]

6. (a) By sketching the curves with equations $y = 4 - x^2$ and $y = e^x$, show that the equation $x^2 + e^x - 4 = 0$ has one negative root and one positive root.

(b) Use the iteration formula $x_{n+1} = -(4 - e^{x_n})^{1/2}$ with $x_0 = -2$ to find in turn x_1, x_2, x_3 and x_4 and hence write down an approximation to the negative root of the equation, giving your answer to 4 decimal places.

An attempt to evaluate the positive root of the equation is made using the iteration formula $x_{n+1} = (4 - e^{x_n})^{1/2}$ with $x_0 = 1.3$.

(c) Describe the result of such an attempt.

[L]

Common errors

1. **Index notation**

   Do not be confused by the notation x_n. For example, do not confuse x_2 with x^2. x_2 is the second approximation in the sequence which started with x_0.

2. **Solution of equations**

   In all the methods be very careful with arithmetic. It is very easy to make mistakes, especially with the negative signs in the linear interpolation and Newton-Raphson formulae.

   When doing several successive approximations, it is a good idea to keep x_n in the memory of your calculator, and then replace it with x_{n+1} after each approximation is completed.

3. **Numerical integration**

   (a) Make sure that your intervals are correct. They must be equal in length.

   (b) When approximating something like $\int y^2 \, dx$, make sure that you square the y values before you use the formula.

   Be careful of the following: $\int y^2 \, dx \neq \left(\int y \, dx \right)^2$

18 Series

A *power series* is an expression of the form:

$$a_0 + a_1 x + a_2 x^2 + \ldots + a_n x^n + \ldots$$

where $a_0, a_1, \ldots a_n, \ldots$ are constants. The series *converges* if it approaches a fixed value as we take more and more terms. Otherwise the series *diverges.*

Two special power series have been defined, in Chapters 2 and 3.

$$\frac{1}{1-x} \equiv 1 + x + x^2 + \ldots + x^n + \ldots \quad \text{(the geometric series)}$$

$$(1 + x)^n \equiv 1 + nx + n(n-1)\frac{x^2}{2!} + n(n-1)(n-2)\frac{x^3}{3!} + \ldots \quad \text{(the binomial series).}$$

Both these series converge for $-1 < x < 1$.

18.1 Series for trig and exponential functions

Some standard series are as follows:

$$\ln(1 + x) \equiv x - \tfrac{1}{2}x^2 + \tfrac{1}{3}x^3 - \tfrac{1}{4}x^4 + \ldots$$

This series converges for $-1 < x \leq 1$.

$$e^x \equiv 1 + x + \frac{x^2}{2!} + \frac{x^3}{3!} + \ldots + \frac{x^n}{n!} + \ldots$$

$$\sin x \equiv x - \frac{x^3}{3!} + \frac{x^5}{5!} - \ldots$$

$$\cos x \equiv 1 - \frac{x^2}{2!} + \frac{x^4}{4!} - \ldots$$

These series converge for all x. In the expansions for $\sin x$ and $\cos x$ the angle x is measured in radians.

18.1.1 Examples

1. Find the series for $e^{2x}\cos x$, up to the term in x^3.
    Solution
    Expand both the series, up to the x^3 term.

    $$e^{2x} \approx 1 + 2x + \frac{(2x)^2}{2!} + \frac{(2x)^3}{3!}$$

    $$\cos x \approx 1 - \frac{x^2}{2!}$$

$$e^{2x}\cos x \approx (1 + 2x + 2x^2 + \tfrac{4}{3}x^3)(1 - \tfrac{1}{2}x^2)$$

$$e^{2x}\cos x \approx 1 + 2x + \tfrac{3}{2}x^2 + \tfrac{1}{3}x^3$$

2. Find the series for $(1 + x^2)^{-1}$, and use it to find the series for $\tan^{-1}x$. (The derivative of $\tan^{-1}x$ is $(1 + x^2)^{-1}$.) Hence find the approximate value of $\tan^{-1}0.1$.

   Solution

   To find the series for $(1 + x^2)^{-1}$ use the geometric series, replacing x by $-x^2$.

   $$(1 + x^2)^{-1} \equiv 1 - x^2 + x^4 - ...$$

   Integrate this series to find $\tan^{-1}x$. The constant of integration is zero, as $\tan^{-1}0 = 0$.

   $$\tan^{-1}x \equiv x - \frac{x^3}{3} + \frac{x^5}{5} - ...$$

   Put in $x = 0.1$ and evaluate:

   $$\tan^{-1}0.1 \approx 0.0996687$$

18.1.2 Exercises

1. Find the first three non-zero terms in the series for the following:

   (a) $\cos 2x$ (b) $\sin 3x$

   (c) e^{3x} (d) e^{-2x}

   (e) $e^x \sin x$ (f $e^{-x}\cos x$

   (g) $\ln(1 + 2x)$ (h) $\ln(1 - x^2)$

2. Use the series expansions to find approximations for the following:

   (a) $e^{1/2}$ (b) $\cos \tfrac{1}{4}$

   (c) $\sin 0.1$ (d) $\dfrac{1}{e}$

   (e) $\ln(1.1)$ (f) $\ln(0.8)$

3. Multiply together the series for $\cos x$ and $\sin x$, and write the result as a power series up to the x^3 term. Verify that your answer is the same as the expansion of $\tfrac{1}{2}\sin 2x$.

4. Find the expansion for $\cos^2 x$ up to the x^4 term,

   (a) by squaring the series of $\cos x$

   (b) by writing $\cos^2 x = \tfrac{1}{2}\cos 2x + \tfrac{1}{2}$, and expanding $\cos 2x$.

   Verify that the results are the same.

5. Integrate the series for $\dfrac{1}{x + 1}$, and verify that the result is the series for $\ln(1 + x)$.

6. By writing $(2 + x)$ as $2(1 + \tfrac{1}{2}x)$, find the series for $\ln(2 + x)$.

7. By expanding the terms concerned, find the limit as x tends to zero of

   $$\frac{e^x - e^{-x}}{e^{2x} - e^{-2x}}$$

8. Use the method of Question 7 to find the limit as x tends to zero of:

   (a) $\dfrac{1 - \cos x}{x^2}$

   (b) $\dfrac{x^2 - x \sin x}{1 - \cos x}$

   (c) $\dfrac{\ln(1 + x)}{x}$

   (d) $\dfrac{e^x - e^{-x}}{\sin x}$

9. By writing 2^x as $e^{x \ln 2}$ find the expansion of 2^x.

10. Find the limit as x tends to zero of $\dfrac{2^x - 2^{-x}}{3^x - 3^{-x}}$.

11. Expand e^{-x} up to the term in x^2. Hence find an approximate solution for the equation $e^{-x} = x$.

12. By the method of Question 11 find approximate solutions for:

    (a) $\cos x = 3x$

    (b) $\sin x = \ln(1 + x)$

13. Express $\dfrac{2}{(1 - x)(1 + x)}$ in partial fractions. Hence find the expansion of this function up to the term in x^2.

14. Find the expansions of the following functions up to the terms in x^2. In each case give the range of values of x for which the series converges.

    (a) $\dfrac{2 + 5x}{(1 + 2x)(1 + 3x)}$

    (b) $\dfrac{5x + 8}{(1 + x)(2 + x)}$

    (c) $\dfrac{x^2 + x + 2}{(1 - x)(1 + x)^2}$

    (d) $\dfrac{x - 1}{(1 + x^2)(1 + x)}$

18.2 Maclaurin series

The *Maclaurin series* for a function $f(x)$ is:

$$f(x) \equiv f(0) + f'(0)\, x + f''(0)\, \frac{x^2}{2!} + \ldots + f^n(0)\, \frac{x^n}{n!} + \ldots$$

Here $f^n(0)$ represents the nth derivative of $f(x)$, evaluated at $x = 0$.

18.2.1 Example

Find the Maclaurin series for $\tan x$, up to the term in x^3. Hence find the approximate value of $\tan 0.2$.

Solution

Let $f(x) = \tan x$. Differentiate three times:

$f'(x) = \sec^2 x; \ \ f''(x) = 2 \sec^2 x \tan x; \ \ f'''(x) = 4 \sec^2 x \tan^2 x + 2 \sec^4 x.$

Put $x = 0$ in each of these derivatives and in $f(x)$ itself.

$f(0) = 0 : f'(0) = 1 : f''(0) = 0 : f'''(0) = 2.$

Put these values into the Maclaurin series.

$\tan x \approx x + \tfrac{1}{3}x^3$

Put $x = 0.2$:

$$\tan 0.2 \approx 0.2027$$

18.2.2 Exercises

1. Use the fact that the derivative of e^x is e^x to verify that the Maclaurin series for e^x is the series given in 18.1.

2. Find the first four derivatives of $\cos x$ and of $\sin x$. Hence verify that their Maclaurin series are the same as the series in 18.1.

3. Find the Maclaurin series for the following functions, up to the term in x^3.
    (a) $\sin^{-1}x$ (b) $\cos^{-1}x$
    (c) $\sec x$ (d) $e^{\tan x}$

4. By writing $f(x) = \sin(\frac{\pi}{6} + x)$, prove that
    $$\sin(\tfrac{\pi}{6} + x) \approx \tfrac{1}{2} + \tfrac{1}{2}\sqrt{3}x - \tfrac{1}{4}x^2.$$

5. Find the expansion of $\cos(\frac{\pi}{3} + x)$ up to the term in x^2.

6. A function $f(x)$ is such that $f(0) = 3$, $f'(0) = 2$, $f''(0) = 4$, $f'''(0) = 12$. Write down the Maclaurin expansion of $f(x)$ up to the term in x^3.

18.3 Examination questions

1. Find the expansions, in ascending powers of x as far as the term in x^5, for
    (i) $\sin^3 x$ (ii) $x(1 - \cos x)$.

    Find the limit, as $x \to 0$, of the function $\dfrac{\sin^3 x}{x(1 - \cos x)}$.
    [O&C]

2. When x is so small that x^3 and higher powers of x can be neglected, find non-zero constants a and b such that
    $$e^{-x} = \frac{1 + ax}{1 + bx}$$
    [L]

3. Use *Maclaurin's expansion* to obtain the first five non–zero terms of the series for $\log_e(1 + x)$. Hence show that
    $$\log_e\left(\frac{1+x}{1-x}\right) = 2x + \frac{2x^3}{3} + \frac{2x^5}{5}$$
    and state the range of values of x for which the expansion is valid

    By using a suitable substitution for x, an infinite series for $\log_e\left(\dfrac{n}{n-1}\right)$ may be obtained.

    Determine this substitution and hence write down the series. Find the range of positive values of n for which this expansion is valid.

    Find k such that $\log_e(\frac{9}{8}) + k \log_e(\frac{6}{5}) = \log_e 1.62$.

    Hence *use your series* for $\log_e(\frac{9}{8})$ and $k \log_e(\frac{6}{5})$ to evaluate $\log_e 1.62$ to 5 decimal places.
    [AEB 1985]

4. Given that $y = e^{\tan^{-1}x}$, where $\tan^{-1}x$ denotes the principal value, show that

$$(1 + x^2)\, \frac{dy}{dx} = y.$$

By repeated differentiation of this result, show also that

$$(1 + x^2)\, \frac{d^4y}{dx^4} + 6x\, \frac{d^3y}{dx^3} + 6\, \frac{d^2y}{dx^2} = \frac{d^3y}{dx^3}.$$

Hence, or otherwise, obtain the expansion of $e^{\tan^{-1}x}$ in ascending powers of x up to and including the term in x^4, and show that, when x is small enough for powers above the fourth to be neglected

$$e^{\tan^{-1}x} = e^x - \tfrac{1}{3}\,(x^3 + x^4).$$

[C]

Common errors

1. **Series**

    (a) The series for $\ln(1 + x)$ only converges if $|x| < 1$. Do not try to use it if $|x| > 1$. And do not omit the 1; there is no series for $\ln x$.

    (b) x must be in radians for the series of $\sin x$ and $\cos x$. Do not use the series if x is in degrees.

2. **Maclaurin series**

    Do not forget the $n!$ factor when using a Maclaurin series.

19 Differential equations

Suppose that y is a function of x. An equation which expresses derivatives of y in terms of y and x is a *differential equation*

To *solve* the equation means to obtain y as a function of x.

If the solution contains constants of integration then it is a *general solution*.

If the constants can be found from given values of x and y, these values are called *initial conditions*.

The solution so found without constants of integration is a *particular solution*.

A collection of functions which obey the same differential equation is a *family of solutions*.

19.1 Equations with separable variables

If a differential equation can be re–arranged so that all the y terms are on one side and all the x terms on the other, then the equation has *separable variables*.

19.1.1 Examples

1. Find the general solution of the equation $\dfrac{dy}{dx} = 2xy$. Find the particular solution with the initial conditions of $y = 2$ for $x = 0$.

    Solution

    Here the y terms can be collected on the left, and the x terms on the right.

    $$\int \frac{dy}{y} = \int 2x\,dx.$$

    Integrate both sides:

    $$\ln y = x^2 + c.$$

    $$y = e^{x^2+c} = e^c e^{x^2} = Ae^{x^2}, \text{ where } A = e^c.$$

    $$y = Ae^{x^2}$$

    Put $y = 2$ and $x = 0$. $2 = Ae^0$. $A = 2$.

    $$y = 2e^{x^2}$$

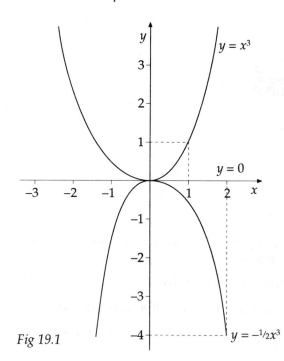

Fig 19.1

2. Find the general solution of the equation $\frac{dy}{dx} = 3\frac{y}{x}$.
   Find and sketch the solutions which go through

   (a) (1,1)   (b) (2,–4)   (c) (1,0).

   Solution

   Separate the variables and integrate.

   $$\int \frac{dy}{y} = \int \frac{3}{x}\,dx.$$

   $\ln y = 3\ln x + c = \ln Ax^3$, where $A = \ln c$.

   $$y = Ax^3$$

   The solution which goes through (1,1) is $y = x^3$.

   The solution through (2,–4) is $y = -\frac{1}{2}x^3$.

   The solution through (1,0) is $y = 0$. The three solutions are illustrated.

19.1.2 Exercises

1. Find the general solutions of the following differential equations:

   (a) $\frac{dy}{dx} = 2xy$

   (b) $\frac{dy}{dx} = \frac{x}{y}$

   (c) $\frac{dy}{dx} = x(1 + y)$

   (d) $\frac{dy}{dx} = \frac{\cos x}{\sin y}$

   (e) $x\frac{dy}{dx} = y(y + 1)$

   (f) $x\frac{dy}{dx} = e^y$

2. Find the particular solutions of the following equations with the initial conditions shown:

   (a) $\frac{dy}{dx} = xy : x = 1$ when $y = 1$ (b) $\frac{dy}{dx} = \frac{y}{x} : x = 3$ when $y = 4$

   (c) $(1 + x)\frac{dy}{dx} = y^2 : x = 0$ for $y = -1$

   (d) $\frac{dy}{dx} = y \sin x : x = \frac{\pi}{2}$ when $y = 1$ (e) $x\frac{dy}{dx} = e^y : x = 1$ for $y = 0$

3. Find the general solution of the equation $\frac{dy}{dx} = 2\frac{y}{x}$. Find and sketch the solutions which go through

   (a) (1,2)

   (b) (3,–9)

   (c) (3,0).

4. Find the general solution of the equation $x^2\frac{dy}{dx} = y^2$. Find and sketch the solutions which go through

   (a) (1,1)   (b) $(1,\frac{1}{2})$ (c) (1,2).

5. If $z = y + x$, show that $\dfrac{dz}{dx} = \dfrac{dy}{dx} + 1$.

   Use the substitution $z = x + y$ to solve the equation $\dfrac{dy}{dx} = x + y$.

6. By the same substitution as in Question 5 solve the following equations:

   (a) $\dfrac{dy}{dx} = (x + y)^2$ (b) $\dfrac{dy}{dx} = \frac{1}{2}(x + y) - 1$

7. Solve the following differential equations, using the substitution suggested:

   (a) $\dfrac{dy}{dx} = x - y.\ (z = x - y)$ (b) $\dfrac{dy}{dx} = 3x + 2y.\ (z = 3x + 2y)$

8. If $y = xz$, find an expression for $\dfrac{dy}{dx}$ in terms of x, z and $\dfrac{dz}{dx}$. Use this substitution to solve the following differential equations:

   (a) $\dfrac{dy}{dx} = \dfrac{y + x}{x}$ (b) $x^2 \dfrac{dy}{dx} = x^2 + xy + y^2$

   (c) $x \dfrac{dy}{dx} = y + \sqrt{(x^2 - y^2)}$

9. Show that all functions of the form $y = Ae^x$ obey the differential equation $\dfrac{dy}{dx} = y$.

10. For each of the following functions find a differential equation, not involving the constant A, which it satisfies.

    (a) $y = Ae^{2x}$ (b) $y = Ae^{-3x}$

    (c) $y = Ax^4$ (d) $y = A \cos x$

    (e) $y = A \sin 2x$ (f) $y = A(\cos x + \sin x)$

19.2 Modelling with differential equations

Many situations can be expressed in terms of a differential equation. When we have solved the equation, we can explain the situation and predict how it will develop.

19.2.1 Example

The weight W of a certain radioactive material decays at a rate proportional to the weight. The half-life, (when half of it has decayed), is 3,000 seconds. If the original weight is 20 grams find the weight after t seconds.

Solution

The rate of change of W is $\dfrac{dW}{dT}$. W is decreasing, so this is equal to $-\lambda W$, where λ is the constant of proportionality.

$$\dfrac{dW}{dT} = -\lambda W$$

The variables can be separated.

$$\int \frac{dW}{W} = -\lambda \int dt$$

Integrate to obtain:

$\ln W = -\lambda t + c : W = e^c e^{-\lambda t}$

$W = 20$ when $t = 0$, so $e^c = 20$.

$W = 20e^{-\lambda t}$

When $t = 3{,}000$, $W = 10$.

$$10 = 20e^{-3000\lambda} : \lambda = \frac{-\ln\frac{1}{2}}{3{,}000} = \frac{\ln 2}{3{,}000}$$

$$W = 20e^{-t(\ln 2/3000)} = 20 \times 2^{-t/3000}$$

19.2.2 Exercises

1. The rate of increase of a population P is proportional to P, with the constant of proportionality being 0.03. Write down a differential equation in P. If the initial population is P_0, find P at time t. Find the time for the population to double.

2. A weed is growing across a pond, so that the rate of increase of the area A it covers is proportional to A. At time $t = 0$ days the area is $1\ m^2$, and after 10 days the area is $2\ m^2$. Find the area covered after t days.

3. The rate of increase of a plant is proportional to the size of the plant, and it takes 12 hours for it to double. Find the height h cm in terms of time t hours, given that it starts from 6 cm.

4. The rate of decrease of a radioactive material is proportional to the amount of material, with constant of proportionality $1/1000$. Find the amount M in terms of time t, and hence find the half–life of the material.

5. A disease afflicts a proportion p of a population. The disease is spreading, so that the rate of change of p, $\frac{dp}{dt}$, is equal to $0.1p(1 - p)$. Initially the proportion is 0.1. What proportion will be affected after time t? When will half the population be affected?

6. A sealed jar initially contains 0.1 kg of substance A, and 0.9 kg of substance B. Substance B is changing into substance A, at a rate proportional to the product of the amounts of A and B present in the jar. After 100 seconds there is 0.2 kg of A and 0.8 kg of B. Find the amount of A after t seconds. When will there be equal quantities of A and B?

7. The mass of a fungus is M kg. New fungus is created at a rate proportional to M, and old fungus dies at a rate proportional to M^2. The equilibrium mass is 10 kg. Find a differential equation obeyed by M.

   Initially $M = 2$ and after 1 hour $M = 5$. Find M after t hours. When is M equal to 9?

19.3 Numerical solution of differential equations

Suppose we cannot solve a differential equation exactly. There are numerical procedures for finding approximate solutions. Below is the *step by step* method.

Suppose we know that $y = y_0$ when $x = x_0$. Let $x_1 = x_0 + \delta$, where δ is small. The approximate corresponding value of y, y_1, is given by

$$y_1 = y_0 + \frac{dy}{dx} \delta$$

This step can be repeated, to obtain y_2, y_3 etc.

By taking more steps, i.e. smaller values of δ, the process can be made more accurate.

19.3.1 Example

It is known that $\dfrac{dy}{dx} = \sqrt{(x + y)}$, and that $y = 1$ when $x = 0$. Use four steps to find the approximate value of y when $x = 1$.

Solution

Here $x_0 = 0$ and $y_0 = 1$. If we take four steps to reach $x = 1$, then $\delta = 0.25$. Find the successive values of y as follows.

$x_1 = 0.25$: $y_1 = 1 + \sqrt{(0 + 1)}\, \delta = 1.25$

$x_2 = 0.5$: $y_2 = 1.25 + \sqrt{(0.25 + 1.25)}\, \delta = 1.556$

$x_3 = 0.75$: $y_3 = 1.556 + \sqrt{(0.5 + 1.556)}\, \delta = 1.915$

$x_4 = 1$: $y_4 = 1.915 + \sqrt{(0.75 + 1.915)}\, \delta = 2.323$

When $x = 1$, the approximate value of y is 2.3

19.3.2 Exercises

1. In each of the following, you are given $\dfrac{dy}{dx}$ and the initial values of x and y. In each case find the approximate value for the given value of x, with the number of steps given.

    (a) $\dfrac{dy}{dx} = \sqrt{(x + 2y)}$. $x_0 = 0$, $y_0 = 1$. Find y when $x = 1$, using 4 steps.

    (b) $\dfrac{dy}{dx} = x + y^2$. $x_0 = 1$, $y_0 = 0$. Find y when $x = 2$, using 4 steps.

    (c) $\dfrac{dy}{dx} = \cos(xy)$. $x_0 = 0$, $y_0 = 0$. Find y when $x = 0.3$, using 3 steps.

2. Suppose that $\dfrac{dy}{dx} = \dfrac{3y}{x}$, and that $y = 1$ when $x = 1$. Evaluate y when $x = 2$:

    (a) exactly, by solving the differential equation
    (b) approximately, by using a step by step method with 4 steps.
    What is the percentage error in your answer to (b)?

3. Suppose that $\frac{dy}{dx} = 2e^x - y$, and that $y = 2$ when $x = 0$. Estimate the value of y when $x = 1$, using a step by step method with 4 steps.

   Verify that a solution of the equation is $y = e^x + e^{-x}$. Find the exact value of y when $x = 1$.

19.4 Examination questions

1. Find the particular solution of the differential equation

$$(y + 1)(x^2 + 1)\, \frac{dy}{dx} = 1 \quad (y \neq -1)$$

   for which $y = 0$ when $x = 1$, in the form $x = g(y)$.

   [W]

2. (i) Find y in terms of x given that $(1 + x)\, \frac{dy}{dx} = (1 - x)y$ and that $y = 1$ when $x = 0$.

   (ii) A curve passes through $(2,2)$ and has gradient at (x,y) given by the differential equation

$$y\, e^{y^2}\, \frac{dy}{dx} = e^{2x}.$$

   Find the equation of the curve. Show that the curve also passes through the point $(1,\sqrt{2})$ and sketch the curve.

   [L]

3. Find the general solution of the differential equation

$$e^x\, \frac{dy}{dx} + y^{\frac{1}{2}} = 0$$

   expressing y in terms of x and an arbitrary constant.

   [O] PART

4. Find the general solution of the differential equation

$$\frac{dy}{dx} - \frac{2y}{x} = 0.$$

   Sketch the two solution curves passing respectively through the points $(2,2)$ and $(-1,-1)$.

   [C] PART

5. The gradient of a curve at any point (x,y) on the curve is directly proportional to the product of x and y. The curve passes through the point $(1,1)$ and at this point the gradient of the curve is 4. Form a differential equation in x and y and solve this equation to express y in terms of x.

   [L]

Common errors

Separable variables

(a) Make sure that you have separated the variables before you integrate. It is not possible to evaluate $\int x^2 \, dy$, for example.

(b) Do not forget the constant of integration. It often provides the most important part of the solution.

(c) When making y the subject of the formula be very careful with logs. Watch out for the following:

From $\ln y = \ln x + c$ do not go to $y = x + \ln c$.

(It should be $y = x \times \ln c$.)

20 Probability

20.1 Probability of successive events

A *Tree Diagram* shows the probabilities of successive events.

20.1.1 Examples

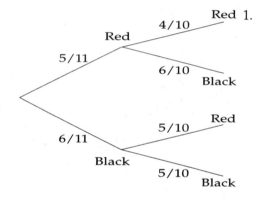

First marble   Second marble

Fig 20.1

1. A bag contains 5 red and 6 black marbles. Two are drawn without replacement. What is the probability that:

   (a) Both are red   (b) They are different colours.

   Solution

   Construct the tree diagram as shown. The top branch corresponds to both marbles being red. Multiply the probabilities along this branch.

   (a) The probability that both are red is $\frac{5}{11} \times \frac{4}{10} = \frac{2}{11}$

   The two middle branches correspond to the marbles having different colours.

   (b) P(Different colours) = $\frac{5}{11} \times \frac{6}{10} + \frac{6}{11} \times \frac{5}{10} = \frac{6}{11}$

2. Four fair dice are rolled. Find the probabilities of

   (a) four 6s   (b) at least one 6.

   Solution

   (a) The probability of four 6s is $(\frac{1}{6})^4$.

   The probability of four 6s is $\frac{1}{1296}$

   (b) There will be at least one 6 unless *none* of the dice show a 6. This has probability $(\frac{5}{6})^4$.

   The probability of at least one 6 is $1 - \frac{625}{1296} = \frac{671}{1296}$

20.1.2 Exercises

1. Two fair dice are rolled. Find the probabilities that:

   (a) Both are sixes   (b) The total is 2

   (c) The total is 7

   (d) The first is greater than the second

   (e) A 'double' is thrown   (f) At least one of the dice is a six.

2. Two cards are drawn without replacement from a well-shuffled pack. Find the probabilities that:

    (a) The first is a heart   (b) Both are hearts

    (c) The first is a heart and the second is a spade

    (d) The first is a King and the second is a Queen.

3. A bag contains 5 blue and 4 green counters. Two are drawn without replacement. Find the probabilities that:

    (a) Both are blue   (b) They are the same colour

    (c) There is at least one blue   (d) The second is green

4. A sweet box contains 5 toffees, 6 liquorices and 8 chocolates. Two are drawn out. Find the probabilities that:

    (a) The first is a toffee and the second is a chocolate.

    (b) At least one is a liquorice   (c) Neither is a toffee

5. Two fair dice are rolled. The score is the larger of the numbers showing. Find the probabilities that:

    (a) The score is 1   (b) The score is 6

6. Two children A and B each pick at random a single digit from 1 to 9. Find the probabilities that:

    (a) They pick the same number   (b) A's number is larger than B's

7. To start a certain board game a die is rolled until a six is obtained. Find the probabilities that:

    (a) A player starts on his first roll   (b) He starts on his second roll

    (c) He starts on his third roll

    (d) He has not started by his fourth roll

8. To start at darts a 'double' must first be thrown. Albert has probability $\frac{1}{10}$ of throwing a double, and Beatrice has probability $\frac{1}{8}$. Albert throws first. Find the probabilities that:

    (a) Both start on their first throw

    (b) Beatrice starts on her second throw but Albert has not started by then.

9. A fair coin is spun five times. Find the probabilities of

    (a) five Heads   (b) at least one Head.

10. A roulette wheel has the numbers 1 to 36. A gambler bets that a number divisible by 3 will turn up. The bet is repeated four times. Find the probabilities that the gambler

    (a) wins all his bets   (b) wins at least one bet.

11. Five people take the driving test. Each has probability $\frac{2}{3}$ of passing. Find the probabilities that:

    (a) they all pass   (b) at least one fails.

20.2 Exclusive and independent events. Conditional probability

If two events cannot happen together, then they are *exclusive.* If events are exclusive then the probability that one or the other occurs is the sum of their probabilities.

$$P(A \text{ or } B) = P(A) + P(B), \text{ provided that A and B are exclusive.}$$

Two events are *independent* if the truth of one of them does not alter the probability of the other.

If events A and B are independent then the probability of them both occurring is the product of their probabilities.

$$P(A \& B) = P(A) \times P(B)$$

The *conditional probability* of A given B is the probability of A, once it is known that B is true.

The conditional probability of A given B is written $P(A \mid B)$. It is obtained from the formula:

$$P(A \mid B) = \frac{P(A \& B)}{P(B)} \quad .$$

If A and B are independent then $P(A \mid B) = P(A)$

The symbols $\cap$ and $\cup$ are sometimes used for 'and' and 'or' respectively.

20.2.1 Examples

1. Two cards are drawn without replacement from a pack. Events A, B, C are as follows:

   A : the first is a heart.   B : the second is a heart.   C : the second is a king

   Which pairs of these events are independent?

   Solution

   If A is true, then there is one fewer heart in the pack. The probability of B is $\frac{12}{51} < \frac{1}{4}$. Hence A and B are not independent.

   If A is true then C is neither more likely nor less likely than before. Its probability is still $\frac{1}{13}$. Hence A and C are independent.

   Similarly the truth of B does not alter the probability of C.

   The pairs A and C, B and C are independent

2. A woman travels to work by bus, car or on foot with probabilities $\frac{1}{6}$, $\frac{1}{3}$, $\frac{1}{2}$ respectively. For each type of transport her probabilities of being late are $\frac{1}{5}$, $\frac{1}{4}$, $\frac{1}{20}$ respectively. If she arrives late one morning, find the probability that she came by bus.

   Solution

   Here let L be the event that she is late, and B the event that she came by bus. Use the formula for conditional probability:

   $$P(B \mid L) = \frac{P(B \& L)}{P(L)}$$

$$P(B \mid L) = \frac{\frac{1}{6} \times \frac{1}{5}}{\frac{1}{6} \times \frac{1}{5} + \frac{1}{3} \times \frac{1}{4} + \frac{1}{2} \times \frac{1}{20}}$$

The probability that she came by bus is $\frac{4}{17}$

20.2.2 Exercises

1. Two cards are drawn from a pack without replacement. Events A, B, C, D are as follows:

   A: the first is an ace   B: the second is an 8

   C: the first is red   D: the second is a spade.

   Which pairs of events are independent? Which are exclusive?

2. Two dice are rolled. Events A, B, C, D are as follows:

   A: the first is a 5   B: the total is 8

   C: the total is 7   D: the dice show the same number

   Which pairs of events are independent? Which are exclusive?

3. Two dice are rolled. Events A, B, C, D are as follows:

   A: the total is 7   B: the second die is a 2

   C: both dice are less than 5   D: at least one die is a 6

   Which pairs of events are independent? Which are exclusive?

4. Three fair coins are spun. Events A, B, C, D are as follows:

   A: the first coin is a head   B: all the coins are heads

   C: there is at least one tail

   D: the first and last coins show the same.

   Which pairs of events are independent? Which are exclusive?

5. With events A, B, C, D as defined in Question 1, find the following:

   (a) $P(B \mid A)$ (b) $P(D \mid C)$

6. With A, B, C, D defined as in Question 2, find the following:

   (a) $P(A \mid B)$ (b) $P(B \mid D)$

7. With events A, B, C, D as defined in Question 3, find the following:

   (a) $P(A \mid B)$ (b) $P(C \mid D)$

8. With events A, B, C, D as in Question 4, find the following:

   (a) $P(B \mid A)$ (b) $P(C \mid A)$

9. A bag contains 5 red and 6 blue marbles. Two are drawn without replacement. If the second is red find the probability that the first was blue.

10. In his drawer a man has 7 left shoes and 10 right shoes. He picks two out at random. Find the probabilities that:

    (a) He has one left shoe and one right shoe.

    (b) He has one left and one right, given that the first was a left.

    (c) The second is a left, given that he has one left and one right.

11. A man travels to work by bus, car and motorcycle with probabilities 0.4, 0.5, 0.1 respectively. With each type of transport his chances of an accident are $\frac{1}{500}$, $\frac{1}{50}$, $\frac{1}{10}$ respectively. Find the probabilities that:

    (a) He goes by car and has an accident.

    (b) He does not have an accident.

    (c) He went by motorcycle, given that he had an accident.

12. 1% of the population has a certain disease. There is a test for the disease, which gives a positive response for $\frac{9}{10}$ of the people with the disease, and for $\frac{1}{50}$ of the people without the disease. A person is selected at random and tested.

    (a) What is the probability that the test gives a negative response?

    (b) If the test is positive, what is the probability that the person has the disease?

    (c) If the test is negative, what is the probability that the person does not have the disease?

13. An island contains two tribes; $\frac{2}{3}$ of the population are Wache, who tell the truth with probability 0.7, and $\frac{1}{3}$ are Oya, who tell the truth with probability 0.8. I meet a tribesman who tells me that he is a Wache. What is the probability that he is telling the truth?

14. In a certain town $\frac{3}{4}$ of the voters are over 25, and they vote for the Freedom Party with probability $\frac{1}{3}$. Voters under 25 support the Freedom Party with probability $\frac{4}{5}$. If a supporter of the Freedom Party is picked at random, what is the probability that he or she is under 25?

15. Events A and B are such that $P(A) = 0.4$, $P(B) = 0.3$ and $P(A \& B) = 0.25$. Show that A and B are neither exclusive nor independent. Find $P(A \mid B)$.

16. Events A and B are such that $P(A) = 0.3$, $P(B) = 0.2$, $P(A \text{ or } B) = 0.4$. Show that A and B are not exclusive. Find $P(A \& B)$ and $P(A \mid B)$.

17. Events A and B are such that $P(A) = 0.4$, $P(B) = 0.3$ and $P(A \mid B) = 0.5$. Find $P(A \& B)$ and $P(A \text{ or } B)$. Find $P(B \mid A)$.

18. Events A and B are such that $P(A) = 0.3$ and $P(B) = 0.5$. Find $P(A \text{ or } B)$ and $P(A \& B)$ in the following cases:

    a) A and B are exclusive   b) A and B are independent

20.3 Examination questions

1. A 2p coin and a 10p coin are thrown on a table. Event A is 'A head occurs on the 2p coin'. Event B is 'A head occurs on the 10p coin'. Event C is 'Two heads or two tails are obtained'.

    State, giving reasons, which of the following statements is (are) true and which is (are) false.

(a)   A and B are independent events

(b)   B and C are independent events.

(c)   A and C are mutually exclusive events

(d)   A and B $\cap$ C are independent events.

(e)   P(A $\cap$ B $\cap$ C) = P(A).P(B).P(C)

[L ADD]

2.   Six balls coloured yellow, green, brown, blue, pink and black have values 2, 3, 4, 5, 6, 7 respectively. They are identical in size and are placed in a box. Two balls are selected together from the box at random and the total number of points is recorded.

(i)   Find the probability that the total score is

(a) 7,   (b) 9,   (c) 10,   (d) greater than 9,   (e) odd.

(ii)   A game between two players, X and Y, starts with the six balls in a box. Each player in turn selects at random two balls, notes the score and then returns the balls to the box. The game is over when one of the players reaches a total score of 25 or more.

(a)   If X starts, calculate the probability that X wins on his second turn;

(b)   if Y starts, calculate the probability that X wins on his second turn.

[O ADD]

3.   (a)   The two electronic systems C_1, C_2 of a communications satellite operate independently and have probabilities of 0.1 and 0.05 respectively of failing. Find the probability that

(i)   neither circuit fails,   (ii)   at least one circuit fails,

(iii) exactly one circuit fails.

(b)   In a certain boxing competition all fights are either won or lost; draws are not permitted.

If a boxer wins a fight then the probability that he wins his next fight is $\frac{3}{4}$; if he loses a fight the probability of him losing the next fight is $\frac{2}{3}$.

Assuming that he won his last fight, use a tree diagram, or otherwise, to calculate the probability that of his next three fights

(i)   he wins exactly two fights,   (ii)   he wins at most two fights.

State the most likely and least likely sequence of results for these three fights.

[NI ADD]

4.   (i)   The events A and B are such that P(A) = 0.4, P(B) = 0.45, P(A $\cup$ B) = 0.68. Show that the events A and B are neither mutually exclusive nor independent.

(ii)   A bag contains 12 red balls, 8 blue balls and 4 white balls. Three balls are taken from the bag at random and without replacement. Find the probability that all three balls are of the same colour.

Find also the probability that all three balls are of different colours.

[L]

147

5. A box contains 25 apples, of which 20 are red and 5 are green. Of the red apples, 3 contain maggots and of the green apples, 1 contains maggots. Two apples are chosen at random from the box. Find, in any order,

   (i) the probability that both apples contain maggots,

   (ii) the probability that both apples are red and at least one contains maggots,

   (iii) the probability that at least one apple contains maggots, given that both apples are red,

   (iv) the probability that both apples are red given that at least one apple is red.

   [C]

(6) (a) Two digits X and Y are taken from a table of random sampling numbers. Event R is that $X = Y + 1$ and event S is that X and Y are both less than 2. Write down

   (i) P(R)   (ii) P(R ∩ S),

   (iii) P(R ∪ S)   (iv) P(R | S)

   (b) Conveyor belting for use in mines is tested for both strength and safety (the safety test is based on the amount of heat generated if the belt snaps). A testing station receives belting from three different suppliers: 30% of its tests are carried out on samples of belting from supplier A, 50% from B; 20% from C. From past experience the probability of failing the strength test is 0.02 for a sample from A, 0.12 from B and 0.04 from C.

   (i) What is the probability that a particular strength test will result in a failure?

   (ii) If a strength test results in a failure, what is the probability that the belting came from supplier A?

   (iii) What is the probability of a sample failing both strength and safety tests given the following further information:

   Supplier A – the probability of failing the safety test is 0.05 and is independent of the probability of failing the strength test;

   Supplier B – 1% of samples fail both strength and safety tests;

   Supplier C – exactly half the samples which fail the strength test also fail the safety test.

   [AEB 1985]

Common errors

1. **Single probability**

   If there are n outcomes to an experiment, then each has probability $\frac{1}{n}$ only if they are *equally likely*.

   When two dice are rolled, there are 11 possible results for the total score. But a total of 12 is less likely than a total of 7, so neither has probability $\frac{1}{11}$.

2. **Addition of probabilities**

   The probability of 'A or B' is only the sum of the probabilities if the events concerned are *exclusive*. In general:

   $$P(A \text{ or } B) \leq P(A) + P(B)$$

3. **Multiplication of probabilities**

The probability of 'A & B' is only the product of the probabilities if the events concerned are *independent*.

4. **Conditional probability**

   (a) Do not forget to divide by P(B) when working out P(A | B).

   (b) In the formula

   $$P(A \mid B) = \frac{P(A \text{ \& } B)}{P(B)}$$

   do not assume that P(A & B) is P(A) × P(B). This is only true if A and B are independent.

   (c) Conditional probability is concerned with belief, not with cause and effect. If P(A | B) ≠ P(A), then it does not follow that B has caused A or prevented A. It may even be that B happened after A did.

21 Representing data

21.1 Mean, median, variance, standard deviation

MEASURES OF CENTRAL TENDENCY

Suppose $x_1, x_2,..., x_n$ are n numbers. The *mean* x is their average:

$$\bar{x} = \frac{x_1 + x_2 + ... + x_n}{n} = \frac{1}{n}\sum x_i$$

This is sometimes known as the *arithmetic mean*. The *geometric mean* is given by:

$$x_G = \sqrt[n]{(x_1 x_2 ... x_n)}$$

If some of the values are thought to be more important than the others, then a *weighted mean* is found. If the weights are $\lambda_1, \lambda_2,... \lambda_n$, then the weighted mean is:

$$= \frac{\lambda_1 x_1 + \lambda_2 x_2 + ... + \lambda_n x_n}{\lambda_1 + \lambda_2 + ... + \lambda_n} = \frac{\sum \lambda_i x_i}{\sum \lambda_i}$$

The *median* of the values is the middle value, in the sense that half of the figures are less than the median and half are greater than it.

MEASURES OF SPREAD

The *Variance* S^2 of the figures is a measure of their spread. It is found from the formula:

$$S^2 = \frac{(x_1 - \bar{x})^2 + (x_2 - \bar{x})^2 + ... + (x_n - \bar{x})^2}{n} = \frac{1}{n}\sum (x_i - \bar{x})^2$$

It can be shown that this is equivalent to:

$$S^2 = \frac{x_1^2 + x_2^2 + ... + x_n^2}{n} - \bar{x}^2 = \frac{1}{n}\sum x_i^2 - \bar{x}^2$$

The *standard deviation* is the square root of the variance.

The *interquartile range,* discussed on page 153, is another measure of spread.

Suppose the x figures are scaled by the function $y = a + bx$, where a and b are constants. Then the mean, variance and standard deviation of the y figures are given by:

$$\bar{y} = a + b\bar{x} \quad : \quad S_y^2 = b^2 S_x^2 \quad : \quad S_y = bS_x$$

21.1.1 Examples

1. Find the mean, median and standard deviation of the following set of figures.

   $$22, 23, 24, 26, 21, 29, 19, 26, 30, 27.$$

   Solution

   For the mean, add these numbers together and divide by 10.

   > The mean is 24.7

   For the median, note that the 5th number is 24 and the 6th is 26. Take half way between these.

   > The median is 25

   It is easier to use the second formula to find the variance.

   $$S^2 = \frac{22^2 + 23^2 + \dots + 27^2}{10} - 24.7^2 = 11.21.$$

   Square root this to find the standard deviation.

   > The standard deviation is 3.35

2. The prices of four commodities A, B, C, D are given weights 3, 4, 1, 2 respectively. Over a year these prices rise by 5%, 10%, 15% and 2% respectively. Calculate the weighted average percentage rise in price.

   Solution

   Find the weighted mean of the percentages, using the weights given.

   $$\text{Average price rise} = \frac{5 \times 3 + 10 \times 4 + 15 \times 1 + 2 \times 2}{3 + 4 + 1 + 2}$$

   > The weighted average is 7.4%

3. The marks for a certain exam have mean 45 and variance 144. In order to harmonise them with previous years they are to be scaled so that their mean is 50 and their variance 64. Find the scaling function, in the form $y = a + bx$.

   Solution

   Use the formulae above, for the mean and variance of figures after they have been scaled.

   $$50 = a + 45b : 64 = b^2 144.$$

   $$b = \tfrac{2}{3} : a = 20.$$

   > The scaling function is $y = 20 + \tfrac{2}{3}x$

4. In a test sat by 37 pupils, 15 scored at most 20 and 6 scored more than 40. Estimate the median mark.

   Solution

   The median mark is the mark of the 19th pupil. 15 scored less than 21, and so we want the 4th mark from the 16 which are between 21 and 40. If these 16 marks are evenly spread, then the 4th mark is a quarter of the way along.

   > The median is approximately $21 + \tfrac{1}{4}(20) = 26$

21.1.2 Exercises

1. Find the means of the following sets of figures:
   (a) 12, 11, 13, 14, 12, 15, 20, 21, 18   (b) 1.3, 1.8, 1.6, 0.9, 1.2
   (c) 67, 65, 58, 59, 71, 62   (d) 103, 132, 122, 134, 112, 108

2. Find the medians of the sets of figures in Question 1.

3. Find the geometric means of the figures in Question 1.

4. Find the variances and standard deviations of the sets of figures in Question 1.

5. Find the means and variances of the sets of figures in Question 1 after they have been scaled by the function $y = 2 + 10x$.

6. A set of figures consists of 5 repeated 4 times, and 7 repeated 6 times. Find the mean and the variance of the figures.

7. The values of a set of figures are given by the following frequency table:

Value	2	3	4	5
Frequency	3	10	12	5

   Find the mean and standard deviation of the figures.

8. The values of a set of figures are given by the following table:

Range	0–10	10–20	20–30	30–40
Frequency	12	35	43	17

   By taking mid–interval values, estimate the mean and standard deviation.

9. Estimate the mean, median and standard deviation from the following table:

Range	0–0.5	0.5–1	1–1.5	1.5–2	2–2.5	2.5–3
Frequency	3	23	33	31	21	9

10. The quantities A, B, C, D, E are given weights 1, 2, 2, 3, 3 respectively. Find the weighted mean if A, B, C, D, E have values 12, 20, 25, 10, 8 respectively.

11. A set of marks has mean 60 and variance 200. The marks are scaled by the function $y = 10 + 0.5x$.
    (a) What is a mark of 80 scaled to?
    (b) What mark is scaled to 40?
    (c) What mark is unaltered by the scaling?
    (d) What are the mean and variance of the scaled marks?

12. How should the marks of Question 11 be scaled so that their mean is 50 and their variance 8?

21.2 Frequency and cumulative frequency

FREQUENCY

A *histogram* is a bar-chart used to represent numerical data. The area of each rectangle is proportional to the frequency in the range it covers.

A *stem and leaf* diagram is a bar chart in which the bars consist of the actual data.

CUMULATIVE FREQUENCY

The *cumulative frequency* at a value is the running total of all the frequencies up to that value.

The median corresponds to a cumulative frequency of $\frac{1}{2}$. The *lower quartile* corresponds to a cumulative frequency of $\frac{1}{4}$, and the *upper quartile* to a cumulative frequency of $\frac{3}{4}$. The *interquartile range* is the difference between the quartiles.

A *box and whisker* diagram shows the middle half of the data as a box, and the range outside the box as lines (whiskers). Extreme values (by convention, more than 1.5 the interquartile range from the nearest quartile) are *outliers*. They are sometimes excluded from the whiskers.

21.2.1 Examples

1. 120 pupils took an exam which was marked out of 100. Their marks are shown in the table below:

Mark range	0–30	31–40	41–50	51–55	56–60	61–70	71–100
Frequency	9	15	23	19	17	17	20

   Plot a histogram to illustrate these figures.

   Solution

   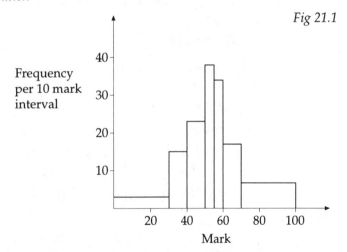

   Fig 21.1

   The most common width of interval is 10 marks. Let that be the standard. The first and last intervals are three times the standard width, hence their heights must be divided by 3. The two intervals in the 50's are half the standard width, hence their heights must be doubled. Plot the histogram as shown.

2. The ages of 40 people at a party are given below. Construct a stem and leaf diagram to illustrate the figures, using stems of 10, 20, 30, 40.

   18 30 19 20 32 29 25 19 31 41   41 37 27 21 29 42 31 49 27 21

   29 31 17 30 41 20 26 37 21 30   26 29 37 34 19 30 42 42 38 22

Solution

Put the stems (the first digits) vertically, and draw a line alongside. Place the leaves (the second digits) next to the appropriate stem. The result is shown below.

```
1 | 7 8 9 9 9
2 | 0 0 1 1 1 2 5 6 6 7 7 9 9 9 9
3 | 0 0 0 0 1 1 1 2 4 7 7 7 8
4 | 1 1 1 2 2 2 9
```

3. The times to the nearest minute taken by 12 people to run a race are given below. Find the median and the quartiles. Draw a box and whisker diagram, identifying any outliers.

$$43 \ 41 \ 46 \ 48 \ 42 \ 44 \ 55 \ 47 \ 45 \ 46 \ 41 \ 42$$

Solution

Arrange these in order.

$$41 \ 41 \ 42 \ 42 \ 43 \ 44 \ 45 \ 46 \ 46 \ 47 \ 48 \ 55$$

The median is between the 6th and 7th values. This is 44.5. The lower quartile is between the 3rd and 4th, and the upper quartile between the 9th and 10th.

The median is 44.5, and the quartiles are 42 and 46.5

The interquartile range is 4.5. The value of 55 is greater than 1.5×4.5 away from the upper quartile, hence it is an outlier. The box and whisker diagram is shown below. The median and quartiles are marked by M, Q_1 and Q_3. Note that the right hand whisker only goes up to 48.

Fig 21.2

21.2.2 Exercises

1. The number of days in a year taken off work by the employees of a factory are shown in the table below. Plot a histogram to illustrate the figures.

Number of days	0– 9	10– 14	15– 19	20– 24	25– 29	30– 40
Frequency	36	10	8	7	6	9

2. The heights of a collection of 80 plants were as given by the table below. Plot a histogram to illustrate the figures.

Height in cm	0– 10	10– 12	12– 14	14– 15	15– 17	17– 20
Frequency	10	9	18	13	14	16

3. 60 children ran a 100 m race. Their times are given by the table below. Plot a histogram to illustrate the figures.

Time in s	11– 12	12– 12.5	12.5– 13	13– 13.5	13.5– 15
Frequency	12	10	16	9	13

4. The ages of 1000 members of a political party were as shown in the table below. Plot a histogram to illustrate the figures.

Age	20– 25	25– 30	30– 35	35– 40	40– 50	50– 70
Frequency	120	230	240	223	112	75

5. 80 cats were weighed, and the results are given in the table below. Plot a histogram to illustrate the data.

Weight in kg	2–2.5	2.5–2.75	2.75–3	3–3.25	3.25–3.5	3.5–4
Frequency	7	12	19	21	11	10

6. The data below gives the temperature, in Fahrenheit to the nearest degree, at midday on thirty days in the summer. Plot a stem and leaf diagram to illustrate the data, taking 60, 70, 80 and 90 as the stems.

   68 73 69 83 77   92 84 89 91 84   72 67 64 72 78

   64 68 70 74 78   83 88 82 72 73   72 80 85 90 85

7. The marks obtained by 40 children in a test are given below. Draw a stem and leaf diagram, taking 0, 5, 10, 15, 20, 25 as stems.

   16 17 28 21 23 19 22 24 19 4   3 12 21 18 14 8 10 14 20 2

   7 11 6 18 21 22 28 24 15 17   28 26 4 14 19 16 27 25 26 9

8. The data below gives the amount in £ spent per day by 20 holidaymakers. Find the median and the quartiles. Illustrate the data in a box and whisker diagram, identifying any outliers.

   43 39 65 72 49   63 70 67 61 58   60 51 47 52 68   93 62 71 51 62

9. The number of hours on homework spent per week by 16 pupils is given below. Find the median and quartiles. Illustrate the data in a box and whisker diagram, identifying any outliers.

   10 12 1 14   15 11 12 20   28 15 10 13   14 12 13 14

21.3 Examination questions

1. During the eight successive hours of a working day at a small television factory, the following numbers of sets were completed.

   10 14 26 20 18 8 10 6.

   Calculate:

   (i) the arithmetic mean   (ii) the median,

   (iii) the mean deviation from the median

   (iv) the variance,   (v) the geometric mean.

   [AEB ADD 1987]

2. The marks of 20 students in a test are given in the table.

Mark x	20	22	24	25	26	27	30	33	34	35	36	38	40
Freqy	1	1	1	1	1	1	8	1	1	1	1	1	1

   Show that the mean and standard deviation are 30 and 5 respectively. Show all necessary working.

   The marks are to be scaled using a transformation $m = px + q$, where p and q are integers, so that the new mean is 50 and the standard deviation is 15. Calculate p and q and hence the scaled mark corresponding to an original test mark of 26.

   [O ADD]

3. Mr and Mrs Smith and Mr and Mrs Jones each decided to calculate a personal cost of living index which is the weighted arithmetic mean of index numbers for the following four categories of expenditure: Food, Fuel and Transport, Housing and Clothing. In January 1980 they allocated a base index number of 100 to each of these categories and the associated weights are shown in the table below.

Index Category	Weights Smith	Jones	Index Jan 1980	Jan 1981
Food	4	3	100	112
Fuel & Transport	3	4	100	110
Housing	2	3	100	115
Clothing	1	2	100	105

Using the index numbers for each category for January 1981 also shown in the table, calculate the cost of living index for each couple at that time.

In January 1982 the index numbers for Fuel and Transport, and for Housing had risen to 130 and 120 respectively. Both couples then found that their cost of living index was 120. Calculate the values of the index numbers for Food and for Clothing at that time.

[MEI ADD]

4. (a) The grouped frequency distribution table gives the lengths, recorded to the nearest mm, of 250 nails produced from a particular machine.

Length (mm)	98–99	100–101	102–103	104–105	106–107	108–109
Number of Nails	12	36	106	58	30	8

Draw the cumulative frequency curve and from your graph estimate

(i) the interquartile range,

(ii) the percentage of nails having a length below 103 mm.

Given that the top 10% and bottom 10% of this distribution are rejected, estimate from your graph the limits between which the length must lie if it is to be accepted.

(b) The masses of 100 male students were recorded to the nearest kg and are grouped in the following table.

Mass (kg)	50–59	60–74	75–94
Number of Students	20	50	30

(i) Draw a histogram to represent this information.

(ii) Estimate the median mass of these students.

[C ADD]

5. Tubs of margarine are claimed on the label to contain 250 grammes. The actual weights of margarine in a random sample of 15 tubs were as follows. The weights are given correct to the nearest gramme.

261 252 242 240 254

257 252 250 265 249

253 248 259 246 252

(i) Construct a stem and leaf diagram to represent these data, taking the stem values to be 240, 245,....

(ii) Comment on the shape of the distribution of weights, with particular reference to the claim that the tubs contain 250 grammes.

(iii) Use your calculator to find the mean and standard deviation of the weights of margarine in this sample.

(iv) Explain very briefly how one could ensure that a greater proportion of tubs contained 250 grammes or more of margarine by adjusting

    (1) the mean,   (2) the standard deviation.

[MEI]

Common errors

1. **Mean and median**

   (a) When finding the mean from grouped data, divide by the number of terms, not by the number of groups.

   (b) When finding a weighted mean, divide by the sum of the weights, not by the number of the weights.

   (c) The median of 19 numbers is not 10. It is the 10th number.

2. **Variance and standard deviation**

   (a) Be very careful when using the formula for variance. In particular, make sure you do the squaring and subtracting in the correct order.

   (b) Most scientific calculator will work out for you the mean and variance of a set of data. But do not rely on your calculator – many questions require you to show how the mean and variance are obtained.

3. **Histograms**

   If the intervals of a histogram are not uniform, then take account of this by dividing or multiplying the height of the bars. It is the *area* of each bar which represents the frequency, not its height.

22 Distance, velocity, acceleration

Time, displacement, velocity and acceleration are often symbolised by the letters t, s, v and a respectively. Velocity is the rate of change of displacement, acceleration is the rate of change of velocity.

$$v = \frac{ds}{dt}, \quad a = \frac{dv}{dt}$$

Conversely, velocity is the integral of acceleration, displacement is the integral of velocity.

$$v = \int a\, dt, \quad s = \int v\, dt$$

The constants of integration in these equations are found from the *initial* velocity and the *initial* displacement.

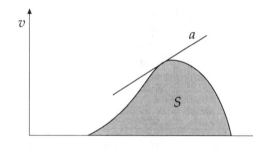

Fig 22.1

If the velocity is plotted on a graph against time, then the gradient of the graph is the acceleration and the area under the graph is the displacement.

UNITS

Unless otherwise stated, distance and time are measured in metres (m) and seconds (s). Velocity is measured in metres per second (m s^{-1}) and acceleration in metres per second squared (m s^{-2}).

22.1 Constant acceleration

If the acceleration a is constant, then the following hold:

$$v = u + at$$

(where u is the initial velocity)

$$s = \tfrac{1}{2}(u + v)t$$

$$s = ut + \tfrac{1}{2}at^2$$

$$v^2 = u^2 + 2as$$

If a body is falling freely under gravity, then its acceleration (neglecting air resistance) is constant with the value $g = 9.8$ m s^{-2}.

158

22.1.1 Examples

1. A car accelerates uniformly for 10 seconds at 1.5 m s^{-2}, then travels at a constant speed for 30 seconds, then brakes uniformly to a halt within a space of 25 m. Find the total distance covered and the total time taken.

    Solution

    The speed it reaches is $10 \times 1.5 = 15$ m s^{-1}. The distance it covers while accelerating is:

    $s = 0 \times 10 + \frac{1}{2} \times 1.5 \times 10^2 = 75$ m.

    The distance it covers at a constant speed is $30 \times 15 = 450$ m.

    Total distance $= 75 + 450 + 25 = 550$ m.

    The deceleration is found from the formula $v^2 = u^2 + 2as$.

    Deceleration $= \dfrac{15^2}{2 \times 25} = 4.5$ m s^{-2}

    The time for deceleration is $\dfrac{15}{4.5} = 3\frac{1}{3}$ sec.

    Total time $= 10 + 30 + 3\frac{1}{3} = 43\frac{1}{3}$ seconds

2. A cliff is 45 m high. A stone is thrown down from the top at 10 m s^{-1}, and at the same time a stone is thrown up from the bottom at 80 m s^{-1}. Find how high the stones are when they collide.

    Solution

    Measure distance s up from the bottom of the cliff. For the first stone:

    $s_1 = 45 - 10t - \frac{1}{2}gt^2$

    For the second stone:

    $s_2 = 80t - \frac{1}{2}gt^2$

    The stones collide when these are equal.

    $45 - 10t - \frac{1}{2}gt^2 = 80t - \frac{1}{2}gt^2$. It follows that $t = \frac{1}{2}$ sec.

    Put this value into either of the distance formulae.

    The height is $80 \times \frac{1}{2} - \frac{1}{2} \times 9.8 \times (\frac{1}{2})^2 = 38.775$ m

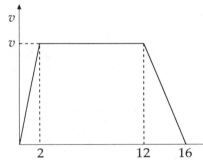

Fig 22.2

3. A vehicle accelerates uniformly for 2 seconds, travels at a constant speed for 10 seconds, then decelerates uniformly to rest in 4 seconds. If the total distance travelled is 520 m, find the maximum speed.

    Solution

    Sketch a velocity-time graph as shown. The height of the trapezium is the maximum velocity v m s^{-1}. The area in the trapezium is the distance, 520 m.

    $520 = \frac{1}{2}v(10 + 16)$.

    The maximum velocity is 40 m s^{-1}.

22.1.2 Exercises

1. A car accelerates at 0.8 m s^{-2} for 5 seconds. Find its speed and the distance it has covered.

2. A particle is accelerated uniformly from rest, so that after 10 seconds it has achieved the speed of 15 m s^{-1}. Find its acceleration and the distance it has covered.

3. A car accelerates uniformly from rest, achieving a speed of 20 m s^{-1} after covering 100 m. How long did it take?

4. The buffers at the end of a railway line can stop a train travelling at 10 m s^{-1}, by being compressed through 10 cm. How long does the deceleration take, assuming that it is uniform?

5. A car accelerates uniformly from rest, and after 12 seconds it has covered 40 m. What is its acceleration and its final velocity?

6. A train slows down from 20 m s^{-1} to 15 m s^{-1}, covering 200 m. How long did it take?

7. A car accelerates uniformly from 5 m s^{-1} to 15 m s^{-1}, taking 7.5 seconds. How far did it travel during this period?

8. A body starts from rest with constant acceleration 1.5 m s^{-2}. How long does it take to cover 12 m?

9. A particle is accelerated from 1 m s^{-1} to 5 m s^{-1} over a distance of 15 m. Find the acceleration and the time taken.

10. A body falls from the top of a 50 m cliff. Find the time taken and the speed at the bottom.

11. A body is thrown down from a 50 m cliff at 10 m s^{-1}. Find the time it takes to reach the bottom and its speed at the bottom.

12. From the top of a 60 m cliff a body is thrown up at 15 m s^{-1}, so that it then falls over the edge of the cliff. Find the greatest height reached and the time it takes to reach the bottom of the cliff. Find its speed at the bottom of the cliff.

13. A sprinter during a 100 m race accelerates uniformly during the first 50 m to his maximum speed of 10 m s^{-1}, and then continues the rest of the race at that speed. Find the time taken and his average speed.

14. A body is thrown up in the air at 30 m s^{-1}, and 2 seconds later a second body is thrown up at 60 m s^{-1}. Find how high the bodies are when they collide.

15. A car accelerates at 2 m s^{-2} for 4 seconds, then travels at a constant speed for 20 seconds, then decelerates uniformly to rest. The total distance travelled is 200 m. Draw a velocity–time graph and hence find the deceleration.

16. A car is travelling at 40 m s^{-1}, then it decelerates uniformly to 25 m s^{-1} over 30 seconds, then travels at the slower speed for 500 m. Draw a velocity–time graph, and calculate how much longer the journey took it than if it had continued at a constant speed of 40 m s^{-1}.

17. A cyclist starts from rest, and accelerates uniformly to a maximum speed of 10 m s^{-1}. This speed is maintained for 20 seconds, and then the cyclist decelerates uniformly to rest. The total distance covered is 250 m. Sketch a velocity–time graph. Find the total time taken and the acceleration.

22.2 Non–constant acceleration

If the acceleration is not constant, then the formulae of 22.1 can no longer be used. The quantities must be derived from each other by differentiation or integration.

22.2.1 Examples

1. A particle travels so that its distance s m from the origin after time t s is given by $s = 8t - \frac{2}{3}t^3$. Find its greatest distance from the origin, and the time when it returns to the origin.

   Solution

   The velocity v m s^{-1} is given by:

   $$v = \frac{ds}{dt} = 8 - 2t^2$$

   The distance is greatest when the velocity is zero, i.e when $t = 2$.

   The greatest distance is $8 \times 2 - \frac{2}{3} 2^3 = 10\frac{2}{3}$ m.

   It returns to the origin when $s = 0$.

   $8t - \frac{2}{3} t^3 = 0$. Hence $t = 0$ or $\pm\sqrt{12}$

   It returns to the origin after 3.46 seconds.

2. The velocity v m s^{-1} of a particle at time t s is given by $v = t^2 + 1$. Find its acceleration after 3 seconds, and the distance it has travelled during that time.

   Solution

   The acceleration a m s^{-2} is given by:

   $$a = \frac{dv}{dt} = 2t.$$

   The acceleration after 3 seconds is $2 \times 3 = 6$ m s^{-2}

   The distance travelled is found by integrating the velocity between $t = 0$ and $t = 3$.

   $$s = \int_0^3 (t^2 + 1)\, dt = \left[\tfrac{1}{3}t^3 + t\right]_0^3$$

   The distance is 12 m

22.2.2 Exercises

1. The displacement of a body is given by $s = 6t - 7t^3$. Find the initial velocity and the acceleration at $t = 3$.

2. A particle moves so that its displacement s m after t seconds is given by $s = 4t - 8t^3$. When it returns to the origin it stops. Find:

   (a) The initial velocity　　　　　　　(b) The maximum velocity

   (c) The time it takes to return to the origin

   (d) The maximum displacement

3. The displacement of a body is given by $s = \frac{1}{2}t^4 - 3t^3 + 6t^2 + 4$. Find the greatest and least values of the velocity, and the distance it travels between reaching these values.

4. The velocity of a particle is given by $v = 3t + t^2$. Find its initial acceleration, and the distance gone at time $t = 3$.

5. The velocity v m s^{-1} of a body t seconds after it starts is given by $v = 4t - t^2$. Find the greatest velocity, and the distance it has travelled when it achieves its greatest velocity. Find the time taken for it to return to its starting point, and the total distance it has moved through during this time.

6. The acceleration a m s^{-2} of a body is given by $a = 1 + 3t$. Find its velocity after 10 seconds, given that it starts at 4 m s^{-1}. Find the distance travelled after 5 seconds.

7. A particle starts at 21 m s^{-1}, and accelerates at a rate given by $a = 20 - 2t$. Find:

   (a) The maximum velocity   (b) The maximum distance

   (c) The time it takes to return to its starting point, and its speed at this time.

8. Two bodies start from the same position: the first has initial velocity 3 m s^{-1} and acceleration $(4 - t)$ m s^{-2}, and the second has initial velocity 1 m s^{-1} and acceleration $(2 + t)$ m s^{-2}. Find:

   (a) When the two bodies are first moving with the same velocity, and their distance apart at this time.

   (b) When the two bodies are at the same position, and the difference in speeds at this time.

9. A body A is projected from the origin with speed 5 m s^{-1} and acceleration $(2 + t)$ m s^{-2}. At the same time a second body B starts from a point 90 m away in the direction of motion of the first body, with initial speed 4 m s^{-1} towards A and acceleration t m s^{-2} away from A. Find when the two bodies collide, and the relative speed with which they do so.

22.3 Vector quantities

The *displacement* **s** of a body is the vector from its starting position to its present position.

Displacement, velocity and acceleration are all *vectors*. Sometimes these vectors are expressed as $a\mathbf{i} + b\mathbf{j} + c\mathbf{k}$, where **i**, **j** and **k** are unit vectors in the x, y, z directions respectively.

If the vectors are given in terms of components, then the components can be differentiated or integrated individually. For example:

If $\mathbf{v} = \mathrm{f}(t)\mathbf{i} + \mathrm{g}(t)\mathbf{j}$, then $\mathbf{a} = \mathrm{f}'(t)\mathbf{i} + \mathrm{g}'(t)\mathbf{j}$.

Speed is the modulus of the vector velocity.

22.3.1 Example

The position **r** m of a vector is given by $\mathbf{r} = 5t\mathbf{i} + 3t^2\mathbf{j} - \mathbf{k}$. Find:

(i) The acceleration.

(ii) The time when the speed is 20 m s^{-1}.

Solution

(i) Obtain the velocity by differentiating the distance.

$\mathbf{v} = 5\mathbf{i} + 6t\mathbf{j}$.

Obtain the acceleration by differentiating the velocity.

$\mathbf{a} = 6\mathbf{j}$.

The acceleration is $6\mathbf{j}$ m s^{-2}

(ii) The speed is the modulus of the velocity.

$$\sqrt{(5^2 + (6t)^2)} = 20$$
$$36t^2 = 375.$$

The speed is 20 m s^{-1} after 3.23 secs.

22.3.2 Exercises

1. Find the (vector) velocity when the displacement **r** m is given by the following:

    (a) $\mathbf{r} = 3t\mathbf{i} + 7t^2\mathbf{j}$ (b) $\mathbf{r} = t\,\mathbf{i} - 2t^2\mathbf{j} + 4\mathbf{k}$

    (c) $\mathbf{r} = \cos t\,\mathbf{i} + \sin t\,\mathbf{j}$ (d) $\mathbf{r} = \sin 2t\,\mathbf{i} + 3\cos 2t\,\mathbf{j} + t\mathbf{k}$

2. Find the speed for each of the parts of Question 1.

3. Find the (vector) acceleration for each of the parts of Question 1.

4. In each of the following, a particle starts from the origin, and moves with velocity vector given by the expressions below. Find the displacements at time t.

    (a) $\mathbf{v} = 3\mathbf{i} + 5\mathbf{j}$ (b) $\mathbf{v} = t\mathbf{i} + 3t\mathbf{j} - 5t\mathbf{k}$

    (c) $\mathbf{v} = \cos 2t\mathbf{i} - \sin 3t\mathbf{j}$ (d) $\mathbf{v} = e^t\mathbf{i} - 3e^{2t}\mathbf{j}$

5. A particle moves so that at time t its position vector is given by $\mathbf{r} = \cos t\,\mathbf{i} + \sin t\,\mathbf{j} + 10\mathbf{k}$. Show that its speed is constant.

6. A particle moves with displacement vector $\mathbf{r} = (3t^2 + 1)\mathbf{i} + (t - t^2)\mathbf{j}$. Find when the particle is moving

    (a) parallel to the x-axis

    (b) parallel to the vector $4\mathbf{i} - \mathbf{j}$.

7. A particle moves so that its displacement is given by $\mathbf{r} = (6 - t)\mathbf{i} + t\mathbf{j}$. Find its velocity vector **v**. When is its velocity perpendicular to its displacement?

8. A particle moves so that its displacement is given by $\mathbf{r} = (t - 1)\mathbf{i} + (t^2 - t)\mathbf{j}$. Find its velocity vector **v**. When is its velocity parallel to its displacement?

22.4 Examination questions

1. A vehicle starts from rest, accelerates at 3.2 m s^{-2} for 12 s and decelerates at 1.8 m s^{-2} until its speed is 10 m s^{-1}.

   Calculate the following, giving your answers corrected to two significant figures:

   (a) the greatest speed;   (b) the time taken to decelerate;

   (c) the distance covered while accelerating;

   (d) the distance covered while decelerating.

   [SMP ADD]

2. A particle P moves in a straight line so that its velocity v m s^{-1} at time t seconds, where $t \geq 0$, is given by $v = 12t - 5t^2$. Calculate

   (a) the value of t when the acceleration of P is zero,

   (b) the distance covered by P between the instants when $t = 0$ and $t = 2$.

   [L ADD]

3. At a certain instant a mass at O has a velocity **u** m s^{-1} given by **u** = 18**i** − 24**j**, where **i** and **j** are unit vectors in the direction of the x −axis and y-axis respectively. What is the magnitude of the velocity at this instant? The mass subsequently has an acceleration **a** m s^{-2} given by **a** = −3**i** + 2**j**. In terms of **i** and **j**, what is the velocity of the mass 5 seconds later? After what further period of time will the mass be instantaneously moving in a direction parallel to the y-axis, and at that time what will its position vector be relative to O?

   [MEI ADD]

4. (a) A particle moves on the x-axis. It starts from rest at the origin O and moves in the positive direction with constant acceleration of 2 m s^{-2} until its velocity reaches 10 m s^{-1}. It then continues with constant velocity 10 m s^{-1} for some time, before decelerating uniformly and coming to rest after a total time of 20 s. The total distance travelled is 160 m. Sketch the velocity-time graph for the motion, and find the magnitude of the deceleration.

   (b) Two particles P and Q move in the positive direction on the x-axis, P with constant acceleration 2 m s^{-2} and Q with constant acceleration of 1 m s^{-2}. At time $t = 0$, P is projected from the origin with speed 1 m s^{-1}, and at time $t = 4$ Q is projected from O with speed 16 m s^{-1}. Find the times between which Q is ahead of P. Find also the distance from O at which Q overtakes P, and the distance from O at which P overtakes Q.

   [C]

5. (i) Two points move in a plane, both starting from the origin, in such a way that, after time t seconds, their position vectors are

   $3(\cos t - 1)\mathbf{i} + (4 \sin t)\mathbf{j}$ and $(3 \sin t)\mathbf{i} + 4(\cos t - 1)\mathbf{j}$.

   Find the value of t when the points are first moving in

   (a) opposite directions,   (b) the same direction.

   (ii) A particle moves in a straight line with acceleration

   $[(t - 1)e^{-t} + 2 \cos t]$ m s^{-2}, starting from rest at the origin at time $t = 0$. Obtain the distance x m travelled from rest in time t seconds.

   [L]

6. The position vector of a particle at time t is given by

$$\mathbf{r} = (a \cos \omega t)\mathbf{i} + (a \sin \omega t)\mathbf{j} + bt\mathbf{k},$$

where a, b and ω are constants. Find the velocity and acceleration vectors. Show that the speed of the particle is constant and that the magnitude of the particle's acceleration is always non–zero.

Comment briefly on these results.

[W]

Common errors

1. **Notation**

    (a) Read a question carefully to make sure that you know which of the quantities distance, speed, acceleration you are dealing with.

    (b) To go from displacement to velocity, or from velocity to acceleration, you must *differentiate*. To go the other way you *integrate*. Do not perform the wrong operation.

    (c) If a body moves with two different velocities u and v, then the *average velocity* is not necessarily $\frac{1}{2}(u + v)$. You must find the total distance and divide it by the total time.

2. **Constant acceleration**

    (a) Make sure that you are consistent with the *signs* of your quantities. Decide that one direction shall be positive, and then displacement, velocity and acceleration in the opposite direction must be negative. Do not have the velocity one way and the acceleration the other.

    (b) Suppose a body is moving backwards and forwards. To find the displacement after a period of time you do not need to split up the motion into its positive period and its negative period. The equations cover both the positive period and the negative period.

    (c) The *displacement* of a body is the directed distance from the starting point. The *total distance travelled* is the amount of distance covered, in both directions. So if a body returns to its starting point then its displacement is zero, but the total distance travelled is not zero.

3. **Non–constant acceleration**

    (a) Do not use formulae such as $s = ut + \frac{1}{2}at^2$ for situations in which the acceleration is not constant. You must use calculus to find, for example, the distance from the velocity.

    (b) Do not ignore negative signs. A negative velocity, for example, means that the particle is moving towards the origin instead of away from it.

    (c) The maximum distance occurs when the *velocity* is 0. Similarly the greatest velocity occurs when the *acceleration* is 0. Make sure that you put the correct expression equal to zero.

23 Force and acceleration

23.1 Newton's first and second laws

Newton's First Law states that:

Unless acted upon by an external force, a body will remain at rest or move with a constant speed in a straight line.

Newton's Second Law states that:

The acceleration experienced by a body is proportional to the external force acting upon it, and is in the same straight line as the force.

a m s⁻²

F N

Fig 23.1

These laws can be summarised by the formula:

$$\mathbf{F} = m\mathbf{a}$$

Here **F** is the force, m is the mass and **a** is the acceleration. Note that **F** and **a** are vectors.

The unit of force is the *Newton* (N). 1 Newton applied to 1 kilogram imparts an acceleration of 1 m s⁻².

23.1.1 Examples

1. A stone of mass 0.3 kg is skimmed across the ice at 10 m s⁻¹ and comes to rest in 100 m. Find the force acting upon it, assuming that it is constant.

    Solution

    Use the formula for constant acceleration.

    $0^2 = 10^2 + 2 \times a \times 100$.

    $a = -\frac{1}{2}$ m s⁻²

    Use the second law:

    $$\text{Force} = 0.3 \times \tfrac{1}{2} = 0.15 \text{ N}$$

2. A man weighs out diamonds in a lift which is accelerating upwards at 1 m s⁻². The balance registers 27 grams. What is the true weight of the diamonds? (Take g to be 9.8 m s⁻²)

    Solution

    If the balance registers 27 grams, then the force it applies is 0.027×9.8 N.

166

If the mass of the diamonds is m grams, then the second law gives:

$0.027 \times 9.8 - m \times 9.8 = m \times 1$

$m = 0.0245$

The diamonds weigh 24.5 grams

3. A body of mass 4 kg moves so that its displacement $\mathbf{r}$ m is given by $\mathbf{r} = (t^2 + 1)\mathbf{i} + t^3\mathbf{j}$. Find in vector form the force acting on the body at time t s.

Solution

Differentiate the displacement twice to obtain the acceleration.

$\mathbf{a} = 2\mathbf{i} + 6t\mathbf{j}$ m s^{-2}

Multiply the acceleration by the mass to obtain the force.

The force is $8\mathbf{i} + 24t\mathbf{j}$ N

23.1.2 Exercises

Throughout these exercises take g to be 9.8 m s^{-2}.

1. A mass of 5 kg is suspended from a string. Find the tension in the string.

2. A body of mass 70 kg is dragged across the floor at a constant speed of $\frac{1}{2}$ m s^{-1}. If the force dragging it is 30 N, find the resistance force.

3. A body of mass 2 kg is accelerated at 12 m s^{-2}. Find the force applied to it.

4. A body experiences a force of 20 N, and accelerates at 60 m s^{-2}. Find the mass of the body.

5. A mass of 4 kg receives a force of 12 kg. Find its acceleration.

6. A train of mass 60,000 kg comes to rest from 2 m s^{-1} in 30 seconds. Find the braking force, assuming that it is constant.

7. A car of mass 1,500 kg accelerates from 1 m s^{-1} to 20 m s^{-1} in 30 seconds. Find the tractive force, assuming that it is constant.

8. A sprinter of mass 70 kg accelerates constantly over 50 metres, reaching a speed of 12 m s^{-1} at the end. Find the force that he exerts.

9. A train of mass 100,000 kg accelerates constantly from rest until it reaches 10 m s^{-1}, over a distance of 500 m. Find the tractive force of the train.

10. A train of mass 80,000 kg is brought to rest from a speed of $\frac{1}{2}$ m s^{-1} by buffers which contract through 20 cm. Find the force, assumed constant, exerted by the buffers.

11. A parachutist of mass 100 kg falls at a steady speed of 1.5 m s^{-1}. What is the force of air resistance?

12. A particle of mass $\frac{1}{4}$ kg is raised on a string at an acceleration of 2 m s^{-2}. Find the tension in the string.

13. A lift cage weighs 1,000 kg. The tension in the supporting cable is 9,500 N. Find the deceleration of the lift.

14. A mass supported by a string is accelerated up at 2.5 m s^{-2}. The tension in the string is 12 N. Find the mass.

15. A parachutist has mass 100 kg, and is falling at 1 m s^{-1}. Air resistance is equal to 500 N at this speed. Find his acceleration at this speed.

16. The air resistance experienced by a 100 kg parachutist is proportional to his velocity, and his maximum speed is 1.5 m s^{-1}. Find the air resistance when he is falling at 1 m s^{-1}, and his acceleration at that speed.

17. A 70 kg man weighs himself on a weighing machine which is in a lift accelerating up at 1.25 m s^{-2}. What does he seem to weigh?

18. A 50 kg woman weighs herself in a lift, and the dial registers 47 kg. What is the deceleration of the lift?

19. When a man weighs himself in a lift accelerating up at 1 m s^{-2}, the dial registers 77 kg. What is his true weight?

20. A man weighs an object in a lift with a spring balance. When it is accelerating up at k m s^{-2}, it appears to weigh 1.4 kg. When it is accelerating down at k m s^{-2}, it appears to weigh 1.1 kg. Find the true weight of the object.

21. A balloon of total mass 500 kg is floating horizontally. If 100 kg of ballast is thrown out, find the acceleration with which the balloon rises.

22. A balloon of total mass 700 kg is accelerating down at $\frac{1}{8}$ m s^{-2}. How much ballast must be ejected to stop the balloon's descent?

23. A body of mass 2 kg experiences a force of $(3\mathbf{i} + 2\mathbf{j})$ N. Find its acceleration in vector form.

24. A body of mass 4 kg experiences an acceleration of $((1 + t)\mathbf{i} + 12\mathbf{j})$ N. Find in vector form the force acting upon it at time t s.

25. A body of mass 6 kg experiences a force of $(24t\mathbf{i} + 60t^2\mathbf{j})$ N. Find its acceleration. If it starts at rest from the origin find its velocity and its displacement.

26. The force experienced by a body of mass 0.4 kg is $((\cos t)\mathbf{i} + (\sin t)\mathbf{j})$ N. Find its acceleration in vector form. If it starts at rest from the point $\mathbf{i}$ m find its velocity and displacement.

23.2 Action and reaction

Newton's Third Law states that:

Action and reaction are equal and opposite.

Hence if two bodies A and B are in contact, the force exerted by A on B is equal and opposite to the force exerted by B on A.

23.2.1 Examples

Fig 23.2

1. A locomotive of mass 50 tonnes drags two coaches of 20 tonnes each, against resistances of 2,000 N for the locomotive and 700 N for each coach. If the acceleration is $\frac{1}{4}$ m s^{-2}, find the force produced by the engine and the tensions in the couplings.

Solution

Considering the train as a whole, and using Newton's first law:

$F - 3400 = 90,000 \times \frac{1}{4}$

Force = 25,900 N

Considering the carriages as a whole, and letting T_1 be the tension in the first coupling:

$T_1 - 1400 = 40,000 \times \frac{1}{4}$

Considering the final carriage on its own, and letting T_2 be the tension in the second coupling:

$T_2 - 700 = 20,000 \times \frac{1}{4}$

The tensions are 11,400 and 5,700 Newtons

2.   Two masses of 4 and 3 kg are at the ends of a light inextensible string, which is slung over a smooth peg. Find the acceleration of the system, and the force exerted by the peg.

Fig 23.3

Solution

Letting a m s^{-2} be the acceleration and T N the tension in the string, obtain the two equations:

$T - 3g = 3a$

$4g - T = 4a$

Add these two equations:

$g = 7a$

The acceleration is $\frac{g}{7} = 1.4$ m s^{-2}

The tension in the string is $3a + 3g = 33.6$ N.

The force exerted by the peg is $2T = 67.2$ N

23.2.2 Exercises

Throughout these exercises take g to be 9.8 m s^{-2}

1.   A car of mass 800 kg tows a caravan of 500 kg, against resistances of 900 N for the car and 400 N for the caravan. If the acceleration produced is 1.5 m s^{-2}, find the force exerted by the car and the tension in the tow-bar.

2.   A tug tows two barges of mass 100 tonnes each, at an acceleration of 0.1 m s^{-2}, through water which exerts a drag of 2,000 N on each barge. Find the tensions in the ropes between the tug and the first barge and between the two barges.

3.   A train consists of three carriages, each of mass 50 tonnes and each experiencing a resistance of 5000 N. The train is travelling at 10 m s^{-1}, then brakes are applied to the front carriage which bring the train to a halt in 100 m. Find the thrust in the couplings.

4.   Two masses of 3 kg and 5 kg are connected by a light inextensible string which is slung over a smooth peg. Find the acceleration of the system and the tension in the string. Find the reaction at the peg.

5.   Repeat Question 4, for masses of 10 kg and 5 kg.

6. Two masses of m and M kg, where $m > M$, are connected by a light inextensible string which is slung over a smooth peg. Show that the acceleration of the system is

$$\frac{(m - M)g}{(m + M)} \text{ m s}^{-2}.$$

7. A mass of 5 kg lies on a smooth horizontal table, and is connected by a light inextensible string to a mass of 3 kg which hangs over the edge. Find the acceleration of the system and the tension in the string.

8. Repeat Question 7, with masses of 10 kg and 5 kg.

9. A mass of m kg lies on a smooth horizontal table, and is connected by a light inextensible string to a mass of M kg which hangs over the edge. Show that the acceleration of the system is

$$\frac{Mg}{(m + M)} \text{ m s}^{-2}.$$

Fig 23.4

Fig 23.5

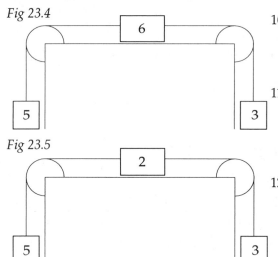

10. Three masses are as shown in Fig 23.4. The table is smooth and horizontal, and the strings are light and inextensible. Find the acceleration of the system and the tensions in the strings.

11. A mass of 4 kg lies on a horizontal table, and is connected by a light inextensible string to a mass of 5 kg which hangs freely. If the system moves with acceleration 2 m s^{-2} find the frictional force acting on the 4 kg mass.

12. Three masses are as shown in Fig 23.5. The table is horizontal, and the strings are light and inextensible. If the system moves with acceleration 1 m s^{-2}, find the frictional force acting on the central mass.

23.3 Examination questions

1. A lift of mass 500 kg accelerates at 2.2 m s^{-2} from rest to its maximum speed and also decelerates at 2.2 m s^{-2} from this maximum speed to rest. What are the maximum and minimum values of the tension in the supporting cable when the lift is not carrying any passengers?

   In fact the lift is designed to carry at most five passengers whose average mass can be taken as 75 kg each. What is the maximum tension that the cable must be able to withstand, and what will be the maximum force on the floor of the lift?

   [MEI ADD]

2. Forces measured in newtons are represented by the vectors

$$\binom{3}{4}, \binom{2}{4}, \binom{-2}{1} \text{ and } \binom{p}{2p}.$$

   They act on a particle to accelerate it in the direction $\binom{-1}{-1}$.
   Find p.

If the mass of the particle is 0.1 kg, show that the magnitude of the acceleration is approximately 42.4 m s^{-2}.

If the particle is initially at the point (0,0) and moving with velocity $\binom{1}{4}$ m s^{-1}, find its position vector after 2 seconds.

[O&C ADD]

3. Two particles A and B of masses 0.4 kg and 0.3 kg respectively, are connected by a light inextensible string which passes over a smooth, light, fixed pulley. The particles are released from rest with the string taut and the hanging parts vertical. Calculate

   (a) the acceleration, in m s^{-2}, of A,

   (b) the tension, in N, in the string.

   [L ADD]

4. A tug is towing two barges along a canal and slowing down at 0.015 m s^{-2}. The mass of each barge is 12 tonnes, and of the tug 8 tonnes.

 Fig 23.6

Each of the barges and the tug experiences the same resistance from the water, R, and the engines give a forward force of 120 N on the tug.

Show that the tension T_1 in the first cable is double the tension T_2 in the second cable.

Calculate the values of T_1 and R.

[SMP ADD]

5. (In this question take g to be 10 m s^{-2})

A balloon of total mass M kg, including the balloonist, his equipment and ballast, is at a height of 2.2 km above the ground, ascending vertically at a steady speed of 10 m s^{-1}. Write down the force of upthrust by the air on the balloon.

The balloonist wishes to land, and he adjusts the balloon so that the upthrust is suddenly reduced to $\frac{9}{10}$ of its previous value, without altering M, and remains constant thereafter. Show that, 1 minute later, his height is 1 km and his velocity is 50 m s^{-1} downwards.

At this moment the balloonist drops overboard pM kg of ballast, where $\frac{1}{10} < p < 1$. Show that the balloon's acceleration changes to

$$\frac{10p - 1}{1 - p} \text{ m s}^{-2} \text{ upwards.}$$

Given that the balloon reaches the ground with zero velocity, find

(a) the value of p,

(b) the time between the ballast hitting the ground and the balloon reaching the ground.

[AEB 1986]

6. In the interval $0 \leq t \leq 6$, where t denotes time in seconds, a particle of mass 2 kg is acted upon by two forces. The first force acts in the direction of the vector $8\mathbf{i} - \mathbf{j} + 4\mathbf{k}$ and has a constant magnitude of 18 N. The second force acts in the direction of the vector $-2\mathbf{i} + 2\mathbf{j} - \mathbf{k}$ and its magnitude decreases

171

uniformly with time from 18 N when $t = 0$ to zero when $t = 6$. Show that the acceleration of the particle during the interval $0 \leq t \leq 6$ is

$$(2 + t)\mathbf{i} + (5 - t)\mathbf{j} + (1 + \tfrac{1}{2}t)\mathbf{k} \text{ m s}^{-2}.$$

Given that the particle has velocity $2\mathbf{i}$ m s^{-1} when $t = 0$, find its velocity when $t = 6$.

[JMB]

Common errors

1. **Force and acceleration**

   (a) Forces on a system only balance if the system is in equilibrium. If the system is accelerating then you cannot equate the forces to zero.

   (b) When drawing a diagram of the forces acting on a body, do not put in a force corresponding to the acceleration. The acceleration is a consequence of the forces, not an extra force itself.

2. **Action and reaction**

   When dealing with problems involving weights hanging from strings, do not assume that the tension in the string is equal to the weight. That will only be true if the system is in equilibrium. If the system is accelerating then the tension will be different from the weight.

24 Resolving forces

24.1 Forces at an angle

If a force F makes an angle θ with a direction, the *resolved part* or *component* of the force in that direction is $F \cos \theta$.

Fig 24.1

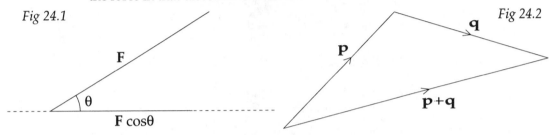

Fig 24.2

If two or more forces are equivalent to a single force, that force is the *resultant*.

Fig 24.3

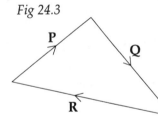

The resultant can be found by components, or by use of a vector triangle, as shown.

If three forces **P**, **Q**, **R** are in equilibrium, then they form a *triangle of forces* as shown.

Suppose a body is acted on by certain forces. Newton's Laws I and II can be generalised as follows:

> **I If a body is not accelerating in a particular direction, then the sum of the resolved parts of the forces in that direction is zero.**

> **II The acceleration of a body in a particular direction is proportional to the net resolved parts of the forces in that direction.**

The process of finding the resolved parts along a certain direction is called *resolving* in that direction.

24.1.1 Examples

Fig 24.4

1. Forces of 12 N and 15 N through the same point, along bearings of 030° and 345°. Find the magnitude and direction of the force needed to counterbalance them.

    Solution

    Let the counterbalancing force have South component S and East component E.

    Resolving North-South:

173

$S = 12 \cos 30° + 15 \cos 15° = 24.88$ N

Resolving East-West:

$E = 12 \cos 60° - 15 \cos 75° = 2.12$ N

The magnitude F of the force is found by Pythagoras, and its direction θ by trigonometry.

$F = \sqrt{(S^2 + E^2)} = 24.97$ N : $\theta = \tan^{-1} \frac{E}{S} = 4.9°$

The balancing force is 25.0 N, at a bearing of 175.1°

Fig 24.5

10°

2. A barge of mass 50 tonnes is pulled by a rope which makes 10° with the keel of the boat. If the water resistance is 2,000 N, find the force in the rope needed to accelerate the barge at 0.1 m s^{-2}.

Solution

Let the force be F. Resolving along the keel:

$F \cos 10° - 2,000 = 50,000 \times 0.1$

The force needed is 7108 N

24.1.2 Exercises

1. Find the North component of a force of 24 N at a bearing of 075°. Find its East component.

2. Find the East components of the following forces:
   (a) 25 N at 023°   (b) 7 N at 180°
   (c) 0.02 N at 113°   (d) 65 N at 337°

3. Find the magnitude and direction of the force needed to counterbalance 5 N at 066° and 3 N at 015°.

4. Find the magnitudes and directions of the forces needed to counterbalance the following sets of forces:
   (a) 17 N due North and 18 N due West
   (b) 4 N at 120° and 3 N at 210°
   (c) 12 N due North, 25 N at 012° and 33 N at 354°
   (d) 5 N at 254°, 7 N at 119°, 10 N at 331°, 14 N at 23°.

5. Find the resultant of 12 N North East and 27 N South West.

6. Find the resultants of the following sets of forces:
   (a) 14 N at 25°, 22 N at 348°   b)   2 N at 47° and 3 N at 183°
   (c) 48 N at 63°, 34 N at 190° and 41 N at 213°.

7. A body of mass 12 kg is acted upon by two forces, one of which is 6 N due north, the other being 7 N North East. Find the magnitude and direction of the acceleration of the body.

8. Find the magnitude and direction of the acceleration of a body of mass 5 kg when it experiences the following set of forces:

   3 N at 012°, 3.5 N at 348° and 4.1 N at 327°.

9. A water skier of mass 80 kg is pulled by a rope which makes 15° with the horizontal. If the water resistance is 20 N, find the force in the rope need to pull him along at a steady speed.

10. If the skier of Question 9 accelerates at 1.5 m s⁻², find the tension in the rope.

11. A body of mass 30 kg lies on a smooth floor, and is pulled by a rope which makes 30° with the horizontal. If the tension in the rope is 12 N find the acceleration of the body.

12. A body of mass 70 kg lies on a rough floor, where the resistance to motion is 43 N. A rope is attached to the body at 20° to the horizontal. Find the force in the rope necessary to accelerate the body at 2 m s⁻².

13. If in Question 12 the force in the rope is 60 N, find the acceleration of the body.

14. Three forces P, Q and R act at a point, and are in equilibrium. Let $\hat{p}$ be the angle between Q and R, with $\hat{q}$ and $\hat{r}$ defined similarly. Prove that:

$$\frac{\sin \hat{p}}{P} = \frac{\sin \hat{q}}{Q} = \frac{\sin \hat{r}}{R}$$

24.2 Problems involving weight

The *weight* of a body is its mass multiplied by g. Throughout this section take g to be 9.8 m s⁻².

Weight always acts vertically downwards. It is sometimes necessary to resolve the weight of a body.

24.2.1. Examples

Fig 24.6

1. A body of mass 3 kg lies on a smooth slope of angle 20°. Find the acceleration of the body down the slope.

   Solution

   The forces are as shown in the diagram. Resolving down the slope:

   $3g \cos 70° = 3a$

   The acceleration is $g \cos 70° = 3.35$ m s⁻²

Fig 24.7

2. A body of mass 12 kg hangs from a string, and is pulled aside by a horizontal force of 30 N. Find the tension in the string and the angle it makes with the vertical.

   Solution

   Resolving vertically:

   $T \cos \theta = 12g$

   Resolving horizontally:

   $T \sin \theta = 30$

   Divide the second equation by the first:

$$\tan \theta = \frac{30}{12g} : \theta = 14.3°$$

Substitute into either equation to find T.

The tension is 121 N and the angle is 14.3°

3. Three particles A, B, C of masses 4 kg, 5 kg, 6 kg respectively, are tied in that order on a light inextensible string. The string is slung over two smooth pegs X and Y, with X between A and B and Y between B and C. Find the angle made by XB with the vertical.

    Solution

    The situation is as shown. The three forces acting at B are $4g$, $5g$, $6g$. Re-arrange the three forces into a triangle of forces.

Fig 24.8

Fig 24.9

Use the cosine rule to find θ.

$\cos \theta = 0.125$

XB makes 83° with the vertical.

24.2.2 Exercises

1. A body of mass 30 kg lies on a smooth slope of angle 35°. Find the acceleration down the slope.

2. A body lies on a smooth slope of angle α. Show that the acceleration down the slope is $g \sin \alpha$.

3. A body of mass 10 kg lies on a smooth slope of angle 20°. Find the normal reaction.

4. A body mass 20 kg lies on a smooth slope of angle 25°. Find the force acting up the slope which will keep it in equilibrium.

5. A body mass 12 kg lies on a smooth slope of angle 10°. A horizontal force of 3 N acts on it up the slope. Find the acceleration down the slope.

6. A body of mass 14 kg lies on a slope of angle 27°, experiencing a frictional force of 57 N. Find its acceleration down the slope.

Fig 24.10

7. A body of mass 5 kg lies on a smooth slope of angle 30°. It is attached to a light inextensible string, which passes over a smooth peg at the top and is attached to a weight of 4 kg which hangs freely. Find the acceleration of the system and the tension in the string.

8. The 5 kg mass of Question 7 is replaced by a heavier mass so that the system is now in equilibrium. Find the new mass.

9. The 4 kg mass of Question 7 is replaced by a lighter mass so that the system accelerates at $\frac{1}{2}$ m s^{-2}. Find the new mass.

10. The 4 kg mass of Question 7 is replaced by a lighter mass so that the system accelerates in the other direction at $\frac{1}{2}$ m s⁻². Find the new mass.

Fig 24.11

11. Bodies of mass 4 kg and 7 kg lie on the sides of smooth slopes of angle 50° and 60° respectively, connected by a light inextensible string as shown in Fig 24.11. Find the acceleration of the system.

12. The 7 kg mass of Question 11 is replaced by a lighter mass so that the system is in equilibrium. Find the new mass.

13. The 7 kg mass of Question 11 is replaced by a heavier mass so that the system accelerates at 5 m s⁻². Find the new mass.

14. A mass of 6 kg hangs at the end of a string and is pulled aside by a horizontal force of 23 N. Find the tension in the string and the angle it makes with the vertical.

15. The mass of Question 14 is pulled aside by a horizontal force, so that the string makes 12° with the vertical. Find the force.

16. The mass of Question 14 is pulled aside by a horizontal force, so that the tension in the string is 65 N. Find the force.

17. The mass of Question 14 is pulled aside by a force of 36 N which is at right angles to the string. Find the tension in the string and the angle which it makes with the vertical.

18. The mass of Question 14 is pulled aside by a force which is at right angles to the string. The string now makes 33° with the vertical. Find the force and the tension in the string.

19. A mass of 7 kg is supported by two strings, which make 30° and 40° with the vertical. Find the tensions in the strings.

20. A mass of 8 kg is supported by two strings, each of which exerts a tension of 45 N. Find the angles that the strings make with the vertical.

21. A mass of 10 kg is supported by two strings. One string exerts 60 N and is at 20° to the vertical. Find the tension in the other string and the angle it makes with the vertical.

22. A mass of 10 kg is supported by two strings. If the tensions in the strings are 60 N and 70 N find the angles which they make with the vertical.

24.3 Examination questions

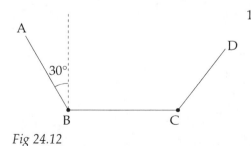

Fig 24.12

1. Particles of masses 500g at B and 250g at C are supported by 3 strings as shown in the figure. The string AB is inclined at an angle of 30° to the vertical and BC is horizontal.

   (a) Draw accurately a triangle of forces for the particle at B and hence find the tension in AB and in BC.

   (b) Find by drawing or by calculation the angle which CD makes with the vertical.

   [AEB ADD 1986]

2. A particle of mass 0.3 kg is suspended in equilibrium by two light strings inclined to the horizontal at 30° and 60° respectively. Calculate the tensions in the strings.

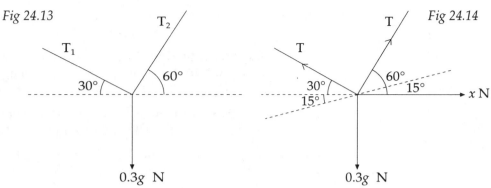

Fig 24.13 *Fig 24.14*

A horizontal force of x newton, acting in the plane of the two strings, as shown in Fig 24.14, is now applied to the particle and the system is held in equilibrium with the tensions in the two original strings now being equal. By resolving in the direction AB shown in the diagram, or otherwise, find the value of x.

[O&C ADD]

3. A particle A of mass 2 kg is placed on a long smooth plane inclined at an angle θ where $\sin \theta = \frac{3}{50}$. It is attached by a light inelastic string to a particle B of mass 2 kg. The string passes over a smooth peg P with the particle B hanging vertically below the peg.

Fig 24.15

The system is released from rest. Calculate the tension in the string and the acceleration of the particles. After 2 seconds B hits the ground without rebounding, and the string becomes slack. Calculate the total distance which A moves before it comes instantaneously to rest.

[O ADD]

4. A sledge with rider, of total mass 100 kg, slides down an 18° slope at constant speed. Calculate the force of resistance to its motion. [Take g to be 10 m s^{-2}, and give your answer to 2 significant figures.]

The angle of the slope increases to 20°. Assuming that the resistance stays the same, and that the sledge remains in contact with the surface, find the rate at which it accelerates.

[SMP]

Fig 24.16

5. Two particles, masses $2M$ and $3M$, fastened to the ends of a light inelastic string which passes over two smooth pegs A and B are kept in equilibrium by a third particle, mass aM, fastened to point C of the string, C lying between A and B. If the line AB is horizontal and if, in equilibrium, the string is such that the angle $\hat{ACB} = 120°$, find a.

[NI]

Common errors

Resolving forces

(a) Do not forget to multiply forces by the factor of $\cos \theta$. The resultant of two forces of 5 N and 6 N is not 11 N, unless they happen to be in the same direction.

(b) Do not assume that the sum of forces is zero, unless the body is in equilibrium.

25 Friction

Suppose two bodies are in contact. If they are sliding over each other or about to slide then friction is said to be *limiting*.

Fig 25.1

The maximum frictional force between them, achieved when friction is limiting, is proportional to the normal force between them.

The constant of proportionality is the *coefficient of friction* μ.

Suppose two bodies are in contact, and R is the resultant of the normal and frictional forces. The greatest possible angle between R and the normal is the *angle of friction*.

The angle of friction λ is given in terms of the coefficient of friction μ by the equation $\mu = \tan \lambda$.

25.1 Examples

1. A stone of mass 0.1 kg is skimmed across ice. It starts at 5 m s^{-1} and comes to rest after 50 m. Find the coefficient of friction μ. (Fig 25.2)

    Solution

    The deceleration is found from the formula $v^2 = u^2 + 2as$.

    The deceleration is 0.25 m s^{-2}.

    The normal force is $0.1g$. As the stone is sliding, friction is limiting.

    $\mu \times 0.1g = 0.1 \times 0.25$

    The coefficient of friction is 0.026

Fig 25.2

Fig 25.3

2. A body of mass 2 kg lies on a slope of angle 30°, where $\mu = \frac{1}{4}$. Find the acceleration of the body down the slope. (Fig 25.3)

Solution

Resolving perpendicular to the slope:

$N = 2g \cos 30°$

Resolving parallel to the slope:

$2g \sin 30° - F = 2a$, where a is the acceleration.

It is sliding, so friction is limiting. $F = \frac{1}{4}N$.

$2a = 2g \sin 30° - \frac{1}{2}g \cos 30°$

The acceleration is 2.78 m s^{-2}

25.1.2 Exercises

1. A mass of 6 kg lies on a rough table where the coefficient of friction μ is 0.5. Find the least horizontal force needed to move it.

2. A mass of 8 kg on a rough floor can just be moved by a horizontal force of 45 N. Find the coefficient of friction.

3. A body of mass 3 kg slides on a rough horizontal table where the coefficient of friction is $\frac{1}{2}$. If it starts with a speed of 5 m s^{-1} find how far it skids.

4. A body of mass 12 kg lies on a rough horizontal table, and a horizontal force of 24 N is applied. If the body does not move find the frictional force.

5. A body of mass 9 kg slides along a rough horizontal table, coming to rest from 3 m s^{-1} in 1 m. Find the coefficient of friction.

6. A body lies on a slope of angle 23°, where the coefficient of friction is $\frac{1}{4}$. Find its acceleration down the slope.

7. A body of mass 12 kg lies on a rough slope of angle 17°. If it does not slip find the frictional force.

8. A body lies on a slope of angle 43°, and accelerates at 5 m s^{-2}. Find the coefficient of friction.

9. A body can just rest on a slope where the coefficient of friction is $\frac{1}{2}$. Find the angle of the slope.

10. A body can just rest on a slope of angle α. Show that the angle of friction is α.

11. A body lies on a slope of angle α, where the angle of friction is λ. ($\lambda < \alpha$).

    Show that its acceleration down the slope is $\dfrac{g \sin(\alpha - \lambda)}{\cos \lambda}$

12. A body of mass 3 kg lies on a slope of angle 30°, where the coefficient of friction is $\frac{1}{4}$. Find the least force parallel to the slope which will prevent it from sliding down. Find the least force parallel to the slope which will push it up the slope.

13. A car of mass 700 kg is travelling at 25 m s^{-1} when the engine seizes, causing the wheels to lock. The coefficient of friction between tyre and ground is 0.75. Find how long it takes to come to a halt

    (a) along level ground   (b) down a slope of angle 10°

    (c) up a slope of angle 5°.

14. A body of mass 23 kg lies on a floor where the coefficient of friction is $\frac{1}{2}$. A rope is attached to it at an angle θ to the horizontal. Find the least tension in the rope which will pull the body along in the cases when θ is

    (a) 0°   (b) 25°   (c) 40°.

15. A body of mass 75 kg lies on a floor where the coefficient of friction is $\frac{1}{4}$. It is pushed by a rod making θ with the horizontal. Find the least force in the rod which will move the body in the cases when θ is

    (a) 0°   (b) 12°

    (c) 20°.

16. A body of mass 3 kg lies on a slope of angle 20°, where the coefficient of friction is $\frac{1}{8}$. A rope is attached to it, making 10° with the slope. Find the least tension in the rope which will prevent the body from sliding down. Find the least tension which will pull the body up.

17. A mass of 3 kg lies on a horizontal table where the coefficient of friction is $\frac{1}{2}$. It is attached to a light inextensible string, which passes over the table and supports a mass of 7 kg which hangs freely. Find the acceleration of the system.

18. A mass of 5 kg lies on a rough horizontal table, and is attached by a light inextensible string to an equal mass which hangs freely. The system moves with an acceleration of 4 m s^{-2}. Find the coefficient of friction.

19. A mass of 4 kg lies on a slope of angle 20° and coefficient of friction $\frac{1}{8}$, and is attached by a light horizontal string to a mass of 6 kg which hangs freely. Find the acceleration of the system.

Fig 25.4

25.2 Examination questions

1. A block of wood is made to slide along a rough horizontal plane by a force $\sqrt{2}\,P$ newtons applied at an angle of 45° as in the left figure. Copy this figure and mark in clearly all the forces acting on the block.

Fig 25.5

Fig 25.6

If the coefficient of friction is $\frac{1}{3}$ and if the force $\sqrt{2}\,P$ newtons causes the block to accelerate along the plane at 0.4 m s^{-2}, calculate the value of P.

If a new force $\sqrt{2}\,Q$ newtons is applied to the block instead of the original force, as in the right figure, and if the acceleration is unaltered, prove that $Q = \frac{1}{2}P$.

[O&C ADD]

2. The diagram shows a particle A of mass 2 kg resting on a horizontal table. It is attached to particles B of mass 5 kg and C of mass 3 kg by light inextensible strings hanging over light smooth pulleys. Initially the plane ABC is vertical, the strings are taut and pass over the pulleys at right angles to the edges of the table. In the ensuing motion from rest find the common acceleration of the particles and the tension in each string before A reaches an edge

    (a) when the table is smooth,

    (b) when the table is rough and the coefficient of friction between the particle A and the table is $\frac{1}{2}$.

    (Take g as 10 m s^{-2}.)

    [L]

Fig 25.7

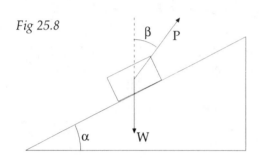

3. A weight W is placed on a rough plane inclined at an angle α to the horizontal and the angle of friction between the weight and the plane is $\lambda\,(<\alpha)$.

    (i) Show that the weight will slide down the plane.

    (ii) If the weight is just prevented from sliding down by a force P inclined to the upward vertical at an acute angle β, show that
    $$P = W\,\frac{\sin(\alpha - \lambda)}{\sin(\alpha - \lambda + \beta)}$$
    Obtain the least value of P as β varies and the corresponding value of β.

    (iii) If $\alpha + \lambda < \frac{1}{2}\pi$, what is the direction and magnitude of the smallest force which will just move the weight *up* the plane?

    [SUJB]

Fig 25.8

Common errors

(a) Do not assume that the frictional force must be equal to μN. This is only the case when friction is limiting, i.e. when the surfaces are sliding or about to slide. In general, $F \leq \mu N$.

(b) When a body lies on a surface, do not assume that $N = mg$. If the surface is not horizontal, or if there are extra forces involved, then you must find N by resolving along the normal.

26 Moments

If a force acts on a large body, then the *moment* of the force about a point is the turning effect of the force about that point.

If the body does not turn about a point, then the sum of the clockwise moments about that point is equal to the sum of the anti-clockwise moments.

The operation of equating the clockwise and anti-clockwise moments about a point is called *taking moments* about that point.

26.1 Perpendicular forces

Suppose a lever is pivoted at A, and the force F acts at d from the pivot and is at right angles to the lever.

The moment of the force about A is Fd.

Fig 26.1

26.1.1 Example

A see-saw is balanced at its centre. Zoe, who weighs 45 kg, sits 2 m from the centre. Where should Yvonne, who weighs 50 kg, sit in order for the see-saw to balance?

Fig 26.2

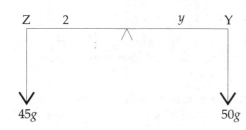

Solution

Suppose that Yvonne sits y m from the centre. Her (clockwise) moment about the centre is $50yg$. This must exactly balance Zoe's (anti-clockwise) moment.

$50yg = 2 \times 45g$. $y = 1.8$

Yvonne should sit 1.8 m from the centre

26.1.2 Exercises

1. In each of the diagrams of Fig 26.3 the system is in equilibrium. Find the unknown forces.

2. In each of the diagrams of Fig 26.4 the system is in equilibrium. Find the unknown distances.

3. A see-saw of length 5 metres is pivoted at its centre. Naomi, weighing 40 kg, sits at one end. Where should Osric, weighing 75 kg, sit to balance the see-saw?

Fig 26.3

Fig 26.4

4. Osric gets off the see-saw of Question 3, and Peregrine sits on it 2 m from the centre. If it is in balance how much does he weigh?

5. A light rod of length 2 m has weights of 7 kg and 13 kg at each end. Where should it be pivoted if it is to balance?

6. A light rod of length 1.4 m is pivoted 0.5 m from one end. 4.5 kg is placed at the shorter end: how much weight should be put at the longer end to balance it?

7. A uniform beam of length 2 m and mass 50 kg is pivoted 0.8 m from one end. What weight should be put at the shorter end in order to balance it?

8. A non-uniform rod of length 2 m and mass 40 kg is such that its weight acts through a point 20 cm from the centre. If it is pivoted at its centre, what weight should be put at an end in order to balance it?

9. A uniform rod of mass 12 kg and length 1.6 m is smoothly hinged at one end. It is held horizontal by a force acting vertically at its free end. What is the force?

10. A uniform rod of mass 20 kg and length 2.4 m is smoothly hinged at one end. It is held horizontal by a force of 15g acting vertically. Where does the force act?

11. A uniform beam of mass 50 kg and length 2 m is held by two supports which act at 0.2 m from one end and 0.1 m from the other. Find the forces exerted by the supports.

12. A non-uniform beam of length 3 m is supported at both ends. The upthrusts from the supports are 30g N and 50g N. Where does the weight of the beam act?

13. A diving-board of mass 70 kg is a uniform plank of length 2 m. It is held in a horizontal position by a bar at one end above the plank, and a bar 0.25 m from the same end acting below the plank. Find the forces exerted by the bars.

14. A pipe of mass 50 g. is such that its weight acts through a point 8 cm from the mouthpiece. It is held horizontal by the upper and lower teeth of the smoker, which act 1 cm and 2 cm respectively from the mouthpiece. Find the forces exerted by the teeth.

26.2 Forces acting at an angle

Fig 26.5

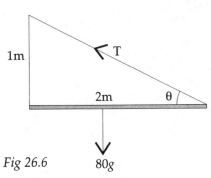

Suppose a lever is pivoted at A, and the force F acts at d from the pivot and makes an angle θ with the lever.

The moment of the force about the pivot is $Fd \sin \theta$. This can be though of as either of the following:

(a) Taking the component of the force which is perpendicular to the lever.

(b) Taking the perpendicular distance from the pivot to the line of action of the force.

26.2.1 Examples

1. A uniform plank of mass 80 kg and length 2 m is freely hinged at one end. It is held horizontal by a rope at the other end which is tied to a point 1 m above the hinge. Find the force in the rope.

Solution

The angle θ between the rope and the plank is $\tan^{-1} \frac{1}{2}$. Taking moments about the hinge:

$$80g \times 1 = T \times 2 \times \sin \theta$$

The force in the rope is 876.5 N

Fig 26.6

2. A uniform ladder of mass 20 kg and length 2 m leans on a rough floor against a smooth wall. If it makes 60° with the horizontal find the least possible coefficient of friction.

Solution

The forces are as shown in the diagram. Resolving vertically:

$$N = 20g$$

Resolving horizontally:

$$F = P$$

Taking moments about the base of the ladder:

$$20g \times 1 \times \cos 60° = P \times 2 \times \sin 60°$$

If friction is limiting, $F = \mu N$.

Fig 26.7

$$\mu = \frac{F}{N} = \frac{P}{N} = \frac{\cos 60°}{2 \sin 60°}$$

The coefficient of friction is 0.29

26.2.2 Exercises

1. Each of the diagrams below shows a uniform rod smoothly pivoted at one end. Each system is in equilibrium. Find the unknown forces.

Fig 26.8

2. Each of the diagrams below shows a non-uniform rod smoothly pivoted. Each system is in equilibrium. Find the unknown distances.

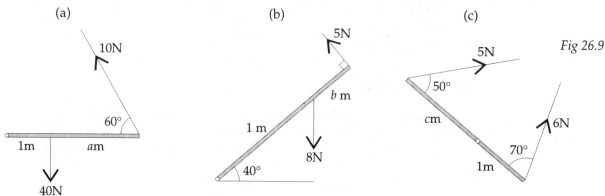

Fig 26.9

3. Each of the diagrams below shows a uniform rod, smoothly pivoted. The system is in equilibrium. Find the unknown angles.

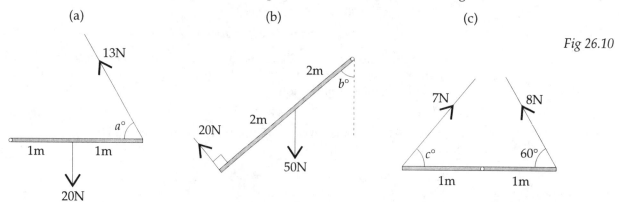

Fig 26.10

4. A light rod of length 1 m is freely hinged at one end. A vertical force of 2 N acts at the other end, and a horizontal force acts in the middle (see Fig 26.11). If the rod makes 30° with the vertical find the horizontal force.

5. A light rod of length 1 m is freely hinged at one end. A force of 12 N acts at the other end, making 20° with the vertical. What vertical force acting through the centre of the rod will keep it horizontal?

6. A light rod of length 1 m is freely hinged at one end. It makes 50° with the downward vertical, under the action of a horizontal force of 3 N through its other end and a vertical force through its centre. Find the vertical force.

7. A light rod of length 1 m is freely hinged at one end. A force of 5 N acts vertically up through its other end, and a force of 3 N acts horizontally through its centre away from the hinge. Find the angle the rod makes with the vertical.

Fig 26.11

8. A uniform plank of mass 10 kg and length 1.2 m is freely hinged at one end. It is held horizontal by a force at the other end acting at 35° to the vertical. Find the force.

9. A uniform plank of mass 10 kg and length 1.2 m is freely hinged at one end. It is held horizontal by a force of 70 N acting at the other end. Find the angle this force makes with the vertical.

10. A uniform plank of length 3 m rests on a rough floor against a smooth wall, making 70° with the horizontal. If it is about to slip find the coefficient of friction.

11. A uniform plank of mass 60 kg and length 3 m rests on a smooth floor against a smooth wall. If it is at 60° to the horizontal find the extra horizontal force at the base of the plank which will prevent it from slipping.

Fig 26.12

12. A uniform plank of mass 20 kg and length 2 m rests on a smooth floor and against a rough wall where the coefficient of friction is $\frac{1}{2}$. If it makes 60° with the horizontal find the least horizontal force at the base of the ladder which will prevent it from slipping.

13. A uniform ladder rests against a smooth wall and on a rough floor where the coefficient of friction is $\frac{1}{4}$. Find the greatest angle it can make with the vertical before it slips.

14. A uniform bar of length 1.2 m and mass 5 kg rests on a rough floor, its other end being held by a horizontal string (see Fig 26.12). If the bar makes 50° with the vertical find the force in the string and the least possible coefficient of friction.

26.3 Examination questions

1. A uniform straight plank AB, of mass 12 kg and length 2 m, rests horizontally on two supports, one at C and the other at D, where AC = CD = 0.6 m. A particle P of mass X kg is hung from B and the plank is on the point of tilting.

(a) Find the value of X.

The particle P is removed from B and hung from A.

(b) Find, in N, the magnitude of the force exerted on the plank at each support.

[L ADD]

2. A uniform ladder of length 6 m and mass 25 kg rests with one end in contact with a smooth vertical wall, and the other end on rough horizontal ground. The ladder is in a vertical plane perpendicular to the wall.

The lower end of the ladder is 1.5 m from the base of the wall, and the coefficient of friction between the ladder and the ground is 0.15.

A man of mass 110 kg ascends the ladder.

Draw a neat diagram showing clearly all of the forces acting on the ladder when the man is 1 m up the ladder.

Find how far along the ladder the man can ascend before the ladder starts to slip.

[NI ADD]

3. A uniform ladder of weight W is inclined at an angle α to the horizontal. Its foot rests on rough horizontal ground (coefficient of friction μ_1) and its top against a smooth vertical wall. Show that slipping will not occur provided

$$\tan \alpha \geq (2\mu_1)^{-1}.$$

(Note that the appearance of $\geq$ in this relation must be justified.)

The same ladder is now moved to lean against a rough vertical wall (coefficient of friction μ_2), with the coefficient of friction between the foot of the ladder and the horizontal ground still being μ_1. Show that the ladder is on the point of slipping when its angle of inclination to the horizontal is

$$\arctan\left(\frac{1-\mu_1\mu_2}{2\mu_1}\right).$$

[MEI]

4. AC is a fixed rough straight horizontal wire of length greater than 4a. A straight uniform rod AP of mass 4M and length 2a is smoothly jointed to the wire at A. The end P of the rod is attached by means of a light inelastic thread PB of length 2a to a bead B of mass M which can slide on the wire.

(a) The system is in equilibrium with $P\hat{A}B$ equal to θ. By taking moments about A for the rod AP, or otherwise, show that the tension in the string is $Mg/\sin \theta$. Find the frictional force at B and show that $\mu \geq \frac{1}{2}\cot \theta$, where μ is the coefficient of friction between the bead and the wire.

(b) With $P\hat{A}B = \theta$, suppose $\mu = \frac{1}{4}\cot \theta$ and that a horizontal force S applied at P in the plane APB keeps the system in equilibrium. If B is on the point of slipping towards A, show that the tension in the string is $Mg/(3 \sin \theta)$ and find the value of S.

(c) When $\hat{PAB} = \theta$, $\mu = \frac{1}{4}\cot\theta$ and no horizontal force is applied at P, what is the minimum value of the mass of B required to ensure equilibrium?

[W]

5. The diagram shows a uniform rod AB, of length $4a$ and weight $2W$, freely jointed at A to a vertical wall. A light inextensible string of length $4a$ joins B to the point C of the wall distant $4a$ vertically above A. A uniform disc of weight W and radius $a/\sqrt3$ rests in equilibrium touching the rod and wall. The points of contact are frictionless. Find

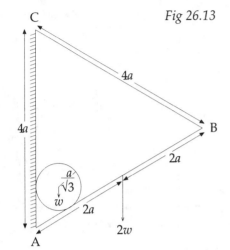

Fig 26.13

   (i) the magnitudes of the reactions of the wall and the rod on the disc;

   (ii) the tension in the string;

   (iii) the magnitude and direction of the reaction of the joint at A on the rod.

[SUJB]

Common errors

Taking moments

(a) State clearly the point about which you are taking moments. In general, the moment will depend on the point.

(b) The point about which you take moments does not have to be a fulcrum or pivot. If a body is in equilibrium then the sum of moments about any point is zero.

(c) If the force and the lever are not at right-angles to each other, then do not forget the factor of $\sin\theta$ when you are taking moments.

(d) The moment of a force about a point is the product of the force and the distance to the *line of action* of the force. It is not the product of the force and the distance to the *point of action* of the force.

27 Centre of gravity

The *centre of gravity* (*c.g.*) of a body is the point through which its weight may be supposed to act.

If a body is symmetrical about a line or a plane, then the c.g. must lie on that line or plane.

The centre of gravity of a body may be found by taking moments.

27.1 One dimensional problems

27.1.1 Examples

1. Masses of 1 kg, 3 kg and 5 kg lie at points (2,0), (4,0), (8,0) along the *x*-axis. Find the coordinates of the centre of gravity.

1kg	3kg		5kg
(2,0)	(4,0)		(8,0)

Fig 27.1

Solution

Let the c.g. be at ($\bar{x}$,0). Take moments about the origin:

$$\bar{x} \times (1 + 3 + 5) = 2 \times 1 + 4 \times 3 + 8 \times 5$$

The c.g. is at (6, 0)

2. A hammer consists of a head which is of mass 0.5 kg and height 3 cm, attached to a shaft which is of mass 0.1 kg and length 20 cm. The top of the shaft is flush with the top of the head. Find the position of the centre of gravity.

Fig 27.2

3cm

20cm

Solution

Let the c.g. be *x* cm from the top of the head. Taking moments about the top of the head:

$$x \times (0.5 + 0.1) = 1.5 \times 0.5 + 10 \times 0.1$$

The c.g. is $2\frac{11}{12}$ cm from the top of the head

27.1.2 Exercises

1. Find the c.g. of masses of 2 kg, 3 kg, 7 kg at $x = 3$, $x = 4$, $x = 6$ respectively.

2. Find the c.g. of masses of 1 kg, $1\frac{1}{2}$ kg, 2 kg at (−1,0), (0,0), (2,0).

3. A mass of 2 kg lies at (1,0). Another mass is at (−1,0), and their c.g. is at ($\frac{1}{2}$,0). Find the size of the second mass.

4. A mass of 3 kg lies at $x = 4$. A second mass of 2 kg is such that their centre of gravity is at $(-1,0)$. Find the position of the second mass.

5. A car aerial consist of four sections, each a uniform cylinder of length 10 cm, and masses 50 g, 45 g, 40 g, 35 g. Find the position of its centre of gravity when fully extended.

6. A fishing rod consists of three sections, each a uniform cylinder. The first is 1.2 m long and of mass 0.1 kg, the second 0.8 m and 0.06 kg, the third 0.5 m and 0.04 kg. Find the position of its c.g.

7. A lollipop consists of a disc of radius 3 cm and mass 50 g, on top of a stick which is 10 cm long and weighs 10 g. Find the position of the c.g.

8. A uniform plank is 2 m. long and weighs 20 kg. Edward, who weighs 50 kg sits at one end and Fiona, who weighs 40 kg sits at the other. Where is the centre of gravity?

9. In Question 8, where should Gordon (55 kg) sit, if the centre of gravity is to be at the centre of the plank?

10. Two solid cubes are made out of the same uniform material: one has side 20 cm and the other side 10 cm. If the smaller is placed symmetrically on top of the larger where is their centre of gravity?

11. A pencil of length 8 cm has the last 2 cm sharpened into a cone. Find the position of its c.g. (The c.g. of a cone of height h is $\frac{1}{4}h$ from its base.)

12. A solid hemisphere of radius 5 cm is placed on top of a solid cylinder of radius 5 cm and height 12 cm. If they are made out of the same material find the position of the c.g. (The c.g. of a solid hemisphere of radius a is $\frac{3}{8}a$ from the centre.)

13. A jar is made out of thin uniform metal, in the form of a cylinder with bottom but no top. Its radius is 3 cm and its height 8 cm. Find the position of its c.g.

14. A uniform disc of radius 10 cm has a disc of radius 1 cm cut out. The centres of the two discs are 3 cm apart. Find the c.g. of the remaining part.

15. A uniform solid sphere has radius 10 cm. A sphere of radius 1 cm is removed from the inside. The centres of the two spheres are 3 cm apart. Find the c.g. of the remaining solid.

27.2 Two and three dimensional problems

27.2.1 Example

The shape shown is made out of a uniform sheet of cardboard. Find the position of its centre of gravity. Give the answer in terms of coordinates, with the x-axis along the base and the y-axis up the side.

Solution

Divide the shape into two rectangles, one 6 by 2 and the other 6 by 1. The total area is 18 cm². Let the c.g. be at $(\bar{x}, \bar{y})$.

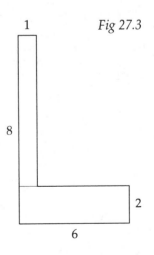

Fig 27.3

Taking moments about the x-axis:

$18 \times \bar{y} = 12 \times 1 + 6 \times 5$

$\bar{y} = 2\frac{1}{3}$

Similarly, taking moments about the y-axis:

$18 \times \bar{x} = 12 \times 3 + 6 \times \frac{1}{2}$

The c.g. is at $(2\frac{1}{6}, 2\frac{1}{3})$

27.2.2 Exercises

1. Masses of 1 kg, 3 kg, 6 kg are at (1,1), (2,3), (1,−1). Find the position of their c.g.

2. Masses of 3 kg, 2 kg, x kg are at (1,1), (3,1), (2,2). If their c.g. is at (1.9, 1.5) find x.

3. Masses of 4 kg and 5 kg are at (1,0) and (0,5). Where should a mass of 8 kg be placed to ensure that the c.g. is at (4,7)?

   In Questions 4 to 7 give the answers in terms of coordinates, with the x-axis along the base of the shape and the y-axis up the side.

4. Find the c.g.s of the following shapes:

(a)   (b)   (c)

Fig 27.4

5. A uniform wire of length 10 cm is bent in half into an L shape. Find the position of the c.g.

6. A uniform wire of length 12 cm is bent so that the base part is of length 7 cm and the side part of length 5 cm, and the two parts are at right angles to each other. Find the position of the c.g.

7. A uniform wire of length 20 cm is bent so that one part of length 12 cm lies along the base, and the other part of length 8 cm is at 45° to the other. Find the position of the c.g.

8. Masses of 4 kg, 3 kg and 5 kg are at (1,0,1), (2,3,2), (4,0,5). Find the position of the c.g.

9. Masses of 3 kg and 8 kg are at (1,1,1) and (2,−1,−2). Where should a mass of 1 kg be placed to ensure that the c.g. is at (4,5,6)?

27.3 Problems involving calculus

Fig 27.5

Suppose a uniform lamina occupies a region bounded by a curve and the x-axis, between $x = a$ and $x = b$. Then its c.g. is at $(\bar{x}, \bar{y})$, where:

$$\bar{x} \int_a^b y\, dx = \int_a^b xy\, dx$$

$$\bar{y} \int_a^b y\, dx = \int_a^b \tfrac{1}{2} y^2\, dx$$

Suppose a uniform solid occupies the region generated when a curve is rotated about the x-axis, from $x = a$ to $x = b$. Then its c.g. is at $(\bar{x}, 0)$, where:

$$\bar{x} \int_a^b \pi y^2\, dx = \int_a^b x\pi y^2\, dx$$

27.3.1 Examples

1. A uniform lamina occupies the region enclosed by the positive axes and the curve $y = 1 - x^2$. Find the position of the c.g.

    Solution

    Say the c.g. is at $(\bar{x}, \bar{y})$. The curve goes from $x = 0$ to $x = 1$. Apply the formula above:

    $$\bar{x} \int_0^1 (1 - x^2)\, dx = \int_0^1 x(1 - x^2)\, dx$$

    $$\bar{x} \times \tfrac{2}{3} = \tfrac{1}{4}$$

    $$\bar{x} = \tfrac{3}{8}$$

    Apply the formula above:

    $$\bar{y} \times \tfrac{2}{3} = \int_0^1 \tfrac{1}{2} y^2\, dx$$

    $$= \int_0^1 \tfrac{1}{2}(1 - x^2)^2\, dx$$

    $$\bar{y} \times \tfrac{2}{3} = \tfrac{4}{15}.$$

    $$\bar{y} = \tfrac{2}{5}.$$

Fig 27.6

The c.g. is at $(\tfrac{3}{8}, \tfrac{2}{5})$

2. The region of Example 1 is rotated about the y-axis. Find the c.g. of the solid of revolution.

    Solution

    By symmetry the c.g. lies on the y-axis. Say it is at $(0, \bar{y})$. Divide the solid into thin discs as shown. Taking moments about the x-axis:

Fig 27.7

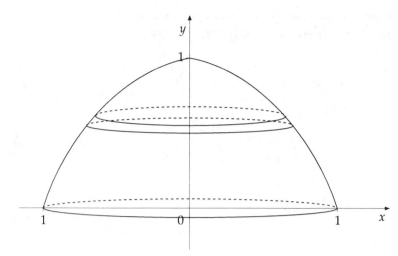

$$\bar{y} \int_0^1 \pi x^2 \, dy = \int_0^1 y\pi x^2 \, dy$$

$$\bar{y} \int_0^1 \pi(1-y) \, dy = \int_0^1 y\pi(1-y) \, dy$$

$$\bar{y} \times \tfrac{1}{2}\pi = \tfrac{1}{6}\pi$$

The c.g. is at $(0, \tfrac{1}{3})$

27.3.2 Exercises

1. A uniform lamina consists of the region enclosed by the x-axis, the line $x = 1$ and the curve $y = x^2$. Find the coordinates of its centre of gravity.

2. The shape of Question 1 is rotated about the x-axis. Find the centre of gravity of the solid of revolution.

3. A uniform lamina occupies the region enclosed by the positive axes and the curve $y = 1 - x^3$. Find its centre of gravity.

4. A uniform lamina occupies the region enclosed by the x-axis, the lines $x = 1$ and $x = 2$ and the curve $y = \dfrac{1}{x^2}$. Find its centre of gravity.

5. The area of Question 4 is rotated about the x-axis. Find the centre of gravity of the solid of revolution.

6. A uniform lamina occupies the region enclosed by the positive axes and the curve $y = 9 - x^2$. Find its centre of gravity.

7. The area of Question 6 is rotated about the y-axis. Find the centre of gravity of the solid of revolution.

8. The area of Question 6 is rotated about the x-axis. Find the centre of gravity of the solid of revolution.

9. A triangle of height h and base $2a$ is enclosed by the region between the lines $y = \dfrac{xa}{h}$, $y = -\dfrac{xa}{h}$, $x = h$. Show that its centre of gravity is at $(\tfrac{2}{3}h, 0)$.

10. A cone of height h and base radius a is formed by rotating the triangle of Question 9 about the x-axis. Show that the centre of gravity of the cone is at $(\frac{3}{4}h, 0)$.

11. A semicircular disc of radius a is contained by the x-axis and the circle $y = \sqrt{(a^2 - x^2)}$. Find its centre of gravity.

12. A hemisphere of radius a is obtained by rotating the disc of Question 11 about the y-axis. Find its centre of gravity.

27.4 Statics problems

When a body is suspended, its centre of gravity is directly below the point of suspension.

A body is about to topple when its centre of gravity is above the edge about which it will topple.

The c.g.s of some simple uniform laminas and solids are as below. Where relevant, the height of the object is h, and its radius is a.

TRIANGLE

Along medians, $\frac{1}{3}h$ from base.

SEMICIRCLE

$\dfrac{4a}{3\pi}$ from centre.

CONE AND PYRAMID

$\frac{1}{4}h$ from base.

SOLID HEMISPHERE

$\frac{3}{8}a$ from centre.

HOLLOW HEMISPHERE

$\frac{1}{2}a$ from centre.

27.4.1 Examples

1. A uniform semi-circular disc is hung from one end of the bounding diameter. Find the angle the diameter makes with the vertical.

   Solution

   The c.g. of the disc must be below the point of suspension.

   $$\tan \theta = \frac{4a}{3\pi} \frac{1}{a} = \frac{4}{3\pi}$$

   The angle is $23°$

2. A cone of height 8 and base radius 3 rests with its base on a rough plane. The plane is gradually tilted: what angle will the plane make when the cone topples?

Fig 27.8

Fig 27.9

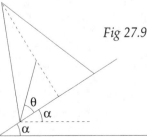

Solution

The angle θ is found from $\tan \theta = \dfrac{\frac{1}{4} \times 8}{3}$.

$\theta = 33.7°$

The cone topples when the c.g. is above the edge A. For this to be true:

$\alpha + \theta = 90°$.

The angle of tilt is $56.3°$

27.4.2 Exercises

1. A uniform lamina consists of a rectangle of sides 6 cm and 8 cm. It is hung from one corner: find the angle made by the longer side with the vertical.

2. A uniform lamina consists of a rectangle, one of whose sides is 10 cm. When the lamina is hung from one corner this side makes 23° with the vertical. Find the other side of the rectangle.

3. A uniform lamina is a square ABCD of mass $5m$. Masses of $m, 2m, 3m, 4m$ are placed at A, B, C, D respectively. If it is hung from A find the angle which AB makes with the vertical.

4. A lamina is in the shape of an isosceles triangle with sides 8, 8, 3. It is suspended from one of the base angles. Find the angle between the base side and the vertical.

5. A wire ABC of length 10 cm is bent into an L shape, where AB = 6, BC = 4 and ABC = 90°. If it is suspended from A find the angle AB makes with the vertical.

6. A uniform cube is placed on a rough plane, which is gradually tilted. Find the angle of the plane when the cube starts to topple.

7. A uniform cuboid with square base of side 4 cm is placed with its base in contact with a rough plane. The plane is gradually tilted, and the cuboid topples when the plane is at 20°. Find the height of the cuboid.

8. A uniform cylinder of height 10 cm is placed with its base on a rough plane. The plane is gradually tilted, and when it is at 40° the cylinder topples. Find the base radius of the cylinder.

27.5 Examination questions

1. A thin uniform wire, of length 40 cm, is bent to form the sides of a right-angled triangle ABC in which AB = 8 cm, BC = 15 cm and CA = 17 cm.

    (a) Show that the centre of mass of the triangular wire is at a distance 6 cm from AB and at a distance 2.5 cm from BC.

    The vertex B is smoothly hinged to a fixed point so that the triangular wire can rotate freely in a vertical plane about B.

    (b) Find, to the nearest degree, the acute angle made by BC with the vertical when the wire rests in equilibrium.

    [L ADD]

2. A uniform solid right circular cone has height h and base of radius r and centre O. From this cone, there is removed a solid right circular cone with the same base but having vertex V, where OV = kh $(0 < k < 1)$. Find the distance of G, the centre of gravity of the remaining body, from O.

   For what value of k will G coincide with V?

   [O&C]

Fig 27.10

3. Three uniform triangular laminas, AOB. BOC, COD, each in the form of an equilateral triangle of side a, have masses m, $2m$, $3m$ respectively. A composite lamina is formed by joining the triangles together along the edges OB, OC (see diagram) so that AOD is a straight line. Using the axes Ox, Oy, shown in Fig 27.10, find the coordinates of the centre of mass of the composite lamina.

   The composite lamina is free to move in a vertical plane about a smooth horizontal axis at C and is maintained in equilibrium with D vertically above C by a vertical force acting at A. Find, in terms of m and g, the magnitude of this force.

   [C]

4. Prove that the centroid of a uniform hemispherical shell of radius a is at a distance $\dfrac{a}{2}$ from O, the centre of the circular rim of the shell.

   A toy tower is constructed of thin uniform sheet metal and consists of a right circular cylinder, with open ends, of height h and radius r, where $h > r$, covered by a hemispherical cap of radius r. Show that for such a tower the centre of gravity is at a distance x from the ground, where

   $$\overline{x} = \tfrac{1}{2}(h + r).$$

   The tower is suspended from a string which is attached to a point on the rim of the hemispherical cap. Show that, when the tower hangs in equilibrium, the axis of symmetry of the tower is inclined at an angle α to the horizontal, where

   $$\tan \alpha = \frac{h - r}{2r}.$$

   [L]

5. Show that the area A of the region in the first quadrant bounded by the axes and the curve whose equation is $\dfrac{x^2}{a^2} + \dfrac{y^2}{b^2} = 1$ satisfies

   $$A = \frac{b}{a} \int_0^a \sqrt{(a^2 - x^2)}\, dx$$

   By means of the substitution $x = a \sin \theta$, or otherwise, show that $A = \tfrac{1}{4}\pi ab$.

   The centre of mass of a uniform lamina in the shape of this region is the point with coordinates $(\overline{x}, \overline{y})$. Show by integration that

   $$\overline{x} = \frac{4a}{3\pi}.$$

   Deduce, or obtain otherwise, the value of $\overline{y}$.

   This lamina is suspended freely from the origin and hangs at rest under gravity. Find the tangent of the angle between the vertical and the edge of the lamina of length a.

   [MEI]

Common errors

1. Make full use of symmetry. The c.g. must lie on a line of symmetry: do not waste time by ignoring this.

2. When using calculus to find centres of gravity, make sure that you do not try to integrate a function of x with respect to y. That is, do not try to evaluate $\int f(x)\, dy$. Write f(x) in terms of y and then integrate.

28 Miscellaneous statics

28.1 Couples

If a system of forces has zero resultant, but does have a turning effect, then it is called a *couple*.

The simplest couple consists of two equal and opposite forces.

The moment of a couple about a point is the same for all points.

The *sense* of a couple is either clockwise or anti-clockwise, depending on the way in which it tends to turn the system.

28.1.1 Examples

Fig 28.1

1. A table ABCD is a square of side 1.4 m. Forces of 2 N, 3 N, 2 N, 3 N act along AB, BC, CD, DA respectively. Show that the forces form a couple, and find its moment.

   Solution

   The force along AB balances that along CD. The force along BC balances that along DA. Hence the system has zero resultant.

   Taking moments about A:

   Moment = $3 \times 1.4 + 2 \times 1.4$

   The moment of the couple is 7 Nm.

Fig 28.2

2. A trapdoor is a uniform square of side 0.8 m. and mass 2 kg. It is hinged along one side, and it can just stay open at 20° to the vertical. Find the couple exerted by the hinge.

   Solution

   The forces are as shown. The door is about to fall clockwise, so the couple C is anti-clockwise. Taking moments about the hinge:

   $C = 2g \times 0.4 \times \sin 20°$

   The couple of the hinge is 2.68 Nm.

28.1.2 Exercises

1. In each of the diagrams below show that the forces form a couple and find its moment.

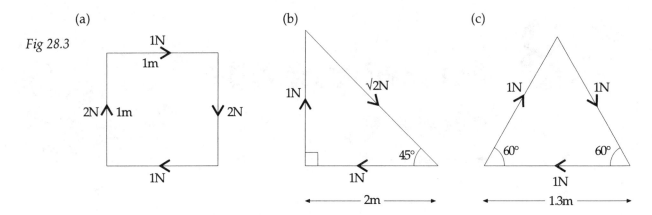

(a)   (b)   (c)

Fig 28.3

2. The forces in each of the diagrams below form a couple. Find the unknown forces, and find the moments of the couples.

(a)   (b)   (c)

Fig 28.4

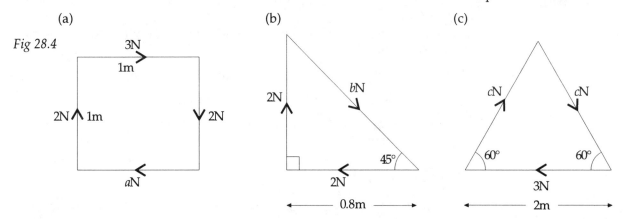

3. ABCD is a square of side 2 m. Forces of 2 N, 3 N and 5 N act along AB, AC, AD respectively. Find the forces along CD and CB which will ensure that the system is a couple, and find its moment.

4. A spanner of length 10 cm can just turn a nut when a force of 150 N is applied to its end. Find the couple exerted by the nut.

5. A stiff tap can just be turned when forces of 20 N are applied at two points 3 cm from its axis. Find the couple that these forces exert.

6. An inn-sign is a uniform square of side 0.6 m and mass 3 kg. It is hinged along its top, and will just rest at 25° to the vertical. Find the couple at the hinges.

7. What is the least horizontal force applied to the base of the inn-sign of Question 6 which will hold it at 40° to the vertical?

8. What is the least horizontal force applied to the base of the inn-sign of Question 6 which will raise it when it is 35° to the vertical?

28.2 Equivalent systems

A system of forces acting in a plane is equivalent either to a single force or to a single couple.

28.2.1 Example

ABCD is a square of side 1 m, and forces of 3 N, 2 N, 2 N act along AB, DC, AC respectively. Show that these forces are equivalent to a single force, and find where the line of action of this force crosses BC.

Show also that the system is equivalent to a force through A and a couple G, which is to be found.

Fig 28.5

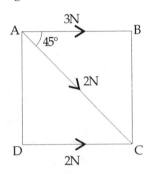

Solution

The force is the resultant of the three forces. Letting F_1 and F_2 be the components of the resultant parallel to AB and BC respectively:

$F_1 = 3 + 2 + 2\cos 45°: F_2 = 2\sin 45°.$

Use Pythagoras and trigonometry to find the resultant.

> The force is 6.57 N at 12° to AB

Suppose the resultant cuts BC at x m from C. Take moments about C. (Only the component of the resultant parallel to AB need be considered.)

$6.414 \times x = 3 \times 1$

> The resultant cuts BC at 0.47 m from C

Suppose instead that the resultant acts through A. Then the extra couple required is found by taking moments about A.

$G = 2 \times 1$

> The couple is 2 Nm

28.2.2 Exercises

1. Both of the following are squares of side 1 m. In both cases find the equivalent force, and the point at which it crosses AB.

    (a)   (b)

Fig 28.6

2. ABCD is a square of side 2 m. Forces of 3 N, 4 N and 5 N act along AB, BC and AC respectively. Find the equivalent force and where it crosses AB.

3. Forces of 2**i**, 3**i**, 4**j** act at the points A(1,0), B(2,0) and C(3,0) respectively. Find the equivalent force and where it crosses the *x*-axis.

4. ABC is a triangle, with AB = AC = 5 cm, BC = 4 cm. Forces of 3 N, 4 N, 7 N act along AB, AC, BC respectively. Find the equivalent force and where it crosses BC.

5. ABCD is a rectangle, AB = 6 cm and AD = 8 cm. Forces of 2 N, 4 N and 5 N act along AB, AD, BD respectively. Find the equivalent single force, and where it crosses AB.

    Show that the system is equivalent to a force through A and a couple, which is to be found.

6. Forces of **i**, 4**j**, 2**i** - 3**j** act through the points A(0,1), B(3,0), C(1,0) respectively. Find the single equivalent force, and where it crosses the *y*-axis.

    Show that the system is equivalent to a force through the origin and a couple, which is to be found.

28.3 Three forces in equilibrium

If there are exactly three forces acting on a body, then either they are all parallel or else they all go through the same point.

This can sometimes be used to solve problems in statics. The method is particularly powerful when combined with the use of the angle of friction.

28.3.1 Example

Fig 28.7

A uniform ladder rests against a smooth wall and on a rough floor. It is about to slip when it makes 30° with the vertical. Find the coefficient of friction.

Solution

The forces are as shown in Fig 28.7. Combine the normal reaction and the friction into a single resultant R making λ with the normal.

The three forces must meet, at the point above the centre of the ladder.

$$\tan \lambda = \frac{AB}{AE} = \frac{\frac{1}{2} \times AC}{AE} = \tfrac{1}{2}\tan 30°.$$

The coefficient of friction is $\tan \lambda = \dfrac{1}{2\sqrt{3}} = 0.289$

28.3.2 Exercises

All these questions can be solved by the method of this section.

1. A non-uniform rod of length 2 m hangs horizontally from two strings, one at each end, which make 40° and 50° with the horizontal. Find the position of the centre of gravity of the rod.

2. A uniform rod of length 2 m hangs from two strings, one at each end, which make 30° and 60° with the rod. Show that the point of suspension must be 1 m above the midpoint of the rod. Hence find the angle to the horizontal of the rod.

3. A uniform bar AB is jointed at A to a wall. It is held horizontal by a string attached to B, which is fixed to a point of the wall above A so that the string makes 70° with the vertical. Find the direction of the reaction at the joint.

4. A uniform bar AB of length 1 m is held horizontal with A against a rough wall, and with a string B of length 2 m fixed to a point on the wall vertically above A. Find the least possible coefficient of friction between A and the wall.

5. A uniform bar AB is hinged at A to a wall. A string is attached to B and makes 90° with the rod. If the bar is raised to 20° above the horizontal find the direction of the reaction at A.

6. A uniform bar AB is hinged at A to a wall, and B is attached to a string which is perpendicular to the bar. If the bar is at 45° below the horizontal find the direction of the reaction between A and the wall.

7. A uniform bar AB rests with A on a smooth slope of angle 30°. It is held horizontal by a string attached to B. Find the angle that the string makes with the vertical.

8. A uniform bar AB rests with A on rough ground, and B is attached to a string which is perpendicular to the bar. If the bar makes 10° with the ground find the least coefficient of friction between A and the ground.

9. Two smooth planes of angles 40° and 50° meet in a horizontal line. A non-uniform bar of length 2 m lies horizontally on the planes. Find the position of the centre of gravity of the bar.

10. Two rough planes of angles 30° and 60° meet in a horizontal line. A uniform bar rests horizontally on the planes. If it is on the point of slipping find the angle of friction between the bar and the planes.

11. A uniform ladder rests on rough ground against a smooth wall. If it is about to slip when it makes 50° with the horizontal find the coefficient of friction.

12. A uniform ladder rests on rough ground against a smooth wall. The coefficient of friction is $\frac{1}{2}$. Find the greatest angle the ladder can make with the vertical.

13. A uniform ladder of mass 50 kg rests on rough ground against a smooth wall. The coefficient of friction is $\frac{1}{2}$. If it is at 40° to the vertical find how far up the ladder a 50 kg man can safely ascend.

28.4 Light frameworks

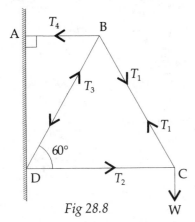

Fig 28.8

A system of light rods smoothly jointed together is a *light framework*.

For each rod, the reactions at each end are equal and opposite and act along the line of the rod.

If the rod is being compressed, it is under *thrust*. If it is being stretched it is under *tension*.

28.4.1 Example

The light framework shown supports a load of *W*. All the angles concerned are 90°, 60° or 30°. Find the force in each rod, indicating whether it is tension or thrust.

Solution

Let the forces in BC, CD, BD and AB be T_1, T_2, T_3 and T_4 respectively.

Resolving vertically at C, $T_1 \sin 60° = W$.

Resolving horizontally at C, $T_2 = T_1 \cos 60°$.

Taking moments about D, $Wa = T_4\, a \cos 30°$. (BD = a)

Resolving vertically at B, $T_3 \cos 30° = T_1 \cos 30°$.

The results are:

$$T_1 = \tfrac{2}{\sqrt{3}}\, W, \text{ tension.}$$
$$T_2 = \tfrac{1}{\sqrt{3}}\, W, \text{ thrust.}$$
$$T_3 = \tfrac{2}{\sqrt{3}}\, W, \text{ thrust.}$$
$$T_4 = \tfrac{2}{\sqrt{3}}\, W, \text{ tension.}$$

28.4.2 Exercises

For each of the following light frameworks, find the forces in the rods, indicating which are thrusts and which tensions.

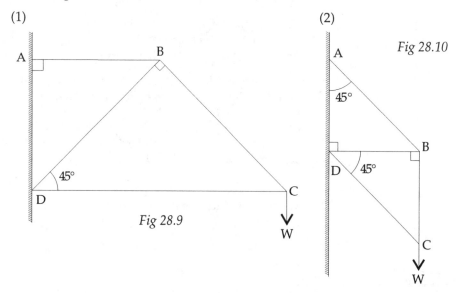

(1)

Fig 28.9

(2)

Fig 28.10

In Questions 3 to 5 A and B are resting on smooth supports.

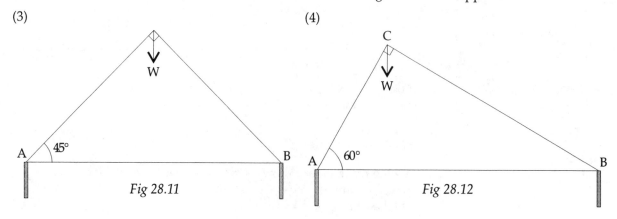

(3)

Fig 28.11

(4)

Fig 28.12

(5)

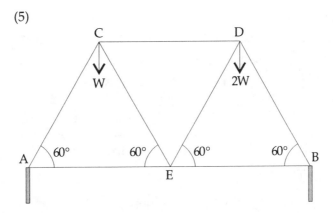

Fig 28.13

28.5 Examination questions

1. A uniform rod AB, of mass 0.5 kg and length 0.4 m, is held at an angle of 30° to the upward vertical by means of a frictional couple applied to the lower end A. Calculate, in Nm, the magnitude of this couple.

   [L ADD]

2. *In this question the unit of distance is the metre.*

   A rectangle OABC has vertices at (0,0), (4,0), (4,3) and (0,3) respectively. Forces of magnitudes 2, 4, 5, 3 and 6 N act along OA, BA, BC, OC and AC respectively, the directions being indicated by the order of the letters. The system is equivalent to a force **R**, acting through O together with a couple G. Calculate

   (a) the magnitude and direction of **R**,

   (b) the equation of the line of action of **R**,

   (c) the magnitude and sense of G, stating the units in which your answer is measured.

   [AEB ADD 1986]

3. Forces of magnitude 2N, 4N, and 4N act in the sense indicated by the letters along the sides AB, BC, CA respectively of an equilateral triangle ABC of side 2 m. Find the magnitude and direction of their resultant and the point where its line of action cuts AC produced.

   This system is to be reduced to equilibrium by the addition of a couple in the plane ABC and a force which acts through A. Find the magnitude and direction of the force and the magnitude and sense of the couple.

   [L]

4. A rectangle ABCD with AB = 2*a* and BC = *a* has forces 6, 3, 2 and P newtons acting along AB, BC, CD and AD in directions indicated by the letters. If the resultant passes through the midpoint of AB find

   (i)   the value of P;

   (ii) the magnitude of the resultant;

   (iii) the distance from C where the line of action of the resultant meets CD.

   The force in AD is reduced to zero. Find at what distance from A the line of action of the new resultant force meets AB. If the rectangle were free to move in its own plane about A what would be the sense and moment of the couple necessary to prevent motion?

   [SUJB]

Common errors

1. **Equivalent systems**

    (a) If a force is said to act along AB, then it acts from A to B. Do not get this the wrong way round.

    (b) A system of forces in a plane can be reduced to either a force *or* a couple. (Not both). If, however, the resultant force must go through a fixed point, then the system is equivalent to that force *and* a couple.

2. **Three forces**

    The rule about forces meeting at a point applies if there are only three forces acting. If there are four or more forces then they may not go through the same point.

29 Work, energy, power

29.1 Work and energy

WORK

If the point of action of a force F moves a distance d in the direction of the force, then the *work* done is Fd. A force of 1 newton acting over 1 metre does 1 joule (J) of work.

A kJ (kilojoule) is a thousand Joules.

If the force $\mathbf{F}$ and the distance $\mathbf{d}$ are vectors which are not parallel then the work done is the scalar product of the force and the distance.

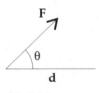

Fig 29.1

$$\text{Work done} = |\mathbf{F}|\,|\mathbf{d}|\cos\theta,$$

where θ is the angle between $\mathbf{F}$ and $\mathbf{d}$.

This is the scalar product of $\mathbf{F}$ and $\mathbf{d}$, $\mathbf{F}.\mathbf{d}$.

ENERGY

Energy is the capacity for doing work.

If a body of mass m is raised through a height of h, it gains *potential energy* (P.E.).

$$\text{P.E.} = mgh.$$

If a body of mass m is moving with speed v, it has *kinetic energy* (K.E.).

$$\text{K.E.} = \tfrac{1}{2}mv^2.$$

The work done by forces on a body is equal to the increase in its kinetic and potential energies.

If no work is done by external forces on a body, then the sum of its potential and kinetic energy is constant.

29.1.1 Examples

1. A car of mass 500 kg brakes to a halt from 20 m s⁻¹ over a horizontal distance of 40 m. Assuming that the braking force is constant, how far would it take to brake to rest from 30 m s⁻¹?

Solution

If the braking force is F N, then the loss of kinetic energy is equal to the work done by the brakes.

$F \times 40 = \frac{1}{2} \times 500 \times 20^2$

$F = 2{,}500$

If it travels d m to brake from 30 m s^{-1}:

$2{,}500 \times d = \frac{1}{2} \times 500 \times 30^2$

The braking distance is 90 m

2.   A roller-coaster starts from rest at its highest point. If resistances are ignored, how fast is it going at its lowest point 20 m below?

Solution

Suppose it moves at v m s^{-1} at the lowest point. The loss of potential energy is equal to the gain in kinetic energy.

$\frac{1}{2}mv^2 = m \times 9.8 \times 20$

It is travelling at 19.8 m s^{-1}

29.1.2 Exercises

1.   A force of 12 N moves through a distance of 5 m. Find the work done.

2.   A force of 8 N performs work of 80 J. Find the distance through which it has moved.

3.   A force performs 0.3 J by moving through 0.1 m. Find the force.

4.   Find the potential energy gained by:
     (a) 2 kg raised through 10 m   (b) 2.5 kg raised through 1 m
     (c) 3 grams raised through 12 cm   (d) 5 kg falling through 2 m

5.   Find the kinetic energy of the following:
     (a) 2 kg moving at 3 m s^{-1} (b) 500 kg moving at 30 m s^{-1}

6.   A constant force acts for 2 m, and accelerates a mass of 3 kg from rest to $1\frac{1}{2}$ m s^{-1}. What is the force?

7.   A force of 12 N acts on a body of mass 3 kg. How far will it have to act to accelerate it to 7 m s^{-1} from rest?

8.   What force is needed to stop in 4 m a mass of 25 kg moving at 10 m s^{-1}?

9.   A car of mass 600 kg slows down from 20 m s^{-1} to 10 m s^{-1} over a distance of 60 m. What force, assumed constant, has achieved this?

10. A car of mass 400 kg travelling at 15 m s^{-1} experiences a force in its direction of motion of 2,000 N. How fast is it travelling after 40 m?

11. A body falls freely. How fast is it going after falling 10 m from rest?

12. A body slides down a smooth slope of angle 20°. If it starts at rest, how fast is it going after moving 2 m?

13. A body is thrown up at 12 m s^{-1}. How high is it when it is moving at 4 m s^{-1}?

14. A body is thrown downwards at 5 m s^{-1}. What is its speed when it has travelled 6 m?

15. A body is projected up a smooth slope of angle 30° at 2 m s^{-1}. How far does it go before it comes to rest?

16. A body of mass 2 kg is projected at 10 m s^{-1} up a slope of angle 30°, where the resistance to motion is 4 N. How far does it go before it comes to rest?

17. A body of mass 6 kg is projected at 12 m s^{-1} down a slope of angle 20° against a resistance of 3 N. What is its speed after it has travelled 20 m?

18. A particle of mass 1.5 kg hangs from a light string of length 2 m, the other end of which is fixed. The string is held horizontal and released. Find the speed of the particle at the bottom of the swing.

19. A particle of mass 0.6 kg hangs from a light string of length 1.2 m. The string is held at 20° to the vertical. Find the speed of the particle at the bottom of the swing.

20. A particle of mass 0.5 kg hangs at the end of a light string of length 1 m. It is given a horizontal velocity of 0.5 m s^{-1}. Find the height it reaches, and hence the greatest angle which the string makes with the vertical.

In Questions 21 – 23 the unit of distance is the metre.

21. A force of 2**i** + 3**j** N moves from the point (2,7) to (4,12). Find the work done.

22. A force of **i** – 3**j** + 2**k** N moves from (1,2,3) to (4,0,5). Find the work done.

23. A body of mass 2 kg is constrained to move along the line $y = x + 3$. It is acted upon by a force of 3**i** + 4**j** N. Ignoring the effect of gravity, find its speed after it has moved from (0,3) to (2,5).

29.2 Power

Power is the rate of doing work. A power of 1 joule per second is 1 watt. (W).

A thousand watts is a kilowatt. (kW).

If the point of action of a force F is moving at speed v then the power is given by

$$\text{Power} = Fv.$$

29.2.1 Examples

1. A car of mass 500 kg drives up a slope of 5° against a resistance of 300 N at a constant speed of 15 m s^{-1}. Find the power developed by the car.

   Solution

   The car has to work against the resistance and the component of its weight down the slope.

   Total Force = $300 + 500g \sin 5°$

   Using the equation: Power = Force × Velocity:

   $P = (300 + 500g \sin 5°) \times 15$

   The power is 10,900 W

2. A pump raises water through 10 m and expels it at 5 m s⁻¹. If the power of the pump is 2,000 W find the volume of water it ejects each second.

   Solution

   Let the volume ejected per second be V litres. Every second V kg is raised through 10 m and given a velocity of 5 m s⁻¹. The work done per second is therefore:

   $$\tfrac{1}{2}V(5)^2 + V \times 10 \times 9.8 = 2{,}000$$

   The volume per second is 18 litres

29.2.2 Exercises

1. A body is dragged at 2 m s⁻¹ against a resistance of 200 N. Find the power.

2. Find the velocity with which a power of 100 W can overcome a resistance of 50 N.

3. A mass of 12 kg is raised at 0.5 m s⁻¹. Find the power needed.

4. A 70 kg man climbs up a rope at 0.5 m s⁻¹. What power is he exerting?

5. A pump raises 20 kg of water per second through 5 m. Find its power.

6. A hose emits 10 kg of water each second at 7 m s⁻¹. Find its power.

7. A hose which exerts 1,000 W of power emits 10 kg of water per second. Find the velocity of the water.

8. A 70 kg man runs up a 10° slope at 5 m s⁻¹. Find his power.

9. A 60 kg man can exert 300 W of power. How fast can he run up a 5° slope?

10. A car of mass 400 kg can exert 4,000 W. If resistances are 250 N what is its maximum speed? What is its acceleration at half the maximum speed?

11. What is the maximum speed at which the car of Question 10 can ascend a slope of 4°? (The resistance is the same.)

12. What is the steepest hill which the car of Question 10 can ascend at 6 m s⁻¹?

13. A car of mass 400 kg experiences resistance which is $20v$, where v is its velocity. If its maximum speed on level ground is 20 m s⁻¹ find its power.

14. Find the maximum speed of the car of Question 13 up a slope of 5°.

15. Find the maximum speed of the car of Question 13 down a slope of 7°.

16. Find the acceleration of the car of Question 13 when it is travelling at 10 m s⁻¹ along level ground.

17. Find the acceleration of the car of Question 13 when it is travelling up a slope of 4° at 5 m s⁻¹.

18. A force of 2**i** + 5**j** moves from (2,5) to (4,7) in 3 seconds. Find the power of the force.

19. A body of mass 3 kg is constrained to move along the line $y = 2x - 3$. A force of 3**i** + 2**j** N acts upon it, and it moves with constant speed 2 m s⁻¹. Ignoring the effect of gravity find the power of the force.

29.3 Examination questions

1. The total mass of a cyclist and his machine is 140 kg. The cyclist rides along a horizontal road against a constant total resistance of magnitude 50 N. Find, in J, the total work done in increasing his speed from 6 m s^{-1} to 9 m s^{-1} whilst travelling a distance of 30 m.

    [L ADD]

2. (a) A pump forces water through a nozzle so as to produce a vertical jet. The mass of water emitted per second is 0.24 kg and the power output of the pump is 7.68 W. Find the height of the jet and the speed with which the water leaves the nozzle.

    (b) A goods vehicle works at a constant power output of 200 kW. Its maximum speed on a horizontal road is 20 m s^{-1}. Calculate the total resistance to motion.

    The vehicle now travels up a slope whose inclination to the horizontal is α, where $\sin \alpha = \frac{4}{15}$. Given that the mass of the vehicle is 2.5×10^3 kg, and that the resistance to motion is unchanged, calculate

    (i) the acceleration of the vehicle when its speed is 8 m s^{-1},

    (ii) the greatest possible speed of the vehicle.

    [C ADD]

3. In this question take g = 10 m s^{-2}.

    The resistance to motion of a motor car is a constant force of R newtons. The engine of the car can work at rates up to 40 kW.

    (i) If the maximum speed that the car can maintain on a straight, level road is 144 km h^{-1}, calculate the value of R.

    (ii) The car accelerates from rest up a hill of inclination θ to the horizontal where $\sin \theta = \frac{1}{15}$. The mass of the car is 1200 kg and the total mass of the driver and passengers is 400 kg. If the engine is working at maximum power, calculate the acceleration when the speed of the car is 36 km h^{-1}.

    (iii) Calculate the total mass of driver and passengers which would just cause the car to freewheel from rest down this hill.

    [NI ADD]

4. [In this question the effect of gravity may be neglected.]

    A small ring, of unit mass, is threaded on a fixed smooth straight wire which passes through the points A(1,–2,3) and B(4,0,–3). The ring moves under the action of a force **F**, where **F** = 2**i** – 8**j** – 18**k**, and starts from rest at A. Show that the work done by **F** in moving the ring from A to B is 98 units, and find the speed of the ring at B.

    The force **F** has two components, **F**$_1$ in the direction of $\underline{AB}$ and **F**$_2$ perpendicular to $\underline{AB}$. Find

    (i) **F**$_1$ and **F**$_2$

    (ii) the reaction, **R**, of the wire on the ring.

    [JMB]

5. The frictional resistance to the motion of a train is k times the combined weight of the engine and its coach. An engine of mass M works at a constant power P and attains a maximum speed U when pulling a coach of mass M up a hill of inclination α to the horizontal. Down the same hill with a coach of mass $\frac{1}{2}M$, the engine can attain a maximum speed $2U$.

Show that P is $\dfrac{12kgUM}{5}$.

The engine pulls a coach of mass $1.5M$ on level ground. Find the acceleration of the train when the speed is $\frac{1}{5}U$ and show that the maximum speed is $\frac{24}{25}U$.

[C]

6. Take the acceleration due to gravity to be 10 m s^{-2}.

A small curtain ring of mass 0.5 kg is moving with constant velocity along a rough horizontal rail, and the coefficient of friction between the ring and the rail is 0.3. The motion is caused by a girl pulling on a light inextensible cord which is attached to the ring and which lies in the same vertical plane as the rail. Given that the cord makes an acute angle θ with the downward vertical and that the girl pulls the cord with tension T N, show that

(a) $T = \dfrac{1.5}{\sin \theta - 0.3 \cos \theta}$ (b) $\tan \theta > 0.3$.

The girl suddenly doubles her pull to $2T$ N without changing θ. Show that the ring then moves with acceleration 3 m s^{-2}.

Given that the ring's initial velocity was 1 m s^{-1} and assuming that it continues to slide along the rail with acceleration 3 m s^{-2} with the tension unaltered at $2T$ N, find, in terms of θ, the work W J done by the girl during the first second of accelerated motion, and show that $W > 7.5$.

[AEB 1986]

Common errors

1. Work done is the product of force and *distance*. It is not the product of force and *time*.

2. Force and distance can only be multiplied together directly if they are in the same direction. If they are not parallel there is an extra factor of cos θ, where θ is the angle between them. In particular, if the force is perpendicular to the distance moved, then no work at all is done.

30 Relative velocity

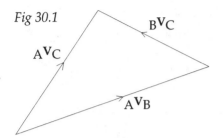

Fig 30.1

The velocity of A as seen by B is the *relative velocity* of A to B. It is written as $_A\mathbf{v}_B$. Relative velocities are combined by the rule:

$$_A\mathbf{v}_B = {_A\mathbf{v}_C} - {_B\mathbf{v}_C}$$

These vectors may be added either by a vector triangle or by components.

30.1 Calculation of relative velocity

30.1.1 Examples

1. A moves with velocity $3\mathbf{i} + 2\mathbf{j}$. B moves with velocity $\mathbf{i} - 4\mathbf{j}$. Find the magnitude of the relative velocity of A to B.

   Solution

   Use the formula above.

   $$_A\mathbf{v}_B = (3\mathbf{i} + 2\mathbf{j}) - (\mathbf{i} - 4\mathbf{j}) = 2\mathbf{i} + 6\mathbf{j}$$

   Use Pythagoras to find the magnitude of this vector.

   The relative velocity has magnitude $\sqrt{(2^2 + 6^2)} = \sqrt{40} = 6.32$

2. A man can row at 5 km h^{-1} in still water. A river is flowing at 3 km h^{-1}. Where should he steer in order to reach a point which is directly opposite?

   Solution

   He wants to travel along PQ. He must row so that his velocity relative to the bank is along the line PQ. Let M, B and R stand for Man, Bank and River respectively. Use the formula:

   $$_M\mathbf{v}_B = {_M\mathbf{v}_R} + {_R\mathbf{v}_B}$$

   Construct a vector triangle of velocities as shown.

Fig 30.2

Fig 30.3

$\sin \theta = \frac{3}{5}$

He should row at 37° to the line directly across the river.

213

30.1.2 Exercises

Where relevant, **i** and **j** are unit vectors along the x and y axes respectively

1. A moves at $\mathbf{i} + 3\mathbf{j}$, and B moves at $3\mathbf{i} + 2\mathbf{j}$. Find the magnitude of the relative velocity of A to B, and the angle it makes with the x-axis.

2. A moves at $3\mathbf{i} - 4\mathbf{j}$ and B moves at $2\mathbf{i} + \mathbf{j}$. Find the magnitude of the relative velocity of A to B, and the angle it makes with the x-axis.

3. A moves at $2\mathbf{i} - 7\mathbf{j}$, and the relative velocity of A to B is $3\mathbf{i} + 2\mathbf{j}$. Find the velocity of B in vector form. Find its magnitude and direction.

4. Ship A sails at 12 km h^{-1} on a bearing of 030°, and ship B sails at 15 km h^{-1} on a bearing of 355°. Find the relative velocity of A to B.

5. A fighter plane flies at 1,000 km h^{-1} on a bearing of 170°, and a bomber flies at 800 km h^{-1} on a bearing of 220°. Find the velocity of the fighter relative to the bomber.

6. A galleon sails at 2 km h^{-1} on a bearing of 080°, and a pirate ship sails at 3 km h^{-1} on a bearing of 130°. Find the velocity of the galleon relative to the pirate.

7. A ship is sailing due north at 14 km h^{-1}. The wind appears to come from 045° with speed 20 km h^{-1}. Find the true direction and speed of the wind.

8. A bomber flies at 900 km h^{-1} on a bearing of 030°. A fighter appears to come from 070° at 2,000 km h^{-1}. Find the true velocity of the fighter.

9. A river 100 m wide is flowing at 3 km h^{-1}. A man can row at 5 km h^{-1}. If he rows directly across the river how far downstream will he land?

10. A wind is blowing at 20 km h–1 from a bearing of 070°. A sparrow, that can fly at 15 km h^{-1} in still air, flies due north. Find its actual speed and direction.

11. A sea-current is flowing at 2 km h^{-1} on a bearing of 220°. A ship sets off on a course of 340° at 12 km h^{-1} relative to the sea. Find the speed and direction of the ship.

12. A river is flowing at 1 m s^{-1}. A man can row at 1.5 m s^{-1}. In which direction should he row if he is to cross the river directly? If the river is 100 m wide how long will it take him?

13. A plane can fly at 200 km h^{-1} in still air. A wind of 50 km h^{-1} is blowing from 045°. If the pilot wishes to reach a place 300 km due north where should he steer? How long will it take him?

14. A current flows at 2 km h^{-1} on a bearing of 140°. A boat which can travel at 10 km h^{-1} is to sail 40 km due east. In what direction should it be steered, and how long will the journey take?

30.2 Interception

If one object A is to intercept another object B, then the relative velocity of A to B is along the straight line joining them.

30.2.1 Example

A cat, which can run at 15 m s⁻¹, spies a mouse 4 m away due north. The mouse is running due east at 5 m s⁻¹. Find the direction the cat should take in order to catch the mouse, and how long it is before interception takes place.

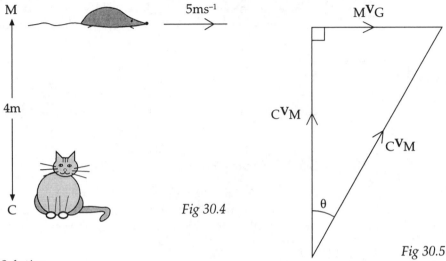

Fig 30.4

Fig 30.5

Solution

The cat C should run so that its velocity relative to the mouse M is due north.

Letting G represent the ground: $_C\mathbf{v}_M = {_C}\mathbf{v}_G - {_M}\mathbf{v}_G$

Draw a vector diagram as shown. The angle of attack is given by $\sin \theta = \frac{1}{3}$.

> The cat should run on a bearing of 19°

The magnitude of the relative velocity is given by Pythagoras.

$$|_C\mathbf{v}_M| = \sqrt{200}$$

> Interception takes place after $\frac{4}{\sqrt{200}} = 0.28$ secs.

30.2.2 Exercises

1. A bomber is flying due west at 800 km h⁻¹. A fighter is 20 km due north of the bomber, and it sets off in pursuit at 1200 km h⁻¹. What course should the fighter pilot set, and how long will interception take?

2. A ship sails due north at 10 km h⁻¹. A submarine is 12 km away on a bearing of 045°. If the submarine can travel at 13 km h⁻¹, what course should be set to intercept the ship? How long will it be before interception?

3. Object A is at the origin and moves with velocity vector $\mathbf{i} + 2\mathbf{j}$. Object B has vector position $10\mathbf{i}$, and can travel with speed 3. What direction should B move in in order to intercept A? What is the vector position of their point of collision?

4. A starts from the origin with vector velocity $3\mathbf{i} + 4\mathbf{j}$. B is at $-3\mathbf{j}$ and can move with a speed of 6. Find the direction B should take in order to intercept A, and the vector position of the point of interception.

5. Ship A is 50 km west of ship B. A sets off at 15 km h⁻¹ on a course of 048°. If ship B can travel at 20 km h⁻¹ find the course it should take to intercept A.

6. In a game of football a forward is running along the touchline at 9 m s⁻¹. A defender, who can run at 8 m s⁻¹, is 20 m from the touchline and 30 m nearer the goal than the forward. What direction should the defender run in in order to intercept the forward? How long will it take?

30.3 Shortest distance

If two objects are moving closer to each other, but not necessarily on a collision course, then there is a *shortest distance* between them.

30.3.1 Example

Ship A is 100 km due west of Ship B. A sets off at 12 km h⁻¹ on a course of 045°, and B sets off at 15 km h⁻¹ on a bearing of 330°. Find the shortest distance between them, and the time when this shortest distance is achieved.

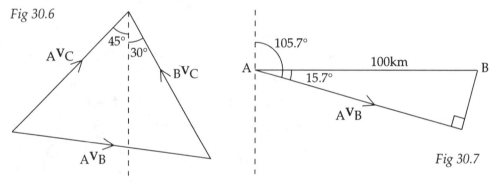

Fig 30.6

Fig 30.7

Solution

First the relative velocity of A to B, $_A\mathbf{v}_B$, must be found, by the methods of Section 30.1.

$_A\mathbf{v}_B$ is 16.6 km h⁻¹, at 105.7°.

From the point of view of B, A is moving with velocity $_A\mathbf{v}_B$. The shortest distance is the perpendicular distance from B to the line of $_A\mathbf{v}_B$.

Shortest distance = $100 \times \sin 15.7° = 27$ km.

To find the time taken, divide the relative distance travelled by A by the relative speed.

Time taken = $\dfrac{100 \times \cos 15.7}{16.6} = 5.8$ hours

30.3.2 Exercises

1. Alfred is 100 m due south of a crossroads, and is walking towards it at 1.5 m s⁻¹. Beatrice is 100 m due east of the crossroads, and is walking towards it at 1.25 m s⁻¹. Find the shortest distance between them, and when this least distance is reached.

2. Clarice is 80 m south of a crossroads, and is walking north at 1.5 m s^{-1}. Dorothy is 60 m due east, and is walking west at 1 m s^{-1}. Find the least distance between them, and how far Dorothy is from the crossroads when they are at this least distance.

3. A starts from the origin with velocity vector $\mathbf{i} + \mathbf{j}$, and at the same time B starts from the point with position vector $5\mathbf{i}$ and moves with velocity vector $-2\mathbf{i} + 3\mathbf{j}$. Find the least distance between them.

4. A starts from the origin with velocity vector $2\mathbf{i} + 3\mathbf{j}$, and at the same time B starts from $-\mathbf{i} + \mathbf{j}$ with velocity $2\mathbf{i}$. Find the shortest distance between them, and B's position when this least distance is reached.

5. Airplane A is 300 km due north of airplane B. A flies at 600 km h^{-1} on a bearing of 097°, and B flies at 400 km h^{-1} at 023°. Find the closest distance apart of the two planes, and the time when they are at this distance.

6. A vessel is sailing due east at 14 km h^{-1}. A second vessel, initially 35 km due north of the first, sails at 9 km h^{-1} on a bearing of 235°. Find the shortest distance between the two ships.

30.4 Examination questions

1. (a) An aircraft flies in a straight line from a point A to a point B 200 km East of A. There is a wind blowing at 40 km h^{-1} from the direction 240° and the aircraft travels at 300 km h^{-1} in still air. Find

   (i) the direction in which the pilot must steer the aircraft,

   (ii) the time, to the nearest minute, for the journey from A to B.

   (b) To an observer in a ship sailing due North at 10 km h^{-1}, a second ship appears to be sailing due East at 24 km h^{-1}. Find the magnitude and direction of the actual velocity of the second ship.

   [C ADD]

2. An aircraft A is 1000 m due north of a second aircraft B. A is flying with constant velocity 170 m s^{-1} due west and B is flying with constant velocity 200 m s^{-1} in a direction 330° (N 30° W). Both aircraft are flying at the same height. Draw a clear velocity diagram and find by drawing or calculation the velocity of A relative to B. How long does it take the two aircraft to reach the closest point to each other, and how far apart are they at that time?

   [O ADD]

3. At noon two boats, A and B, are at sea with B 40 km due East of A. A moves with constant velocity 50 km h^{-1} in a direction N 20° E and B with constant velocity 25 km h^{-1} in a direction N 40° W.

   Find, each correct to 2 significant figures,

   (i) the magnitude and direction of the velocity of A relative to B;

   (ii) the shortest distance between A and B and the time interval (in minutes) during which A is within 30 km of B.

   When A is due North of B it changes course without changing speed in order to intercept B. Calculate A's new course correct to 2 significant figures.

   [SUJB]

4. The vectors $\mathbf{i}$ and $\mathbf{j}$ are unit vectors in the directions East and North respectively. A man walks with constant speed 6 km h^{-1} due North and to him the wind appears to have a velocity $u_1(\sqrt{3}\mathbf{i} - 3\mathbf{j})$ km h^{-1}. Without changing speed the man alters his course so that he is walking in the direction of the vector $(-\frac{1}{2}\sqrt{3}\mathbf{i} + \frac{1}{2}\mathbf{j})$ and the velocity of the wind now appears to him to be $u_2\mathbf{i}$ km h^{-1}. Find u_1 and u_2. Find also the actual velocity of the wind.

    [L]

5. The wind velocity is $W(\cos\alpha\,\mathbf{i} + \sin\alpha\,\mathbf{j})$, where $\mathbf{i}$ and $\mathbf{j}$ are unit vectors due North and due West respectively. An aeroplane makes a journey from a place O to a place A, where A is due North of O, and then it returns to O. The aeroplane works at constant power so that, if there were no wind, its constant speed on both parts of the journey would be V, where $V > W$.

    On the outward journey, the aeroplane is steered parallel to the unit vector $(\cos\beta\,\mathbf{i} - \sin\beta\,\mathbf{j})$, so that the resultant velocity relative to the ground is $U_1\mathbf{i}$. Find $\sin\beta$ in terms of V, W and α, and deduce that

    $$U_1 = W\cos\alpha + \sqrt{(V^2 - W^2\sin^2\alpha)}.$$

    Obtain a similar expression for U_2, where $-U_2\mathbf{i}$ is the velocity of the aeroplane relative to the ground for the return journey. Given that OA = a, deduce that the difference between the times of flight for the two parts of the journey is

    $$\frac{2aW\cos\alpha}{V^2 - W^2}.$$

    [MEI]

6. In this question the units of distance, time and speed are km, h and km h^{-1} respectively.

    A, B and C are three small spheres. At time $t = 0$, A is at the origin O, and B and C have position vectors $6\mathbf{i} + 8\mathbf{j}$ and $16\mathbf{i} + 8\mathbf{j}$ respectively where $\mathbf{i}$ and $\mathbf{j}$ are unit vectors due E and N respectively. They move with constant velocities given by $\mathbf{v}_A = 3\mathbf{i} + 4\mathbf{j}$, $\mathbf{v}_B = \lambda\mathbf{i} + \mu\mathbf{j}$ and $\mathbf{v}_C = -\mathbf{i} + 2\mathbf{j}$.

    (i)   Show that A and C collide and find the time when this happens. Find the distance of the point of collision from O.

    (ii) To an observer on A, B appears to be moving due N and to an observer on C, B appears to be moving due NE. Find the values of λ and μ and the shortest distance between B and C.

    [SUJB]

Common errors

1. **Relative velocity**

    When adding or subtracting velocities, remember that you must treat them *as vectors*. Do not just add or subtract the magnitudes.

2. **Shortest distance**

   (a) When solving a 'shortest distance' problem, do not confuse your distance diagram and your velocity diagram. The velocity diagram is used to find the relative velocity, and the distance diagram is used to find the shortest distance.

   (b) Once you have found $_A\mathbf{v}_B$, then the shortest distance is the line from B perpendicular to the relative velocity line of A. It is not perpendicular to the line AB.

31 Projectiles

Throughout this chapter the effect of air resistance is ignored.

When a body is projected, its *horizontal* motion has constant velocity. Its *vertical* motion is subject to a constant acceleration g.

Throughout this chapter take g to be 9.8 m s^{-2}.

If the initial horizontal and vertical velocities are u_h and u_v respectively, then the equations of motion for horizontal and vertical motion are:

Fig 31.1

$$\frac{dx}{dt} = u_h \qquad \frac{dy}{dt} = u_v - gt$$

$$x = u_h t \qquad y = u_v t - \tfrac{1}{2}gt^2$$

31.1 Horizontal projection

If a body is projected horizontally with speed u, then $u_h = u$ and $u_v = 0$.

31.1.1 Example

Fig 31.2

A body is projected horizontally with speed 10 m s^{-1} from the top of a cliff of height 50 m. Find

(a) the time it takes to reach the bottom

(b) its speed at the bottom

(c) its distance from the base of the cliff

(d) the angle at which it is travelling when it lands.

Solution

(a) Suppose it lands at the bottom after t secs.

$$-50 = -\tfrac{1}{2} \times 9.8 \times t^2$$

It lands after 3.19 secs

(b) The horizontal speed is constant at 10 m s⁻¹. The vertical speed can be found by $v = gt = 31.3$ m s⁻¹. Combine these velocities by Pythagoras:

The speed at the bottom is 32.9 m s⁻¹

(c) The horizontal distance it has travelled is found by multiplying the horizontal speed by the time.

It lands 31.9 m from the base of the cliff

(d) The tan of the angle θ at which it is travelling is given by the ratio of the vertical velocity to the horizontal velocity.

$$\tan \theta = \frac{31.3}{10}$$

It travels at 72° to the horizontal

31.1.2 Exercises

1. A body is projected at 20 m s⁻¹ from the top of a cliff. It hits the bottom after 3 seconds. Find how high the cliff is, and how far from the base of the cliff the body lands.

2. A body is projected at 15 m s⁻¹ from the top of a 70 m cliff. Find the time it takes to reach the bottom, and its distance from the foot of the cliff.

3. A marble rolls off the top of a 1.5 m table at 1 m s⁻¹. Find how long it takes to reach the floor, and how far from the table it lands.

4. A dart is thrown horizontally at 20 m s⁻¹ at a board 3 m away. Find how far it has fallen when it hits the board.

5. A gun is fired horizontally at 1000 m s⁻¹. If the target is 500 m distant find how far the bullet has fallen below the level of the gun.

6. A gun is fired horizontally at a target 200 m distant. When it strikes it has fallen 5 cm. Find the muzzle velocity of the bullet.

7. A tennis ball is struck horizontally at 5 m s⁻¹. When it reaches the net it has fallen 30 cm. How far away is the net?

8. A car is driven off the top of a 50 m cliff at 25 m s⁻¹. Find the speed with which it hits the sea. Find the angle to the horizontal at which it is travelling when it hits the sea.

9. A cricket ball is struck horizontally from a height of 1 m at a speed of 13 m s⁻¹. Find its speed when it lands, and the angle to the horizontal with which it is travelling.

10. A bomber flies horizontally at 300 m s⁻¹ at a height of 3,000 m when it drops its bomb to hit a certain target on the ground. Find the distance from the target. Find the speed with which the bomb hits the target, and the angle with which it does so.

31.2 Projection at an angle

If a body is projected at θ to the horizontal, its initial horizontal velocity u_h is $u \cos \theta$, and its initial vertical velocity u_v is $u \sin \theta$. The equations of motion are:

$$\frac{dx}{dt} = u\cos\theta \qquad \frac{dy}{dt} = u\sin\theta - gt$$

$$x = ut\cos\theta \qquad y = ut\sin\theta - \tfrac{1}{2}gt^2$$

The horizontal range of a projectile is $\dfrac{u^2\sin 2\theta}{g}$.

The greatest horizontal range is $\dfrac{u^2}{g}$, achieved when $\theta = 45°$.

The greatest height is $\dfrac{\tfrac{1}{2}u^2\sin^2\theta}{g}$

31.2.1 Example

Fig 31.3

A body is projected at 20 m s^{-1} at 30° to the horizontal. Find its range and its time of flight.

Solution

Put $u = 20$ and $\theta = 30°$ into the formula above.

$$\text{Horizontal range} = \frac{20^2\sin 60°}{9.8} = 35 \text{ m.}$$

It will hit the ground when its vertical displacement is 0.

$20 \times \sin 30° \, t - \tfrac{1}{2} \times 9.8t^2 = 0$. Hence $t = 0$ or 2.04 secs.

Its time of flight is 2.04 secs

31.2.2 Exercises

1. A particle is projected at 40 m s^{-1} at 40° to the horizontal. Find its range, the time it is in flight and the greatest height it reaches.

2. A particle is projected at 30 m s^{-1} at 60° to the horizontal. Find the greatest height it reaches, and the time it takes to reach this height.

3. A gun fires a bullet at 1,000 m s^{-1}, at an elevation of 5°. Find the horizontal range of the gun.

4. A particle is projected at 50 m s^{-1} at 35° to the horizontal. Find how high it has risen after 1 second. Find the angle at which it is moving at that time.

5. A particle is thrown at 15 m s^{-1} at an elevation of 25°. Find its range, and the greatest height it reaches.

6. A particle is thrown at 20 m s^{-1} at an elevation of 30°. Find its speed after $\frac{1}{2}$ second. At what angle is it travelling at this time? When is the particle moving at 20° to the horizontal?

7. A cricket ball is hit at 15 m s^{-1} at an elevation of 50°. Find the angle of its direction after $\frac{1}{4}$ sec. When is it descending at an angle of 30° to the horizontal?

8. A stone is thrown at 20 m s^{-1} at an elevation of 40°, from the top of a 60 m cliff. Find how long it takes to reach the bottom, and its distance from the foot of the cliff. At what angle does it enter the sea?

9. A particle is projected at 30 m s^{-1} at 50° to the horizontal. A vertical wall is 10 m distant from the point of projection: how high up the wall does the particle strike? At what angle does it strike?

10. An arrow is fired at a speed of 30 m s^{-1} at an angle of 20°, from the top of a 30 m castle tower. How far from the base of the tower does it land?

11. An aircraft is diving at 200 m s^{-1} at an angle of 20° to the horizontal. It releases a bomb when it is 1,000 m above a certain point on the ground. How far from the point does the bomb land?

31.3 Trajectory

The path along which a projectile travels is its *trajectory*.

If the particle is projected at speed u with an elevation of θ, its trajectory is:

$$y = x \tan \theta - \frac{\frac{1}{2}gx^2}{u^2 \cos^2 \theta}$$

If the angle of elevation θ is to be found, the equation is written as:

$$y = xT - \frac{\frac{1}{2}gx^2(1+T^2)}{u^2}$$

where $T = \tan \theta$.

31.3.1 Example

Fig 31.4

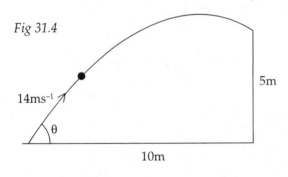

14ms^{-1}

θ

10m

5m

A boy can throw a stone at 14 m s^{-1}. At what angle should he throw in order to hit a window which is 10 m away horizontally and 5 m higher than him?

Solution

In the equation above, put $u = 14$, $x = 10$ and $y = 5$.

$$5 = 10T - \frac{\frac{1}{2}g(10)^2(1+T^2)}{(14)^2}$$

Re-arrange this into a quadratic equation.

$T^2 - 4T + 3 = 0$

$T = 1$ or 3. Recall that $T = \tan \theta$.

He should throw at an elevation of 45° or of 72°

31.3.2 Exercises

1. The muzzle velocity of a gun is 400 m s^{-1}. What are the possible angles of elevation to achieve a horizontal range of 10,000 m?

2. A boy can throw a stone at 20 m s^{-1}. What angle should he throw at to achieve a range of 30 m?

3. A particle can be projected at 21 m s^{-1}. What should be the angle of projection if it is to hit a target 2 m high and 15 m distant?

4. A gun can be fired at 200 m s^{-1}. What should be the angle of elevation to hit a target 1 m high and 2,000 m distant?

5. An arrow can be fired at 42 m s^{-1}. What should be the angle of elevation to strike a target 10 m high and 25 m distant?

6. An archer stands on the top of a 30 m tower. He can shoot an arrow at 49 m s^{-1}. What is the lower angle at which the arrow should aimed to hit a target which is 250 m from the base of the tower? At what angle does it enter the target?

7. From a window 25 m above the street a boy throws stones at a target 40 m away from the foot of the house. If he can throw at 21 m s^{-1} find the angle at which he should throw.

8. A ball is thrown at an elevation of 45°, and just clears the top of a tree which is 2 m higher than the point of projection and 4 m distant horizontally. Find the speed of projection.

9. A shot is fired from the top of a 200 m high cliff, at 20° above the horizontal. It strikes a boat which is 2000 m out to sea. Find the speed at which the shot was fired.

31.4 Examination questions

1. A particle is projected from a point O on horizontal ground with velocity 40 m s^{-1} at an angle of 30° to the horizontal.

    Given that, 0.7 seconds after projection, the particle is at a point P, calculate

    (i)   the height of P above the ground,

    (ii) the magnitude and direction of the velocity of the particle at P.

    The particle reaches the ground again at a point Q. Calculate

    (iii) the time of flight,

    (iv) the greatest height reached

    (v)   the distance OQ.

    [C ADD]

2. The height in metres of a stone above ground level t seconds after being thrown until it hits the ground, is given by

    $$h = 80 + 15t - 5t^2.$$

    (a) State the height from which it was thrown.

    (b) Calculate, to the nearest tenth of a second, when it hits the ground.

    (c) Rewrite h in the form $5[B - (A - t)^2]$, stating the values of the positive numbers A and B.

    (d) Hence, or otherwise, state when the stone is highest and give this height.

    (e) Find the height after 0.8 second and calculate for how long it is above this.

    [SMP ADD]

3. A boy threw a ball directly at the vertical wall of a building which was 42 m in front of him. 2s later the ball struck a window in that wall at a point which was 2.8 m above the point from which the ball was thrown.

    (i) Show that the ball was thrown at an angle θ to the horizontal where $\tan \theta = \frac{8}{15}$.

    (ii) Calculate the maximum height reached by the ball above the point from which it was thrown.

    (iii) Calculate the distance from the building at which the boy would have needed to stand in order that the ball, thrown in exactly the same manner, would have hit the wall at a point which was at the same level as the point from which the ball was thrown.

    [JMB ADD]

4. A particle is projected vertically upwards with speed V from a point O. Find H, the maximum height of the particle above O.

    When the particle is projected from O with the same speed V, but at an angle of elevation θ to the horizontal, the maximum height of the particle above the horizontal plane through O is h and the range on the horizontal plane is R.

    (a) When $R = H$, show that there are two possible values of θ, and find the two corresponding values of h.

    (b) When $h = \frac{1}{2}H$, show that there is only one possible value of θ, and find the corresponding value of R.

    [L]

5. A boy throws a small ball towards a wall so that the flight of the ball is in a vertical plane perpendicular to the wall. The boy and the wall stand on horizontal ground 9 m apart.

    (a) The ball leaves the boy's hand in a horizontal direction with a speed of 20 m s^{-1} at a height of 1.1 m above the ground. Calculate, to the nearest cm, the height above the ground of the point at which the ball strikes the wall.

    (b) A can stands on the wall, directly opposite the boy, at a height of 2m above the ground. In order to knock the can off the wall it is necessary for the ball to strike the can with a velocity whose horizontal component is at least 16 m s^{-1}. Determine the speed, in m s^{-1} to 1 decimal place, with which the ball must be thrown just to knock the can off the wall.

    In this case determine, in degrees to 1 decimal place, the angle which the ball's trajectory makes with the horizontal

    (i) as the ball leaves the boy's hand,

    (ii) at the moment of impact.

    [AEB 1985]

6. (a) A particle is projected under gravity from a point O with speed u at an angle α to the horizontal. Write down expressions for the horizontal and vertical displacements x and y of the particles from O at time t.

    (b) A boy throws a ball from the foot of a plane inclined at an angle β to the horizontal and later the ball falls on to the plane. The motion of the ball takes place in the vertical plane containing the line of greatest slope of the plane. The initial velocity of the ball has magnitude u and is inclined at an angle α ($\alpha > \beta$) to the horizontal.

(i) By using the results given in (a), show that the ball meets the inclined plane after a time

$$\frac{2u\sin(\alpha-\beta)}{g\cos\beta}.$$

[Hint: the equation of the line of greatest slope of the plane is $y = x\tan\beta$.]

(ii) Find the range on the inclined plane.

(iii) Given that the ball strikes the plane at right–angles, show that

$$\tan\alpha = \cot\beta + 2\tan\beta.$$

[W]

Common errors

Equations of motion

(a) Be very careful with signs. The positive direction for y is upwards. So g is negative. If a body is thrown down 50 m then put $y = -50$.

(b) Do not confuse the various quantities. When a body strikes the ground, then $y = 0$. When it is at its greatest height, then $\frac{dy}{dx} = 0$. Do not get these the wrong way round.

(c) When finding the angle at which a projectile is moving, you must take the ratio of the vertical and horizontal *velocities*. Do not take the ratio of the *distances*.

32 Momentum

If a body of mass m is moving with velocity v, then its momentum is given by:

$$\text{Momentum} = mv.$$

The *Principle of Conservation of Momentum* states that:

If there are no external forces acting on a system, its total momentum is constant.

32.1 Impulse

If a force F acts on a body for a time t, then the *impulse* it gives to the body is Ft. The impulse is equal to the change of momentum of the body.

A *light inextensible string* is one whose weight is negligible and whose length is constant. When such a string becomes taut then the bodies at each end of the string receive equal and opposite impulses along the direction of the string.

Impulse and momentum are vectors. If the motion does not take place in a straight line then impulses can be found from a vector triangle or by components.

Suppose a continuous stream of matter strikes a body. The force on the body can be found by considering the rate of loss of the matter.

UNITS

A force of 1 newton acting for 1 second provides an impulse of 1 Ns.

32.1.1 Examples

1. A sphere of mass 1 kg travelling north at 3 m s^{-1} strikes a stationary sphere of mass 2 kg. After the collision the second sphere travels North East with speed $\frac{1}{2}$ m s^{-1}. Find the velocity of the first sphere, and the impulse received by the second sphere.

   Solution

   Let the first sphere be travelling at v m s^{-1} north and u m s^{-1} west. By conservation of momentum in the north-south direction:

   $$1 \times 3 = 1 \times v + 2 \times \tfrac{1}{2} \cos 45°$$

   $$v = 2.293 \text{ m s}^{-1}$$

   By conservation of momentum in the east-west direction:

   $$0 = 1 \times u - 2 \times \tfrac{1}{2} \sin 45°$$

Fig 32.1

$u = 0.707$ m s^{-1}

Combine these velocities:

The velocity of the first sphere is 2.4 m s^{-1} at 343°

The impulse given to the second sphere is its change of momentum.

The impulse is 1 Ns at 045°

2. A shell of mass 5 kg is travelling horizontally at 100 m s^{-1} when it explodes into two parts. One part of mass 2 kg travels in the original direction at 200 m s^{-1}. Find the speed of the other part, and find the gain in energy due to the explosion.

Solution

Suppose the 3 kg part moves at v in the original direction. By conservation of momentum:

$5 \times 100 = 2 \times 200 + 3 \times v$

The 3 kg part travels at $33\frac{1}{3}$ m s^{-1} in the original direction

The energy gained is the difference between the kinetic energies before and after the explosion.

Energy gained $= \frac{1}{2} \times 2 \times 200^2 + \frac{1}{2} \times 3 \times 33.33^2 - \frac{1}{2} \times 5 \times 100^2$

The energy gained is 16,667 joules

3. Two bodies A and B, of masses 1 kg and 3 kg respectively, are connected by a light inextensible string of length h m. They lie a distance $\frac{1}{2}h$ apart on a smooth horizontal table, with A on the edge. A is tipped over the edge. Find the speed of B immediately after the string becomes taut.

Solution

Body A falls freely under gravity for a distance of $\frac{1}{2}h$. Its speed is then found from the formula $v^2 = u^2 + 2as$:

Speed is $\sqrt{(gh)}$ m s^{-1}.

After the string becomes taut, the two bodies move as one with speed w. By conservation of momentum,

$4w = \sqrt{(gh)}$.

B starts to move with speed $\frac{1}{4}\sqrt{(gh)}$ m s^{-1}

4. A body of mass 3 kg is travelling with velocity $3\mathbf{i} + 2\mathbf{j}$ m s^{-1}. It receives a blow, and then travels with velocity $2\mathbf{i} - 4\mathbf{j}$ m s^{-1}. Find the magnitude of the impulse it has received.

Solution

The change of velocity is obtained by subtracting the two vectors. The change of momentum is the mass times the change of velocity.

Change of momentum $= 3(-\mathbf{i} - 6\mathbf{j}) = -3\mathbf{i} - 18\mathbf{j}$ Ns.

Use Pythagoras to find the magnitude of this vector.

The magnitude of the impulse is 18.25 Ns

5. A hose delivers 5 kg of water every second at 15 m s^{-1}. The water is played horizontally on a wall. Assuming that the water does not rebound, find the force exerted on the wall.

Solution

In every second, 5 kg loses 15 m s^{-1} of speed. The rate of loss of momentum is 75 Ns.

The force on the wall is 75 N

32.1.2 Exercises

1. Find the momentum of the following:
   (a) A car of mass 500 kg moving at 20 m s^{-1}.
   (b) A ball of mass 0.1 kg moving at 5 m s^{-1}.

2. An impulse of 12 Ns is applied to a stationary mass of 3 kg. Find its velocity afterwards.

3. An impulse of 20 Ns is applied to a mass of 4 kg moving at 3 m s^{-1} in the direction of the impulse. Find the new velocity of the mass.

4. A stationary ball of mass 0.2 kg is struck so that it moves at 12 m s^{-1}. Find the impulse it has been given.

5. A body of mass 3 kg moving at 6 m s^{-1} is struck by an impulse acting in the same direction as the motion. If it now moves at 9 m s^{-1} find the impulse.

6. A cricket ball of mass 0.12 kg is bowled at 20 m s^{-1}. The batsman hits it back to the bowler at 25 m s^{-1}. Find the impulse he has given to the ball.

7. A car of mass 500 kg moves at 10 m s^{-1} and collides with a stationary car of mass 400 kg. If they move on together find their common speed. Find the loss of energy in the collision.

8. A car of mass 500 kg moving at 20 m s^{-1} bumps into a car of mass 600 kg which is moving in the same direction at 15 m s^{-1}. If they stay fixed together find their speed.

9. A car of mass 500 kg travelling at 20 m s^{-1} has a head–on collision with another car travelling in the opposite direction at 25 m s^{-1}. If they are both brought to a halt find the mass of the second car.

10. An arrow of mass 50 g flying horizontally at 40 m s^{-1} strikes a hanging target of mass 4 kg and sticks in it. Find the speed with which they move after impact. Find the loss of energy. If the arrow penetrates to a depth of 3 cm find the average force of resistance of the target.

11. An arrow of mass 50 g travelling horizontally at 30 m s^{-1} strikes an apple of mass 100 g and embeds itself in it. Find the speed with which they begin to move. If the arrow penetrates to a depth of 10 cm find the force of resistance of the apple.

12. A stake of mass 10 kg is to be driven vertically into the ground. It is struck by a sledgehammer of mass 20 kg moving at 15 m s^{-1}. The hammer and stake stay together after collision. Find their velocity after collision. If the stake penetrates 20 cm find the force of resistance of the ground.

13. Two particles of masses 2 kg and 4 kg are connected by a light inextensible string. The lighter particle is projected away from the heavier with speed 3 m s^{-1}. Find their common speed after the string becomes taut. Find the loss of energy caused by the tightening of the string.

14. A and B, of masses 2 kg and 6 kg respectively, are connected by a light inextensible string. They are projected away from each other with speeds 4 m s^{-1} and 3 m s^{-1} respectively. Find their speeds after the string becomes taut. Find the impulse in the string.

15. A particle of mass 4 kg moves with velocity 5**i** − 3**j** m s^{-1}. After a blow it moves with velocity 7**i** + 4**j** m s^{-1}. Find the magnitude of the impulse it has received.

16. A particle of mass 2 kg and velocity 2**i** + 3**j** m s^{-1} receives an impulse of 4**i** + 7**j** Ns. Find its new velocity, and the energy it has gained.

17. Two particles, of masses 5 kg and 2 kg and velocities **i** + 2**j** m s^{-1} and −2**i** − 3**j** m s^{-1}, collide and coalesce. Find their new velocity, and the impulse each has received.

18. A ball of mass 3 kg travelling at 2 m s^{-1} strikes a stationary ball of mass 1 kg. The smaller ball then travels at 1.5 m s^{-1} at 30° to the original line of motion of the larger. Find the new velocity of the larger ball.

19. A ball of mass 0.3 kg strikes a stationary ball of mass 0.8 kg at 2 m s^{-1}, and is deflected through 90° and its velocity is reduced to 1 m s^{-1}. Find the velocity of the larger ball.

20. A rifle of mass 4 kg fires a bullet of mass 10 g at 800 m s^{-1}. Find the initial speed of recoil of the rifle. Find the energy of the explosion.

21. A shell of mass 20 kg travelling horizontally at 200 m s^{-1} explodes into two equal halves, one of which is brought to a halt. Find the speed of the other. Find the energy of the explosion.

22. A cricket ball of mass 0.12 kg, bowled at 20 m s^{-1}, is struck so that it travels at right–angles to its original direction at 30 m s^{-1}. Find the impulse given to the ball.

23. A cricket ball of mass 0.12 kg, bowled at 25 m s^{-1}, is deflected through 20° and its speed is reduced to 15 m s^{-1}. Find the impulse given to the ball.

24. A cricket ball of mass 0.12 kg, bowled at 17 m s^{-1}, is struck back to the bowler so that it travels at 35 m s^{-1} and makes 20° with its original direction. Find the magnitude of the impulse given.

25. If the cricket ball of Question 22 is struck by an impulse of 3 Ns at right angles to its original direction find its new velocity.

26. The cricket ball of Question 24 is struck back to the bowler by an impulse of 5 Ns in a direction which makes 10° with its original direction. Find its new speed.

27. A jet of water plays horizontally on a wall. The jet delivers 2 kg of water per second, and its speed is 10 m s^{-1}. Assuming that the water does not rebound, find the force exerted on the wall.

28. Suppose that in Question 27, the water rebounds at 5 m s^{-1}. Find the force on the wall.

29. The muzzle of a hose has cross section 5 cm^2. Water emerges at 20 m s^{-1}. Find the force necessary to hold the hose.

30. A machine gun fires 20 bullets per second, at a speed of 400 m s^{-1}. If each bullet has mass 5 grams, find the force needed to hold the gun.

32.2 Elastic collisions

When two bodies collide, their relative velocity is reversed and multiplied by a constant factor e. This factor is the *coefficient of restitution*.

$$e = \frac{\text{relative speed after}}{\text{relative speed before}}$$

e lies between 0 and 1. Bodies for which $e = 1$ are called *perfectly elastic*. Bodies for which $e = 0$ are *perfectly inelastic*.

32.2.1 Examples

1. A body is dropped from a height of 10 m onto a horizontal surface for which the coefficient of restitution is $\frac{3}{4}$. Find the height it rises to after the first bounce.

   Solution

   The velocity with which it strikes the floor is found from the formula $v^2 = 2as$. The speed is $\sqrt{(2g \times 10)} = 14$ m s^{-1}. This is then multiplied by e.

   Speed after bounce = 10.5 m s^{-1}

   The height can be found from the same formula.

   $$\text{The height is } \frac{10.5^2}{2g} = 5.625 \text{ m.}$$

2. Three spheres A, B, C of masses 2, 2, 1 respectively lie in that order on a horizontal table. The coefficient of restitution is $\frac{1}{2}$. A is given a speed of 4 m s^{-1} towards B. Find the speed with which C begins to move.

   Solution

   The three diagrams below show the situations

   (a) before the first collision

   (b) after the first collision but before the second

   (c) after the second collision.

   (a)   A $\to 4$ B   C

   (b)   A $\to u$ B $\to v$ C

   (c)   A $\to u$ B $\to p$ C $\to q$

   By conservation of momentum in the first collision:

   $2 \times 4 = 2 \times u + 2 \times v$

   By restitution in the first collision:

   $v - u = \frac{1}{2} \times 4$

   Solve these to find that $u = 1$ and $v = 3$.

   Repeat the process for the second collision.

   $2v = 2p + q$ (Conservation of momentum)

   $q - p = \frac{1}{2} v$ (Restitution)

   Solve these equations to find q, using $v = 3$.

   $$\text{The velocity of C is 3 m s}^{-1}.$$

32.2.2 Exercises

1. A ball falls from a height of $2\frac{1}{2}$ m, onto a floor where the coefficient of restitution is $\frac{7}{8}$. Find the height it reaches after the first bounce.

2. A ball falls from a height of 8 m, and after the first bounce it reaches a height of 2 m. Find the coefficient of restitution.

3. A ball of mass 3 kg moving at 4 m s^{-1} strikes a stationary ball of mass 2 kg. If the coefficient of restitution is $\frac{1}{4}$ find their speeds after collision.

4. Two balls collide, the first being of mass 2 kg and travelling at 2 m s^{-1} and the second of mass 3 kg and travelling at 1 m s^{-1} in the opposite direction. If the coefficient of restitution is $\frac{1}{3}$ find their speeds after impact.

5. A ball of mass 1 kg moving at 5 m s^{-1} strikes a stationary ball of mass 2 kg. If the larger ball moves off at 2 m s^{-1} find the coefficient of restitution.

6. A ball of mass 3 kg travelling at 2 m s^{-1} strikes a ball of mass 2 kg travelling in the same direction at $1\frac{1}{2}$ m s^{-1}. If the first ball now moves at $1\frac{3}{4}$ m s^{-1} find the coefficient of restitution.

Fig 32.2

In Questions 7 to 10 two balls A and B lie as shown. A is projected towards B with speed 2 m s^{-1}. B bounces off the wall, and returns to strike A. The coefficients of restitutions between A and B and between B and the wall are e and e' respectively. In each of the following find the speed of A after striking B for the second time.

7. $e = e' = \frac{1}{2}$. A and B have equal mass.

8. $e = e' = \frac{1}{2}$. A has twice the mass of B.

9. $e = e' = \frac{1}{2}$. A has half the mass of B.

10. $e = \frac{1}{2}$, $e' = \frac{1}{3}$. A and B have equal mass.

In Questions 11 to 14, three balls, A, B and C lie in a straight line as shown. A is projected towards B at 2 m s^{-1}. The coefficient of restitution is $\frac{3}{4}$. In each case find the velocity of C after it has been struck. Will there be a third collision?

Fig 32.3

11. A, B, C have equal mass.

12. The mass of A is twice that of B or C.

13. The masses of A, B and C are in the ratio 3:2:1.

14. The masses of A, B, C are in the ratio 1:2:3.

32.3 Oblique impact

Suppose two smooth objects collide at an angle. Their relative velocity along the line of collision is multiplied by the coefficient of restitution. The relative velocity perpendicular to the line is unchanged.

32.3.1 Examples

Fig 32.4

1. A body strikes a wall at an angle of 40° to the wall. If the coefficient of restitution is $\frac{1}{2}$ find the angle it makes with the wall after striking it.

    Solution

    Let the speed of the ball be u. The velocity parallel to the wall is $u\cos 40°$. This is unchanged. The velocity perpendicular to the wall is $u\sin 40°$. This is multiplied by $\frac{1}{2}$. Find the angle θ which the ball now makes with the wall, by considering the ratio of the velocities.

    $$\tan\theta = \tfrac{1}{2}\,\frac{u\sin 40°}{u\cos 40°} = \tfrac{1}{2}\tan 40°$$

    It now makes 23° with the wall

2. A smooth sphere A is travelling at 8 m s⁻¹. It strikes a similar stationary sphere B, so that the line joining the centres is at 60° to the original direction of A. Find the velocity of A after the collision, given that the coefficient of restitution between the spheres is $\frac{3}{4}$.

Fig 32.5

Before

After

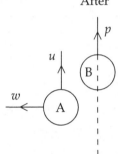

    Solution

    Suppose that after the collision, the velocity of sphere A has components u m s⁻¹ along the line of centres and w m s⁻¹ perpendicular to the line of centres. Let sphere B have velocity p m s⁻¹ along the line of centres. Let the mass of each sphere be m kg.

    $m(8)\sin 60° = mw$ (momentum, perpendicular to loc)

    $m(8)\cos 60° = mu + mp$ (momentum, along loc)

    $\tfrac{3}{4}(8)\cos 60° = p - u$ (restitution along loc)

    Solve these equations to find that $w = 4\sqrt{3}$ and $u = \frac{1}{2}$. Combine these speeds by Pythagoras and trigonometry.

    The velocity of A is 6.95 m s⁻¹, at 86° to the line of centres

32.3.2 Exercises

1. A ball strikes a wall at 60° to the wall. If the coefficient of restitution is 0.7 find the angle it makes with the wall after collision.

2. A ball strikes a wall at 40° to the wall. After collision it makes 35° with the wall. Find the coefficient of restitution.

3. In Questions 1 and 2 find the impulses experienced by the ball, if it is initially travelling at 12 m s⁻¹ and has mass 0.5 kg.

4. A smooth sphere A, moving at 10 m s⁻¹, strikes an identical stationary sphere B so that the line of centres makes 30° with the original direction of A. If the collision is perfectly elastic find the velocities of A and B after the collision.

5. A smooth sphere A strikes an identical stationary sphere B so that the line of centres makes 10° with the original direction of A. After the collision A is moving at 45° to the line of centres. Find the coefficient of restitution between the spheres.

6.   A smooth sphere of mass 2 kg strikes a stationary sphere of mass 1 kg, so that the line of centres makes 45° with the original direction of motion. If the coefficient of restitution is $\frac{1}{2}$ find the angle through which the sphere is deflected.

7.   A smooth sphere of mass 1 kg strikes a stationary sphere of mass 2 kg. The line of centres makes 30° with the original direction. If the collision is perfectly elastic, show that the speeds of the spheres are equal after the impact.

8.   A smooth sphere of mass m kg strikes a stationary sphere. The collision is perfectly elastic, and the line of centres makes 30° with the original direction. After the collision, the first sphere travels at 45° to the line of centres. Find the mass of the second sphere.

32.4 Examination questions

1.   In a traffic pile up on a smooth icy road, a car, of mass 800 kg travelling at 14 m s^{-1}, hits a stationary car of mass 1100 kg and the two move on together. Calculate their common velocity in m s^{-1} after impact, and the loss of energy on impact, giving your answer in joules.

Without losing any further velocity the two cars slide until they come to rest on hitting a stationary lorry, of mass 10,000 kg, which is just in front. Calculate the velocity of the lorry, in m s^{-1}, immediately after the impact.

If the lorry is brought to rest by a uniform frictional force after moving 10 m, calculate the retarding force in newtons.

[O&C ADD]

2.   In using a pile driver, a mass of 3000 kg is released from rest to fall freely through 2.5 m to strike a pile of mass 500 kg. What is the velocity of the 3000 kg mass immediately before it hits the pile? What is the common velocity of the total mass of 3500 kg immediately after impact, assuming that there is no rebound?

If the constant resistance of the ground is R N, write down the net force acting on the mass of 3500 kg (allowing for the weight), and hence calculate the value of R if the mass penetrates 0.5 m into the ground before coming to rest.

[MEI ADD]

3.   A shot of mass 8 kg is fired horizontally from a stationary gun of mass 0.5 tonne. The gun is free to recoil. The impulse given by the gun to the shot is 2000 N s.

      (a)   Calculate the speed of the shot and the speed of the gun immediately after firing.

      The gun is subsequently brought to rest by a constant horizontal force F in 2 seconds. Calculate

      (b)   the magnitude of F,   (c)   the distance the gun moves.

[AEB ADD 1986]

4.   A Thark of mass 5.7×10^{-7} kg, initially travelling at 3.4×10^6 m/s, receives an impulse which deflects it through 90° and doubles its speed.

(a) Calculate the magnitude and direction of this impulse.

Shortly afterwards the Thark disintegrates into two. One third of the mass deflects through 40° and moves at 7.9×10^6 m s^{-1} at 50° to the direction in which it was initially travelling.

(b) Find, by drawing or calculation, the speed and direction of the other two-thirds.

[SMP ADD]

5. (Take the acceleration due to gravity to be 10 m s^{-2})

An archer shoots an arrow of mass 0.2 kg at a wooden target of mass 5 kg which he has hung from a fixed point by a cord of length 2 m. The target is free to move in the direction of the arrow's motion, and it is hanging at rest when the arrow strikes it horizontally with a speed of 39 m s^{-1}, and sticks into it. Find the velocity with which the target begins to move.

The maximum angle which the cord makes with the vertical in the subsequent swinging motion is θ. Regarding the target and arrow as a particle, and using conservation of energy, find the value of θ to the nearest degree.

The archer recovers his arrow by tugging it horizontally out of the target as it is passing through the lowest point of its swing, moving away from him. This action leaves the target at rest and the arrow moving away from it at a speed of 2 m s^{-1}. Draw a diagram to show the impulse acting on the arrow and on the target, and find the magnitude of the impulse which the archer exerts on the arrow.

[AEB 1987]

6. A ball is thrown vertically downwards from a height d above a level floor with speed $\sqrt{(3gd)}$. Find the time taken to reach the floor, and show that the ball rebounds with speed $e\sqrt{(5gd)}$, where e is the coefficient of restitution between the ball and the floor.

The height of the ceiling above the floor is $2d$. Find the minimum value of e that ensures that the ball reaches the ceiling.

Find the maximum height of the ball above the floor for the case when $e^2 = \frac{3}{5}$ and determine its speed when it returns to the point of projection after striking the floor once.

[MEI]

7. Three perfectly elastic smooth spheres A, B, C of equal radii but of masses $3m$, $2m$ and $1m$ respectively, lie at rest on a horizontal plane with their centres in a straight line. Sphere A is projected with speed u to collide directly with sphere B which then collides directly with sphere C. Find the speed of each sphere after each of these collisions. Explain why there are only two collisions between the spheres.

[L]

8. A particle A of mass m is attached to a particle B of mass $2m$ by a light inextensible string of length a. The particles lie at rest on a frictionless horizontal plane and A is projected towards B with speed u. If the coefficient of restitution between the particles is $\frac{3}{4}$ show that the direction of motion of A is reversed after impact with B.

Find

(i)   the speeds of A and B immediately after the string tightens;

(ii) the magnitude of the impulsive tension in the string;

(iii) the time that elapses between the impact and the tightening of the string;

(iv) the total loss of energy due to the impact and tightening of the string.

[SUJB]

9.   (a) Two particles A and B of masses $3m$ and $5m$ respectively are placed on a smooth horizontal table. The particle A is projected along the table with speed u directly towards B, which is at rest. After impact A continues to move in the same direction with speed $\frac{u}{6}$. Find

(i)   the speed of B after impact,

(ii) the coefficient of restitution between A and B,

(iii) the loss in kinetic energy due to the collision.

(b) The same particles A and B are now connected by a light inextensible string and are placed side by side on the smooth horizontal table. The particle A is projected horizontally, directly away from B, with a speed v. Calculate

(i)   the resulting common speed of the two particles after the string has tightened,

(ii) the magnitude of the impulse in the string when the string tightens,

(iii) the loss in kinetic energy due to the tightening of the string.

[AEB 1986]

Common errors

1.   **Momentum**

Momentum and impulse are both vectors. So if a body changes direction as well as speed, the change in velocity is not just the difference between its speeds before and after. Find the change of velocity by components or by a vector triangle.

2.   **Impact problems**

(a) Do not forget that energy is usually lost in collisions. Do not try to solve problems by claiming that energy is conserved before and after a collision has taken place.

(b) When working with problems which involve penetration, do not ignore gravity. Note the difference between:

(i)   An arrow enters a target horizontally. The energy lost will be kinetic energy.

(ii) A stake enters the ground vertically. The energy lost will be kinetic energy plus potential energy.

3. **Coefficient of restitution**

    Be careful with signs. It is probably wise to take all the velocities in the same direction. Then if a body is travelling in the opposite direction its velocity is negative.

33 Variable acceleration

The equations of motion such as $s = ut + \frac{1}{2}at^2$ apply only to situations in which the acceleration is constant. If the acceleration is not constant then calculus must be used.

Acceleration can be a function of time, or of velocity, or of distance.

Situations in which the acceleration was a function of time were dealt with in Chapter 22.

Frequently the identity $\dfrac{dv}{dt} = v\dfrac{dv}{ds}$ is applied.

Throughout the letters t, s and v will represent time, distance and velocity respectively.

33.1 Force as a Function of Velocity

The *terminal* velocity of an object is its final velocity. The acceleration is zero when the terminal velocity is reached.

33.1.1 Examples

1. A body of mass 2 kg falls under gravity, experiencing air resistance which is proportional to the square of its velocity. The terminal velocity is 14 m s^{-1}. Find the constant of proportionality.

    Solution

    Let the force of resistance be kv^2.

    The equation of motion is: $2\dfrac{dv}{dt} = 2g - kv^2$.

    When $v = 14$, $\dfrac{dv}{dt} = 0$. This gives $k = 0.1$.

    The constant of proportionality is 0.1

2. A body with mass 1 kg moves under a force of $3\sqrt{v}$ N directed towards the origin, where v is the velocity. It is projected at 9 m s^{-1} away from the origin. Find the distance X it travels before coming to rest.

    Solution

    The equation of motion is:

    $$\dfrac{dv}{dt} = -3\sqrt{v}$$

Use the identity $\dfrac{dv}{dt} = v\,\dfrac{dv}{ds}$, to obtain:

$$v\,\frac{dv}{ds} = -3\sqrt{v}$$

Separate the variables and integrate. While v goes from 9 to 0, s goes from 0 to X.

$$\int_9^0 \sqrt{v}\,dv = -3\int_0^X ds$$

$$-3X = \left[\frac{2}{3}v^{\frac{3}{2}}\right]_9^0 = -18$$

It travels 6 m before coming to rest.

3. A vehicle of mass 1200 kg exerts a constant power of 8000 W and experiences a constant resistance of 400 N. It accelerates from rest to 5 m s⁻¹. Find the time taken.

Solution

The force exerted by the vehicle is obtained by dividing the power by the speed. Hence the equation of motion is

$$1200\,\frac{dv}{dt} = \frac{8000}{v} - 400$$

Separate the variables and integrate.

$$\begin{aligned}
\text{Time} &= \int_0^5 \frac{1200\,v\,dv}{8000 - 400v} \\[2mm]
&= \int_0^5 \frac{3\,v\,dv}{20 - v} \\[2mm]
&= \int_0^5 \left(-3 + \frac{60}{20 - v}\right) dv \\[2mm]
&= \left[-3v - 60\ln(20 - v)\right]_0^5
\end{aligned}$$

The time taken is 2.26 seconds

33.1.2 Exercises

1. A body of mass 5 kg falls under gravity against a resistance equal to a quarter of its velocity. Find the terminal velocity.

2. A body of mass 3 kg falls under gravity against a force equal to half its velocity squared. Find its terminal velocity.

3. A car drives along horizontal ground, with constant power equal to 10,000 W, and against a constant resistance of 400 N. Find its terminal velocity.

4. A car of mass 500 kg rolls down a slope of angle 10°, against a resistance equal to twenty times its velocity. Find the terminal velocity.

5. A body of mass 10 kg falls under gravity against a resistance proportional to its velocity. If its terminal velocity is 50 m s^{-1}, find the constant of proportionality.

6. A body of mass 2.5 kg falls under gravity against a resistance proportional to the velocity squared. If the terminal velocity is 8 m s^{-1} find the constant of proportionality.

7. A car of mass 800 kg rolls down a slope of 5°, against a resistance proportional to its velocity. If the terminal velocity is 4 m s^{-1} find the constant of proportionality.

8. A body of unit mass experiences a force of $2v^{3/2}$ away from the origin. It starts at the origin with speed 16. Find the time it takes to reach a speed of 25.

9. Find the distance covered by the body of Question 8.

10. A body starts from the origin with speed 10. It experiences an acceleration towards the origin of $(1 + v)$. Find the time it takes to come to a halt.

11. A body starts from rest at the origin and experiences an acceleration away from the origin of $(2 - v)$. Find the terminal velocity, and the time it has taken to reach half the terminal velocity. Find the distance covered over this period.

12. A body starts from the origin with speed 20, and experiences an acceleration of $(1 + v^2)$ directed towards the origin. Find the time it takes to come to rest.

13. Find the distance covered by the body of Question 12.

14. The resistance experienced by a body of unit mass is $v + v^2$. It starts from the origin with speed 12. Find the distance it has covered when it is brought to rest.

15. A body of mass m falls under gravity against resistance of $0.1gmv$. Find the terminal velocity. Find the time taken to reach half the terminal velocity if it has been dropped from rest.

16. Find the distance travelled by the body of Question 15 while it falls from rest to half its terminal velocity.

17. A body of mass 1 kg is thrown upwards at 50 m s^{-1}, against a resistance of $0.05v^2$ N. Find the time taken to reach its greatest height.

18. Find the greatest height reached by the body of Question 17.

19. A vehicle has mass 1000 kg, and exerts a power of 10,000 W. It experiences a constant resistance of 250 N. Find the greatest speed, and the time to reach half this greatest speed from rest.

20. Find the distance travelled by the vehicle of Question 19 in reaching half its greatest speed from rest.

21. A vehicle has mass 1000 kg and can exert a power of 10,000 W. It experiences a resistance of $16v$ N. Find its greatest speed. Find the time taken to reach a speed of 10 m s^{-1} from rest, and find the distance travelled during this time.

33.2 Force as a function of distance

33.2.1 Example

A body of mass 2 starts at rest from $x = 3$, under a force of $\dfrac{2x}{9}$ directed towards the origin. Find its speed when it reaches the origin.

Solution

Write down the equation of motion:

$$2v\,\frac{dv}{dx} = -\frac{2x}{9}$$

Separate the variables and integrate:

$$v^2 = k - \frac{x^2}{9}$$

When $x = 3$, $v = 0$. This gives $k = 1$.

$$v = \sqrt{\left(1 - \frac{x^2}{9}\right)}\,.\text{ Put } x = 0:$$

At the origin the velocity is 1.

33.2.2 Exercises

1. The equation of motion of a body is $\dfrac{dv}{dt} = 3s$. It is at rest at the origin, and is displaced slightly. Find its speed after travelling 10 m.

2. A body starts from the origin with an initial speed of 1 m s^{-1}, and its equation of motion is $2\,\dfrac{dv}{dt} = \dfrac{1}{1+s}$. Find its speed after travelling 2 m.

3. A body moves from rest at the origin so that its equation of motion is $\dfrac{dv}{dt} = \dfrac{2}{1+s}$. Find how far it has travelled when its speed is 1 m s^{-1}.

4. A body moves from the origin with an initial speed of 2 m s^{-1}, and its equation of motion is $3\,\dfrac{dv}{dt} = s$. Find how far it has travelled when its speed is 10 m s^{-1}.

5. A body of mass 3 kg experiences a force equal to $2s$ N, where s m is its distance from the origin. It is at rest at the origin, and is displaced slightly. Find its velocity when it has moved 2 m.

6. A body of mass 1 kg experiences a force of $\dfrac{1}{s^2}$ N, directed towards the origin, where s m is its distance from the origin. It starts 2 m away from the origin with a speed of 1 m s^{-1} towards the origin. Find
    (a) its speed when it is 0.5 m from the origin
    (b) the time it takes to reach this position.

7. A planet has radius R. When a particle is r from the centre the acceleration due to gravity towards the centre is $\dfrac{gR^2}{r^2}$. A body is projected from the surface of the planet with speed u. Show that when it has come to rest its distance r from the centre of the planet is given by

    $$r = \frac{2gR^2}{2gR - u^2}.$$

8. A particle is projected from the surface of the earth at 3,000 m s^{-1}. Use Question 7 to find the greatest height it reaches. (Ignore air resistance: take R to be 6.4×10^6 m.)

9. Use Question 7 to find the 'escape velocity' from the earth, i.e. the velocity a particle must have to escape completely from the earth's gravitational field.

33.3 Examination questions

1. A particle moves in a straight line so that its speed is inversely proportional to $(t + 1)$, where t is the time in seconds for which it has been moving. After 2 seconds, the particle has a retardation of $\dfrac{10}{9}$ m s^{-2}.

    Calculate the distance moved in the first second of the motion.

    [L]

2. A particle moves in a straight line with variable velocity. When its displacement from a fixed point O on the line is x its velocity is v. Show that the acceleration is then $v\dfrac{dv}{dx}$.

    The particle is projected from O with velocity u (where $u > 0$) and moves under the action of a force directed towards O and proportional to $v^{3/2}$. When $x = a$ the velocity of the particle is $\dfrac{u}{4}$. Find its velocity when $x = \dfrac{4a}{3}$.

    [JMB]

3. Given that $v = \dfrac{dx}{dt}$, show that $\dfrac{dv}{dt} = \dfrac{d}{dx}(\tfrac{1}{2}v^2)$.

    A particle of mass 0.1 kg moves in a straight path under the action of a variable force F, such that when the particle is at distance x metres from a fixed point O on the path, the force F has magnitude $\dfrac{0.4}{x^3}$ newtons, and acts towards O. If v m s^{-1} is the speed at time t seconds, and the particle starts (at $t = 0$) from position $x = 1$ with initial speed $v = 2$ (in the direction of x increasing), show that

    (i) $v = \dfrac{2}{x}$

    (ii) after 2 seconds x has increased to 3.

Find the loss of kinetic energy as the particle moves from $x = 1$ to $x = 3$, and *verify* that this is the work done by F in retarding the particle over this interval.

[SMP]

4. A train of mass 2.4×10^5 kg travelling at a speed v m s^{-1} on a horizontal track experiences a resistance of $40(100 + bv)$ N. The engine exerts a constant force of F newtons. When the train is travelling at a constant speed of 20 m s^{-1} the power output of the engine is 1.6×10^5 watts. Find F and b.

    If the train starts from rest,

    (i)   how long does it take to reach speed 10 m s^{-1}?

    (ii) how far has it travelled when its speed reaches 10 m s^{-1}?

[NI]

5. (a) A particle P moves along the x–axis with acceleration $6e^{-3t}$ at time t. Its velocity at time t is denoted by v. When $t = 0$, $v = 1$. Find the value of t when $v = 2$. Find also the limiting value of the speed as t becomes very large.

    (b) At time t the displacement from the origin O of a particle Q of mass m moving on the x–axis is x and its velocity is v. The particle moves under the action of a force directed towards O and of magnitude F given by

    $$F = \begin{cases} mn^2x & \text{when } x \geq a \\[2mm] \dfrac{mn^2x^3}{a^2} & \text{when } x \leq a \end{cases}$$

    where n is a positive constant. At time $t = 0$, the particle is released from rest at the point where $x = 2a$. Show that when it reaches the point where $x = a$ its speed V satisfies the equation $V^2 = 3a^2n^2$.

    Find the speed of the particle when it reaches O.

[C]

6. An aeroplane of mass M kg moves along a horizontal runway, starting from rest. The aeroplane's engines exert a constant thrust of T newtons and, when the speed of the aeroplane is v m s^{-1}, the magnitude of the resistance to motion is kv^2 newtons, where k is a positive constant.

    Show that, to reach a speed of V m s^{-1} on the runway, the aeroplane travels a distance

    $$\frac{M}{2k} \ln\left(\frac{T}{T - kV^2} \right)$$

[L]

Common errors

(a) Do not forget the constant of integration. It is often the most important part of the solution. In a numerical example the constant can be found from the initial conditions.

(b) Do not try to integrate a function of s with respect to t. That is, do not attempt to evaluate $\int f(s)\, dt$.

Usually writing $v\,\dfrac{dv}{ds}$ in place of $\dfrac{dv}{dt}$ will help you to avoid this.

(c) Be careful with signs. If a body experiences a force *towards* the origin, then its acceleration *away* from the origin is negative.

34 Circular motion

If a body is moving round a circle, the angle (in radians) through which the radius passes per second is the *angular velocity*.

If the circle has radius r and the angular velocity is ω then the speed v of the body is ωr.

Fig 34.1

A body moving in a circle of radius r, with angular velocity ω or speed v accelerates towards the centre of the circle at

$\omega^2 r$ or $\dfrac{v^2}{r}$. This is the *centripetal acceleration*.

The force which produces the centripetal acceleration is the *centripetal force*.

34.1 Two-dimensional problems

34.1.1 Examples

1. A body of mass 2 kg is on a smooth horizontal table, and moves in a circle at the end of a light string of length 1.5 m. The body makes 70 revolutions per minute. Find the tension in the string.

    Solution

    Convert 70 r.p.m. to angular velocity.

    $\omega = 70 \times 2\pi \div 60$ rads/sec.

    The body accelerates at $r\omega^2$ m s⁻². Multiply this by 2.

    The tension in the string is $mr\omega^2 = 161.2$ N.

2. A turn-table rotates at 4 rads/sec. A body lies on the table, and the coefficient of friction between it and the table is $\frac{1}{4}$. Find the greatest distance it can be from the centre of the table.

    Fig 34.2

    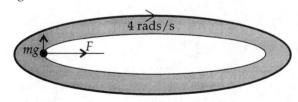

    Solution

    Let the mass of the body be m, and let the body be on the point of slipping when the radius is r. The normal force is mg, and hence the frictional force is $\frac{1}{4}mg$.

    This force provides the centripetal acceleration.

    $\frac{1}{4}mg = mr4^2$

    The greatest radius is $\frac{1}{4}\dfrac{g}{16} = 0.153$ m.

34.1.2 Exercises

1. Convert the following to angular velocities:
   (a) 24 revolutions per second
   (b) 77 revolutions per minute
   (c) 15° per second
   (d) 1,000° per hour.

2. Find the angular velocities of the following:
   (a) The hour hand of a clock
   (b) The minute hand of a clock
   (c) The earth about its axis
   (d) The earth about the sun.

3. A turntable rotates at 40 rads/sec. Find the speed of a point 0.2 m from the centre.

4. A roundabout rotates at 8 revolutions per minute. Find the speed of a child 2 m from the centre.

5. A roundabout rotates so that it takes 12 seconds to make a full circle. Find the speed of a child 1 m from the centre.

6. A body of mass 3 kg moves in a horizontal circle of radius 2.5 m with angular speed 12. Find its acceleration. Find the horizontal force experienced by the body.

7. A body of mass 0.3 kg moves in a horizontal circle with angular speed 3 under a horizontal force of 12 N. Find the radius of the circle.

8. A body of mass 1.5 kg moves in a horizontal circle of radius 1.25 m under a horizontal force of 13 N. Find its angular velocity.

9. A turntable rotates at 2 rads/sec. The coefficient of friction between it and a body on it is 0.5. Find the greatest possible distance of the body from the centre.

10. A turntable rotates at 40 r.p.m. A body can just stay on the table at a distance of 12 cm from the centre. Find the coefficient of friction.

11. The coefficient of friction between a body and a turntable is $\frac{3}{8}$. It is on the point of slipping when it is 5 cm from the centre. Find the angular speed of the turntable.

12. The coefficient of friction between the tyres of a car and the ground is 0.9. It travels in a horizontal circle.
    (a) Find the greatest speed with which it can go round a circle of radius 50 m.
    (b) What is the least radius of a circle which it can go round at a speed of 20 m s^{-1}?

13. A car can just go round a circle of radius 45 m at 25 m s^{-1}. Find the coefficient of friction between the tyres and the ground.

14. Bodies A and B of masses 3 kg and 4 kg are connected by a light string. A lies on a smooth horizontal table. The string passes through a hole in the table and supports B. If A moves in a horizontal circle of radius $1\frac{1}{2}$ m find its speed.

15. The 'Rotor' at a funfair consists of a vertical cylinder of radius $2\frac{1}{2}$ m, which rotates at 2 rads/sec. Customers stand against the inside wall of the cylinder, and the floor gradually sinks away. Find the least coefficient of friction between the customers and the wall if they are to remain fixed on it.

34.2 Three–dimensional problems

34.2.1 Examples

1. A conical pendulum consists of a mass m suspended by a string of length h from a fixed point. The mass performs horizontal circles at ω rads/sec. Find the angle the string makes with the vertical.

Fig 34.3

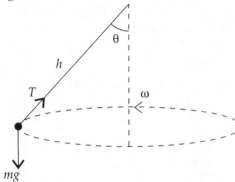

Solution

The mass does not move vertically. Hence, resolving vertically:

$T \cos \theta = mg$.

Resolving horizontally:

$T \sin \theta = m\, h \sin \theta\, \omega^2$.

Eliminate T by dividing the first equation by the second.

$$\cos \theta = \frac{g}{h\omega^2}$$

The angle is $\cos^{-1} \dfrac{g}{h\omega^2}$

2. A race track of radius 50 m is banked at 20° to the horizontal. If the coefficient of friction between a car's tyres and the track is 0.9, find the greatest speed at which it can go round the track without slipping.

Fig 34.4

Solution

Resolving vertically:

$R \cos 20° - F \sin 20° = mg$

Resolving horizontally:

$$R \sin 20° + F \cos 20° = \frac{mv^2}{50}$$

If it is about to slip, $F = 0.9\,R$. Eliminate R by dividing the second equation by the first:

$$\frac{v^2}{50g} = \frac{\sin 20° + 0.9 \cos 20°}{\cos 20° - 0.9 \sin 20°}$$

The maximum speed is 30.3 m s^{-1}

34.2.2 Exercises

1. A conical pendulum consists of a mass 0.5 kg at the end of a string of length 1.2 m. It performs horizontal circles at 3 rads/sec. Find the angle the string makes with the vertical.

2. If the conical pendulum of Question 1 rotates so that the string is at 30° to the vertical, find its angular velocity.

3. A conical pendulum makes an angle of 20° to the vertical, and rotates at an angular velocity of 0.8 rads/sec. Find the length of the string.

4. Two strings each of length 1.5 m are attached to a mass of 1 kg. Their free ends are attached to points A and B, where A is 2.4 m vertically above B.

The mass rotates in horizontal circles about AB. Find the least angular speed if the lower string is not to become slack. (Fig 34.5)

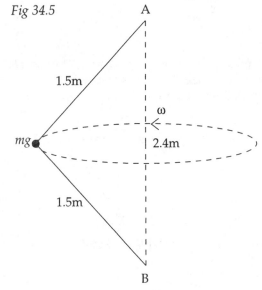

Fig 34.5

5. If, in Question 4, the mass rotates at 4 rads/sec, find the tension in the lower string.

6. In Question 4 the mass rotates so that the tension in the upper string is twice that in the lower string. Find the angular velocity.

7. Point A is 1.2 m above B. A string of length 1.8 m is attached to A and B, and a mass of 2 kg is smoothly threaded on it. The mass rotates around AB at the same level as B. Show that the mass is 0.5 m from B. Find its angular speed.

8. A circular race track of radius 50 m is banked at 30°. Find the speed at which a car travelling round the track has no tendency to side–slip.

9. If, in Question 8, the coefficient between tyres and track is 0.8, find the greatest speed with which a car can go round the track.

10. If, in Question 8, a car can just go round the track at 40 m s⁻¹, find the coefficient of friction between its tyres and the track.

11. A race track is banked at 25°, and the coefficient of friction between tyre and track is $\frac{1}{2}$. If the greatest safe speed is 35 m s⁻¹ find the radius of the track.

12. A race track is of radius 60 m. The coefficient of friction is $\frac{3}{4}$. At what angle should the track be banked if the fastest speed is 30 m s⁻¹?

13. A particle performs horizontal circles on the smooth inner surface of a sphere of radius 10 cm. If the particle is 5 cm below the centre of the sphere find its speed.

14. A particle moves in horizontal circles round the inner surface of a smooth vertical cone of angle 30°, which is held with its axis vertical and its point downwards. If the body moves at 3 m s⁻¹ find its height above the point.

34.3 Motion in a vertical circle

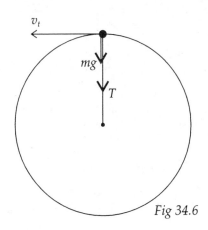

Fig 34.6

If a particle moves freely in a vertical circle then its velocity will vary. The velocity is best found by considerations of energy.

34.3.1 Example

A particle of mass m kg hangs at the end of a light inextensible string of length 1.4 m, the other end of which is fixed. Find the least velocity the particle must be given if it is to perform vertical circles.

Solution

Let v_b and v_t be the speeds at the bottom and the top respectively.

By conservation of energy:

$$mg \times 2.8 = \tfrac{1}{2}mv_b^{\,2} - \tfrac{1}{2}mv_t^{\,2}$$

$$g \times 5.6 = v_b^{\,2} - v_t^{\,2}$$

The string is most likely to collapse when the particle is at the top. Resolving vertically:

$$mg + T = \frac{mv_t^{\,2}}{1.4}$$

Vertical circles will be performed provided that $T \geq 0$.

$$\frac{mv_t^{\,2}}{1.4} \geq mg$$

$$v_t^{\,2} \geq 9.8 \times 1.4$$

$$v_b^{\,2} \geq 9.8 \times 1.4 + 9.8 \times 5.6$$

The least velocity is 8.28 m s^{-1}

34.3.2 Exercises

1. A particle hangs at the end of a light inextensible string of length 0.6 m. Find the least velocity it must be given to perform vertical circles.

2. A particle hangs at the end of a light inextensible string, and when it is given an initial speed of 6 m s^{-1} it just performs vertical circles. Find the length of the string.

3. A hollow cylinder with inside radius 20 cm is held with its axis horizontal. A smooth stone makes vertical circles inside it: find the least speed that the stone has at its lowest point.

4. A roller–coaster contains a vertical circle of radius 10 m. Find the least speed that the cars must have at the bottom of the circle if they are not to fall off the track at the top of the circle.

5. A body of mass 2 kg is at the end of a light inextensible string of length 2 m. It is given a speed of 20 m s^{-1}. Find
    (a) the speed at the top of the swing
    (b) the tension in the string at the top of the swing.

6. Find the speed of the body of Question 5 when the string is horizontal. Find also the tension in the string at this time.

7. A body of mass 1 kg is tied to the end of a string of length 1.4 m. It is given a velocity of 1 m s^{-1}. Find
    (a) the greatest angle θ the string makes with the vertical
    (b) the tension in the string when the string makes $\tfrac{1}{2}\theta$ with the vertical.

8. A smooth wire is bent into a vertical circle of radius 0.5 m. A bead of mass 0.05 kg is threaded on it. At the lowest point of the wire the bead is given a speed of 5 m s^{-1}. Find its speed at the top of the circle and the reaction of the wire.

9. The bead of Question 8 is instead given a velocity of 2 m s⁻¹. Find the greatest height the bead rises to. Find the reaction of the wire when it has reached half this height.

34.4 Examination questions

1. A particle B of mass 200 g is attached to two light inextensible strings AB and BC, where AB = BC = 0.5 m. The ends A and C are held fixed so that A is vertically above C and AC = 0.6 m. The particle is made to rotate in a horizontal circle.

   (a) Calculate the tensions in both strings if the angular speed is $3\sqrt{10}$ rad/s.

   (b) Calculate the minimum angular speed if both strings are to remain taut.

   [AEB ADD 1986]

2. Write down the magnitude and indicate the direction of the acceleration of a particle travelling in a fixed circular path of radius r at a constant speed v.

   A satellite is in steady circular orbit at height h above the surface of the earth. At this height the gravitational pull on the satellite has magnitude

   $$\frac{GmM}{(R+h)^2}$$

   where m is the mass of the satellite, M is the mass of the earth, R is the radius of the earth, and G is constant. Find the speed of the satellite, and show that it will take a time

   $$2\pi(R+h)^{\frac{3}{2}}(GM)^{-\frac{1}{2}}$$

   to travel once round the orbit.

   [SMP]

Fig 34.7

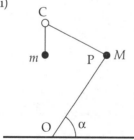

(i) (ii)

3. A light inextensible string has one end fastened to a fixed point at O. A particle of mass m is attached to the other end of the string. The string passes through a small smooth ring at the fixed point C, vertically above O, and carries a smooth bead P of mass M, which is free to move on the string. The system rotates about OC with constant angular velocity ω.

   (a) Given that the bead moves on a smooth horizontal plane, in a circle of radius r and centre O (see Fig. (i)), with $\hat{OPC} = 60°$, show that

   $$\frac{m}{M} \le \frac{2}{\sqrt{3}} \quad \text{and that} \quad \frac{m}{M} = \frac{2r\omega^2}{3g}$$

   (b) Given that the bead moves, in a horizontal circle of radius R, above the plane (see Fig. (ii)), with $\hat{OPC}$ a right–angle and with OP inclined to the horizontal at an angle α, where $\cos\alpha = \frac{4}{5}$, show that $m = 5M$ and that $R\omega^2 = 7g$.

   [C]

4. A small bead P of mass m is threaded on a smooth thin wire, in the form of a circle of radius a and centre O, which is fixed in a vertical plane. The bead is initially at the lowest point A of the circle and is projected along the wire with a velocity which is just sufficient to carry it to the highest point. Denoting the angle POA by θ, find, in terms of m, g and θ, the magnitude of the reaction of the wire on the bead.

   Express $\dfrac{d\theta}{dt}$, where t denotes time, in the form $C\cos\dfrac{\theta}{2}$, where C is a constant. Show that the time taken for the bead to reach the horizontal diameter is

   $$\left(\frac{a}{g}\right)^{\frac{1}{2}} \ln(\sqrt{2}+1)$$

   [JMB]

5. One end of a light inextensible string of length a is fastened to a fixed point O. The other end of the string is fastened to a particle P of mass m. The particle is projected vertically upwards with speed u from the position in which the particle is at the same level as O, the string being taut. When OP makes an acute angle θ with the upward vertical through O, the speed of the particle is v and the tension in the string is T. Find expressions for v^2 and T in terms of m, a, u, θ and g, assuming that the string is still taut.

   If $u^2 = \frac{1}{2}(3\sqrt{3})\,ag$, show that the string becomes slack when $\theta = 30°$ and verify that in the subsequent motion the string again becomes taut when OP is horizontal.

   [O&C]

Common errors

1. **Angular velocity**

   Do not measure angular velocity in degrees. It must be measured in radians.

2. **Centripetal force**

   (a) A body moving in a circle is accelerating towards the centre. This must be provided by the *centripetal* force. It is incorrect to put in a *centrifugal* force.

   (b) When working out the forces acting on a body moving in a circle, do not forget that the body is accelerating towards the centre.

3. **Motion in a vertical circle**

   For a body on the end of a string to reach the top of a circle, it is not sufficient for it to have enough energy to get there. It must also have sufficient speed for the tension in the string to be non–zero at the top.

35 Elasticity

35.1 Elasticity

Suppose forces are applied to a body. If the body reverts to its original shape when the forces are removed, then the body is made from *elastic* material.

If an elastic string under tension T extends by a length x, then *Hooke's Law* states:

The tension is proportional to the extension. $T \propto x$.

The constant k of proportionality is the *spring rate*.

For different lengths of the same string, k is inversely proportional to the length. The constant λ of proportionality is the *modulus of elasticity*.

$$T = \frac{\lambda x}{L}$$

where L is the unstretched length of the string.

Energy is stored in the string in the form of *elastic potential energy*. If a string of length L and modulus λ is stretched by x, the energy stored is:

$$\tfrac{1}{2} \frac{\lambda x^2}{L}.$$

35.1.1 Examples

Fig 35.1

20cm

5cm

1kg

1. An elastic string of natural length 20 cm stretches to 25 cm under a load of 1 kg. Find the modulus of elasticity. What will its length be under a load of 2.5 kg?.

   Solution

   Here the extension is 5 cm. Using Hooke's Law:

   $$1 \times g = \frac{\lambda \times 0.05}{0.2}.$$

   The modulus of elasticity is $4g = 39.2$ N.

   If the load is 2.5, then the extension x is given by:

   $$2.5g = \frac{4gx}{0.2}. \text{ Hence } x = 0.125 \text{ m}.$$

   The new length will be 32.5 cm.

2. A man of mass 80 kg jumps off a bridge, tied to the bridge by an elastic rope of natural length 20 m and modulus 1568 N. Find the greatest depth that he reaches, and his depth below the bridge when he stops bouncing.

   Solution

   Suppose that his greatest depth occurs when the string is stretched by x m. The loss of gravitational potential energy must equal the gain of elastic potential energy.

   $$80 \times g \times (x + 20) = \tfrac{1}{2} \frac{1568}{20} x^2.$$

   $$x^2 - 20x - 400 = 0.$$

   $$x = 32.4 \text{ m or } -12.4 \text{ m}.$$

   His greatest depth is 52.4 m below the bridge.

   When he stops bouncing his weight must equal the tension in the rope. Let y be the extension when this occurs:

   $$80g = \frac{1568}{20} y. \text{ Hence } y = 10 \text{ m}.$$

   When he stops bouncing he will be 30 m below the bridge.

35.1.2 Exercises

1. An elastic string of natural length 2 m and modulus 40 N supports a mass of 3 kg. Find the extension of the string.

2. An elastic string of unstretched length 0.4 m and modulus 49 N supports a load. If the extension is 5 cm find the load.

3. An elastic string of natural length 0.6 m extends 9 cm under a load of 0.5 kg. Find its modulus of elasticity.

4. An elastic string of modulus of elasticity 49 N extends by 30 cm under a load of 2 kg. Find its natural length.

5. When a mass of 2 kg hangs from the end of an elastic string its length doubles. Find its modulus of elasticity.

6. A spring of natural length 10 cm is compressed 0.1 cm when it supports a mass of 5 kg. Find the modulus of elasticity.

7. The length of a string is 1.2 m under a load of 4 kg, and 1.4 m under a load of 6 kg. Find its natural length and its modulus of elasticity.

8. A string, of natural length 1.5 m and modulus 19.6 N, is tied to a similar string, and a mass of 1.3 kg is suspended from the free end of the second string. Find the total extension of the strings.

9. The two strings of Question 8 are joined together at both ends. A mass of 1.3 kg is hung from the combined string. Find the extension.

10. Point A is 3 m above point B. Two elastic strings, of natural length 1 m and moduli 19.6 N, are tied at A and B. The free ends of the strings are tied to a mass of 0.5 kg. Find the height of the mass above B.

11. Find the energy stored in an elastic string of length 50 cm and modulus 9.8 N when it is extended by 10 cm.

12. Find the energy stored in an elastic string of length 2 m and modulus 49 N when it supports a mass of 3 kg.

13. A spring of length 20 cm and modulus 98 N is compressed by 5 cm. It fires a mass of 10 grams. Assuming that all the elastic potential energy is changed into the kinetic energy of the mass, find its velocity after it is fired.

14. A catapult consists of two parallel elastic strings, each of natural length 15 cm and modulus 49 N. A 10 gram stone is placed between the strings and they are pulled back 20 cm and released. Assuming that all the elastic energy is changed to kinetic energy of the stone, find its initial velocity.

15. A body of mass 0.1 kg travelling horizontally at 25 m s^{-1} is brought to rest by a spring of natural length 40 cm and modulus 490 N. Find the compression of the spring.

16. A mass of 4 kg is tied to the end of an elastic string of length 2 m and modulus 98 N. The other end is attached to a point A on a smooth horizontal surface. The mass is thrown horizontally at 12 m s^{-1} away from A. Find the extension of the string when it is brought to rest.

17. A mass of 40 kg hangs at the end of an elastic rope of natural length 10 m and modulus 4900 N. Find the extension of the string. It is then given a downward velocity of 1 m s^{-1}. Find the greatest depth to which it falls.

18. A mass of 60 kg is tied to the end of an elastic string of natural length 15 m and modulus 2450 N. The other end is tied to the top of a building, and the mass is dropped from the level of the top. Find.

    (a) the greatest depth it sinks to.

    (b) the speed with which it is moving when it has fallen 20 m.

    (c) its depth when it stops bouncing.

19. A mass of 20 kg rests on top of a spring of natural length 0.2 m and modulus 490 N. Find the compression of the spring. The mass is then pushed down a further 2 cm and released. Find the speed of the mass when it passes through its original position.

35.2 Simple harmonic motion

If a body moves to and from about a fixed point, it is *oscillating* about that point.

An oscillation in which the motion of a body is given by

$$x = a \sin(\omega t + \varphi)$$

is called *simple harmonic motion*. (S.H.M.).

The motion can also be written as

$$x = A \cos \omega t + B \sin \omega t,$$

where $a^2 = A^2 + B^2$ and $\tan \varphi = \dfrac{A}{B}$.

The *amplitude* of the motion is a.

The *period* of the motion is $\dfrac{2\pi}{\omega}$

The *frequency* of the motion is $\frac{\omega}{2\pi}$.

The *phase angle* of the motion is φ

35.2.1 Example

A body executes simple harmonic motion, with amplitude 3 cm and period $\frac{2\pi}{5}$ seconds. When $t = 0$ the displacement is zero. Find

(a) the value of the displacement at time t

(b) the maximum velocity

(c) the time for it to reach 1 cm.

Solution

(a) Let x be the displacement. Then $a = 3$ and $\omega = 5$. When $t = 0$ $x = 0$, and hence $\varphi = 0$. Write down the equation for x:

$$x = 3 \sin 5t.$$

(b) Differentiate x to find the velocity.

$$\frac{dx}{dt} = 15 \cos 5t.$$

The maximum velocity is 15 cm s^{-1}.

(c) Put $x = 1$.

$$1 = 3 \sin 5t.$$
$$\sin 5t = \tfrac{1}{3}.$$
$$t = \tfrac{1}{5} \sin^{-1}\tfrac{1}{3}$$

It reaches 1 cm after 0.068 secs.

35.2.2 Exercises

1. For each of the following equations of simple harmonic motion, write down the amplitude, the period and the phase angle.

    (a) $x = 3 \sin(2t + 1)$ (b) $x = 4 \sin(\tfrac{1}{2}t - 2)$.

    (c) $x = 3 \cos t + 4 \sin t$ (d) $x = 12 \cos 3t - 5 \sin 3t$.

    (e) $x = 2 \cos(3t - \tfrac{1}{4}\pi)$

    (f) $x = \cos(\tfrac{1}{2}t + \tfrac{1}{6}\pi) + 2 \sin(\tfrac{1}{2}t + \tfrac{1}{6}\pi)$.

2. A point moves with S.H.M. of period π, and its maximum velocity is 3. Find its amplitude.

3. A point starts from the origin and performs S.H.M. with period $\tfrac{1}{3}\pi$ and amplitude 10. Find the displacement in terms of time.

4. A point moving with S.H.M. has maximum velocity 12 and amplitude 4. Find its period.

5. A point moving with S.H.M. has frequency 6 and maximum velocity 8. Find its amplitude.

6. A point moves with S.H.M. of period π. If its amplitude is 10 cm find the time it takes to travel 5 cm from the origin.

7. A point moves with S.H.M of period $\frac{1}{4}\pi$. It takes 0.1 secs to go 5 cm from the origin. Find its amplitude.

8. A point moves with S.H.M. of amplitude 6 cm. It takes 3 secs to travel 3 cm from the origin. Find its period.

9. A point moves with S.H.M. of period $\frac{1}{3}\pi$ and amplitude 10 cm. Find its distance from the origin when its speed is 4 cm s^{-1}.

10. A point executes S.H.M. with period 4π and amplitude 20 cm. What is its maximum velocity? How long does it take for its speed to change from zero to 4 cm s^{-1}?

35.3 Systems which perform S.H.M.

Let x measure the displacement of a system. If $\dfrac{d^2x}{dt^2} = -\omega^2 x$, then the system performs S.H.M. of period $\dfrac{2\pi}{\omega}$

A heavy particle which swings in a vertical plane at the end of a light inextensible string is a *simple pendulum*.

35.3.1 Examples

Fig 35.2

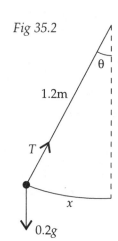

1. A simple pendulum consists of a mass of 0.2 kg at the end of a light inextensible string of length 1.2 m. Find the period of small oscillations.

   Solution

   Suppose the mass is pulled aside through a distance x. Resolving perpendicular to the string:

   $$0.2\,\frac{d^2x}{dt^2} = -0.2 \times g \sin\theta$$

   If θ is small, then $\sin\theta \approx \dfrac{x}{1.2}$.

   $$0.2\,\frac{d^2x}{dt^2} = -0.2\,g\,\frac{x}{1.2}.$$

   $$\frac{d^2x}{dt^2} = -\frac{9.8}{1.2}\,x.$$

   The pendulum performs S.H.M. with period $2\pi\sqrt{\dfrac{1.2}{9.8}} = 2.2$ seconds.

2. An elastic string of unstretched length 1.5 m and modulus 21 N supports a mass of 0.1 kg. It is displaced slightly. Find the period of the following oscillations.

   Solution

   When it is hanging in equilibrium, the extension e is given by:

   $$0.1 \times 9.8 = \frac{21}{1.5} \times e. \text{ Hence } e = 0.07 \text{ m.}$$

If it falls a further distance x, the equation of motion is:

$$0.1 \, \frac{d^2x}{dt^2} = 0.1 \times 9.8 - \frac{21}{1.5} \, (e + x).$$

The constant terms on the right hand side cancel. Divide both sides by 0.1 to obtain:

$$\frac{d^2x}{dt^2} = -140 \, x.$$

The period of the oscillations is $\frac{2\pi}{\sqrt{140}} = 0.53$ secs.

35.3.2 Exercises

1. A simple pendulum consists of a mass of 1 kg at the end of a string of length 2 m. Find the period of small oscillations.

2. A simple pendulum has period 5 seconds. Find its length.

3. On a certain planet a simple pendulum of length 1.5 m has period 3 secs. Find the acceleration due to gravity on that planet.

4. Through long use the length of a simple pendulum increases by 1%. Find the approximate percentage increase in its period.

5. The bob of a simple pendulum of length 1 m has a velocity of $\frac{1}{2}$ cm s^{-1} at its lowest point. Find the amplitude of the displacement of the bob.

6. A simple pendulum of length 1.4 m swings through a total angle of 2°. Find the maximum speed of its bob.

7. A mass of 5 kg hangs from an elastic string of length 0.5 m and modulus 49 N. If it is displaced slightly downward, find the frequency of its oscillations.

8. A mass of 10 kg lies on a smooth horizontal table, and is attached to a spring of length 0.4 m and modulus 500 N. The mass is given an initial velocity of 0.02 m s^{-1}. Find the period and amplitude of the following oscillations.

9. A mass of 1 kg lies on a smooth horizontal table, and is attached to a spring of length 0.2 m and modulus 100 N. It is pulled through a distance of 1 cm. Find the period of the following oscillations, and its maximum velocity.

10. A smooth wire is bent into the shape of a circle of radius a, and is fixed in a vertical plane. A small bead is threaded on the wire, and is disturbed slightly from the lowest position. Find the frequency of the following oscillations.

11. A cube of side a cm has a uniform density of ρ. ($\rho < 1$). It floats in a large lake, with two faces horizontal. If it is pushed a small distance x downwards, show that the net upthrust is a^2xg. Hence find the period with which it bobs up and down in the water.

35.4 Examination questions

1. State Hooke's law

   (a) A particle of mass 2 kg is attached to one end of a spring of natural length 0.5 m and modulus of elasticity 160 N. The other end is fastened to a point on a smooth horizontal table. If the particle is made to describe circles on the table at $\frac{4}{\pi}$ revolutions per second, find the extension of the spring.

   (b) A particle of mass 5 kg describes horizontal circles suspended on the end of an extended elastic string whose natural length is 0.16 m and modulus of elasticity is 400 N. The string is extended by 0.04 m beyond its natural length. Find the inclination of the string to the vertical and the speed with which the particle is rotating.

   (Assume that the acceleration due to gravity is 10 m s^{-2}).

   [NI].

2. A uniform rod AB, of length 2a and mass m, rests in equilibrium with its lower end A on a rough horizontal floor. Equilibrium is maintained by a horizontal elastic string, of natural length a and modulus λ. One end of the string is attached to B and the other end to a point vertically above A. Given that θ, where $\theta < \frac{1}{3}\pi$, is the inclination of the rod to the horizontal,

   show that the magnitude of the tension in the string is $\frac{1}{2}mg \cot \theta$.

   Prove also that $2\lambda = \dfrac{mg \cot \theta}{2 \cos \theta - 1}$.

   Given that the system is in limiting equilibrium and that the coefficient of friction between the floor and the rod is $\frac{2}{3}$, find $\tan \theta$. Hence show that

   $$\lambda = \frac{10\,mg}{9}.$$

   [L].

3. A uniform rod AB of length 2a and weight W has its ends joined by a light elastic string of natural length a and modulus of elasticity λ. The string passes over a small smooth peg at C and the rod rests in equilibrium at an angle 30° to the horizontal with A in contact with a rough horizontal plane. C is vertically above A and AC = 2a. Show that

   (i) $\lambda = \dfrac{W}{6}$;

   (ii) $\mu \geq \sqrt{3}$, where μ is the coefficient of friction between the rod and the plane.

   Find the magnitude and direction of the force that the peg exerts on the string.

   [SUJB].

4. A particle of mass 0.02 kg is performing simple harmonic motion with centre O, period 6 s and amplitude 2 m. Find, correct to 2 significant figures in each case,.

   (i) the maximum speed V of the particle;.

   (ii) the distance of the particle from O when its speed is 0.9V;.

(iii) the magnitude of the force on the particle when it is 1 m from O.

Show also that the power exerted by the force on the particle is a periodic function of time, and state its period.

(Simple harmonic motion formulae may be quoted without proof.).

[MEI].

5. A particle P moves along the *x*–axis so that its displacement *x* from the origin at time *t* satisfies the differential equation

$$\frac{d^2x}{dt^2} + 9x = 18.$$

At times $t = \frac{\pi}{6}, \frac{\pi}{3}$ the values of *x* are 6, 5 respectively.

Assuming that the solution to the equation is $x = A \cos nt + B \sin nt + c$, find values for *A*, *B*, *c* and *n*.

Prove that the solution may be written in the form $x = 5 \sin(3t - \alpha) + 2$,

where α is the angle in the first quadrant such that $\tan \alpha = \frac{3}{4}$.

Assuming that the motion starts at $t = 0$, determine.

(i)   the initial displacement and the greatest displacement.

(ii) the initial speed and the greatest speed.

Draw rough sketches of *x* and of $\frac{dx}{dt}$ against *t* in the range $0 \le t \le \pi$.

[O&C].

6. A point P moves along the line A'OA, where A'O = OA = *a* such that when OP = *x*, its acceleration $\frac{d^2x}{dt^2} = -\omega^2 x$.

Without assuming any formulae relating to simple harmonic motion show that.

(i)   if the speed $v = 0$ when $x = a$ then $v^2 = \omega^2(a^2 - x^2)$,

(ii) a solution of the differential equation such that $v = 0$ when $t = 0$ is $x = a \cos \omega t$.

At time $t = 0$, P is at A and it moves a distance of 1 m to B where its speed is 6 m s^{-1} and after moving a further 1 m to C its speed is 8 m s^{-1}. If C and B are between O and A find the values of *a* and ω and the time taken for P to move from B to C.

A rough horizontal platform moves horizontally according to the above law with these values of *a* and ω. When the platform is instantaneously at rest a weight is placed on it. If the coefficient of friction between the weight and the platform is 0.8 and the acceleration due to gravity is 9.8 m s^{-2} determine whether the weight slides or remains at relative rest.

[SUJB].

7. A light elastic string AB obeying Hooke's law is of natural length 1 m and has the end A fixed. When a particle of mass 2 kg is attached to the string at B and is allowed to hang freely, the string is extended by a length of 0.14 m. Find the modulus of elasticity, stating the units in which it is measured.

The particle is pulled down a further 0.2 m and is then released from rest at time $t = 0$. Show that until the string becomes slack, the motion is simple harmonic. Show also that the particle passes through the equilibrium position after approximately 0.19 seconds and find the speed of the particle at that time.

From energy considerations or otherwise, find how high above the point of release the particle reaches during the subsequent motion.

[W].

Common errors

1. **Hooke's Law.**

   Do not confuse the spring rate and the modulus of elasticity. If you are given the modulus λ then you must divide by the natural length in order to use Hooke's law.

2. **S.H.M.**

   When dealing with simple harmonic motion, all angles must be measured in radians. Do not measure them in degrees.

36 Permutations and combinations

The number of ways in which n objects can be arranged in a definite order is:

$$n(n-1)(n-2)(n-3)...3.2.1$$

This is pronounced 'n factorial', and written $n!$. By convention, $0! = 1$.

If r objects are to be permuted from n objects, i.e. arranged in a definite order, then the number of ways in which this can be done is:

$$^nP_r = \frac{n!}{(n-r)!} = n(n-1)(n-2)...(n-r+1)$$

If r objects are to be *combined* from n objects, i.e. selected in any order, then the number of ways in which this can be done is:

$$^nC_r = \frac{n!}{r!\,(n-r)!} = \frac{n(n-1)(n-2)\,...\,(n-r+1)}{r!}$$

^nC_r is often written as $\binom{n}{r}$

The expression ^nC_r was also defined as the binomial coefficient in Chapter 3.

36.1 Simple arrangement problems

Examples 36.1.1

1. Find

   (a) $^{10}P_3$ (b) $^{100}C_3$

   Solution

   (a) Use the definition.

   $$^{10}P_3 = \frac{10!}{7!} = 720$$

   (b) The second form of the definition will be used, as a calculator may not be able to handle 100!.

   $$^{100}C_3 = \frac{100 \times 99 \times 98}{3!} = 161{,}700$$

2. In a game of poker, 5 cards are dealt from a pack of 52. How many possible poker hands are there?

Solution

Here 5 cards are selected from 52, without regard to order. This is a combinations problem.

$$\text{Number of hands} = {}^{52}C_5 = 2{,}598{,}960$$

3. A telephone number contains 6 digits. How many possible telephone numbers are there in which no digit is repeated?

Solution

There are ten digits. For a telephone number the order of digits is important. Hence the total number of possible telephone numbers in which no digit is repeated is:

$$^{10}P_6 = 151{,}200$$

36.1.2 Exercises

1. Evaluate the following:
   - (a) 6!
   - (b) 10!
   - (c) 11!
   - (d) $^5P_2$
   - (e) $^{12}P_4$
   - (f) $^{20}P_5$
   - (g) $^6C_2$
   - (h) $^{12}C_5$

2. Evaluate the following:
   - (a) $^5P_5$
   - (b) $^{100}P_4$
   - (c) $^{10}C_{10}$
   - (d) $^{1001}C_2$
   - (e) $^{1001}C_{999}$

3. Show that $^{20}C_6 = {}^{20}C_{14}$

4. Show that $^nC_r = {}^nC_{n-r}$. Explain in words why this is true.

5. Is it true that $^nP_r = {}^nP_{n-r}$?

6. How many ways can you arrange the letters from the word CODES?

7. At Scrabble™ you have the letters XZJYPVK. How many 3 letter arrangements can be made from them?

8. A travelling salesman must visit 15 towns. In how many different ways can he plan his journey?

9. How many numbers between 100 and 1000 use only odd digits, no digit being repeated?

10. In Mastermind a code is picked using 4 out of 7 colours. How many codes are possible, if no colour can be used twice?

11. There are 14 horses in a race. In how many ways can the first 3 places be filled?

12. A class contains 25 pupils. In how many ways can prizes be awarded in Latin, French and Mathematics, if no pupil can win more than one prize?

13. In how many ways can eight books be arranged along a shelf?

14. At Scrabble the letters QWYPKGDZXBM are left in the bag. In how many ways can you draw out four of them?

15. You are given 12 points on a plane, no three of them being in a straight line. How many triangles can be drawn using the points as vertices?

16. You are given 9 points on a circle. How many chords do they form?

17. You have 10 blue flowers and 5 red flowers. In how many ways can they be planted in a row, if we do not distinguish between flowers of the same colour?

18. The travelling salesman of Question 8 decides to visit only 5 towns. In how many ways can his selection be made? How many possible journeys does he have now?

19. In Bridge each player receives 13 out of the 52 cards. How many possible Bridge hands are there?

20. A coin is tossed 10 times, and heads comes up 4 times. In how many ways can this have happened?

21. You win a tennis set 6–4. How many ways can this have happened?

36.2 Compound problems

36.2.1 Examples

1. How many arrangements are there of the letters of the word SCROOGE? In how many of these are the O's together?

   Solution

   If the O's were different, there would be 7! arrangements. But the O's can be permuted without changing the arrangement. Hence there are:

   $$\frac{7!}{2!} = 2520 \text{ arrangements.}$$

   If the O's are kept together, then they can be considered as one single letter. The number of arrangements is therefore:

   $$6! = 720.$$

2. A squash team is to contain 3 men and 2 women, chosen from 15 men and 9 women. In how many ways can the team be chosen?

   Solution

   The men can be picked in $^{15}C_3 = 455$ ways. The women can be picked in $^9C_2 = 36$ ways. The total number of possible teams is therefore:

   $$455 \times 36 = 16{,}380$$

3. 4 six-sided dice are rolled. What is the probability that the numbers they show are all different?

   Solution

   The number of ways in which 4 different numbers could be selected is $^6P_4 = 360$.

   The number of ways in which the 4 numbers, not necessarily different, could be selected is $6 \times 6 \times 6 \times 6 = 1296$.

The probability is therefore:

$$\frac{360}{1296} = \frac{5}{18}$$

36.2.2 Exercises

1. Find the number of arrangements of the letters of:
    (a) DREAD   (b) CASSETTE
    (c) TERROR   (d) HORROR
    (e) INTERDENOMINATIONAL

2. How many arrangements are there of the letters from ABACUS in which the A's are together?

3. How many arrangements are there of the letters from ABACUS in which the A's are not together?

4. How many arrangements are there of the letters from BRAINS in which the vowels are together?

5. How many arrangements are there of the letters from IDAHO in which the consonants are separated?

6. A library contains 10 thrillers and 18 science–fiction books. In how many ways can a borrower select 2 of each?

7. A committee must contain 3 men and 4 women. In how many ways can the committee be chosen from 10 men and 6 women?

8. In how many ways can 7 men and 8 women sit on a bench, if no 2 women can sit next to each other?

9. A shelf contains 5 Western books and 4 Romances. In how many ways can they be arranged
    (a) without any restrictions
    (b) if all the Westerns are together and all the Romances are together
    (c) if all the Westerns are together
    (d) if no two Westerns are together?

10. How many codes are there in the Mastermind game of Question 10, 36.1.2, without the restriction that colours may not be repeated?

11. How many numbers are there between 100 and 1000 in which the digit 0 does not appear?

12. How many numbers between 500 and 1000 are there using only the digits 1, 3, 4, 6, 7?

13. How many odd numbers are there between 5000 and 10000 are there using only the digits 1, 3, 6, 7, 8?

14. 12 circles are drawn on a piece of paper. What is the greatest possible number of intersection points?

15. In a certain country car registration numbers consist of 3 letters followed by 4 numbers. How many registrations are possible if
    (a) no letter or digit may be repeated
    (b) without such a restriction?

16. How many 3 letter arrangements can be taken from the letters of DREAD?

17. In its sweet-box a child has 3 toffees, 2 chocolates and 1 liquorice. Its mother only allows it to eat 3. In how many ways can this be done?

18. There are 27 children in a class. Find the probability that:

    (a) Their birthdays are all different.

    (b) At least two children have the same birthday.

    (Ignore leap years; assume that all days of the year are equally likely; leave your answer in factorial form)

19. In Bridge the 52 cards are dealt to 4 players. How many possible Bridge deals are there?

20. Find the probability that a Bridge hand of 13 cards contains:

    (a) 7 spades   (b) 7 cards all of the same suit.

21. In a game of Bridge, North and South have 8 hearts between them. What is the probability that the remaining 5 are split 3–2 or 2–3 between East and West?

22. A railway carriage has 4 seats on each side. In how many ways can 6 men and 2 women sit if

    (a) the women sit opposite each other

    (b) the women do not sit next to each other?

23. A diagonal of a polygon is a line joining two vertices which are not next to each other. How many diagonals are there for a

    (a) 10 sided polygon   (b) n-sided polygon.

24. In how many ways can two taxis, each of which will take at most 4 passengers, take a party of 7 people if 2 of them refuse to be in the same taxi?

36.3 Examination questions

1. In the small country of Ruritania, car registration plates consist of different arrangements of groups of 4 letters taken from the Ruritanian alphabet which consists of 10 letters. Calculate the number of different registration plates which can be made if

   (a) repetitions of letters are not allowed,

   (b) the letters can be repeated any number of times.

   In case (b), all the different possible arrangements are listed and one arrangement is then to be chosen at random. Calculate the probability of choosing an arrangement which has

   (c) two or more letters the same,

   (d) different letters at the beginning and the end of the arrangement.

   [L ADD]

2. Three girls and three boys enter a railway compartment in which there are six seats altogether, three on each side. In how many different ways can the seats be occupied?

If the girls all sit on one side and the boys sit opposite in how many different ways can the seats be occupied?

If the girls enter the compartment first and occupy three of the four corner seats and the boys then follow them and occupy the remaining seats, in how many different ways can the seats be occupied?

[MEI ADD]

3. John and Mary are members of a group of eight boys and two girls.

    (a) In how many ways can they all be seated in a row if John and Mary always sit together? (Leave your answer in factorial form.)

    (b) In how many ways can a sub-committee of five be chosen from the same group of ten if:

        (i)   both John and Mary are on it,

        (ii) either John or Mary is on it but not both,

        (iii) at least one girl is on it?

[O&C ADD]

4. A certain game is played with a number of cards, each of which has a single letter printed on it. A player has ten cards, which are lettered A, C, E, E, E, F, L, L, W, X respectively.

    (i) A 'word' is any arrangement of these ten letters, for example LXCELWFEEA.

        (a) Find the total number of different 'words' that the player can make.

        (b) Find the number of these 'words' which begin and end with E and in which the two letters L are consecutive.

    (ii) A second player chooses three of the first player's ten cards at random, and takes them from the first player. Calculate the probability that

        (a) the three cards will all carry the letter E or L,

        (b) the first player's remaining seven cards will all carry different letters.

[C]

5. How many distinguishable arrangements of the 10 letters of the word STATISTICS are possible?

    Three letters are selected without replacement from these ten and the number of distinguishable ways of arranging them is calculated. What is the total number of distinguishable arrangements for all possible such selections?

    The ten letters are written one on each of ten cards. Two cards are selected at random and from these any card not carrying an S or a T is discarded and another selected in its place from the remaining cards. What is the probability that the cards now chosen are either two S's or two T's?

[O&C]

Common errors

1. Make sure you do not confuse ^nP_r and ^nC_r. If the order is important then ^nP_r is used, if it is not important then ^nC_r is used.

2. $0! = 1$, not 0. In particular, $^nC_0 = 1$. If we select 0 objects out of n, then there is 1 way of doing it. (Don't pick any!)

3. Suppose you are making two different selections, say of 5 from a group of 10 and 6 from another group of 9. The total number of ways is the *product* of $^{10}C_5$ and $^9C_6$. Do not add the expressions.

4. Suppose r items are selected out of n. If repetition is allowed, then the number of ways is n^r. If repetition is not allowed, the number of ways is ^nP_r. Do not confuse these.

37 Discrete random variables

37.1 Distribution of discrete random variables

A variable X whose values are determined by chance is a *random variable*.

The *distribution* of a random variable X gives the possible values of X with their appropriate probabilities. The distribution may be given by a formula or by a table.

Suppose that X take the values $x_1, x_2, x_3,..., x_n,...$, with associated probabilities $p_1 = P(X=x_1)$, $p_2 = P(X=x_2),..., p_n = P(X=x_n)$ and so on. Each p_i is greater or equal to 0, and their sum must be 1.

$$p_i \geq 0 \text{ and } \sum p_i = 1.$$

A random variable whose distribution can be described in this way is a *discrete* random variable.

Usually, but not always, X takes whole number values, i.e. each x_i is an integer.

X may take either finitely many or infinitely many values.

37.1.1 Examples

1. X is a discrete random variable with distribution given by the table below. Find the value of c.

i	1	2	3	4
P($X=i$)	0.1	0.3	c	0.2

    Solution

    The sum of all the probabilities must be 1.

    $0.1 + 0.3 + c + 0.2 = 1$

    $\qquad c = 0.4$

2. 3 fair coins are spun, and X is the number of heads obtained. Write down the distribution of X.

    Solution

    Denoting heads by H and tails by T, the 8 possible outcomes are

    HHH, HHT, HTH, HTT, THH, THT, TTH, TTT.

In one of these outcomes, HHH, there are 3 heads. Hence $P(X = 3) = \frac{1}{8}$. In 3 of the outcomes $X = 1$. Hence $P(X = 1) = \frac{3}{8}$. The other probabilities are found similarly. Fill in the table below:

i	0	1	2	3
$P(X=i)$	$\frac{1}{8}$	$\frac{3}{8}$	$\frac{3}{8}$	$\frac{1}{8}$

37.1.2 Exercises

1. The discrete random variable X has the distribution given by the table below. Find the value of a.

i	0	1	2	3
$P(X=i)$	a	0.1	0.3	0.2

2. The discrete random variable X has the distribution given by the table below. Find the value of m.

i	2	3	4	5	6
$P(X=i)$	m	0.1	0.5	$2m$	0.05

3. The discrete random variable X takes values $i = 0, 1, 2, 3$ with probabilities $\lambda i + 0.1$. Find λ.

4. X takes values $i = 1, 2, 3, 4, 5$ with probabilities $\dfrac{i}{20} + \mu$. Find μ.

5. X takes values $i = 1, 2, 3, 4$ with probabilities $\dfrac{i^2}{100} + \beta$. Find β.

6. A fair die is rolled, and X is the score. Write down the distribution of X.

7. Two fair dice are rolled, and X is the total score. Write down the distribution of X.

8. Two fair dice are rolled, and X is the larger of the scores showing. (If the dice show the same number, then X is that number.) Write down the distribution of X.

9. 10 cards are numbered 1, 2, 2, 3, 3, 3, 4, 4, 4, 4. They are shuffled and one is drawn at random. Let X be the number on the drawn card. Write down the distribution of X.

10. A bag contains 4 red and 3 blue marbles. Two are drawn without replacement. X is the number of red marbles drawn. Write down the distribution of X.

37.2 Expectation

The *expectation* or *mean* of a random variable X is the average value that X takes. For a discrete random variable expectation is given by the formula:

$$E(X) = \sum i\, P(X = i)$$

37.2.1 Examples

1. X has the distribution given by the table below. Find $E(X)$.

i	2	3	4	5	6
$P(X=i)$	0.05	0.1	0.4	0.4	0.05

Solution

Use the formula for expectation:

$E(X) = 2 \times 0.05 + 3 \times 0.1 + 4 \times 0.4 + 5 \times 0.4 + 6 \times 0.05$

$E(X) = 4.3$

2. Michelle and Robert play a game as follows: from a bag containing 4 red and 5 blue marbles two are drawn without replacement. If both are red Robert wins 50p, if exactly one is red it is a draw. If both are blue Michelle wins: how much should she gain if the game is to be fair?

Solution

The probabilities of the number of red marbles are as follows:

$$P(2 \text{ red}) = \frac{4}{9} \times \frac{3}{8} = \frac{1}{6}$$

$$P(1 \text{ red}) = \frac{4}{9} \times \frac{5}{8} + \frac{5}{9} \times \frac{1}{2} = \frac{5}{9}$$

$$P(0 \text{ red}) = \frac{5}{9} \times \frac{1}{2} = \frac{5}{18}.$$

If Michelle wins x p when two blues are drawn, then Robert's expected gain for the game is:

$$50 \times \frac{1}{6} + 0 \times \frac{5}{9} - x \times \frac{5}{18}$$

For the game to be fair Robert's expected gain is zero.

$50 \times \frac{1}{6} - x \times \frac{5}{18} = 0$. Hence $x = 30$

Michelle should gain 30p if both marbles are blue

37.2.2 Exercises

1. If X has the distribution given by the table below, find $E(X)$.

i	1	2	3	4	5
$P(X=i)$	$\frac{1}{8}$	$\frac{1}{4}$	$\frac{3}{8}$	$\frac{1}{8}$	$\frac{1}{8}$

2. X has the distribution given by the table below. Find $E(X)$.

i	11	12	13	14
$P(X=i)$	0.3	0.4	0.1	0.2

3. & 4.

Find the expectations for the distributions given in Examples 1 and 2 of 37.1.1.

5. to 14.

Find the expectations for the distributions given in Exercises 1 to 10 of 37.1.2.

15. X has the distribution given by the table below. $E(X) = 3$. Find a.

i	1	2	a	4	5
$P(X=i)$	$\frac{1}{8}$	$\frac{1}{4}$	$\frac{3}{8}$	$\frac{1}{8}$	$\frac{1}{8}$

16. X has the distribution given by the table below. $E(X) = 2.8$. Find a and b.

i	1	2	3	4
$P(X=i)$	0.2	0.1	a	b

17. Cards numbered 1, 1, 2, 2, 2, 3, 3, 3, 4, 4, 4, 4, 4 are shuffled and one is drawn out. Find the expected value of the number on the drawn card.

18. A bag contains 5 black and 7 white beads. Two are drawn out without replacement. Find the expectation of the number of white beads.

19. In a dice game a fair die is rolled once. The player receives the score on the die in pounds, except when it is 1, in which case he has to pay the banker. If it is a fair game, how much does he pay?

    If instead he pays £21, how much will he expect to lose if he plays the game 100 times?

20. A coin game is follows. A fair coin is tossed either 3 times or until a head has turned up, whichever is the sooner. If a head first appears on the 1st, 2nd, 3rd go then the player receives £1, £3, £7 respectively. If no head appears on all three goes then the player has to pay the bank. If the game is fair, how much should be paid to the bank if no head appears?

37.3 Variance

The *variance* of a random variable is a measure of how widely spread the values are.

If X is a random variable with expectation μ, then the variance of X is given by:

$$\text{Var}(X) = E((X - \mu)^2)$$

An equivalent formula for the variance is:

$$\text{Var}(X) = E(X^2) - \mu^2$$

(The mean of the square minus the square of the mean)

The square root of the variance is the *standard deviation* σ.

$$\sigma = \sqrt{\text{Var}(X)} : \sigma^2 = \text{Var}(X)$$

37.3.1 Example

X has the distribution given by the table below. Find $\text{Var}(X)$.

i	0	1	2	3	4
$P(X=i)$	$\frac{1}{8}$	$\frac{1}{4}$	$\frac{3}{8}$	$\frac{1}{8}$	$\frac{1}{8}$

Solution

First find the expectation μ.

$\mu = 0 \times \frac{1}{8} + 1 \times \frac{1}{4} + 2 \times \frac{3}{8} + 3 \times \frac{1}{8} + 4 \times \frac{1}{8} = 1\frac{7}{8}$.

To find $E(X^2)$, average the value of X^2.

$E(X^2) = 0^2 \times \frac{1}{8} + 1^2 \times \frac{1}{4} + 2^2 \times \frac{3}{8} + 3^2 \times \frac{1}{8} + 4^2 \times \frac{1}{8} = 4\frac{7}{8}$.

Use the second version of the formula for variance:

$\mathrm{Var}(X) = 4\frac{7}{8} - \mu^2 = 1\frac{23}{64}$.

37.3.2 Exercises

1. X has a distribution given by the following table. Find $\mathrm{Var}(X)$.

i	1	2	3	4
$P(X=i)$	$\frac{1}{6}$	$\frac{1}{6}$	$\frac{1}{4}$	$\frac{5}{12}$

2. X has a distribution given by the table below. Find $\mathrm{Var}(X)$.

i	−1	0	1	2	3
$P(X=i)$	0.1	0.05	0.35	0.25	0.25

3. & 4.

   Find the variance for each of the distributions in Examples 1 & 2 of 37.1.1.

5. X has distribution given by the table below. $E(X) = 3.5$ and $\mathrm{Var}(X) = 2.65$. Find a and b, given that they are integers.

i	1	2	a	b
$P(X=i)$	0.1	0.3	0.4	0.2

6. A bag contains 4 red and 6 blue balls. Two are drawn without replacement. Find the mean and variance of the number of red balls.

7. A fair die is rolled twice. Let X and Y be the scores on the first and second throw respectively, and let $Z = X + Y$ be the total score. Find $E(X)$ and $\mathrm{Var}(X)$. Write out the distribution table for Z, and find $E(Z)$ and $\mathrm{Var}(Z)$.

8. With X and Y as defined in Question 7, let $W = X - Y$ be the *difference* between the scores. Write down the distribution table for W. Find the mean and variance of W.

37.4 Examination questions

1. Two dice, each in the shape of a regular tetrahedron, have the numbers 0, 1, 2, 3 respectively on their four faces. When the dice are thrown the score recorded is the product of the numbers on the two faces resting on the ground.

X	0	1	2	3
0	0	0	0	0
1	0	1	2	3
2	0	2	4	6
3	0	3	6	9

Copy and complete the table of scores recorded when the dice are thrown, and write down the probability of achieving each possible score. What is the expected score when the two dice are thrown?

In a game played with these two dice, and scores calculated in the same way, a player wins 10p if he makes a maximum score; wins 4p if he scores an odd number other than the maximum; loses 4p if he scores an even number (not zero); and loses 2p if he scores zero. Calculate the expected loss or gain for a player in 100 throws.

[MEI ADD]

2. (i) An urn contains 2 black and 3 white balls. Balls are drawn successively from the urn, at random and without replacement, until a black ball is obtained. Given that X is the random variable representing the number of draws required, copy and complete the following table:

n	1	2	3	4
$P(X = n)$				

Hence show that $E(X) = 2$.

(ii) A bag contains 4 red and 2 blue counters. Pairs of counters are drawn successively from the bag, at random and without replacement, until a pair of counters with the same colour is obtained. Given that Y is the random variable representing the number of draws required, copy and complete the following table:

m	1	2	3
$P(Y = m)$			

Hence find the value of $E(Y)$.

[L ADD]

3. In a shooting competition competitors aim at a target which consists of a central circle surrounded by three concentric rings. If a competitor hits the central circle he is awarded 5 points; the points awarded for hitting the rings are 4, 3 and 1 respectively. Each competitor hits the target with every shot. The object of the competition is to score at least 3 points in as few shots as possible.

The probabilities that a certain competitor, A, will score 5, 4, 3 or 1 points with any one shot are given in the table below.

Points	5	4	3	1
Probability	$\frac{1}{8}$	$\frac{3}{16}$	$\frac{5}{16}$	$\frac{3}{8}$

Find the probability that A will require

(i) one shot, (ii) two shots,

(iii) three shots, to score at least 3 points.

Given that X denotes the number of shots required by A to score at least 3 points, calculate $E(X)$, $E(X^2)$ and the variance of X.

The probabilities that a second competitor, B, will score 5, 4, 3 or 1 points with any one shot are all equal. Find the probability that B will require

(iv) one shot,   (v) two shots,

(vi) three shots, to score at least 3 points.

Given that Y denotes the number of shots required by B to score at least 3 points, calculate $E(Y)$, $E(Y^2)$ and the variance of Y.

Using these results, explain briefly who, in a series of contests between A and B, is the more likely to be

(vii)   the first to score at least 3 points on most occasions,

(viii) the more consistent marksman.

[C ADD]

4. Each trial of a random experiment must result in one and only one of the events A, B and C occurring, the probabilities of these events being $\frac{1}{2}$, $\frac{1}{4}$ and $\frac{1}{4}$, respectively.

Independent trials of the experiment are to be conducted until one of the three events occurs for the second time.

(i)   Show that the probability that the trials will stop with A occurring for the second time (a) in the second trial is $\frac{1}{4}$, (b) in the third trial is $\frac{1}{4}$, (c) in the fourth trial is $\frac{3}{32}$.

(ii) Determine the corresponding probabilities that the trials will stop with B occurring for the second time.

(iii) Let X denote the number of trials that will be conducted. Find the distribution of X. Hence determine the most probable value of X and the expected value of X.

[W]

5. Two riflemen, A and B, shoot independently at a target; a game consists of 10 shots each. Their probabilities of hitting the target with any one shot are $\frac{1}{5}$ and $\frac{1}{10}$ respectively.

N_A is the number of shots taken by A before A first hits the target, if at all. N_B is similarly defined for B. A wins if $N_A < N_B$, B wins if $N_B < N_A$, and otherwise a game is drawn. Find the probability that A wins a game.

Since A is a better shot than B, they play a series of games in which A has to win 2 games before B wins 1 game in order that A should win the series; otherwise B wins the series. Who is most likely to win the series, and with what probability?

[O&C]

Common errors

1. **Distributions**

    Do not forget the condition that the sum of all the probabilities must be 1. If this is not the case then you must have made a mistake in your calculations.

2. **Expectation**

   Suppose that X takes the values 1, 2, 3, 4 with probabilities p_1, p_2, p_3, p_4. The mean is $\sum i\, p_i$. Do not divide this answer by 4.

3. **Variance**

   (a) When working out $E(X^2)$ you must square X first and then average it. If you do this the other way round then you will obtain zero for your variance.

   (b) When working out $E(X^2)$ it is the values of x that are squared. Do not square the probabilities.

38 Binomial and Poisson distributions

38.1 The binomial distribution

Suppose there is a trial for which the probability of success is p, and the probability of failure is $q = 1 - p$.

This trial is repeated independently n times. Let X be the number of successes. X is said to have a *binomial distribution*. This is often written as:

$$X \sim B(n, p)$$

The distribution of X is given by the formula:

$$P(X = r) = {}^nC_r\, p^r q^{n-r}, \text{ for } r = 0, 1, 2, ..., n.$$

Recall that ${}^nC_r = \dfrac{n!}{r!\,(n-r)!}$, as defined in Chapters 3 and 36.

If $X \sim B(n, p)$, then the mean and variance of X are given by:

$$E(X) = np \; : \; Var(X) = npq$$

38.1.1 Examples

1. A fair die is rolled 10 times. Find the probability that there are

    (a)   2 sixes   (b)   at least 1 six.

    Solution

    Here the trial consists of rolling the die, and obtaining a six is called a success. Letting X be the number of sixes, X has a binomial distribution, $X \sim B(10, \frac{1}{6})$.

    (a) $P(X = 2) = {}^{10}C_2(\frac{1}{6})^2(\frac{5}{6})^8$

          The probability that there are 2 sixes is 0.291

    (b)   There will be at least one six unless there are no sixes.

          $P(X \geq 1) = 1 - P(X = 0) = 1 - (\frac{5}{6})^{10}$

          The probability that there is at least one six is 0.838

2. Seven children are picked at random. Find the mean and standard deviation of the number of girls. (Assume that boys and girls are equally likely.)

   Solution

   Picking a girl is counted as a success. Letting X be the number of girls, $X \sim B(7, \frac{1}{2})$. Use the formulae for mean and variance:

   $$E(X) = 7 \times \tfrac{1}{2} : \mathrm{Var}(X) = 7 \times \tfrac{1}{2} \times \tfrac{1}{2}$$

   The mean is 3.5 and the standard deviation is $\sqrt{1.75} = 1.32$

38.1.2 Exercises

1. A trial with probability $\frac{1}{4}$ of success is repeated independently 6 times. Let X be the number of successes. Find the probability that:

   (a) $X = 2$ (b) $X = 5$

   (c) $X > 0$ (d) $X \leq 4$

2. $X \sim B(12, \frac{1}{3})$. Evaluate the following:

   (a) $P(X = 4)$ (b) $P(X = 5)$

   (c) $P(X \leq 2)$ (d) $P(X \geq 2)$

3. When a dart is thrown at the dartboard, the probability of hitting the bullseye is 0.1. If the dart is thrown 20 times, and each throw is independent, find the probability of:

   (a) Exactly 3 bullseyes   (b) No bullseyes

   (c) At least one bullseye   (d) Less than 2 bullseyes

4. It is estimated that 3 out of 4 tulip bulbs will flower. If I buy 10, find the probability that:

   (a) All flower   (b) exactly 8 flower

   (c) At least 9 will flower.

5. A multiple choice exam contains 20 questions, with 5 possible answers for each question. A candidate answers the questions at random. Find the probabilities that:

   (a) He gets none right   (b) He gets all right

   (c) He gets 4 right   (d) He gets at least 2 right

6. One in ten of a batch of apples is bad. If 6 are bought, find the probabilities that:

   (a) One is bad   (b) At least 2 are bad

7. Find the expectation and variance of the number of bullseyes in Question 3.

8. Find the mean and variance of the number of flowering bulbs in Question 4.

9. Find the mean and variance of the number of correct answers obtained by the candidate in Question 5.

10. Find the mean and variance of the number of bad apples among the six bought, as described in Question 6.

11. When a fair die is rolled several times, the expected number of sixes is 3. How many times was it rolled?

12. A fair coin is tossed several times, and the expected number of heads is 4.5. How many times was it rolled?

13. A biased coin is tossed 20 times, and the expected number of heads is 16. What is the probability that a single toss will give heads?

14. When an arrow is fired at a target 50 times, the expected number of golds is 5. What is the probability that a single arrow will hit the gold?

38.2 The Poisson distribution

X has a *Poisson distribution* when its distribution is given by the following formula:

$$P(X = r) = \frac{e^{-\mu} \mu^r}{r!} , \text{ where } r = 0, 1, 2, 3, \dots$$

The mean and variance of X are both equal to μ.

$$E(X) = \mu \text{ and } Var(X) = \mu.$$

A Poisson distribution is often used as an approximation to the binomial distribution $B(n, p)$, when n is very large and p is very small.

If $X \sim B(n, p)$, for large n and small p, then X is approximately Poisson with mean $\mu = np$.

38.2.1 Examples

1. X has a Poisson distribution with mean 3. Find the probability that

    (a) $X = 2$ (b) $X \geq 2$.

    Solution

    (a) Use the formula with $\mu = 3$ and $r = 2$.

    $$P(X = 2) = \frac{e^{-3} 3^2}{2!}$$

    The probability that X is 2 is 0.224

    (b) If X is greater or equal to 2, then it cannot be 0 or 1.

    $$P(X \geq 2) = 1 - P(X = 0 \text{ or } X = 1) = 1 - \left(\frac{e^{-3} 3^0}{0!} + \frac{e^{-3} 3^1}{1!} \right)$$

    The probability that X is at least 2 is 0.801

2. On average, there are 2 misprints on each page of a newspaper. Assuming a Poisson distribution for the number of misprints, find the probabilities that there are

    (a) 3 misprints on page 1

    (b) 5 misprints on the first two pages.

    Solution

    (a) For the first page, the distribution of the number of misprints is Poisson with mean 2. Use the formula:

    $$\text{The probability of 3 misprints is } \frac{e^{-2} 2^3}{3!} = 0.180$$

(b) The number of misprints on the first two pages has a Poisson distribution with mean 4. Use the formula:

The probability of 5 misprints is $\dfrac{e^{-4}4^5}{5!} = 0.156$

38.2.2 Exercises

1. X has a Poisson distribution with mean 1.5. Find the probabilities that:

   (a) $X = 3$ (b) $X = 0$

   (c) $X \leq 2$ (d) $X \geq 2$

2. The distribution of X is Poisson with mean 5. Find the following probabilities:

   (a) $P(X = 3)$ (b) $P(X = 2 \text{ or } 4)$

   (c) $P(X < 3)$ (d) $P(X \geq 2)$

3. The number of letters a man receives each day has a Poisson distribution with mean 3. Find the probabilities that:

   (a) In one day he receives 4 letters.   (b) In two days he receives 6 letters.

4. The number of meteorites which fall on a field in a year has a Poisson distribution with mean $\frac{1}{2}$. Find the probabilities that:

   (a) 2 meteorites fall in a year   (b) No meteorites fall in 6 months.

5. The number of customers entering an antique shop in an hour follows a Poisson distribution with mean 4. Find the probabilities that:

   (a) There will be 6 customers in an hour.

   (b There will be 5 customers in two hours.

   (c) There will be at least one customer in half an hour.

6. The number of goals in a football match follows a Poisson distribution with mean 3. Find the probability that:

   (a) There will be 2 goals in the match.

   (b) The score will be 0–0 at half–time.

7. The number of buses which arrive at a bus–stop over a period of an hour follows a Poisson distribution with mean 4. Find the probabilities of:

   (a) 3 buses in one hour   (b) 6 buses in 2 hours

   (c) 1 bus in 15 minutes   (d) At least 1 bus in half an hour.

8. The number of cases of a certain rare disease in a town follows a Poisson distribution. The probability that there are no cases at all in the town is $\frac{1}{2}$.

   (a) Find the expected number μ of cases.

   (b) Find the probability that there are exactly 2 cases.

9. The number of telephone calls I receive in a day has a Poisson distribution. The probability that I receive no calls is 0.25. Find the average number of calls I receive in a day, and find the probability that in 2 days I receive a total of 5 calls.

10. The number of flaws in a length of cloth follows a Poisson distribution. One in twenty of the lengths has no flaws at all. Find the probability that a length has 4 flaws.

11. A certain rare disease afflicts 0.000002 of the population. A town has a population of 100,000. Assuming that the number of cases in the town follows a Poisson distribution, find the probability that there are 2 cases in the town.

12. It is thought that the proportion of bad eggs is 0.002. Find the probability of 1 bad egg in a batch of 1000.

13. The probability that an answer in the back of a Mathematics textbook is wrong is 0.003. Find the probability that in a hundred answers there will be at least two mistakes.

14. 2% of the population has a certain disease. 60 people are chosen at random. Find the probability that there are 2 cases of the disease among them:

    (a) By using the binomial distribution.

    (b) By using the Poisson approximation.

38.3 Examination questions

1. In order to qualify for a quiz contest, at least three students out of a team of four have to pass a test. To pass this test, a student has to answer correctly at least two questions out of five. The probability of a student answering any particular question correctly is $\frac{1}{3}$. Show that the probability of a student passing the test is $\frac{131}{243}$.

   Hence calculate, to three significant figures, the probability that the team qualifies for the quiz contest.

   [L ADD]

2. A golfer has a probability of $\frac{1}{3}$ of holing his first putt. In a round of nine holes he attempts five such putts. What is the probability that he holes

   (i) exactly three of these putts;

   (ii) less than three of these putts?

   If he fails to hole a putt at the first attempt, the probability that he will hole the putt at the second attempt is $\frac{3}{4}$. In another round of nine holes he fails on four occasions to hole his first putt. What is the probability that at the second attempt he holes more putts than he misses?

   [MEI ADD]

3. The server at tennis is required to serve the ball into a specified region of the court. If a first attempted serve is out of this region (a fault) then a second serve is allowed. If the second serve is also out of the specified region then this is called a double-fault. Forty per cent of McLendl's first serves are faults as are ten per cent of his second serves. Assuming that the outcome of each of McLendl's attempted serves is independent of all previous outcomes, determine the probability that

   (i) a sequence of four of his first attempted serves contains precisely one fault,

   (ii) McLendl serves a double-fault.

After each of McLendl's serves (or pair of serves) either he or his opponent wins a point. If his first serve is not a fault then there is a probability of 0.8 that he wins the point; the corresponding probability for a second serve is 0.3. In the event of his serving a double–fault his opponent wins the point. Show that the overall probability of McLendl winning the point is 0.588.

In competing for four successive points, McLendl has three first serves that are not faults and one second serve that is not a fault. Determine the probability that he wins exactly three of the four points.

[C]

4. A discrete random variable X has a Poisson distribution given by

$$P(X = r) = \frac{e^{-a} a^r}{r!} , r = 0, 1, 2, \ldots$$

Prove that the mean of X is a.

A garage has two cars A and B which it hires out on a daily basis (for a complete day). The number of demands per day follows a Poisson distribution with mean 2.5. Find the most probable number of demands per day.

Calculate, each correct to 3 significant figures,

(i)   the percentage of days when at least one demand would have to be refused;

(ii) the probability that on two successive days a total of two demands will have to be refused;

(iii) the probability of car A being idle on a particular day if the cars are used equally.

[SUJB]

5. A randomly chosen doctor in general practice sees, on average, one case of a broken nose per year and each case is independent of other similar cases.

(i)   Regarding a month as a twelfth part of a year,

(a) show that the probability that, between them three such doctors see no cases of a broken nose in a period of one month is 0.779, correct to three significant figures,

(b) find the variance of the number of cases seen by three such doctors in a period of six months.

(ii) Find the probability that, between them, three such doctors see at least three cases in one year.

(iii) Find the probability that, of three such doctors, one sees three cases and the other two see no cases in one year.

[C]

6. An advertising display contains a large number of light bulbs which are continually being switched on and off. Individual lights fail at random times, and each day the display is inspected and any failed lights are replaced. The number of lights that fail in any one-day period has a Poisson distribution with mean 2.2. Calculate

(i)   the probability that no light will need to be replaced on a particular day,

(ii)   the probability that at least four lights will need to be replaced on a particular day,

(iii) the least number of consecutive days after which the probability of at least one light having to be replaced exceeds 0.9999.

Calculate also the probability that, in a period of seven days, at least four lights will need to be replaced on at least two days.

[C]

Common errors

1. **Binomial distribution**

    (a) You can only use the binomial distribution if the repeated trials are independent. If this is not the case then some other distribution must be used.

    (b) Do not forget the ^nC_r term when working out binomial probabilities.

    (c) Do not be vague about what you are dealing with. If a problem involves the number of sixes when a die is rolled 20 times, do not write: *The sixes are binomial.* State clearly:

    'Let X be the number of sixes: X has a binomial distribution, with n equal to 20 and p equal to $\frac{1}{6}$'.

    To save space you may use the abbreviation: $X \sim B(20, \frac{1}{6})$

2. **Poisson distribution**

    (a) Suppose X is Poisson with mean μ, and you are asked for $P(X > 2)$. You cannot calculate this directly: you must calculate this by taking $P(X > 2) = 1 - P(X \leq 2)$.

    (b) The Poisson approximation to the binomial is only valid for large n and small p. As a rough guide, n should be at least 50 and p at most 0.02.

39 Continuous random variables

If X is a random variable which can take any value from a continuous range, then X is a *continuous random variable*.

The *probability density function*, or *p.d.f.*, f(x) of X gives the density of the probability of X at each point. Hence if δx is a small number:

$$P(x \leq X \leq x + \delta x) \approx f(x)\,\delta x.$$

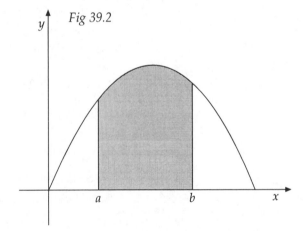

The probability that X lies within a certain range is found by integrating the p.d.f of X along that range.

$$P(a \leq X \leq b) = \int_a^b f(x)\,dx$$

If f(x) is a p.d.f., then it must be non-negative and the total area under its curve must be 1.

$$f(x) \geq 0 \quad \text{and} \quad \int_{-\infty}^{\infty} f(x)\,dx = 1.$$

A random variable whose p.d.f. is constant is called *uniform* or *rectangular*.

The *Expectation* E(X) of X is found by the formula:

$$E(X) = \int_{-\infty}^{\infty} x\,f(x)\,dx$$

283

The *variance* of X is found from the same formula as for a discrete random variable.

$$\text{Var}(X) = E(X^2) - (E(X))^2$$

Here $E(X^2)$ is $\displaystyle\int_{-\infty}^{\infty} x^2 f(x)\, dx$

39.1.1 Example

X is a continuous random variable which takes values between 0 and 1, with p.d.f. $f(x) = kx^2$ for $0 \leq x \leq 1$, where k is a constant. Find

(a) k,

(b) the mean of X

(c) the variance of X,

(d) the median of X.

Solution

(a) The total amount of probability must be 1.

$$\int_0^1 kx^2\, dx = 1$$

$$\left[\tfrac{k}{3}x^3\right]_0^1 = 1$$

$$k = 3$$

(b) Use the formula for expectation.

$$E(X) = \int_0^1 x.3x^2\, dx = \left[\tfrac{3}{4}x^4\right]_0^1$$

The mean of X is $\tfrac{3}{4}$

(c) First find the expectation of X^2.

$$E(X^2) = \int_0^1 x^2.3x^2 dx = \left[\tfrac{3}{5}x^5\right]_0^1 = \tfrac{3}{5}$$

Now use the formula for variance.

The variance of X is $\tfrac{3}{5} - (\tfrac{3}{4})^2 = 0.0375$

(d) The median m is such that the probability that X is less than m is $\tfrac{1}{2}$.

$$P(X \leq m) = \int_0^m 3x^2 dx = \tfrac{1}{2}$$

$$\tfrac{1}{2} = \left[x^3\right]_0^m = m^3$$

The median is $\sqrt[3]{\tfrac{1}{2}} = 0.794$

39.1.2 Exercises

1. X is a continuous random variable with p.d.f given by the function:

$$f(x) = \begin{cases} 0 & \text{for } x < 0 \\ 4x^3 & \text{for } 0 \leq x \leq 1 \\ 0 & \text{for } x > 1 \end{cases}$$

    (a) Check that $f(x)$ is a p.d.f.   (b) Find $P(X \geq \frac{1}{2})$

    (c) Find $P(\frac{1}{4} \leq X \leq \frac{3}{4})$ (d) Find $P(X \leq \frac{1}{8})$

2. X is a continuous random variable with p.d.f. as follows:

$$f(x) = \begin{cases} 0 & \text{for } x < 0 \\ 1 - \frac{1}{2}x & \text{for } 0 \leq x \leq 2 \\ 0 & \text{for } x > 2 \end{cases}$$

    (a) Check that $f(x)$ is a p.d.f.   (b) Sketch the graph of $f(x)$

    (c) Find $P(X \geq 1.5)$ (d) Find $P(0.5 \leq X \leq 1.8)$

3. The p.d.f of X is given by the formula:

$$f(x) = \begin{cases} 0 & \text{for } x \leq 1 \\ \dfrac{2}{x^3} & \text{for } x \geq 1 \end{cases}$$

    (a) Check that $f(x)$ is a pdf.   (b) Sketch the graph of $f(x)$

    (c) Find $P(1 < X < 2)$ (d) Find $P(X \geq 3)$

4. The p.d.f. of X is $f(x) = kx$ for $0 \leq x \leq 1$, and 0 elsewhere. Find the value of k.

5. The p.d.f. of X is $f(x) = 2 - kx$ for $0 \leq x \leq 1$, and 0 elsewhere. Find the value of k.

6. The p.d.f of X is $f(x) = \dfrac{k}{x^2}$ for $x \leq 2$, and 0 elsewhere. Find the value of k.

7. The p.d.f. of X is $f(x) = x^2$ for $0 \leq x \leq b$. Find the value of b.

8. The p.d.f. of X is $f(x) = \frac{1}{2} + x$ for $1 \leq x \leq c$. Find the value of c.

9. and 10.

    For each of the distributions in Questions 1 and 2, find

    (a) the mean   (b) the variance

    (c) the median.

11. Find the mean and median for the distribution of Question 3. Show that the variance does not exist.

12. X is uniform between 2 and 5. Find the p.d.f. of X.

13. X is uniform between a and b, where $a < b$. Find the p.d.f. of X.

14. X is uniform between -1 and k, with p.d.f. $f(x) = 0.1$ for $-1 \leq x \leq k$. Find the value of k.

15. X has p.d.f given by the function:

$$f(x) = \begin{cases} 0 & \text{for } x < -1 \\ \frac{1}{2}(x+1) & \text{for } -1 \leq x \leq 0 \\ \frac{1}{2}\left(1 - \frac{1}{3}x\right) & \text{for } 0 \leq x \leq 3 \\ 0 & \text{for } x > 3 \end{cases}$$

    (a) Check that $f(x)$ is a p.d.f.   (b) Find $P(X \geq 1)$

    (c) Find $P(-0.5 \leq X \leq 2)$ (d) Find $E(X)$

    (e) Find $\text{Var}(X)$.

39.2 Cumulative frequency

The *Cumulative Frequency* of a random variable X at a point x is the probability that X is less than x.

$$P(X < x) = \int_{-\infty}^{x} f(x)\, dx$$

Fig 39.3

The function $F(x)$ giving the cumulative frequency is the *cumulative distribution function*, or c.d.f. The c.d.f. is the integral of the p.d.f., and the p.d.f is the derivative of the c.d.f.

$$F(x) = \int f(x)\, dx \; ; \quad f(x) = \frac{d}{dx}[F(x)]$$

39.2.1 Examples

1. X is a continuous random variable with p.d.f. given by:

    $$f(x) = \begin{cases} 0 & \text{for } x < 0 \\ ke^{-\lambda x} & \text{for } x \geq 0 \end{cases}$$

    Express k in terms of λ and find the c.d.f. of X.

    Solution

    Use the definition of a p.d.f.

    $$1 = \int_{0}^{\infty} k\,e^{-\lambda x}\, dx = \left[-\frac{k}{\lambda}e^{-\lambda x}\right]_{0}^{\infty} = \frac{k}{\lambda}$$

    $$k = \lambda$$

    Use the definition of a c.d.f.

    $$F(x) = \int_{0}^{x} \lambda\,e^{-\lambda x}\, dx = \left[-e^{-\lambda x}\right]_{0}^{x}$$

    $$F(x) = 1 - e^{-\lambda x}$$

2. The probability that a light-bulb will last more than x years is e^{-2x}. Find the p.d.f. of the lifetime of a bulb. Find the probability that a 1 year old bulb will last for a further 2 years.

    Solution

    Let X be the lifetime. X is a continuous random variable. From the information given:

$P(X > x) = e^{-2x}$

The c.d.f. of x is given by:

$F(x) = P(X \le x) = 1 - P(X > x) = 1 - e^{-2x}$

The p.d.f. of X is $\dfrac{d}{dx}[F(x)] = 2\,e^{-2x}$

If the bulb is a year old then X is at least 1. Use the formula for conditional probability:

$$P(X > 3 \,|\, X > 1) = \frac{P(X > 3 \;\&\; X > 1)}{P(X > 1)} = \frac{P(X > 3)}{P(X > 1)}$$

The probability is $\dfrac{e^{-6}}{e^{-2}} = e^{-4}$

39.2.2 Exercises

1. Find the c.d.f. for the distributions with p.d.f.s given below.

   (a) $f(x) = 5x^4$ for $0 \le x \le 1$

   (b) $f(x) = \frac{1}{4} + \frac{1}{4}x$ for $0 \le x \le 2$

   (c) $f(x) = \sin x$ for $0 \le x \le \frac{\pi}{2}$

   (d) $f(x) = \dfrac{1}{x^2}$ for $x \le 1$

2. Find the p.d.f. for the functions with the following c.d.f.s:

   (a) $F(x) = \frac{1}{2}x + \frac{1}{2}x^2$ for $0 \le x \le 1$

   (b) $F(x) = 1 - \dfrac{4}{x^2}$ for $x \ge 2$

   (c) $F(x) = \sin 2x$ for $0 \le x \le \frac{\pi}{4}$

   (d) $F(x) = 1 - e^{-3x}$ for $x \ge 0$

3. to 5.

   Find the c.d.f. of each of the distributions given in Questions 1 to 3 of 39.1.2.

6. The c.d.f. of a continuous random variable is $F(x) = x + \frac{1}{2}x^2$ for $0 \le x \le k$. Find the value of k.

7. The c.d.f of X is $F(x) = kx + \frac{1}{8}x^2$ for $0 \le x \le 2$. Find the value of k.

8. The lifetime X of a car tyre is a continuous random variable with p.d.f.
   $f(x) = \dfrac{1}{(x + 1)^2}$, where x is measured in thousands of miles. Find the probability that the tyre lasts more than 5,000 miles.

9. If the tyre of Question 8 has lasted 1,000 miles, what is the probability that it will last for a further 3,000 miles?

10. When I arrive at a bus stop, the probability that I will have to wait more than x minutes for a bus is $e^{-x/15}$.

    (a) Find the p.d.f. of the time I have to wait.

    (b) Find the mean time that I must wait.

    (c) Find the median time that I must wait.

    (d) If I have waited for 30 minutes, what is the probability that I will have to wait a further 15 minutes?

11. X is uniformly distributed between a and b. Find the c.d.f. of X. Find the mean and the variance of X.

39.3 Examination questions

1. The size, X mm, of a certain component used in the construction of an electrical appliance is found to have a continuous probability density function given by

    $$f(x) = \begin{cases} cx(4-x) \text{ for } 0 \le x \le 3 \\ 0 \text{ otherwise} \end{cases}$$

    where c is a positive constant.

    (i)   Show that $c = \frac{1}{9}$

    (ii) Calculate the mean and variance of X.

    [AEB ADD 1987]

2. A random variable X has probability density function

    $$f(x) = \begin{cases} k(4-x^2) \text{ for } 0 \le x \le 2 \\ 0 \text{ otherwise} \end{cases}$$

    Prove that $k = \frac{3}{16}$. Find the probability that X has a value greater than 1.5. Find also the mean and variance of X.

    [You may leave your answers as fractions in their lowest terms]

    [O&C]

3. A continuous random variable X has probability density function

    $$f(x) = k(2-x) \quad 0 \le x \le 2$$

    $$f(x) = 0 \quad \text{otherwise}$$

    where k is a constant. Obtain an expression for $P(X \le t)$, the probability that x is less than or equal to t, in terms of k and t, where t is a value such that $0 \le t \le 2$. By substituting $t = 2$, verify that $k = \frac{1}{2}$.

    Using the expression for $P(X \le t)$ above, or otherwise, determine the probability $P(\frac{1}{2} \le X \le \frac{3}{2})$.

    [NI]

4. The guarantee by a retailer ensures that a faulty television tube is replaced within the first year of purchase. The probability distribution of the life of the tube can be modelled by

    $$f(x) = \frac{A}{x^4} \text{ for } 1 \le x \le \infty,$$

    $$f(x) = 0 \text{ for } x < 1,$$

    where x is the lifetime in years. Find,

    (i)   the value of A;   (ii) the mean and variance of x;

    (iii) the probability that the tube lasts longer than five years.

    Show that, if a tube has lasted for n years, the probability that it will fail during the next year is

    $$1 - \left(\frac{n}{n+1}\right)^3$$

    [SUJB]

5. The random variable X has a rectangular distribution whose probability density function f(x) is given by

$$f(x) = \begin{cases} \frac{1}{6} & \text{for } -2 \le x \le 4 \\ 0 & \text{otherwise} \end{cases}$$

Sketch the probability density function of X and hence, or otherwise, find the probabilities that

(i) $X \le 2$,

(ii) $|X| \le 2$,

(iii) $|X| \le x$ for $0 \le x \le 2$,

(iv) $|X| \le x$ for $2 < x \le 4$,

(v) $|X| \le x$ for $x > 4$.

Hence obtain, and sketch, the probability density function of $|X|$. Thus determine the mean of $|X|$.

[MEI]

6. A continuous random variable T has a negative exponential distribution given by

$f(t) = Ae^{-t/a}, t \ge 0$

$= 0$ elsewhere

Show that $A = \dfrac{1}{a}$ and that the mean and variance of T are a and a^2 respectively.

(You may assume that $\displaystyle\int_0^\infty t^n e^{-t/a}\, dt = a^{n+1} n!$ for integral values of n.)

The life in hours of a type of electric battery can be modelled by the above distribution and when a sample of 800 is tested the mean life is found to be 92.2 h. What are the values of A and a based on this figure?

(i) What is the probability that a battery will last for at least 200 h?

(ii) If a battery has lasted 200 h what is the probability that it will last for at least a further 100 h?

(iii) If two batteries are bought what is the probability that one fails before 200 h and the other after 200 h?

[SUJB]

Common errors

1. **Continuous variables**

(a) The p.d.f. f(x) does not give the probability that $X = x$. (For a continuous variable that probability is zero.) Probabilities are only obtained after f(x) has been integrated, as in:

$$P(a \le x \le b) = \int_a^b f(x)\, dx$$

(b) Do not worry about whether you have $P(X < a)$ or $P(X \le a)$. If X is continuous, these are numerically equal.

(c) Do not forget the conditions that $f(x) \ge 0$ and $\displaystyle\int f(x)\, dx = 1$.

(d) Mistakes are often made when evaluating the definite integral of the exponential function. That is:

$$\int_0^\infty e^{-x}\,dx = \left[-e^{-x}\right]_0^\infty$$

At the top end, when x tends to ∞ then e^{-x} tends to 0. (Not 1, or ∞).

At the bottom end, when $x = 0$ then $e^{-x} = 1$. (Not 0).

2. **Expectation and variance**

(a) When finding $E(X)$ you must integrate $xf(x)$. You do not integrate $f(x)$ and then multiply by x.

(b) When finding $E(X^2)$ you integrate $x^2f(x)$. You do not integrate $x\,f(x)$ and then square the result.

3. **Cumulative frequency**

(a) A c.d.f. must be positive and increasing, and it must be 0 at its left hand end and 1 at its right hand end. If it does not obey these conditions then it cannot be a c.d.f.

(b) To go from the p.d.f. to the c.d.f. you integrate. To go from the c.d.f. to the p.d.f. you differentiate. Do not get these the wrong way round.

40 Sampling and estimation

40.1 Sums of random variables

Suppose X and Y are random variables, and a and b are constant. The means and variances of combinations of X and Y are given by the following:

$$\mathrm{E}(X + Y) = \mathrm{E}(X) + \mathrm{E}(Y) : \mathrm{E}(X - Y) = \mathrm{E}(X) - \mathrm{E}(Y)$$

$$\mathrm{E}(aX) = a\mathrm{E}(X) : \mathrm{E}(aX + bY) = a\mathrm{E}(X) + b(\mathrm{E}(Y).$$

$$\mathrm{E}(X + a) = \mathrm{E}(X) + a$$

$$\mathrm{Var}(aX) = a^2\mathrm{Var}(X) : \mathrm{Var}(X + a) = \mathrm{Var}(X).$$

If X and Y are independent, then the following are also true:

$$\mathrm{E}(XY) = \mathrm{E}(X) \times \mathrm{E}(Y).$$

$$\mathrm{Var}(X + Y) = \mathrm{Var}(X) + \mathrm{Var}(Y) : \mathrm{Var}(X - Y) = \mathrm{Var}(X) + \mathrm{Var}(Y).$$

$$\mathrm{Var}(aX + bY) = a^2\mathrm{Var}(X) + b^2\mathrm{Var}(Y).$$

40.1.2 Example

Suppose X and Y are independent variables with means 2 and 3 respectively and variances 3 and 4 respectively.

(i) Find the mean of $X + 2Y^2 + 1$.

(ii) Find integer constants a and b so that $aX + bY$ has mean 13 and variance 48.

Solution

(i) First use the fact that $\mathrm{Var}(Y) = \mathrm{E}(Y^2) - (\mathrm{E}(Y))^2$ to show that $\mathrm{E}(Y^2) = 13$.

$\mathrm{E}(X + 2Y^2 + 1) = \mathrm{E}(X) + 2\mathrm{E}(Y^2) + 1$

The mean of $X + 2Y^2 + 1$ is 29

(ii) Use the formulae above to find two equations in a and b.

$2a + 3b = 13 : 3a^2 + 4b^2 = 48.$

Solve these equations simultaneously. The value of a is 2 or $\frac{122}{43}$, and the value of b is 3 or $\frac{105}{43}$. Take the integer values.

$a = 2$ and $b = 3$

40.1.2 Exercises

1. X is a random variable with mean 3 and variance 5. Find the following:

   (a) $E(2X)$
   (b) $Var(3X)$
   (c) $E(X^2)$
   (d) $E(3X - 13)$
   (e) $Var(2X + 3)$
   (f) $E(2X^2 - 3X + 2)$

2. X and Y are independent random variables with expectations 5 and 3 respectively, and variances 4 and 1 respectively. Find the following:

   (a) $E(X + Y)$
   (b) $Var(X + Y)$
   (c) $E(3XY)$
   (d) $Var(X - Y)$
   (e) $E(X + 3Y^2)$
   (f) $Var(2X - 3Y - 1)$
   (g) $E((X + Y)^2)$
   (h) $E((X - Y)^2)$

3. X is a variable with expectation 5 and variance 12. Find positive constants a and b so that $aX + b$ has expectation 13 and variance 48.

4. Y is a variable with mean 8 and variance 64. Find constants a and b so that $aY + b$ has mean 0 and variance 1.

5. Z is a variable with mean μ and variance σ^2. Find constants a and b so that $aZ + b$ has mean 0 and variance 1.

6. X and Y are independent variables, each with mean 2 and variance 4. Find constants a and b so that $aX + bY$ has mean 0 and variance 72.

7. The amount in cm^3 of coffee dispensed by a drinks machine is a variable, with mean 200 and variance 12. The amount of milk it adds has mean 10 and variance 6. Find the mean and variance of the total drink.

   While taking it back to her table a customer spills an amount which has mean 40 and variance 20. Find the mean and variance of the amount left to be consumed.

8. The weight of a person naked has mean 70 kg and variance 4 kg^2. The weight of clothes he puts on has mean 3 kg with variance 1 kg^2. Find the mean and variance of his weight when clothed.

9. Four people run a relay race. The times in seconds they will take are independent of each other, and have means 10, 10.3, 11.7, 11.4 and variances 1.2, 0.8, 1.1 and 2.5. Find the mean and variance of the total time of the race.

10. The exports of a country (in billions of £) have mean 8.3 and variance 4.7. The imports have mean 9.7 and variance 3.2. Assuming that exports and imports are independent, find the mean and variance of the trade balance.

40.2 Estimation from samples

SAMPLES AND POPULATIONS

A distribution from which values are taken at random is a *parent* or *background* or *population* distribution.

A value taken from this distribution is a *sample* value.

A *sample of size n* consists of n independent sample values $X_1, X_2, \ldots X_n$.

A function of the sample is an *unbiased* estimate of the mean μ if the expectation of the function is μ itself.

The function is *consistent* if its variance tends to zero as the sample size n tends to infinity.

If we have two estimators of μ, then the estimator with the smaller variance is more *efficient*.

SAMPLE MEAN AND PROPORTION

Let a background distribution X have mean μ and variance σ^2. Suppose $X_1, X_2, \ldots X_n$ is a sample from X of size n. The *sample mean* is the average of the sample.

$$\overline{X} = \frac{X_1 + X_2 + \ldots + X_n}{n}$$

The expectation and variance of the sample mean are given by:

$$\mathbf{E}(\overline{X}) = \mu \quad \text{and} \quad \mathbf{Var}(\overline{X}) = \frac{\sigma^2}{n}$$

It follows that $\overline{X}$ is an unbiased and consistent estimator of μ.

The standard deviation of $\overline{X}$ is the *standard error*. It is given by the formula:

$$\mathbf{S.E.}(\overline{X}) = \frac{\sigma}{\sqrt{n}}$$

Suppose a proportion π of a large population has a certain property. A sample of size n is taken from the population, and m of the sample have the property. The *sample proportion* is the proportion of the sample which have the property.

$$\theta = \frac{m}{n}$$

The expectation and variance of the sample proportion are given by:

$$\mathbf{E}(\theta) = \pi \quad \text{and} \quad \mathbf{Var}(\theta) = \frac{\pi(1 - \pi)}{n}$$

The sample proportion is an unbiased and consistent estimator of the population proportion.

40.2.1 Examples

1. A machine produces ball-bearings whose diameter has variance 0.001 cm but whose mean μ is unknown. A sample of 12 ball-bearings had diameters:

    1.11, 1.12. 1.12, 1.13, 1.09, 1.08, 1.09, 1.11, 1.10, 1.11, 1.12, 1.11

    Estimate the background mean, and give the standard error of your estimation.

    Solution

    Estimate the background mean μ by the sample mean $\overline{X}$.

$$\overline{X} = \frac{1.11 + 1.12 + \ldots + 1.11}{12}$$

The estimate for the true mean is 1.1075

The standard error is the square root of $\frac{0.001}{12}$.

The standard error is 0.009

2. An opinion poll was taken on two days: on the first day 200 people were questioned, of whom 45% supported the Freedom Party. The next day 42% of a sample of 300 supported it. Estimate the true support for the party.

Solution

In all, 500 people were questioned. The number who supported the Freedom Party was $200 \times 0.45 + 300 \times 0.42 = 216$.

The proportion is estimated at $\frac{216}{500} = 43.2\%$

40.2.2 Exercises

1. The following figures were taken from a distribution with variance 20. Estimate the mean of the distribution, and state the standard error.

    23, 25, 16, 30, 29, 17, 17, 24, 26

2. The following figures were taken from a distribution with variance 0.01. Estimate the mean, and find the standard error.

    3.04, 3.21, 3.11, 3.09, 2.99, 2.97, 3.05

3. The average weight of a group of 100 people was 70 kg, and that of a further group of 200 people was 73 kg. Assuming that the two groups come from the same parent distribution, estimate the mean of that distribution.

4. Three groups containing 100, 250, 400 tomatoes had average weights 100 g, 90 g, 95 g respectively. Assuming that the tomatoes all came from the same background distribution estimate the mean of that distribution.

5. A sample of 100 eggs was examined, and 3 were found to be bad. Estimate the probability that an egg picked at random will be bad.

6. Two samples of apples, of sizes 100 and 250, were tested. The proportion of underweight apples was 0.1 in the first and 0.16 in the second. Assuming that the apples come from the same parent distribution estimate the proportion of underweight apples.

7. A distribution X is thought to be binomial $B(n,p)$ with $n = 3$. A sample of 100 was tested, with the following results:

Value of X	0	1	2	3
Frequency	40	44	14	2

    Estimate the mean of X. Hence estimate the value of p.

8. A distribution X is thought to be binomial $B(n,p)$ with $n = 4$. A sample of 200 was tested, with the following results:

Value of X	0	1	2	3	4
Frequency	0	5	31	82	82

    Estimate the value of p.

9. A distribution is thought to be Poisson with unknown mean μ. A sample of 50 gave the following results:

Value of X	0	1	2	3+
Frequency	27	16	5	2

Estimate the value of μ.

10. A distribution is thought to be Poisson with unknown mean μ. A sample of 200 gave the following results:

Value of X	0	1	2	3	4+
Frequency	60	72	43	18	7

Estimate the value of μ.

11. X and Y are independent variables with the same (unknown) mean μ. Constants a and b are found so that $Z = aX + bY$ is an estimator of μ.

    (i) Show that if Z is an unbiased estimator, then $a + b = 1$

    (ii) Suppose that Var(X) = 1 and Var(Y) = 4. How should a and b be chosen so that Z has minimal variance?

12. 50 pedigree cats were weighed and found to have mean weight $\overline{X}$ kg: 100 mongrel cats had mean weight $\overline{Y}$ kg. Assume that the population mean for pedigree and mongrel cats is the same, μ kg. We want to estimate μ.

    (i) Suppose that the variance of the cats is the same, at σ^2.
    Let $Z = \frac{1}{2}(\overline{X} + \overline{Y})$, and $W = \frac{1}{150}(50\overline{X} + 100\overline{Y})$.

    Show that Z and W are both unbiased. Find Var(Z) and Var(W). Which of Z or W is more efficient?

    (ii) Suppose that the variance of the pedigree cats is three times that of the mongrel cats. An estimate of μ is $Q = aX + bY$. Find the values of a and b which make Q unbiased and most efficient.

13. An opinion poll is taken to find the level of support for the Purple Party. 1000 men and 1500 women were questioned, and the proportions of those supporting the party were p_m and p_w. Let $Z = \frac{1}{2}(p_m + p_w)$ and $W = 0.4p_m + 0.6p_w$. Assume that the true level of support is the same for men and women, at π. Show that Z and W are both unbiased estimators of π. Find the variances of Z and W, and state which is more efficient.

40.3 Estimation of the sample variance

Let $X_1, X_2, \dots X_n$ be a sample from a distribution with mean μ and variance σ^2. The *sample variance* S^2 is defined by:

$$S^2 = \frac{\sum(X_i - \overline{X})^2}{n} = \frac{\sum X_i^2 - n\overline{X}^2}{n}$$

S^2 is biased, in that $E(S^2) = \dfrac{(n-1)\sigma^2}{n}$.

The unbiased sample variance is defined by:

$$\hat{\sigma}^2 = \frac{nS^2}{n-1} = \frac{\sum(X_i - \overline{X})^2}{n-1} = \frac{\sum X_i^2 - n\overline{X}^2}{n-1}$$

It follows that $E(\hat{\sigma}^2) = \sigma^2$.

40.3.1 Example

Find the unbiased sample variance for the following figures:

$$23, 22, 31, 26, 25, 25, 26, 26, 24, 28, 30$$

Solution

The mean is found as in 40.2.

$$\overline{X} = 26$$

Use the formula for the unbiased sample variance:

$$\hat{\sigma}^2 = \frac{\sum X_i^2 - n\overline{X}^2}{n-1} = \frac{23^2 + 22^2 + ... + 30^2 - 11 \times 26^2}{10}$$

The unbiased sample variance is 7.6

40.3.2 Exercises

1. Find the sample variance and the unbiased sample variance for the following sets of figures:
   (a) 55, 56, 54, 54, 55, 56, 57, 53, 52
   (b) 10^2, 02, 99, 110, 94, 112, 120, 89, 100
   (c) 0.014, 0.009, 0.017, 0.012, 0.010, 0.011, 0.019
   (d) −1.7, −1.2, −2, 0.2, 0.1, −1, −1.5, −1.6, −0.8, −0.4

2. Find the sample variance and the unbiased sample variance for the samples which have frequency tables as below:

   (a)

Value	1	2	3	4	5
Frequency	14	9	4	2	1

   (b)

Value	−1	0	1	2	3
Frequency	2	9	18	16	4

   (c)

Value	98	99	100	101	102
Frequency	12	23	38	16	3

3. A sample of size 10 was taken from a distribution. The sum of the values was 23, and the sum of the squares of the values was 55. Find the unbiased sample variance.

4. In the following, n is the sample size, $\sum X$ is the sum of the sample values, $\sum X^2$ is the sum of the squares of the values. Find the unbiased sample variance in each case.

   (a) $n = 8$, $\sum X = 300$, $\sum X^2 = 20,000$ (b) $n = 15$, $\sum X = 23$, $\sum X^2 = 60$

40.4 Examination questions

1. The continuous random variable X has probability density function $f(x)$. Define the variance $V(X)$ of x in terms of $f(x)$ and deduce from your definition that, for any constants a and b,

$$V(aX + b) = a^2 V(X).$$

   Explain why $V(X) \geq 0$.

   The random variables X_1 and X_2 are independent and each has probability density function

   $$\frac{1}{\sqrt{x}} - 1, \text{ where } 0 < x < 1, 0 \text{ elsewhere.}$$

   Find the variance of $Y = 2X_1 - 4X_2 + 2$. What range of values does Y take?
   [O&C]

2. What are the values of the mean and variance of the number of successes in n independent repetitions of a trial in which the probability of success is p?

   An ordinary shaped die is biased in such a way that the probabilities of throwing a 1 and a 6 are equal but different from $\frac{1}{6}$. Denote this common probability by θ. Two methods are suggested for estimating θ. These are:

   Method 1: Toss the die 20 times; record the number X of sixes that occur; take $P_1 = X/20$ as the estimate of θ.

   Method 2: Toss the die 10 times; record the total number Y of ones and sixes that occur; take $P_2 = Y/20$ as the estimate of θ.

   Show that $E(P_1) = E(P_2) = \theta$. Calculate the variances of P_1 and P_2, and hence decide which of the methods is the better one for estimating θ.
   [MEI]

3. (i) At a garden centre, the sales of flower pots are investigated. A sample of 20 flower pot sales is taken and the number of sales, f, of each size, x inches, of flower pot is recorded below.

x	4	5	6	8	12
f	2	3	6	4	5

   Calculate, each to 2 decimal places, the mean and the variance of the sizes of the 20 flower pots sold.

   Find, to 2 decimal places, unbiased estimates of the mean and the variance of the population of sizes of flower pots sold by this garden centre.

    (ii) The discrete random variable R has probability function p(r) defined by

$$p(0) = p(6) = \tfrac{1}{16}, p(1) = p(4) = \tfrac{1}{4}, p(3) = \tfrac{3}{8}, p(r) = 0 \text{ elsewhere.}$$

Find E(R) and Var(R). Find the mean and variance of

    (a) $2R - 5$,   (b) $R_1 - R_2$,

where R_1 and R_2 are independent observations of R.

[L]

4.   The discrete random variable X has the distribution

$P(X = 1) = 0.4, P(X = 2) = 0.2, P(X = 3) = 0.4$. Calculate the variance of X.

Let X_1 and X_2 denote two independent observations of X. Derive the sampling distribution of $T = \tfrac{1}{2}(X_1 - X_2)^2$, and verify that T is an unbiased estimator of the variance of X.

[W]

Common errors

1.   **Sums of random variables**

    (a) If X and Y are subtracted, their variances are added. (Not subtracted).

    (b) The variance of $X + Y$ is only equal to Var(X) + Var(Y) if X and Y are independent.

    (c) If X is multiplied by c, then its variance is multiplied by c^2. (Not by c).

    (d) If c is added to X, then its variance is unchanged. Do not add c to the variance.

2.   **Samples**

Do not confuse the population mean μ and the sample mean $\overline{X}$. μ is a fixed number, even though it may be unknown. $\overline{X}$ is a random variable, though as the sample size increases $\overline{X}$ tends to the fixed value μ.

Be careful to distinguish between the unbiased and biased sample variances.

41 Normal distribution

The probability density function of the *normal distribution* has a graph which is the familiar bell–shaped curve.

The fact that a random variable X is normal with mean μ and variance σ^2 is often written as $X \sim N(\mu, \sigma^2)$.

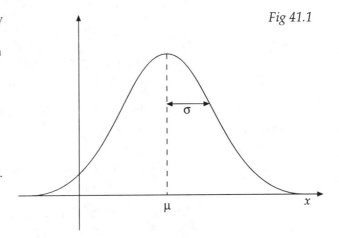

Fig 41.1

41.1 Use of tables

If Z is normal with mean 0 and variance 1, then Z has the standard normal distribution. In symbols, $Z \sim N(0, 1)$.

The cumulative distribution function of Z is called $\Phi(z)$.

$$\Phi(z) = P(Z < z)$$

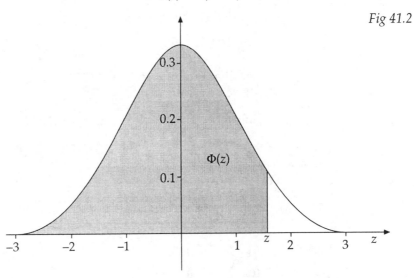

Fig 41.2

Values of $\Phi(z)$ can be found from the statistical tables on page 400. The tables give $\Phi(z)$ for $z \geq 0$. For negative values of z use the formula $\Phi(z) = 1 - \Phi(-z)$.

If X is a normal variable, then X can be converted to the standard normal variable as follows:

If $X \sim N(\mu, \sigma^2)$, then $\dfrac{X - \mu}{\sigma} = Z \sim N(0, 1)$

41.1.1 Examples

1. Let $X \sim N(3, 25)$. Find the probability that X is less than 5.

    Solution

    Convert X to the standard form by the formula above.

    $$P(X < 5) = P\left(\frac{X - 3}{5} < \frac{5 - 3}{5} \right) = P(Z < 0.4) = \Phi(0.4)$$

    Use the tables to find $\Phi(0.4)$

    > The probability that X is less than 5 is 0.655

2. Find the upper quartile of the standard normal distribution.

    Solution

    The upper quartile is the value u such that $P(Z < u) = 0.75$. Look through the normal tables for the value of z such that $\Phi(z) = 0.75$.

    > The upper quartile of Z is 0.674

3. The weights of the apples from a certain tree follow a normal distribution. A quarter of the apples weigh less than 70 g, and a third weigh more than 120 g. Find the average weight of the apples.

    Solution

    Let X be the weight of an apple picked at random. $X \sim N(\mu, \sigma^2)$. From the information given:

    $P(X < 70) = 0.25$ and $P(X > 120) = 0.33$.

    Standardise these values:

    $$\Phi\left(\frac{70 - \mu}{\sigma} \right) = 0.25 \text{ and } \Phi\left(\frac{120 - \mu}{\sigma} \right) = 0.67$$

    Use the tables to obtain:

    $70 - \mu = -0.674\sigma$ and $120 - \mu = 0.43\sigma$

    Solve to find that $\sigma = 45.3$ and $\mu = 100.5$.

    > The average apple weighs 100.5 g.

41.1.2 Exercises

1. Z has the standard normal distribution $N(0, 1)$. Find the following:

    (a) $P(Z < 2\frac{1}{2})$ (b) $P(Z > 1\frac{1}{2})$

    (c) $P(Z < -1.4)$ (d) $P(Z > -2.7)$

    (e) $P(0.3 < Z < 1.4)$ (f) $P(-0.2 < Z < 1.2)$

2. $Z \sim N(0, 1)$. Find the values of a satisfying the following:

    (a) $P(Z < a) = 0.8$ (b) $P(Z > a) = 0.3$

    (c) $P(Z > a) = 0.54$ (d) $P(Z < a) = 0.12$

3. X has a normal distribution with mean 3 and variance 4. Find the following:

   (a) $P(X < 4)$ (b) $P(X > 5.5)$

   (c) $P(X > 2\frac{1}{2})$ (d) $P(X < 1\frac{3}{4})$

4. $X \sim N(2, 9)$. Find the quartiles of X.

5. $X \sim N(5, 1.44)$. Find the value of a such that $P(X < a) = 0.85$.

6. $X \sim N(75, 100)$. Find the values of a which satisfy the following:

   (a) $P(X < a) = 0.9$ (b) $P(X > a) = 0.23$

   (c) $P(X > a) = 0.83$ (d) $P(X < a) = 0.02$

7. X is a normal variable with mean 4, such that $P(X < 5) = 0.6$. Find the variance of X.

8. X is a normal variable with mean 93. $P(X < 90) = 0.48$. Find the standard deviation of X.

9. X is a normal variable with standard deviation 2.5. $P(X < 4) = 0.54$. Find the mean of X.

10. X is a normal variable with variance 121. $P(X > 76) = 0.7$. Find the mean of X.

11. The number of c.c. in cartons of orange juice follows a normal distribution. A tenth of the cartons are below 995 c.c., and a twentieth are above 1010 c.c. Find the mean and variance of the contents.

12. The width of certain bolts follows a normal distribution. 1% of the bolts are above 2.001 cm, and 5% are below 1.995 cm. Find the mean width.

13. The distance that a javelin thrower can reach follows a normal distribution. A third of her throws exceed 40 m., and a quarter exceed 45 m. Find the average distance she can throw.

41.2 Sums and differences of normal variables

If X and Y are independent normal variables with means μ and λ, variances σ^2 and υ^2 respectively, then their sum and difference are also normal, as follows:

If $X \sim N(\mu, \sigma^2)$ and $Y \sim N(\lambda, \upsilon^2)$, then:

$X + Y \sim N(\mu + \lambda, \sigma^2 + \upsilon^2)$; $X - Y \sim N(\mu - \lambda, \sigma^2 + \upsilon^2)$

In general, for a and b constant, $aX + bY \sim N(a\mu + b\lambda, a^2\sigma^2 + b^2\upsilon^2)$

Suppose $X_1, X_2, X_3, ..., X_n$ are independent normal variables, each with mean μ and variance σ^2.

The sum $S = X_1 + X_2 + ... + X_n$ is normal with mean $n\mu$ and variance $n\sigma^2$

The average $\dfrac{S}{n}$ is normal with mean μ and variance $\dfrac{\sigma^2}{n}$.

41.2.1 Examples

1. X and Y are independent variables with $X \sim N(2, 4)$ and $Y \sim N(3, 6.25)$. Find

    (a) the probability that $X + Y$ is less than 6

    (b) the upper quartile of $Y - X$.

    Solution

    (a) $X + Y$ has a distribution given by $X + Y \sim N(5, 10.25)$.

    $$P(X + Y < 6) = \Phi\left(\frac{6 - 5}{\sqrt{10.25}}\right)$$

    The probability that $X + Y$ is less than 6 is 0.62

    (b) Similarly, $Y - X \sim N(1, 10.25)$. The upper quartile is obtained by finding the value of z for which $\Phi(z) = \frac{3}{4} = 0.75$.

    $$\Phi(0.674) = 0.75$$

    The upper quartile is $1 + 0.674 \times \sqrt{10.25} = 3.16$

2. Jason and Daniel run a 100 m race. Jason's time for this distance is normal with mean 12 seconds and variance 1.3, while Daniel's time is normal with mean 12.5 and variance 4. Their times are independent of each other. Find the probability that Daniel wins the race.

    Solution

    Letting X be Jason's time and Y Daniel's, Daniel will win if $Y < X$. But $Y - X$ is normal, with mean 0.5 and variance 5.3.

    $$P(Y < X) = P(Y - X < 0) = \Phi\left(\frac{0 - 0.5}{\sqrt{5.3}}\right)$$

    The probability that Daniel wins is 0.41

3. The contents in c.c. of cartons of orange juice is normal with mean 1,000 and variance 12. Find the probability that the average contents of 20 cartons is less than 998 c.c.

    Solution

    Let $X_1, X_2,..., X_{20}$ be the contents of the cartons. The distribution of their average $\overline{X}$ is normal with mean 1,000 and variance $\frac{12}{20}$.

    $$P(\overline{X} < 998) = \Phi\left(\frac{998 - 1000}{\sqrt{\frac{12}{20}}}\right)$$

    The probability is 0.005

41.2.2 Exercises

1. X and Y are independent normal variables with means 4 and 7 and variances 5 and 4. Find the following:

    (a) $P(X + Y < 11)$ (b) $P(X + Y > 9.5)$

    (c) $P(X - Y < 1)$ (d) $P(2X + 3Y < 30)$

    (e) $P(3X - 2Y > -1\frac{1}{2})$ (f) $P(X > Y)$

    (g) $P(4X > 3Y)$ (h) $P(3Y > 23)$

2. X and Y are independent normal variables with means 23 and 19, and variances 3 and 2. Find the values of a for which:

(a) $P(X + Y < a) = 0.8$

(b) $P(X - Y < a) = 0.75$

(c) $P(3X + 2Y > a) = 0.2$

(d) $P(5X - 4Y < a) = 0.35$

(e) $P(2X < a) = 0.78$

(f) $P(5Y > a) = 0.23$

3. The weight of an empty can is normal with mean 20 g and variance 2, and the weight of its contents is normal with mean 100 g and variance 5. Find the probability that the full can weighs more than 125 g.

4. When a man goes to work he walks to the bus–stop, waits for a bus, takes the bus to his office. The times for all three stages are independent, and are normal with means 3 min, 10 min, 20 min and variances 0.5, 8, 5 respectively. Find the probability that he takes more than 35 minutes for the whole journey.

5. The width of a bolt is normal with mean 1 cm and standard deviation 0.001: the width of the hole of a nut is normal with mean 1.005 and standard deviation 0.002. Find the probability that the bolt will go into the nut.

6. A bus leaves the bus-stop at 9.00 precisely; the time it takes to reach the station is normal with mean 10 minutes and variance 4. The train arrives at the station at a time after 9.00 which is normal with mean 11 minutes and variance 0.25. Find the probability that a passenger on the bus will be able to catch the train.

7. $X_1, X_2,..., X_{16}$ are independent normal variables with mean 3 and variance 0.5. S is their sum and A is their average. Find the following:

(a) $P(S < 50)$

(b) $P(S > 40)$

(c) $P(A < 3.01)$

(d) $P(A < 2.98)$

(e) $P(|A - 3| < 0.05)$

(f) $P(2.97 < A < 3.03)$

8. With the variables as defined in Question 7, find the values of a for which:

(a) $P(S < a) = 0.7$

(b) $P(S > a) = 0.77$

(c) $P(A < a) = 0.99$

(d) $P(A > a) = 0.95$

(e) $P(|A - 3| < a) = 0.98$

(f) $P(|A - 3| > a) = 0.05$

9. The weight of a ball-bearing is distributed normally with mean 5 g and variance 0.001 g. If 100 ball-bearings are chosen, find the probabilities that

(a) the total weight is greater than 500.5 g

(b) the average weight is less than 4.999 g.

10. I calculate that my journey to work is normally distributed with mean 25 minutes and variance 12. Over 50 journeys, evaluate the probabilities that

(a) my total journey time is more than 1300 mins

(b) my average journey time is more than 26 minutes.

41.3 The central limit theorem

The normal distribution is the limit distribution of most other kinds of distributions. The *Central Limit Theorem* states:

Let $X_1, X_2, X_3,...$ be independent variables taken from the same distribution with mean μ and variance σ^2. Let A_n be the average of the first n of them.

Then, as n tends to ∞, the distribution of A_n tends to $N(\mu, \dfrac{\sigma^2}{n})$.

This approximation is especially useful for finding approximations to the Binomial and Poisson distributions and for sample proportions.

When n is large, B(n, p) is approximately N(np, npq).

If λ is large, a Poisson distribution with mean λ is approximately N(λ, λ).

Suppose a proportion π of a large population has a certain property. A sample of size n is taken, and the sample proportion is p. Then, if n is large, p is approximately N(π, $\dfrac{\pi(1-\pi)}{n}$).

When using the normal distribution to approximate a discrete distribution, the *continuity correction* is used, as follows:

If X only takes whole number values, then $X > 3$ means the same as $X \geq 4$. So when the normal approximation is applied the compromise $X > 3.5$ is used.

41.3.1 Examples

1. The lifetime of a certain brand of battery has mean 12 hours and standard deviation 3 hours. 50 batteries are tested. Find the probability that the average lifetime is less than $12\frac{1}{2}$ hours.

    Solution

    Apply the central limit theorem to the average A of the 50 lifetimes X_1, X_2,..., X_{50}.

    A is approximately N($12, \frac{9}{50}$).

    $$P(A < 12\tfrac{1}{2}) = \Phi\left(\frac{12\frac{1}{2} - 12}{\sqrt{\frac{9}{50}}}\right) = \Phi(1.18)$$

    The probability is 0.88

2. X has a Poisson distribution with mean 25. Find the probability that X is greater than 30.

    Solution

    25 is large enough for the normal approximation to be used. The condition $X > 30$ is equivalent to $X \geq 31$, so apply the continuity correction and use $X > 30.5$.

    X is approximately N(25, 25)

    $$P(X > 30.5) \approx 1 - \Phi\left(\frac{30.5 - 25}{5}\right)$$

    The probability is approximately 0.14

3. A multiple choice test contains 100 questions, each of which contains 4 possible answers. A candidate answers at random. What is the probability that he scores at least 28?

    Solution

    Let X be the number of correct answers. X is B($100, \frac{1}{4}$). The value of n is large enough for the normal approximation to be valid. Applying the continuity correction, find the probability that X is greater than 27.5.

    X is approximately N(25, 18.75).

$$P(X > 27.5) \approx 1 - \Phi(\frac{2.5}{\sqrt{18.75}})$$

The probability is approximately 0.28

41.3.2 Exercises

1. The height of a certain species of plant has mean 160 cm and variance 200. 20 plants are measured. Find the probability that the average height is more than 164 cm.

2. The time that a boy takes to run 200 m has mean 30 seconds and standard deviation 3.5 seconds. He runs the distance 30 times. Find the probability that his average time is more than 29 seconds.

3. The weights of a certain grade of egg have mean 50 g and variance 100. 40 eggs are tested. Find the probability that the average weight is more than 48 g.

4. $X \sim B(60, \frac{1}{4})$. Find the probability that X is more than 20.

5. $X \sim B(200, 0.4)$. Find the probability that X is less than 75.

6. $X \sim B(1000, 0.44)$. Find the probability that X is at least 420.

7. A fair die is rolled 60 times. Find the probability that there are more than 15 sixes.

8. On average, 2 in 5 potatoes have blemishes. Find the probability that in a batch of 100 potatoes at least 65 have no blemishes.

9. A fair coin is tossed 200 times. Find the probability of obtaining more than 115 heads.

10. Four fifths of a sort of tulip bulbs give flowers. If I buy 100, what is the probability that more than 25 fail to give flowers?

11. It is thought that support for the Conservative Party in a certain town is at 40%. A poll questions 1,000 voters. What is the probability that more than 380 support the Conservative party?

12. It is thought that 15% of the population are left-handed. What is the probability that the proportion of left-handers in 100 people will be more than 20%?

13. The proportion of candidates who pass the Driving Test is 0.6. Find the probability that, out of 200 candidates, the proportional pass rate was less than 0.55.

14. X has a Poisson distribution with mean 40. What is the probability that X is less than 35?

15. The number of misprints in a page of a newspaper follows a Poisson distribution with mean 4. The newspaper has 20 pages. What is the probability of more than 90 misprints in all?

16. The number of meteorites which fall in a field each year follows a Poisson distribution with mean 2. What is the probability that over a 15 year period more than 33 meteorites fall?

17. The number of letters I receive each day follows a Poisson distribution with mean 2. What is the probability that over 30 days I receive less than 50 letters?

18. A fisherman reckons that the number of fish he catches in a day follows a Poisson distribution with mean 2.5. What is the probability that over 12 days he catches no more than 25 fish?

41.4 Examination questions

1. From a large sample of bars of soap produced by a machine it is found that the mean weight of the bars is 425.1 grams with a standard deviation of 1.6 grams. Assuming that the weights are distributed normally, calculate the percentage of bars of soap produced by the same machine that will weigh

   (i) less than 424 grams;

   (ii) not more than 425.5 grams;

   (iii) between 426 grams and 428 grams.

   If an adjustment can be made to the machine which alters the mean but leaves the standard deviation unchanged, what should the new mean weight be if it is required that 95% of the bars of soap weigh less than 427 grams?

   [Give all your answers correct to one decimal place.]

   [MEI ADD]

2. The length of worms in a certain plot is Normally distributed. About 97% of the worms are found to be under 25 cm long.

   (a) How many standard deviations more than the mean, to the nearest tenth, is a 25 cm worm?

   (b) About 69% of the worms are over 13 cm long. How many standard deviations less than the mean is a 13 cm worm?

   (c) Hence show that the standard deviation of worm length is about 5 cm and calculate the mean length.

   (d) Calculate the percentage of the worms which would have length

   (i) less than 8 cm,   (ii) between 18 cm and 19 cm.

   [SMP ADD]

3. Calculate

   (a) the mean $\bar{x}$ and   (b) the standard deviation s

   for the following sample of weights, in kilograms, of 11 children. Show all necessary working.

   $$37, 38, 38, 42, 42, 44, 46, 46, 48, 50, 53.$$

   Find the percentage of the sample lying between $\bar{x} - s$ and $\bar{x} + s$.

   This sample of 11 was chosen at random from a population of 1000 children of the same age. Estimate how many children from the whole population would have a weight within s of $\bar{x}$.

   [O ADD]

4. The times taken by two runners A and B to run 400 m races are independent and normally distributed with means 45.0 s and 45.2 s, and standard deviations 0.5 s and 0.8 s respectively. The two runners are to compete in a 400 m race for which there is a track record of 44.5 s.

    (i)   Calculate, to three decimal places, the probability of runner A breaking the track record.

    (ii) Show that the probability of runner B breaking the track record is greater than that of runner A.

    (iii) Calculate, to three decimal places, the probability of runner A beating runner B.

    [JMB]

5. An analysis of the membership of a large organisation shows that 60% of the members are over 50 years old and 2.5% are under 20 years old.

    (i)   Using appropriate distributional approximations *when necessary*, calculate the probabilities, correct to three decimal places, that a random sample of 100 members will include

       (a) 60 or more members over 50 years old,

       (b) 3 or fewer members under 20 years old,

       (c) exactly 40 members aged from 20 years to 50 years, inclusive.

    (ii) Use a normal approximation to find the smallest number of members that should be sampled at random in order that the probability is at least 0.9 that 55% or more of the sampled members will be over 50 years old.

    [W]

6. X_i ($i = 1, 2,..., n$) are n random variables each distributed normally with mean μ and variance σ^2. If $Y = X_1 + X_2 +... + X_n$ state precisely the distribution of Y.

    A lift can carry with safety a load of no more than 725 kg. The masses of the people using the lift are normally distributed with mean 67.3 kg and standard deviation 7.2 kg. Show that if 9 people enter the lift it is practically certain that the maximum load will not be exceeded. Calculate the probabilities of the maximum load being exceeded when the number of people in the lift is (i) 10 (ii) 11.

    A notice is placed in the lift stating the maximum number of passengers, N. What should be the value of N in order that with N passengers, the probability of the maximum load being exceeded is less than 1%?

    During a certain time of the day the number of passengers in the lift has a Binomial distribution with parameters N and p. If $p = 0.8$, calculate the probability that during the journey there will be 9 passengers with a total mass of under 650 kg.

    [SUJB]

7. The random variable X has a rectangular distribution with probability density function f(x), where f(x) = $\frac{1}{6}$ for $1 \le x \le 7$ and f(x) = 0 for all other x.

    (i)   Why is it obvious that the expectation of X is 4? Show by integration that the variance of X is 3. What is the probability that $3.7 < X < 4.3$?

(ii) Use results in (i) to write down the values of the expectation and variance of the mean $\overline{X}_{100}$ of 100 independent observations of X. Estimate to 2 decimal places the probability that $3.7 < \overline{X}_{100} < 4.3$.

(iii) One observation x of X is made, dividing the interval [1,7] into two segments. For what values of x is the ratio of the length of the shorter segment to that of the longer segment less than $\frac{1}{4}$? What is the probability that this event occurs?

[MEI]

Common errors

1. **Use of tables**

   (a) Be careful when you solve problems of the form:

   'Find c such that $P(Z < c) = \frac{3}{4}$ '

   You must look through the tables until you find 0.75. Do not look up 0.75 directly.

   (b) Do not confuse the standard deviation σ with the variance σ^2. When standardising normal variables, for example, you divide by the standard deviation σ.

2. **Sums and differences**

   (a) If X has variance σ^2, then aX has variance $a^2\sigma^2$. (Not $a\sigma^2$)

   (b) If X has variance σ^2 and Y has variance v^2, then $X - Y$ has variance $\sigma^2 + v^2$. (Not $\sigma^2 - v^2$)

3. **Central limit theorem**

   (a) The continuity correction is only used when the original distribution is discrete. Do not use it for continuous distributions.

   (b) Make sure you go the correct way with the continuity correction. Suppose you are asked to find the probability that $X < 6$; this is equivalent to $X \leq 5$, so compromise by putting $X < 5.5$.

   (c) The normal approximation is only valid when n is large. As a rough guide, when approximating the Poisson distribution λ must be at least 20. When approximating the Binomial both np and nq must be at least 10.

42 Hypothesis testing

Suppose a sample is taken from a distribution whose mean μ is not known. The use of the sample to check whether or not μ has a certain value is a *hypothesis test*.

Suppose we are checking whether or not the parent mean μ has a certain value μ_0. The *null hypothesis* H_0 states that it does have the value. The *alternative hypothesis* H_1 is that it does not.

ONE AND TWO TAILED TESTS

If H_1 is of the form $\mu \neq \mu_0$, then this is a *two-tailed* test.

If H_1 is of the form $\mu < \mu_0$ (or $\mu > \mu_0$), then this is a *one-tailed* test.

A two-tailed test is always performed, unless there is prior reason to think that μ could only be less than μ_0 (or only greater than it).

Fig 42.1

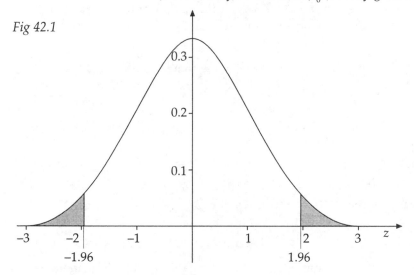

TYPE I AND TYPE II ERRORS

A Type I error is to reject H_0 even though it is true. The probability of doing this is the *significance level* of the test.

A Type II error is to retain the H_0 even though it is false. The probability of doing this depends on the true value of μ.

If H_0 is false, for a given value of μ the probability of rejecting H_0 is the *power* of the test.

42.1 Tests on the mean

Throughout it is assumed that the parent distribution is normal.

A *critical value* for the normal distribution is a value of z which cuts off a certain percentage of probability.

For example, the 5% critical value is 1.96. This means that $P(|Z| > 1.96) = 0.05$. (See Fig 42.1). Critical values can be found in the table on page 401.

42.1.1 Examples

1. A distribution is thought to be normal with mean 12 and variance 5. A sample of size 10 has sample mean 11. Does this provide evidence at a significance level of 5% to show that the parent mean is not 12?

   Solution

   There is no prior reason to think that μ should be greater or less than 12. Hence a two-tailed test is performed.

   $H_0: \mu = 12$ and $H_1: \mu \neq 12$

   Assuming H_0, the distribution of the sample mean $\overline{X}$ is $N(12, \frac{5}{10})$. The difference between the sample mean and the true mean is 1.
   Find the corresponding z value.

   $$z = \frac{\left|\overline{X} - 12\right|}{\sqrt{\frac{1}{2}}} = 1.41$$

   This is less than 1.96, the 5% critical value for a two–tailed test. The null hypothesis is retained.

   > We have failed to disprove that the mean is 12

2. A manufacturer of orange juice claims that the volumes of the cartons which his firm produces are normal with mean 1000 c.c. and variance 16. A weights and measures inspector tests a sample of 20 cartons and finds that their average volume is 997.5 c.c. Is this significant at 1% to show that the manufacturer is giving short measure?

   Solution

   The inspector is only interested in showing that μ is less than 1,000. Hence we do a one–tailed test.

   $H_0: \mu = 1000$ and $H_1: \mu < 1000$

   Assuming H_0, the distribution of the sample mean $\overline{X}$ is $N(1000, \frac{16}{20})$. Find the z–value corresponding to 997.5:

   $$z = \frac{\left|997.5 - 1000\right|}{\sqrt{0.8}} = 2.795$$

   This is greater than 2.33, the critical value for a 1% one–tailed test. The alternative hypothesis is proved at this significance level.

   > At 1% significance we have proved that the mean is below 1000.

3. The weight of certain apples should have mean 112 grams and standard deviation 15 grams. A new spraying technique is introduced, and it will be concluded that the technique is effective if the mean weight of a sample of 20 apples increases to 120 grams. If the mean weight increases to 125 grams, find the power of the test.

   Solution

   Let the new mean be μ. The null hypothesis H_0 is that the mean is still 112. The alternative hypothesis is that it is greater than 112. H_0 will be rejected if the sample mean $\overline{X}$ is greater than 120. If in fact $\mu = 125$:

$$P(\text{reject } H_0) = P(\overline{X} > 120)$$

$$= 1 - \Phi\left(\frac{120 - 125}{\frac{15}{\sqrt{20}}}\right) = 0.932$$

If $\mu = 125$, the power of the test is 0.932

42.1.2 Exercises

1. It is thought that a distribution has mean 2 and variance 0.4. A sample of 8 has sample mean 2.45. Test at the 5% level whether the mean is 2.

2. Repeat Question 1 for a significance level of 1%.

3. It is claimed that the mean of X is 40 and its variance 60. It is suspected that the mean might be greater than this, and a sample of size 15 has mean 45. Does this confirm the suspicion, at a level of 5%?

4. It is thought that a distribution has mean 4. A sample of 10 was as follows:

    4.1, 4.2, 4.0, 3.9, 4.1, 4.2, 4.3, 4.4, 4.3, 4.1

    Assuming that the unbiased sample variance is the correct one, test at a 5% significance level whether or not the mean is 4.

5. The national average mark for a certain exam is 47.5%. The marks of 12 children were:

    47, 46, 45, 44, 49, 53, 54, 44, 42, 41, 42, 40

    Assuming that the unbiased sample variance is the correct one, test at a 5% significance level whether or not the children differ from the average.

6. A factory produces string which, it is claimed, has a breaking strength of 60 N. A sample of 10 pieces of string had breaking strengths as follows:

    50, 58, 64, 55, 52, 53, 54, 57, 50, 51

    Test at the 5% level whether the breaking strength is lower than claimed.

7. Over the year a man finds that the time it takes him to drive to work has mean 20 minutes and variance 20. A new set of traffic-lights is introduced on his route: for the next ten days his average time of journey was 23 mins. Does this show at a significance level of 2% that the traffic-lights have affected his journey time?

8. A light-bulb manufacturer claims that its bulbs have a mean lifetime of 1000 hours. A sample of 10 were tested, and their lifetimes were:

    900, 950, 1100, 800, 700, 850, 930, 900, 920, 940

    Is this significant at 5% to show that the average lifetime is less than 1000 hours?

9. The breaking strength of an elastic band should have mean 3 N and standard deviation 1 N. A sample of 50 will be tested, and the day's production will be rejected as substandard if the sample mean is less than 2.5 N. Find the power of the test if the mean breaking strength is 2.3 N.

10. The mean lifetime of an electric bulb should be 8000 hours, with variance 2000^2. A sample of size 20 is tested, and it is concluded that the mean lifetime is less than 8000 if the sample mean is less than 7000. Find the power of the test if the mean is in fact 7500 hours.

42.2 Testing for differences

Suppose we wish to test whether the means μ_1 and μ_2 of two distributions are the same. Then we test whether the difference $\mu_1 - \mu_2$ is zero.

If there is a natural association between the samples from the two distributions, then the test is a *paired sample test.*

42.2.1 Examples

1. A factory has two machines which make bolts. Samples were taken from both machines: the mean diameter of 100 bolts from Machine A was 1.274 cm, and the mean diameter of 150 bolts from Machine B was 1.271 cm. Assuming that the standard deviation of the bolts is 0.01 for both machines, test at the 5% level whether there is any difference between the machines.

   Solution

   Let μ_1 and μ_2 be the mean diameters of the bolts from Machines A and B respectively.

   $H_0 : \mu_1 = \mu_2$ and $H_1 : \mu_1 \neq \mu_2$

   The distributions of the sample means are

   $$\overline{X} \sim N(\mu_1, \frac{0.01^2}{100}) \quad \text{and} \quad \overline{Y} \sim N(\mu_2, \frac{0.01^2}{150}).$$

   Assuming H_0, the difference between these means is

   $$\overline{X} - \overline{Y} \sim N(0, \frac{0.01^2}{100} + \frac{0.01^2}{150})$$

   The standardised statistic is $\dfrac{\left|1.274 - 1.271\right|}{\sqrt{(0.01)^2\left(\frac{1}{100} + \frac{1}{150}\right)}} = 2.32$

   This is greater than 1.96. The null hypothesis is rejected.

   At 5% we have shown there is a difference between the machines

2. A farmer wishes to see whether the addition of a certain ingredient to his hens' diet will increase the weight of their eggs. Ten hens were selected, and the weights of their eggs before and after receiving the ingredient were as follows:

Hen	A	B	C	D	E	F	G	H	J	K
Weight of egg before	30	35	40	35	43	39	41	37	49	42
Weight of egg after	33	32	43	36	43	41	44	37	50	44

   Assuming that the unbiased sample variance of the difference is correct is this sufficient evidence at 5% to show that the ingredient has increased egg weight?

   Solution

   The same hens appear in the both samples. Hence this is a paired sample test. The farmer is only interested in showing that there has been an increase, hence this is a one tailed test. Write out a table of the differences D:

Hen	A	B	C	D	E	F	G	H	J	K
Difference in weight	3	–3	3	1	0	2	3	0	1	2

$H_0: E(D) = 0$ and $H_1: E(D) > 0$

The sample mean of D is 1.2. The unbiased sample variance is 3.51.

Assuming H_0, $\overline{D}$ is $N\left(0, \dfrac{3.51}{10}\right)$. Find the coresponding z value.

$z = \dfrac{1.2}{\sqrt{0.351}} = 2.03$. This is greater than 1.645.

There is sufficient evidence to show that the weight has increased

42.2.2 Exercises

1. A group of 15 left-handed people had an average I.Q. of 105, while a group of 20 right-handed people had an I.Q. of 99. Assuming that the variance of I.Q is 225, test at a 5% significance level whether left-handers have different intelligence from right-handers.

2. The variance of the marks obtained in an exam is 300. Two classes took the exam, having received different teaching methods. In Class A, 20 pupils had an average mark of 67. In Class B, 25 pupils had an average mark of 56. Test at the 5% level whether there is a difference between the teaching methods.

3. The standard deviation of the midday temperature in a town in July is 70. For the 31 days in July the average midday temperature was 77° in 1993, and 80° in 1994. Test at the 5% level whether the temperature was significantly different in 1994 than in 1993.

4. The standard deviation of the lifetime of certain batteries is 8 hours. A new manufacturing technique is claimed to increase the lifetime. A batch of 15 of the old batteries had a mean lifetime of 30 hours, and a batch of 12 of the new batteries had a mean lifetime of 36 hours. Is this significant at 5% to show that the lifetime has been increased?

5. The same scripts for an exam were marked twice by two different examiners. The results were as follows:

Candidate	A	B	C	D	E	F	G	H	J	K
Examiner 1's mark	66	74	59	54	63	72	60	81	71	58
Examiner 2's mark	64	75	53	50	59	67	61	75	68	53

Assuming that the unbiased sample variance for the differences is correct, is this significant evidence at 5% to show that one examiner is more strict than the other?

6. Two drivers dispute who is the more economical. They select 9 routes, equal in length, and each drives along them. The results of the petrol consumption for the journeys are:

Route	A	B	C	D	E	F	G	H	J
m.p.g. for first driver	35	33	37	48	29	32	34	27	30
m.p.g. for second driver	33	32	37	50	27	30	34	24	28

Test at the 5% significance level whether there is any difference between the petrol consumption of the two drivers.

7. The I.Q.s of 10 couples of husbands and wives were tested. Test at a 5% significance level whether there is any difference between their intelligences.

Couple	A	B	C	D	E	F	G	H	J	K
Husband's I.Q.	103	112	99	107	103	91	88	121	117	102
Wife's I.Q.	111	121	103	101	98	99	95	107	110	120

8. The scores of 9 golfers were found before and after receiving coaching. Test at a 2% significance level whether or not coaching has improved their performance.

Golfer	A	B	C	D	E	F	G	H	J
Score before	103	101	99	97	111	123	88	93	108
Score after	96	94	91	92	101	127	86	90	101

42.3 Testing proportion

A proportion of a population has a certain property. Let that proportion be π. If a sample of size n is taken, then the number of that sample with the property has a $B(n,\pi)$ distribution.

If n is large then $B(n,\pi)$ is approximately $N(n\pi, n\pi(1-\pi))$. Here a continuous distribution is used to approximate to a discrete distribution. Hence the continuity correction is used.

Let p be the *proportion* of the sample which has the property. Then p has expected value π and variance $\dfrac{\pi(1-\pi)}{n}$. If n is large then p is approximately $N(\pi, \dfrac{\pi(1-\pi)}{n})$.

42.3.1 Examples

1. A garden-centre claims that at least 80% of its bulbs will give flowers. When 20 were tested only 12 gave flowers. Is this significant at 5% to discredit the claim?

Solution

We are only interested in showing that the proportion is less than 80%. Hence a one-tailed test is used. Let the proportion be p.

$H_0: p = 0.8$ and $H_1: p < 0.8$

Assuming H_0, the number X of flowering bulbs in the sample is $B(20,0.8)$. This is approximately $N(16, 3.2)$. Using the continuity correction, the corresponding z value is:

$$z = \frac{16 - 12.5}{\sqrt{3.2}} = 1.96.$$ This is greater than 1.645.

At a 5% significance level the claim is false

2. In an opinion poll 100 men and 150 women were asked whether they would vote for the Prosperity Party. The support was 35% and 30% respectively. Is there evidence at 5% significance level that support for the party is different for men and for women?

    Solution

    Let p_m and p_w be the true proportions of support for men and women respectively.

    $H_0: p_m = p_w$ and $H_1: p_m \neq p_w$

    Assume H_0. Estimate the true proportion p by a pooled sample:

    $$p \approx \frac{100 \times 0.35 + 150 \times 0.3}{250} = 0.32$$

    The variance of the difference D is $0.32 \times 0.68 \left(\frac{1}{100} + \frac{1}{150} \right) = 0.0036$

    The distribution of the difference D between the sample proportions is $N(0, 0.0036)$. Find the corresponding z value.

    $$z = \frac{0.35 - 0.3}{\sqrt{0.0036}} = 0.833.$$ This is less than 1.96.

    There is no evidence to show that the proportions are different

42.3.2 Exercises

1. A politician claims that 40% of the population will vote for him. A sample of 30 people produced only 10 supporters. Is this significant at 5% to show that he overestimates his support?

2. In an experiment to verify telepathy a pack of 100 cards is dealt out face down. The pack contains 5 different types of cards, in equal numbers, and a person is asked to guess the type of each card. The person guesses correctly 28 times. Is this significant at 5% to show that the person is telepathic?

3. Leah claims that she can tell which of the 12 signs of the zodiac a person belongs to. She guesses the sign for 100 people, and gets it right 20 times. Is this significant at 5% to show that her claim is correct?

4. A multiple choice exam contains 50 questions, each of which has 5 alternative answers. A candidate gets 15 correct. Is this significant at 5% to show that he has not been answering at random?

5. It is suspected that a coin is biased. It is thrown 100 times, and the proportion of heads is 0.6. Test at whether or not the coin is biased, at

    (a) 5%   (b) 2%.

6. It is thought that a die might be weighted towards 6. It is rolled 180 times, and the number of sixes was 37. Test at 5% whether or not the die is biased.

7. There are two driving-schools in a town. In one of them there were 80 pupils, 50 of whom passed at their first test. The other had 120 pupils of whom 100 passed at their first attempt. Is there evidence at 5% that one school is better than the other?

8. I buy 20 light-bulbs from one shop, and 32 from another shop. 25% of the bulbs from the first shop last less than 6 months, while the corresponding figure for the second shop is 12%. Is there evidence at 5% to show that one shop sells more reliable bulbs?

9. A school has 500 pupils. 200 are given an anti-flu jab, and 300 are not. Over the winter 25% of the first group and 30% of the second has flu. Is there evidence at 5% that the jab has some effect?

10. A rust-proofing process is tested as follows. 40 cars were proofed, and 2 years later 5 had severe rust. 50 similar cars were not proofed, and 2 years later 10 had severe rust. Is there evidence at 5% to show that the process is efficacious?

11. It is suspected that a die is biased towards 4. It is decided to roll it 60 times, and to decide that it is biased if there are more than 20 4s. If the probability of a 4 is in fact 0.4, find the power of the test.

12. It is suspected that a coin is biased towards Heads. It is decided to spin it 40 times, and to conclude that it is biased if there are more than 30 Heads. If the probability of Heads is 0.7, find the power of the test.

42.4 Confidence intervals

Suppose a sample of size n is taken from a population with unknown mean μ. A *confidence interval* for μ is an interval within which μ is expected to be.

A 95% *confidence interval* is one for which there is a 0.95 probability that it contains μ.

Suppose the sample mean is $\overline{X}$ and the population variance is σ^2. Assuming that the distribution of $\overline{X}$ is normal, then a 95% confidence interval for μ is:

$$\overline{X} - \frac{1.96\,\sigma}{\sqrt{n}} < \mu < \overline{X} + \frac{1.96\,\sigma}{\sqrt{n}} \ .$$

Figures for other levels of confidence may be found from a table of critical values of the normal distribution.

Suppose a population has a proportion π with a particular property. The proportion of a sample of size n with that property is p. Provided that n is reasonably large, a 95% confidence interval for π is:

$$p - 1.96\sigma < \pi < p + 1.96\sigma, \text{ (where } \sigma^2 = \frac{p(1-p)}{n} \text{)}.$$

42.4.1 Examples

1. A machine produces ball–bearings whose diameter is normally distributed with mean μ and variance 0.10 mm^2. A sample of size 10 had mean 11.5 mm. Find a 95% confidence interval for μ.

   Solution

   Use the formula above. $\overline{X} = 11.5$, $\sigma = \sqrt{0.1}$, $n = 10$.

   $11.5 - 1.96(\sqrt{0.01}) < \mu < 11.5 + 1.96(\sqrt{0.01})$

   The 95% confidence interval is from 11.3 to 11.7

2. Before a general election, a sample of 2,000 voters was asked which party they would support. 800 said they would support the Freedom Party. Find a 99% confidence interval for the true level of support for the Freedom Party.

    Solution

    Here the sample proportion p is 0.4. Looking up 1% in the table of critical values, we find 2.58. The variance σ^2 is $0.4 \times \dfrac{0.6}{2000}$. The confidence interval is:

    $$0.4 - 2.58\sigma < \pi < 0.4 + 2.58\sigma$$

    The 99% confidence interval is from 0.37 to 0.43

42.4.2 Exercises

1. X has a normal distribution with unknown mean μ and variance 4. A sample of size 12 has sample mean 13. Find a 95% confidence interval for μ.

2. A factory produces cartons of orange juice, whose volume is normally distributed with mean μ and variance 120. A sample of 20 cartons had average volume 995 c.c. Find a 99% confidence interval for μ.

3. A machine produces bolts, whose weight is normally distributed with variance $0.2\ \mathrm{g}^2$. A sample of 15 bolts had average weight 12 g. Find a 99% confidence interval for the mean weight of the bolts produced by the machine.

4. The heights of a certain plant are thought to be normally distributed with variance $12\ \mathrm{cm}^2$. 10 plants had heights (in cm.):

    $$23, 25, 20, 26, 19, 25, 27, 23, 22, 23$$

    Find a 95% confidence interval for the mean height of the plants.

5. The weight of the contents of certain bags of sugar has variance $40\ \mathrm{g}^2$. 8 bags were weighed as follows:

    $$245, 251, 259, 263, 253, 247, 240, 248 \text{ (grams)}$$

    Find a 98% confidence interval for the mean weight of the bags.

6. The diameters of 12 ping-pong balls were (in cm.):

    $$3.18, 3.21, 3.25, 3.22, 3.21, 3.22, 3.19, 3.17, 3.20, 3.22, 3.21, 3.19$$

    Using the unbiased sample variance find a 95% confidence interval for the mean diameter of a ping-pong ball.

7. The lifetimes of 10 light-bulbs were as follows (in hours):

    $$1034, 1132, 1453, 1234, 1372, 1402, 1362, 1222, 1192, 1365$$

    Find a 99% confidence interval for the mean lifetime of the bulbs.

8. In an investigation to find the proportion of left-handed people in the population, 200 people were asked and 35 said they were left-handed. Find a 95% confidence interval for the proportion of left-handers in the population.

9. An opinion poll of 1,000 voters found that 30% of the sample would vote for the Magenta Party. Find a 95% confidence interval for the support for the Magenta Party in the population.

10. Out of 400 households which were investigated, 320 were found to contain a pet. Find a 99% confidence interval for the proportion of households in the country which contain pets.

42.5 Examination questions

1. (a) A news agency wishes to try to predict the result of an election as soon as the polls close. For this purpose they interview a random sample of electors emerging from the polling stations and ask them how they have voted. On a particular occasion 1012 electors were interviewed and 473 of them said they had voted for Party X. Use these figures to calculate an approximate 95% confidence interval for the proportion of the whole electorate supporting Party X.

   (b) The petrol consumption of a new model of car is being tested. In one trial, 50 cars chosen at random were driven under identical conditions, and the distances, x miles, that were covered on precisely 1 gallon of petrol were recorded. The results gave the following totals: $\sum x = 2685$, $\sum x^2 = 144{,}346$. Calculate a 99% confidence interval for the mean petrol consumption, in miles per gallon, of cars of this type.

   [C]

2. The table below summarises the diameters (in mm) of a random sample of 100 rods made at factory A.

Centre of interval	5.8	6.0	6.2	6.4
Frequency	3	40	50	7

   Find

   (a) the mean and variance of these measurements,

   (b) Symmetric 98% confidence limits for the mean diameter of all rods made at factory A.

   A random sample of 80 similar rods made at factory B had a mean diameter 6.16 mm and a variance 0.024 mm². Test the hypothesis that the mean diameter of all rods made at B is equal to the mean diameter of all rods made at A.

   What assumption have you made about the variances of the two underlying populations?

   [O&C]

3. In an examination taken by a very large number of candidates it was found that the mean mark was 43.6 with a standard deviation of 16.8.

   200 candidates from centre A had a mean mark of 45.7 and 80 candidates from centre B had a mean mark of 46.4. For each centre test, at the 5% level of significance, whether the examination performance of the candidates was better than that of the population.

If the marks of the candidates from the two centres are combined, find the mean mark of all 280 candidates. Test, at the 5% level of significance, whether the examination performance of these 280 candidates was different from that of the population.

Given that the standard deviations of the marks of the candidates at centres A and B were 14.2 and 16.6 respectively, calculate the variance of the marks of all 280 candidates.

[AEB 1985]

Common errors

1. **Hypotheses**

   (a) State the null-hypothesis H_0 clearly. It must always be definite – that μ has some fixed value. You cannot have a null-hypothesis of the form $\mu > 3$.

   (b) If your result is not significant, then do not state: *Hence we have proved H_0*. The most that can be said is that: *We have failed to disprove H_0*.

   (c) Only use a one-tailed test if you have *prior* reason to think that a sample mean is less than stated. You cannot look at the figures and then decide to do a one-tailed test.

2. **Differences**

   Only use a paired sample test if there is a natural association between the samples. In example 2 of 42.2.1 the same hen was tested. If the farmer had tested two lots of ten different hens then they would not have been paired.

3. **Proportion**

   Make sure that you get the continuity correction the right way round. If a result can be written either as $X > 12$ or as $X \geq 13$ then compromise by putting $X > 12.5$.

4. **Confidence intervals**

   The mean μ of a population is not a variable, even though it may be unknown. It is better to say: *The confidence interval has probability 0.95 of containing μ* than: *μ has probability 0.95 of lying within the confidence interval*.

43 Sign, t and χ^2 tests

43.1 The sign test

The *sign test* can be used when we do not know anything about the distribution from which the data comes. We examine whether data is positive or negative, i.e. we examine the sign of data.

43.1.1 Examples

1. Test at 5% significance whether the following data could come from a distribution with median 9.5.

$$12\ 13\ 14\ 9\ 15\ 12\ 18\ 11\ 10\ 11$$

Solution

The null hypothesis H_0 is that the median is 9.5. Here we have 10 data. Assuming H_0, the number of data falling below the median is:

$X \sim B(10, \frac{1}{2})$.

Here only one figure is less than the median. The probability of a result as extreme as this is:

$P(X = 0 \text{ or } 1) + P(X = 9 \text{ or } 10) = 2 \times [\ (\frac{1}{2})^{10} + 10 \times (\frac{1}{2})^{10}\ ] = 0.02$

This is less than 0.05. The null hypothesis is rejected.

At 5% significance, we have shown that the median is not 9.5

2. Twelve teenagers played the computer game 'Trollslayer', before and after consuming a large meal of hamburgers, chips and cola. The results are below. Is this significant at 5% to show that the meal has slowed their reflexes?

Score before   11 27 15 92 84 41 27 18 87 46 61 185

Score after   9 19 98 81 79 30 20   0 81 10 62 582

Solution

The null hypothesis H_0 is that there is no change. Assuming H_0, when we subtract the scores the number of negative differences is $X \sim B(12, \frac{1}{2})$.

Here three differences are negative. The probability of a result as extreme as this is

$P(X = 0, 1, 2 \text{ or } 3) = (\frac{1}{2})^{12}(1 + 12 + 66 + 220) = 0.07$

At 5% significance, we have not shown that the meal has slowed their reflexes

43.1.2 Exercises

Throughout take the level of significance to be 5%

1. Test whether the following data could come from a distribution with median 100.

    93 98 94 110 83 77 83 84

2. Test whether the following data could come from a distribution with median 63.

    59 35 –27 84 91 74 92 75 81 90

3. It is claimed that the median wage in a town is £15,000. Eleven wage-earners were picked at random and their salaries found as shown below. Is this significant to show that the median wage is less than £15,000?

    12,100   11,500   10,580   45,000   14,600   16,050
    13,500   10,100   13,450   14,100   13,900

4. The ages of nine people at a party are as below. Is there evidence that the median age is less than 30?

    23 29 19 46 25 18 17 28 23

5. Ten couples in a community were picked at random and their ages found. In all but two cases the husband was older than the wife. Is this significant to show that in this community it is likely that the husband is older than the wife?

6. The following data gives the fuel economy of eight cars using two different brands of petrol. Is there evidence to show that there is a difference between the brands?

    m.p.g. with Brand A   27 37 29 19 41 32 25 35
    m.p.g. with Brand B   26 35 27 20 39 31 24 33

7. Thirteen pigs were weighed before and after they had received a food additive. Is there evidence that the additive is effective? The weights are in kg.

    Weight before   123 153 195 172 172 184 136 143 152 128 188 147 143
    Weight after   129 140 207 183 189 179 140 139 163 140 191 153 151

43.2 The *t* distribution

Suppose a sample is taken from a normal distribution, for which the mean and the variance are both unknown. The unbiased sample variance may be inaccurate. The distribution which takes account of this is *Student t distribution*.

Suppose a sample of size n is taken from a normal distribution with mean μ. Let $\overline{X}$ be the sample mean and let $\hat{\sigma}^2$ be the unbiased sample variance. Then:

$$T = \frac{\overline{X} - \mu}{\sqrt{\dfrac{\hat{\sigma}^2}{n}}}$$

has a t distribution with $n-1 = v$ degrees of freedom.

As *n* tends to infinity the distribution of *T* tends to the standard normal distribution.

Critical values of *T* can be found from the tables on page 401. They are used in exactly the same way as critical values for the normal distribution.

The p.d.f. of the *t* distribution is flatter than that of the normal. The critical value for 5% cuts off 2.5% of the area from each end.

Fig 43.1

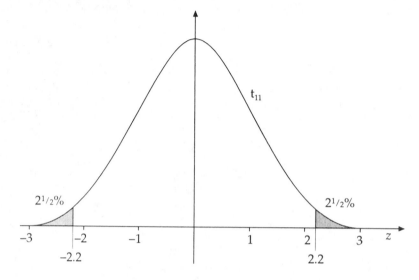

Note that the critical values are given for two-tailed tests. If a one-tailed test at 5% is required, then use the critical value for 10%.

43.2.1 Example

An athlete ran a race 9 times, with results (in seconds) as below. Assuming that the underlying distribution is normal, find a 95% confidence interval for his mean time μ seconds.

$$20.12, 21.11, 20.96, 20.55, 21.32, 21.65, 20.85, 21.63, 20.45$$

Solution

The sample mean and unbiased sample variance are 20.96 and 0.278 respectively. The number of degrees of freedom is $9 - 1 = 8$. Look up the critical value of the *t* distribution, for $v = 8$, at the 95% significance level, finding 2.31. The standard deviation of the sample mean is $\sqrt{(0.278/9)} = 0.176$

The confidence interval is $20.96 \pm 2.31 \times 0.176$.

The confidence interval is $20.55 < \mu < 21.4$

43.2.2 Exercises

1. The following sets of figures come from normal distributions. Find 95% confidence intervals for the means of those distributions.

    (a) 1.3, 1.2, 1.25, 1.22, 1.25, 1.27, 1.31

    (b) 54, 56, 57, 49, 63, 63, 60, 57, 48, 44, 56

    (c) −0.3, −0.4, −0.05, 0.0, 1.1, 0.3, 0.5, 0.6, 0.15

    (d) 150, 162, 166, 143, 169, 171

2. Find 99% confidence intervals for the figures in Question 1.

3. The mean time to perform a certain task in a factory is 12 minutes. An employee performs this task 8 times, with the following times (in minutes)

    13.5, 12.5, 13.6, 12.1, 12.9, 11.8, 13.4, 13.5

    Is there evidence at a significance level of 95% that his time differs from the average?

4. The average height of a certain type of plant is 130 cm. 9 plants from a garden were found to have heights (in cm) : 129, 134, 122, 121, 119, 138, 113, 100, 98. Is there evidence, significant at 95%, that these plants differ from the average?

5. A manufacturer of soup cans claims that the average contents of each can is 500 cm^3 . An inspector measured 11 cans, and found that the volumes of their contents were

    495, 498, 501, 485, 491, 497, 499, 482, 489, 490, 493.

    Test at a 99% significance level whether or not the manufacturer is giving short measure.

6. The times taken by 8 employees at a factory to perform a task, before and after lunch, were as given in the table below. Conduct a test on the differences to see whether lunch has made them any slower.

Employee	A	B	C	D	E	F	G	H
Before lunch	12	12.6	13	14	13.3	14.3	12.9	16.2
After lunch	13	14	16	12	14.3	15.3	13.5	18.1

7. The mean weight of eggs laid by 7 hens, before and after an additive had been given to their diet, were as in the table below. Has the additive increased the weight of the eggs?

Hen	A	B	C	D	E	F	G
Before additive	20	20.3	25.4	26.7	19.6	22.2	23.8
After additive	22.3	21.9	24.1	28.0	21.3	24.5	25.7

43.3 Testing goodness of fit

Suppose it is suspected that a sample comes from a particular distribution. To find whether or not this is the case a χ^2 test is used.

Divide the sample up into n groups. The frequency in each group is the *observed frequency* f_o.

The null Hypothesis is that the figures do come from the suspected distribution. Find the corresponding frequencies for this distribution. These are the *expected frequencies* f_e. These frequencies cannot be too small. If any f_e is less than 6 then amalgamate its group with a neighbouring group.

There are n groups. Say there are m restrictions when fitting the distribution. The number of *degrees of freedom*, υ , is $n - m$. Then:

$$\chi^2(\upsilon) = \sum \frac{(f_o - f_e)^2}{f_e} \quad \text{has a } \chi^2 \text{ distribution with } \upsilon \text{ degrees of freedom.}$$

Critical values of χ^2 are found from the tables on page 402.

The p.d.f. for $\chi^2(\upsilon)$ is shown for different values of υ. The critical value for 5% cuts off 5% of the area as shown.

Fig 43.2

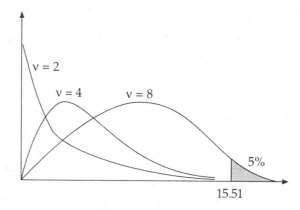

43.3.1 Example

A die is rolled 120 times. The results are given in the table below. Check whether or not it is biased.

Number	1	2	3	4	5	6
Frequency	14	13	21	16	27	29

Solution

These are the observed frequencies. If the die is fair, then the expected figures are each equal to $\dfrac{120}{6}$ = 20. The total of the frequencies must be 120. This is a restriction. Hence the number of degrees of freedom is 6 − 1 = 5. Apply the formula:

$$\chi^2(5) = \frac{6^2 + 7^2 + 1^2 + 4^2 + 7^2 + 9^2}{20} = 11.6.$$

Look up the critical value of χ^2 for $\upsilon = 5$. Notice that 11.6 is between the 5% value and the 1% value.

At a 5% significance level we have shown that the die is biased.

43.3.2 Exercises

Throughout use a 5% level of significance

1. 100 digits from the random number generator of a calculator are given by the table below. Test whether or not the digits are all equally likely.

Number	0	1	2	3	4	5	6	7	8	9
Frequency	6	4	8	13	15	9	7	17	10	11

2. It is thought that X might come from a binomial distribution with $n = 3$ and $p = \frac{1}{2}$. 60 values are as below. Find the expected frequencies for X, and hence test whether this distribution fits the figures.

Value of X	0	1	2	3
Frequency	6	18	24	12

3. Test whether the following figures could come from a binomial distribution with $n = 2$ and $p = \frac{1}{3}$.

Value of X	0	1	2
Frequency	35	40	15

4. The number of passengers in 100 cars were found to be as in the table below. Find the average number of passengers. Test whether the number of passengers follows a binomial distribution, with the value of p as found. (Note: there is an extra restriction introduced, because the mean is found from the data.)

No. of passengers	0	1	2	3
Frequency	45	32	15	8

5. Test whether the following could have come from a binomial distribution.

Value of X	0	1	2	3	4
Frequency	10	25	34	48	23

6. Test whether the following could have come from a Poisson distribution with mean 1.

Value of X	0	1	2	3+
Frequency	30	43	17	10

7. Test whether the following could have come from a Poisson distribution.

Value of X	0	1	2	3	4+
Frequency	35	45	36	18	16

8. Test whether or not the following could have come from a normal distribution with mean 1 and variance 4.

Values of X	$X<-2$	$-2<X<1$	$1<X<4$	$4<X$
Frequency	7	40	43	10

9. It is thought that the following figures might come from a normal distribution with variance 25. Find the sample mean, and hence test whether the figures do fit a normal distribution with that mean. (Note: there is an extra restriction introduced, as the mean is found from the data.)

Values of X	$X<10$	$10<X<20$	$20<X<30$	$30<X<40$	$40<X$
Frequency	10	167	587	195	41

10. Find the mean and variance of the following figures. Test whether they come from a normal distribution. (Note: two extra restrictions are introduced, as the mean and variance are found from the figures.)

Values of X	$0<X<5$	$5<X<10$	$10<X<15$	$15<X<20$	$20<X$
Frequency	151	318	345	123	63

43.4 Testing association

The χ^2 distribution can also be used to test whether or not there is a connection between two properties.

A chart which gives the frequencies of the two properties is a *contingency table*. The entries in this table are the observed frequencies.

The null Hypothesis is that there is no association. The chart containing the expected frequencies must have the same row totals and the same column totals as the contingency table.

If the contingency table has n rows and m columns, then the number of degrees of freedom is $v = (n-1)(m-1)$.

The value of $\chi^2(v)$ is then worked out as in 43.3.

For a 2 by 2 table, *Yates' Correction* is sometimes used. This involves subtracting 0.5 from each of the absolute differences between f_e and f_o.

43.4.1 Example

It is thought that there is an association between the ages of young candidates for the driving test and whether or not they pass at the first attempt. Analysis of 200 cases gave the following contingency table. Test at a 5% level of significance whether there is an association.

	Age			
	17	18	19	20
Fail	21	33	25	1
Pass	24	32	55	9

Solution

These are the observed frequencies. Note that 45 out of 200 were 17 years old, and that 80 out of 200 failed. If there is no association, then the expected number in the top left hand box is

$$\frac{45}{200} \times \frac{80}{200} \times 200 = 18.$$

Fill in the rest of the expected frequencies similarly.

	Age			
	17	18	19	20
Fail	18	26	32	4
Pass	27	39	48	6

Note that the top right box has less than 6 terms in it. Amalgamate the 20 column with the 19 column.

	Age		
	17	18	19 & 20
Fail	18	26	36
Pass	27	39	54

This is now a 3 by 2 table, so the number of degrees of freedom is $(2–1)(3–1) = 2$. The 19 and 20 columns of the observed frequency table are also amalgamated. Evaluate $\chi^2(2)$ as in 43.2.

$$\chi^2 = \frac{3^2}{18} + \frac{7^2}{26} + \frac{10^2}{36} + \frac{3^2}{27} + \frac{7^2}{39} + \frac{10^2}{54} = 8.6$$

This is greater than the critical figure at 5%. We conclude:

There is an association between age and pass-rate

43.4.2 Exercises

Throughout take a significance level of 5%

1. The following contingency table shows the numbers of men and women in high and low positions in a certain firm. Test whether there is an association.

	High	Low
Women	16	80
Men	20	28

2. It is thought that there might be a connection between colour of hair and colour of eye. The results of a survey of 80 people are given below. Test whether or not there is a connection.

		Hair	
		Fair	Dark
Eye	Dark	28	32
	Light	12	8

3. The sixth form of a school contained 300 pupils doing at least one of Maths, Physics, Chemistry. They were asked which was their favourite subject: the results, classified by sex, are given below. Test whether or not there is a connection.

	Maths	Physics	Chemistry
Girls	22	61	37
Boys	28	89	63

4. The connection between A-level passes and television watching was investigated. Group A watched less than 2 hours television a week, Group B watched at least 2 hours. Their exam results are as below:

	0, 1 passes	2 passes	over 2 passes
Group A	6	6	8
Group B	42	48	10

    Is there an association?

5. A group of people were classified by their age and their political convictions. The results are given below. Is there evidence of an association?

	Left	Centre	Right
Young	16	22	25
Middle	16	2	24
Old	16	24	23

43.5 Examination questions

1. (a) Five independent measurements of the diameter of a ball bearing were made using a certain instrument. The results obtained, in millimetres, were 8.9, 9.1, 9.1, 8.9, 8.9.

   (i) Given that the true diameter of the ball bearing is 9 mm, calculate unbiased estimates of the mean and variance of the measurement error of the instrument.

   (ii) Assuming that the measurement errors are independent and normally distributed, calculate 90% confidence limits for the mean measurement error.

   (b) The weekly wages received by a random sample of 80 personnel employed in factory A had a mean of £86.40 and a standard deviation of £3.80. Use this information to calculate an approximate 99% confidence interval for the mean weekly wage of all personnel employed in factory A.

   The weekly wages received by a random sample of 100 personnel employed in factory B had a mean of £87.60 and a standard deviation of £5.20. Calculate an approximate 95% confidence interval for the difference between the mean weekly wages in the two factories. State, with your reason, whether or not your interval discredits the claim that the mean weekly wages in the two factories are equal.

   [W]

2. State the basic assumptions which underlie the use of

   (i) the paired sample *t* test,   (ii) the independent sample *t* test.

   A tyre manufacturer has produced a new tyre and claims that it wears better than the old tyre. In order to test the claim eight cars were selected at random and fitted with one old tyre and one new tyre on the driving wheels. The cars were then driven for one month under normal conditions and the amount of wear measured on each of the tyres in mm. The results were as follows:

Car	A	B	C	D	E	F	G	H
Old tyre	3.41	2.61	0.77	1.60	0.87	2.28	1.92	3.21
New tyre	3.19	2.36	0.47	1.28	0.93	2.05	2.04	3.11

   Show that these data do offer evidence that the new tyre wears significantly less than the old. State your null and alternative hypotheses and the best level at which the null hypothesis can be rejected.

   Calculate a 90% confidence interval for the difference in mean wear between the new and old tyres.

   [SUJB]

3. In order to determine whether or not the number of books borrowed from a school library depends on the day of the week, the librarian noted the numbers of books borrowed daily during a particular week, with the following results.

	Mon	Tue	Wed	Thu	Fri
Number borrowed	68	74	78	85	92.

Not being a statistician, she concluded that, since the figures were different, the numbers borrowed do depend on the day of the week. Why is the argument incorrect? Perform a significance test at the 5% level to resolve the problem.

During another week the figures were

Mon	Tue	Wed	Thu	Fri
70	80	83	92	98.

Determine if the extra data alter your conclusion.

[SUJB]

4. At the end of the first year of a polytechnic course, 105 students sat an examination in statistics. The arithmetic mean and standard deviation of the marks obtained were 46.8 and 12.1 respectively. The marks were then grouped into classes as follows:

Mark	less than 30	30–34	35–39	40–49	50–59	60–69	70 & over
No of Students	6	11	4	40	26	14	4

(a) Use a χ^2 test at a 5% significance level to test whether the normal distribution provides an adequate model for the data.

(b) The pass mark is 40 and it is customary to review all scripts which have scored between 35 and 39 to see if it is possible to award any more marks. The marks given in the table have been subject to such a review. Comment on your results in the light of this further information and suggest how the test might be modified.

[AEB 1985]

5. As part of a survey into transport, the following information was collected on a sample of passenger carrying vehicles arriving in a city.

	Passenger Transport		
	Privately operated buses	Executive buses	Trains
Arrived on time	23	62	33
Arrived late	47	28	7

(a) Use a χ^2 test to show that the difference between the proportions of late arrivals for the three different forms of transport is significant at the 1% level.

(b) A spokeswoman for the private bus company said that the apparent poor performance of their buses was due to the observers using different criteria of lateness for each form of transport. To check this, four observers independently observed the arrivals of a sample of privately operated buses. The resulting contingency table gave a value of 8.12 for $\sum \dfrac{(O-E)^2}{E}$. Test, at the 5% significance level, whether there is a difference between observers, and say how this result would affect your previous conclusions (if at all).

(c) After further training the four observers were asked to classify the arrivals of a sample of trains as 'on time', 'slightly late' or 'late'. The resulting 4×3 contingency table gave a value of 9.32 for $\sum \dfrac{(O-E)^2}{E}$.

Test, at the 5% significance level, whether there is still a difference between observers.

[AEB 1986]

Common errors

1. Both the t–test and the χ^2 test assume that the underlying distribution is normal. Exam questions often ask you to show that you appreciate this.

2. **t–tests**

(a) A t–test is used when the variance is estimated from a small sample. If you are told the variance, then an ordinary normal test can be used, however small the sample is.

(b) You must use the *unbiased* estimate of the variance. But the variance of the sample mean is $\dfrac{\hat{\sigma}^2}{n}$, not $\dfrac{\hat{\sigma}^2}{n-1}$.

(c) The critical values for T are given for two-tailed tests. If you are doing a one-tailed test you must allow for this, by using the 10% figure instead of the 5% figure.

3. **χ^2 tests**

(a) It is easy to get wrong the number of degrees of freedom. Think of it as the number of free choices you have when putting numbers into the boxes – this is the number of boxes minus the number of conditions you have to satisfy.

(b) Boxes are amalgamated if the *expected* frequency in them is less than 6. It does not matter if the *observed* frequency is small.

44 Correlation and regression

44.1 Fitting straight lines

Suppose x and y are related variables. Let several pairs of values (x_i, y_i) be found. When they are plotted on a graph they form a scatter diagram.

Sometimes these points almost lie on a straight line. Sometimes a change of variables will ensure that the points lie almost on a straight line.

44.1.1 Examples

1. It is thought that there is a relationship of the form $y = ax^2 + bx$ between the variables x and y. The following experimental values were obtained:

x	1	2	3	4	5
y	8	24	42	76	95

    By a suitable change of variables, put the relationship in a straight line form. Plot the points, and hence find a and b.

    Solution

Fig 44.1

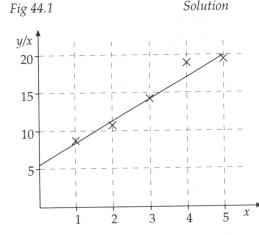

Divide by x, to obtain $\dfrac{y}{x} = ax + b$.

Write out a new row of the table for the values of $\dfrac{y}{x}$.

x	1	2	3	4	5
$\dfrac{y}{x}$	8	12	14	19	19

Plot these points, obtaining the graph shown.

The graph has a gradient of 2.8, and it crosses the $\dfrac{y}{x}$-axis at 6.

The relationship is $y = 2.8x^2 + 6x$

2. r and s are related by the formula $r = as^n$. The table below gives experimental values of r and s. Re-write the formula so that a straight line can be fitted to the data, and hence find a and n.

s	0.25	0.5	1	2	3	4	5
r	2	2.1	3	3.3	3.4	3.6	3.7

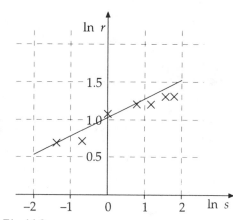

Fig 44.2

Solution

Take logs of both sides. $\ln r = \ln a + n \ln s$. Write out a new table of values of $\ln r$ and $\ln s$.

$\ln s$	−1.4	−0.7	0	0.7	1.1	1.4	1.6
$\ln r$	0.7	0.74	1.1	1.2	1.2	1.3	1.3

Plot $\ln r$ against $\ln s$, obtaining the graph shown.

The gradient is 0.25, and it crosses the y-axis at 1. Hence $n = 0.25$ and $\ln a = 1$.

The relationship is $r = 2.7s^{0.25}$.

44.1.2 Exercises

1. y is given in terms of x by $y = ax^2 + b$. By plotting y against x^2 for the following figures, find the values of a and b.

x	1	2	3	4	5
y	1.8	10.5	25	45	71

2. The relationship between T and S is thought to be of the form $T = a\sqrt{S} + b$. Reduce the equation to a linear form, and hence use the table below to find the values of a and b.

S	1	2	3	4	5
T	45	17	20	22	25

3. x and y are related by $y = \dfrac{a}{x} + b$. Reduce this to a linear form, and use the table below to find the values of a and b.

x	0.25	0.5	1	1.5	2
y	6	−1	−3	−4.5	−5

4. F and v are related by $F = av^3 + bv^2$. Reduce this to a linear form, and hence find the values of a and b, using the data below.

v	10	20	30	40	50
F	15	100	320	720	1400

5. P and V are related by $P = aV^n$. Reduce this to a linear form, and use the data below to find the values of a and n.

V	1	1.2	1.4	1.6	1.8	2.0
P	4	6.2	9.4	13.5	18.6	25

6. It is thought that x and y are related by $y = ab^x$. Use the table below to find the values of a and b.

x	0	1	2	3	4	5
y	0.3	0.4	0.6	0.8	1.2	1.6

7. x and y are related by $y = ax^n$. One of the values of y in the table below is incorrect. Find which it is, and estimate what the correct value should be.

x	1	2	3	4	5
y	7	94	420	900	8000

8. For the following relationships, find the change of variables which will turn them into a linear form.

   (a) $y = ax^3 + b$

   (b) $y^2 = ax + b$

   (c) $y = \dfrac{a}{\sqrt{x}} + b$

   (d) $y = ax + \dfrac{b}{x}$

   (e) $y = a\sqrt{x} + \dfrac{b}{\sqrt{x}}$

   (f) $y = \dfrac{a}{x} + \dfrac{b}{x^2}$

   (g) $y = ax^{-n}$

   (h) $y = ab^{x^2}$

   (i) $y^a = bx$

   (j) $(ay)^x = b$

44.2 Linear regression

Linear regression of y on x expresses y as a linear function of x. If y is dependent on x, then x is the *independent* or *explanatory* variable, and y is the *dependent* or *response* variable.

Suppose the function $y = ax + b$ is to be found from pairs of values (x_1, y_1), (x_2, y_2), ... , (x_n, y_n). The difference between an actual y-value and the predicted y-value, i.e. $y_i - (ax_i + b)$, is a *residual*. The *Method of Least Squares* finds the equation $y = ax + b$ such that the sum of the squares of the residuals is as small as possible,

i.e. $\sum (y_i - (ax_i + b))^2$ is as small as possible.

A value with a large residual is an *outlier*.

Let $\bar{x}$ and $\bar{y}$ be the sample means of x and y respectively. Let S_{xx}^2 be the sample variance of x.

Define the *covariance* of x and y as $S_{xy} = \dfrac{1}{n} \left(\sum x_i y_i - nxy \right)$.

Then the linear relationship is given by:

$$y - \bar{y} = a(x - \bar{x}), \text{ where } a = \dfrac{S_{xy}}{S_{xx}^2}.$$

The line goes through the point $(\bar{x}, \bar{y})$. The line of regression of x on y is found by interchanging the roles of x and y. In general, the two lines will not be equal.

44.2.1 Examples

1. 10 values of x and y are found. $\sum x = 50$, $\sum y = 200$, $\sum x^2 = 300$, $\sum y^2 = 6000$, $\sum xy = 1250$. Find the lines of regression of y on x and of x on y.

   Solution

   $\bar{x} = 5$, $\bar{y} = 20$. $S_{xx}^2 = 5$, $S_{yy}^2 = 200$. Use the formula above to show that $S_{xy} = 25$. The regression coefficients can also be found from the formulae. The equations are:

$$y - 20 = 5(x - 5) \text{ and } x - 5 = \tfrac{1}{8}(y - 20)$$

The equations are $y = 5x - 5$ and $x = \tfrac{1}{8}y + 2\tfrac{1}{2}$

2. Five children sat a test. They were asked how many hours they had spent preparing for the test. Their responses and the test scores are below.

Child	A	B	C	D	E
Hours	2	3	0	5	1
Score	32	47	43	61	27

Calculate the equation of regression of the dependent variable on the independent. Calculate the residuals. Which value is the outlier?

Solution

Here the hours provide the independent variable x, and the score the dependent variable y. Calculate the line of regression by the formulas above.

The equation is $y = 5.07x + 31$

The residual for A is $32 - (5.07 \times 2 + 31) = -9.14$. Calculate the other residuals similarly.

The residuals are $-9.14, 0.79, 12, 4.65, -9.07$

The largest residual is 12.

The outlier is for child C

44.2.2 Exercises

1. Find the line of regression of y on x from the following values:

    (a $n = 5$, $\sum x = 10$, $\sum x^2 = 30$, $\sum y = 13.1$, $\sum y^2 = 54.41$, $\sum xy = 40.3$.

    (b) $n = 6$, $\sum x = 15$, $\sum x^2 = 55$, $\sum y = 6.4$, $\sum y^2 = 8.06$, $\sum xy = 20.4$

    (c) $n = 5$, $\sum x = 20$, $\sum x^2 = 90$, $\sum y = 18.7$, $\sum y^2 = 75.77$, $\sum xy = 82.3$

    (d) $n = 5$, $\sum x = 15$, $\sum x^2 = 55$, $\sum y = 77$, $\sum y^2 = 1503$, $\sum xy = 177$.

2. For each of the situations in Question 1, estimate the value of y when $x = 10$.

3. For each of the situations in Question 1, find the line of regression of x on y.

4. 7 pairs of values of x and y are given below. There is a relationship between y and x of the form $y = ax + b$. Find the line of regression of y on x.

    (1, 2.5) (2, 5) (3, 7.4) (4, 9.3) (5, 11.9) (6, 14) (7, 16)

5. The following pairs of values of x and y are found. Find (a) the line of regression of y on x (b) the line of regression of x on y.

    (2.1, 4), (3.3, 8), (4, 10), (5.9, 13.7), (6.4, 14.2), (8.8, 16).

6. It is thought that there is a relationship of the form $y = ax^2 + b$. Six pairs of values are given below. Use the method of least squares to find the line of regression of y on x^2.

    (2, 9), (3, 15), (4, 30), (5, 50), (6, 74).

7. Use the method of least squares to find the line of regression of $\frac{y}{x}$ on x for the figures in Example 1 of 44.1.1.

8. Use the method of least squares to find the line of regression of $\ln r$ on $\ln s$ for the figures in Example 2 of 44.1.1. Hence find the equation in the form $r = as^n$.

9. There is a relationship between y and x of the form $y = ax + b$. Five pairs of values are given below, of which one is inaccurate. Find the sum of the squares of the residuals. Find the outlier, and find the sum of the squares of the residuals when the outlier is omitted.

x	1	2	3	4	5
y	23	35	48	51	71

10. There is a relationship between x and y of the form $y = ax^2 + b$. Pairs of values are given below. Use linear regression to find the equation.

    One of the values is inaccurate. Find the equation after this value has been omitted.

x	1	2	3	4	5	6
y	5.8	12.3	23.4	41.3	58.6	82.8

44.3 Correlation

Two random variables X and Y are *independent* if for each pair of values i for X and j for Y, the events $(X=i)$ and $(Y=j)$ are independent. i.e.:

$$P(X = i \ \& \ Y = j) = P(X = i) \times P(Y = j)$$

If X and Y are not independent, then the *correlation coefficient* measures the degree to which they are dependent on each other.

The *correlation coefficient* or *product moment correlation coefficient* for two variables X and Y is defined by:

$$\rho_{XY} = \frac{E(XY) - E(X)E(Y)}{\sqrt{[\text{Var}(X)\text{Var}(Y)]}}$$

ρ lies between -1 and 1.

If $\rho = 1$ then there is a linear positive relationship between X and Y.

If $\rho = -1$ there is a linear negative relationship between X and Y.

The significance levels of values of ρ are found from the table on page 402.

If ρ is to be estimated from n values (x_i, y_i) of X and Y, then the estimation is given by:

$$r_{xy} = \frac{\sum x_i y_i - n\overline{x}\overline{y}}{\sqrt{\left(\sum x_i^2 - n\overline{x}^2\right)\left(\sum y_i^2 - n\overline{y}^2\right)}}$$

Suppose that n values of X and Y are found. Let the values be ranked in order. The correlation coefficient between the ranks is Spearman's coefficient of rank correlation.

If d represents the difference between the X and Y ranks, then Spearman's coefficient is:

$$r_s = 1 - \frac{6\sum d^2}{n(n^2 - 1)}$$

The significance level of Spearman's coefficient is found from the table on page 402.

If ranks are tied, say there are two at 5=, then allot them 5.5 each.

44.3.1 Examples

1. The height and the weight of 10 boys were measured and the results are given by the table below. Find the correlation coefficient between the height and the weight. Is the correlation significant at 5%?

Wt (kg)	38	39	43	44	35	32	31	42	49	41
Ht (cm)	150	152	146	158	142	144	135	145	155	150

   Solution

   Letting X be the weight of a randomly selected boy, and Y his height, we have:

   $n = 10 : \bar{x} = 39.4 : \bar{y} = 147.7 : \sum x^2 = 15806 : \sum y^2 = 218559 : \sum xy = 58456.$

   Substitute these values into the formula for correlation.

   $$r = \frac{58456 - 10 \times 39.4 \times 147.7}{\sqrt{(15806 - 10 \times 39.4^2)(218559 - 10 \times 147.7^2)}} = 0.774$$

   The correlation coefficient is 0.774

   The critical value for r with 10 values at 5% is 0.549. This is less than 0.774.

   There is significant correlation between weight and height

2. Two judges at a diving competition marked the 8 candidates in order as follows. Find Spearman's coefficient for the two orders. Is the correlation significant at 5%?

Candidate	A	B	C	D	E	F	G	H
First Judge	4	1	7	8	3	2	6	5
Second Judge	3	2	8	7	5	6	1	4

   Solution

   The differences are 1, –1, –1, 1, –2, –4, 5, 1. $\sum d^2 = 50$. Apply the formula for Spearman's coefficient:

   $$r_s = 1 - \frac{6 \times 50}{8(8^2 - 1)} = 0.405$$

   The 5% critical value of Spearman's coefficient with 8 pairs is 0.643. This is greater than 0.405.

   There is no significant correlation between the scores

44.3.2 Exercises

Where relevant, use a significance level of 5%

1. In each of the following, find the correlation coefficient between y and x from the information given:

	n	$\sum x$	$\sum y$	$\sum x^2$	$\sum y^2$	$\sum xy$
(a)	12	129	63	1500	800	700
(b)	9	56	76	500	830	620
(c)	10	69	436	585	31218	1858

2. Evaluate the correlation coefficient between x and y for each of the sets of sample pairs given below. In each case say whether there is significant correlation.

   (a)

Sample	1	2	3	4	5	6	7	8
x	21	32	39	29	25	31	36	27
y	3.1	4.3	5.7	3.8	3.0	4.1	4.8	3.2

   (b)

Sample	1	2	3	4	5	6	7	8	9
x	159	190	128	177	155	132	199	207	236
y	163	121	180	111	166	219	98	87	63

   (c)

Sample	1	2	3	4	5	6	7
x	93	88	99	70	105	83	123
y	21	17	16	27	23	34	24

3. Select 6 pairs $(x_1, y_1), \ldots, (x_6, y_6)$ on the line $y = 3x + 1$. Check that the correlation coefficient between the x and y values is 1.

4. Select 6 pairs $(x_1, y_1), \ldots, (x_6, y_6)$ on the line $y = -2x + 3$. Check that the correlation coefficient between the x and y values is -1.

5. Find Spearman's rank correlation coefficient for the rankings given below:

   (a)

Item	A	B	C	D	E	F	G	H
First rank	4	3	8	1	6	5	7	2
Second rank	2	1	7	3	4	6	8	5

   (b)

Item	A	B	C	D	E	F	G	H	I	J
First rank	5	3	2	10	8	7	9	1	4	6
Second rank	5	7	10	2	1	3	4	9	6	8

   (c)

Item	A	B	C	D	E	F	G
First rank	6	3	5	7	1	2	4
Second rank	1	2	5	7	3	6	4

6. The following marks were obtained by 8 candidates in Maths and English:

Candidate	A	B	C	D	E	F	G	H
Maths mark	63	54	73	88	48	58	74	61
English mark	53	39	67	66	42	50	83	51

   Rank these results and hence find Spearman's rank correlation coefficient between the two sets of results. Is there significant correlation?

7. For each part of Question 2, find the x and y ranks, and hence find the Spearman rank correlation coefficient. Is the correlation significant?

44.4 Examination questions

1. If experimental readings for x and y obey a formula of the type $y = Ax^B$, where A and B are constants, explain how, by using logarithms, the readings may be plotted to obtain a straight line graph.

   For the following pairs of reading construct a suitable table of values to three decimal places and plot such a graph accurately.

x	1.20	1.38	1.58	1.85	2.24	2.71	3.09
y	1.86	2.29	2.63	3.55	4.74	6.31	7.67

   Show that all but one of the points do lie very close to a straight line. Hence find A and B.

   State which pair of readings does not obey the formula and, assuming that the value of x is correct, estimate what the value of y should be, either by calculation from the formula or by reading from the graph.

   [MEI ADD]

2. (a) The table shows experimental values of two variables x and y.

x	0.2	0.6	1.0	1.4
y	0.69	0.81	0.55	0.06

   It is expected that x and y are related by an equation of the form $y = ax\sqrt{x} + b\sqrt{x}$, where a and b are constants. Express this equation in a form suitable for drawing a straight line graph. Draw the graph for the given data and use it to evaluate a and b.

   (b) It is expected that the variables x, y and X, Y are related by the equations $y = he^{-kx}$ and $Y = p(X + 1)^q$ respectively, where h, k and p, q are unknown constants. Given experimental values of x, y and X, Y,

   (i) determine the variables whose values should be plotted in order to obtain straight line graphs,

   (ii) explain how these graphs may be used to determine the values of h, k and p, q.

   [C ADD]

3. A sample of n pairs (x_i, y_i), $i = 1, 2, \dots, n$, is drawn from a bivariate population (X, Y) and a rank correlation coefficient, r, calculated.

   (i) What range of values is it possible for r to have?

   (ii) What information about the sample does r indicate?

(iii) What can be concluded about the sample points when $r = 1$? Can the same be said about the population from which the sample is drawn? Explain your answer.

The table gives the average share rate and average mortgage rate calculated on the first day of the months shown for the years 1976 to 1985.

Year	1976	1977	1978	1979	1980	1981	1982	1983	1984	1985
Month	Nov	Nov	Dec	Dec	Jan	Nov	Dec	Jul	Dec	Apr
Share%	7.8	6.0	8.0	10.5	10.5	9.8	6.2	7.2	6.8	8.2
M'ge%	12.2	9.5	11.8	11.8	15.0	15.0	10.0	11.2	11.5	14.0

Plot a scatter diagram and comment on its implication for r. Indicate on your diagram which point appears to be an outlier (i.e. one that is far from the trend line).

Calculate a rank correlation coefficient between share rate and mortgage rate.

Under the null hypothesis that the population $r = 0$ against the alternative $r \neq 0$ the following are critical values of Spearman's and Kendall's coefficients for a sample size of 10.

Significance Level	10%	5%	2%	1%
Spearman's r	0.564	0.648	0.745	0.794
Kendall's r	0.467	0.511	0.600	0.644

Comment on the significance of your calculated value of r.

[SUJB]

Common errors

1. **Fitting straight lines**
   (a) Your equation must be reduced to linear form before you plot points. Do not, for example, plot points of the function $y = ax^2 + b$, and try to fit a parabola. This would have no accuracy at all.
   (b) The straight line which you fit does not have to go through the origin. It does not have to go through the first and last points.
   (c) The gradient and intercept must be found from the line which you have drawn. They should not be found from the line joining the first and last points.

2. **Regression and correlation**

   Some calculators can work out regression and correlation coefficients. But do not rely on your calculator – you will get very few marks unless you show that you know the formulae for finding these coefficients.

AEB style Examination papers

Paper 1 Pure Mathematics

Time $2\frac{1}{2}$ hours. *Answer all the questions.*

1. The numbers below are in increasing order.

$$12;\ 26;\ x;\ y;\ 57$$

The numbers have mean 34 and variance 232.4. Show that

$$x + y = 75 \text{ and } x^2 + y^2 = 2873$$

Find x and y.

[8]

2. Complete the square of $x^2 + 3x + 1$. Hence or otherwise find the values of k such that $x^2 + 3x + 1 = k$ has no real roots.

[4]

3. State the periods of

(i) $\cos 3x$ (ii) $\sin \frac{1}{2}x$ (iii) $2 \cos x + 3 \sin x$.

[4]

4. Express in partial fractions:

$$y = \frac{2}{(x-1)(x+1)}$$

Hence find

$$\int_2^3 \frac{2}{(x-1)(x+1)} dx$$

[5]

5. Differentiate and simplify as far as possible:

(i) $y = \ln \sin 2x$ (ii) $y = \ln \sin x + \ln \cos x$

Show that your answers are the same. Give an explanation, not involving calculus, why your answers are the same.

[6]

6. (i) Expand $(1 + 2x)^4$.

(ii) Find the term independent of x in $(x - \frac{2}{x})^6$.

(iii) Solve the equation $4^{x-1} = 5$

[6]

7. Find the tangent to $y = 2 - x^2$ at the point $(1,1)$. Find where this tangent crosses the axes. Find the area enclosed by the tangent and the axes.

    [7]

8. Show that $\cos 2A = 2\cos^2 A - 1$. Hence or otherwise evaluate the integral:

    $$\int \frac{1}{\cos x + 1}\,dx$$

    [7]

9. Show that $x - 1$ is a factor of the cubic $2x^3 + 5x^2 - 4x - 3$. Hence factorize the cubic completely.

    Sketch the graph of $y = 2x^3 + 5x^2 - 4x - 3$.

    Solve the inequality $2x^3 + 5x^2 - 4x - 3 < 0$.

    [7]

10. Suppose that $u_1, u_2, u_3, ..., u_n$ is a geometric progression. Show that $\log u_1$, $\log u_2$, $\log u_3, ..., \log u_n$ is an arithmetic progression.

    Give an equation relating the common ratio of the geometric progression with the common difference of the arithmetic progression.

    [7]

11. Show that $x^3 + x - 17 = 0$ has a root between n and $n + 1$, where n is to be found. Use linear interpolation between these values to find an approximation for the root.

    Use Newton Raphson iteration to find this root to 4 decimal places.

    [8]

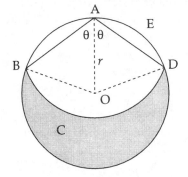

Fig 1.1

12. The diagram shows a circle with centre O and radius r. The three points A, B, D on the circle are such that $B\hat{A}O = D\hat{A}O = \theta$ radian, and BCD is an arc of the circle with centre A and radius AB. The point E lies on the arc AD. Find, in terms of r and θ, expressions for

    (i)   the length of the straight line AD,

    (ii) the area of the sector of the circle (centre A) bounded by the lines AB and AD and the arc BCD,

    (iii) the area of triangle OAD   (iv) the area of the segment ADE.

    Hence show that the area of the shaded segment may be expressed as

    $$r^2(\sin 2\theta - 2\theta \cos 2\theta).$$

    Deduce that, when $\theta = \frac{1}{4}\pi$, this region has an area approximately one third that of the circle with centre O.

    [C]
    [13]

13. The fixed circle C_1 has equation $x^2 + y^2 = 4$, and the variable circle C_2 has equation $x^2 + y^2 - 2kx = 1 - k^2$. Find the two positive values of k for which C_1 touches C_2, and illustrate both situations.

    [11]

341

14. A curve is such that its gradient at any point (x,y) is three times its y value. Set up a differential equation for y and find the general solution.

    If the curve goes through the point $(1,1)$ find y in terms of x.

    Sketch the curve for $0 \le x \le 1$, and find the area between the curve and the x-axis for this range.

    [11]

15. A bag contains 4 red balls and 2 blue balls and balls are withdrawn at random, with replacement. Find the probability that the third ball drawn is the second blue ball to be drawn.

    Two additional bags, labelled B and C, are such that bag B contains 3 red balls and 5 blue balls whilst bag C contains 2 red balls and 1 blue ball. One of the three bags is selected at random and a ball is withdrawn from it. Find the probability that

    (a) bag B is selected and a red ball withdrawn,

    (b) a red ball is selected,

    (c) the ball was selected from bag C, given that it is blue.

    [L]
    [12]

Paper 2 Statistics

Time $2\frac{1}{2}$ hours. *Answer all the questions*

1. At a fairground stall the customer has 3 attempts to knock a tin off a shelf. Once the tin is knocked off he wins a prize and has no more attempts. The prize is £5, £3, £1 if he knocks the tin off on the first, second or third attempt respectively.

   The chance that a customer will knock the tin off with a single shot is $\frac{1}{20}$. Assuming that each shot is independent, complete a table showing the distribution of the amount of prize money the customer wins.

   If the stall–holder hopes to gain, on average, 10 p per customer, how much should he charge?

   [10]

2. The connections between crime rate and poverty are investigated. Ten cities are chosen at random, and ranked in order of crime rate and of average income. In both cases the rankings run from 1 (low) to 10 (high). The results are given in the table below.

City	A	B	C	D	E	F	G	H	I	J
Crime ranking	1	2	3	4	5	6	7	8	9	10
Income ranking	9	6	8	2	5	4	10	7	3	1

   Calculate a Spearman's rank correlation coefficient for the two rankings. Stating your null and alternative hypotheses clearly, find whether the table provides evidence, significant at 5%, to show that high crime is associated with low income.

   [10]

3. I never had a piece of toast
   Particularly long and wide
   But fell upon the sanded floor
   And always on the buttered side.

   [JAMES PAYN]

   To test this poem 80 pieces of toast were dropped, and 52 of them landed on the buttered side. Test the hypothesis that the toast is more likely to land on its buttered side.

   From the data calculate a 95% confidence interval for the probability that a piece of toast will land on its buttered side.

   [10]

4. A college has 100 home students and 50 overseas students. They are asked to classify the food provided in the canteen. Their responses are below.

	good	medium	bad
Home	23	35	42
Overseas	19	18	13

   The caterers want to know whether the opinion of the students is affected by whether or not they come from overseas. Formulate suitable null and alternative hypotheses, and use a χ^2 test with a 5% significance level to test your hypotheses.

   [10]

5. The weights of coffee in tins used by the catering trade are distributed Normally with standard deviation 0.071 kg.

   A random sample of n tins is taken in order to determine a symmetric 99% confidence interval for the mean weight μ kg of coffee in a tin. How large should n be for the total width of this interval to be less than 0.05 kg?

   In a separate investigation a random sample of 36 tins has a mean weight of 0.981 kg. Test at the 1% significance level the null hypothesis H_0 that $\mu = 1$, the alternative hypothesis H_1 being $\mu < 1$.

   Suppose now that it is subsequently discovered that $\mu = 0.950$. Determine the probability that a significance test at the 1% level, using a new random sample of 36 tins and the same H_0 and H_1 as in the previous paragraph, would give the wrong conclusion, i.e. would lead to the acceptance of H_0.

   [MEI]
   [15]

6. The proportion of defectives in a large batch is p. Two testing schemes are devised.

   Method I. Test 10 : reject the batch if there is more than 1 defective.

   Method II. Test 5 : accept the batch if there is no defective, and reject if it there is more than 1 defective. If there is 1 defective test a further 10 and reject the batch unless there are no defectives.

   For each method, find the probabilities of

   (i) rejecting the batch if $p = 0.05$

   (ii) accepting the batch if $p = 0.3$. Comment on your results.

   [10]

7. There are ten adult males in the Smith family. Their heights and masses (where known) are given in the table below.

	Height (cm)	Mass (kg)		Height (cm)	Mass (kg)
Adam	?	80	Fred	167	62
Ben	170	?	George	184	89
Colin	174	83	Harry	168	90
David	150	55	Ivor	173	72
Eric	153	63	John	159	70

(i) Plot the eight complete pairs on a scatter diagram.

(ii) For these eight complete pairs, determine the coordinates of the point of intersection of the regression line of mass on height with the regression line of height on mass.

(iii) Denoting mass by m and height by h, the equation of the regression line of mass on height is $m = -76.1 + 0.898h$, correct to three significant figures. Draw, on the scatter diagram, this regression line. Also draw on the scatter diagram, by eye, the regression line of height on mass, labelling the line clearly.

(iv) Use the regression lines to estimate the height of Adam, and to estimate the mass of Ben, showing your methods clearly.

(v) For the eight complete pairs of observations, calculate the value of a rank correlation coefficient.

[C] [15]

8. The time that Alan takes for the 100 m race is normally distributed with mean 11.4 seconds and standard deviation 0.2 sec. Bertram's times are also normal, with mean 11.5 seconds and standard deviation 0.3 seconds. If they race against each other find the probability that Alan wins.

Cedric now challenges Alan. In 10 runs of 100 m his results are summarised by $\Sigma x = 116$ and $\Sigma x^2 = 1347$. Calculate his average time and an unbiased estimate of the variance of his times.

Assuming that the estimate of the variance is correct, is there evidence at a significance level of 5% that Cedric's mean time is greater than Alan?

[10]

Paper 3 mechanics

Time $2\frac{1}{2}$ hours. *Answer all the questions*

1. (a) A bullet of mass 0.02 kg is moving horizontally with speed 505 m s^{-1} when it hits a wooden block of mass 2 kg which is free to move on a smooth horizontal table. Given that the bullet remains embedded in the block, find the loss of kinetic energy.

(b) A particle of mass 0.5 kg is moving at constant speed on a rough horizontal table in the direction of the constant unit vector **i**. The particle is acted on by three forces, namely (i) its weight, (ii) an applied force **P**, and (iii) the total reaction of the table **R**. Given that **P** = (3**i** + 8**j**) N, where **j** is a unit vector vertically downwards, and taking $g = 9.8$ m s^{-2}, determine **R** in the form **R** = (k**i** + l**j**) N, where k and l are numbers. Hence determine the coefficient of friction between the particle and the table, to 2 decimal places.

[MEI] [10]

2. [Throughout this question take g as 10 m s^{-2}.]

(i) A ball is kicked from a point A on level ground and hits a goalpost at a point 4 m above the ground. The goalpost is at a distance of 32 m from A. Initially the velocity of the ball makes an angle $\tan^{-1}(3/4)$ with the ground. Show that the initial speed of the ball is 20 m s^{-1}. Find the speed of the ball when it hits the goalpost.

(ii) A particle is attached to one end of a light string, the other end of which is fixed. When the particle moves in a horizontal circle with speed 2 m s^{-1} the string makes an angle $\tan^{-1}(5/12)$ with the vertical. Show that the length of the string is approximately 2.5 m.

[L] [12]

3. A body of mass 240 kg is dropped by parachute with negligible initial speed. Whilst the parachute is opening, the body is subject at time t to a resistance due to the atmosphere of $40v$N, where v is its speed at that time. Show that whilst the parachute is opening, the speed v satisfies

$$6 \frac{dv}{dt} = 6g - v.$$

If the parachute is fully open after 6 seconds, prove that its speed will then be $6g(1 - e^{-1})$ ms^{-1}.

Find an expression for the distance fallen by the body at time t seconds ($t \le 6$). Show that the body has fallen through a distance $36ge^{-1}$ m whilst the parachute is opening.

Find the distance fallen by the body when the speed is v ms^{-1} where $v < 6g(1 - e^{-1})$.

[W] [15]

4. A uniform ladder of mass 20 kg and length 2 m rests against a smooth wall and on a rough floor. It is at 60° to the horizontal. A man of mass 60 kg can just walk $\frac{3}{4}$ of the way up it. Find the coefficient of friction between the floor and the ladder.

Show that a ladder cannot rest on a smooth floor against a wall, however rough the wall is.

[10]

Fig 3.1

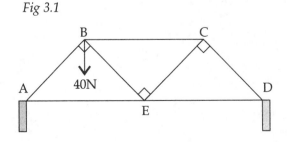

5. The framework shown consists of light rods. The angles are all either 45° or 90°. A load of 40 N is placed at B. The framework rests on smooth supports at A and D.

Find the forces in the rods, specifying which are thrusts and which are tensions.

[10]

6. A *Daruma Doll* is a Japanese toy, which will return to the upright position when it is tipped to one side.

   The doll can be thought of as a solid hemisphere, base radius 2 cm and relative density 11, surmounted by a solid cone of base radius 2 cm, height h cm and relative density 1. Find in terms of h the height of the centre of gravity above the ground when the doll is upright.

   (The cg of a solid uniform hemisphere of radius r is $\frac{3}{8}r$ from the centre of the flat face.

   The cg of a solid cone of height h is $\frac{1}{4}h$ above the centre of the flat face.)

   Hence find the values of h for which the toy will rest in stable equilibrium with the cone above the hemisphere.

   (The doll is named after Daruma, the founder of Zen Buddhism, who sat for so long in meditation that his legs fell off.)

   [10]

7. A particle moves in a circle of radius a with constant speed v. State the magnitude and direction of its acceleration.

   A small sphere of mass m is attached to the end A of a light inextensible string of length $2a$ and a similar sphere but of mass $2m$ is attached to the other end, B. The mid-point of the string is fixed to a point O of a smooth horizontal table and the spheres lie at rest on the table with each part of the string taut and angle AOB 90°. The coefficient of restitution between the spheres is e. The sphere at A is given a speed u along the table in a direction perpendicular to OA. Find

   (i) the speeds of the spheres just after the first impact;

   (ii) the ratio of the tensions in OA and OB just after the first impact;

   (iii) the interval of time between the first and second impacts.

   What happens to the system ultimately?

   [15][SUJB]

8. A uniform cylinder of height L and relative density ρ ($\rho < 1$) floats with its axis vertical in a large lake. Show that a proportion ρL of the cylinder is submerged.

   It is then pushed down vertically by a small amount δ and released. Show that, if the proportion submerged in the subsequent motion is $\rho L + x$, then x obeys the equation $x = -\omega^2 x$, where ω is to be found.

   Find the greatest speed it reaches and the time taken to achieve this greatest speed.

   [10]

UCLES style Examination papers

Paper 4 Pure Mathematics

Time 3 Hours. *You may answer all the questions*

1. The first term of a geometric progression is $\frac{3}{4}$ of its sum to infinity. Find the ratio of the second to the fourth term.

   [4]

2. Find the equations of the tangents to $y = \sin 3x$ at $x = 0$ and at $x = \pi/3$. Find where these tangents cross.

   [4]

3. The first three terms of $\sqrt{(1 + x)}$ and $\dfrac{1 + ax}{1 + bx}$ are the same. Find a and b.

   [6]

4. Solve the equation $2 \cos x + 3 \sin x = 2.5$, for $0° \le x \le 360°$.

   [6]

5. Find the solution of the equation $\dfrac{dy}{dx} = 2x(y + 1)$, for which $y=0$ when $x=0$. Sketch the graph of the curve.

   [7]

Fig 4.1

6. A sketch of $y = f(x)$ is shown. On four separate diagrams sketch the graphs of:

   (a) $y = f(x) - b$ (b) $y = f(x + a)$
   (c) $y = f(-x)$ (d) $y = -f(x)$

   [8]

7. Solve the equations:

    (a) $\log_2(x+1) - \log_2 x = 3$ (b) $e^x + 3 - e^{-x} = 0$.

                                                                                                      [8]

8. Find the remainders when $4x^3 - 4x^2 - 7x - 2$ is divided by

    (a) $x - 1$ (b) $x - 2$.

    Factorize $4x^3 - 4x^2 - 7x - 2$ completely.

    Sketch the graph of $y = 4x^3 - 4x^2 - 7x - 2$, and hence solve the inequality $4x^3 - 4x^2 - 7x - 2 \geq 0$.

                                                                                                [14]

9. [In this question $\cos^{-1}x$ and $\tan^{-1}x$ refer to the principal values.]

    Show on the same diagram sketches of the graphs of $y = \cos^{-1}x$ and $y = \tan^{-1}x$.

    Show that, if $\cos^{-1}x = \tan^{-1}x$, then $x^2(1 + x^2) = 1$, and hence find the value of x such that $\cos^{-1}x = \tan^{-1}x$, giving your answer correct to 3 decimal places.

                                                                                         [C][9]

10. Find the stationary points of $y = x^n e^{-x}$ in the cases

    (a) $n = 0$,   (b) $n = 1$ (c) $n = 2$.

    Sketch the graph of the function for

    (i) n large and odd   (ii) n large and even.

    Letting $I_n = \displaystyle\int_0^\infty x^n e^{-x}\,dx$, show that $I_n = nI_{n-1}$.

                                                                                               [10]

11. Three spheres are placed on a horizontal plane in such a way that each sphere is touching the other two. The radii of the spheres are 2 cm, 3 cm and 4 cm; their centres are A, B, C, respectively; the points of contact with the horizontal plane are P, Q, R, respectively.

    (i) Show that $\cos \hat{ACB} = \frac{5}{7}$

    (ii) Show that $PQ = \sqrt{24}$ cm, and find the lengths of QR and RP.

    (iii) Show that $\sin \hat{PRQ} = \sqrt{\dfrac{47}{96}}$.

                                                                                              [C][12]

12. (a) Using the substitution $u = 1 + x$, or otherwise, evaluate the following integral.

$$\int_3^8 x\sqrt{x+1}\,dx$$

    (b) Use the identity $\sin^2 x + \cos^2 x = 1$ to evaluate the following integral.

$$\int \cos^3 x\,dx$$

    (c) The curve $x^2 + 4y^2 = 1$ is rotated about the x-axis. Find the volume enclosed.

                                                                                              [14]

13. The position vectors, with respect to a fixed origin, of the points L, M and N are given by **l**, **m** and **n** respectively, where

$$\mathbf{l} = a(\mathbf{i} + \mathbf{j} + \mathbf{k}), \quad \mathbf{m} = a(2\mathbf{i} + \mathbf{j}), \quad \mathbf{n} = a(\mathbf{j} + 4\mathbf{k})$$

and a is a non–zero constant. Show that the unit vector **j** is perpendicular to the plane of the triangle LMN.

Find a vector perpendicular to both **j** and (**m** – **n**), and hence, or otherwise, obtain a vector equation of that perpendicular bisector of MN which lies in the plane LMN.

Verify that the point K with position vector $a(5\mathbf{i} + \mathbf{j} + 4\mathbf{k})$ lies on this bisector and show that K is equidistant from L, M and N.

[L][14]

14. (i) Set up a table of values of the function $y = 3^x$, taking x from 1 to 2 at intervals of 0.2. Give the values to 3 decimal places. Show that the values form a geometric progression, and find its common ratio.

(ii) Use the trapezium rule to estimate $\int_1^2 3^x dx$

(iii) Express 3^x as $e^{\lambda x}$, where λ is to be found. Hence find the exact value of the integral.

(iv) Show by graphical means that, however many intervals are taken, the trapezium rule will always result in an overestimate of the integral.

[14]

Paper 5

Section A: Pure Mathematics

Time 3 hours. *You may answer all the questions*

1. Solve the equation $3 \sin^2 \theta + 2 \cos \theta - 1 = 0$, for $0° \leq \theta \leq 180°$

[4]

2. Air is being pumped into a spherical balloon at 20 cm^3 per sec. At the moment when the radius is 12 cm, find

    (i) the rate of change of the radius

    (ii) the rate of change of the surface area.

[4]

3. A test was marked out of 100. 80 pupils took the test, with the following results.

Mark range	0–30	31–40	41–50	51–60	61–70	71–100
Frequency	5	12	17	23	18	5

    (i) Estimate the mean and standard deviation of these figures. Explain why your value for the mean is only an estimate.

    (ii) Draw a cumulative frequency curve, and hence find the interquartile range.

[8]

4. (a) Events A and B are such that P(A) = 0.3, P(B) = 0.5 and P(A ∪ B) = 0.7. Find (i) P(A ∩ B), (ii) P(A | B).

   (b) A disease afflicts 1% of the population. A test gives positive results for 95% of people with the disease and for 2% of those without the disease. If a test result is positive, what is the probability that the person tested has the disease?

   [8]

Section B: Mechanics

Throughout take g to be 9.8 m s^{-2}

5. A particle of mass 1.5 kg lies at rest on a slope of angle 35°. Find the least possible coefficient of friction.

   [3]

Fig 5.1

6. The diagram shows a block of mass 10kg on a floor where the coefficient of friction μ is $\frac{1}{2}$. A rope at 20° above the horizontal is attached to the block. If the tension in the rope is 70 N find the acceleration of the block.

   [5]

7. A horse pulls a barge of mass 50 tonnes, against resistances of 2000 + 1000v N, where v is the speed in m s^{-1}. The tow–rope makes an angle of 10° with the direction of motion of the barge and horse. Find:

   (i) the resistances at a speed of 2 m s^{-1}

   (ii) the tension in the rope at a constant speed of 2 m s^{-1}

   (iii) the acceleration of the barge at a speed of 2 m s^{-1} if the tension in the rope is 5000 N.

   [8]

8. A mass of 2 kg lies on a horizontal table, where the coefficient of friction is $\frac{1}{4}$. A light inextensible string is attached to the mass, and the other end of the string is tied to a mass of 1 kg which hangs over the end of the table. Calculate the acceleration of the system.

   After 1 second the string is cut. Find the time which then elapses before the first mass comes to rest, and the total distance it has travelled.

   [8]

9. An express train approaches a station at a speed of 108 kilometres per hour. When the front of the train is one kilometre from the start of the platform the driver applies the brakes, which cause a constant deceleration. When it reaches the start of the platform it is still travelling at 36 kilometres per hour, and it finally comes to rest 10 metres from the further end of the platform.

   (a) Calculate

   (i) the speed on m s^{-1} of the train before the brakes are applied;

   (ii) the uniform deceleration in m s^{-2};

   (iii) the total length of the platform in metres.

(b) From the moment that the brakes are applied, how many seconds elapse before the train comes to rest?

[MEI ADD][10]

10. Two particles P and Q move in a plane so that at time t seconds, where $t \geq 0$, P and Q have position vectors $\mathbf{r}_P$ and $\mathbf{r}_Q$ respectively, relative to a fixed origin O, where

$$\mathbf{r}_P = (3t^2 + 4)\mathbf{i} + (2t - \tfrac{1}{2})\mathbf{j}; \quad \mathbf{r}_Q = (t + 6)\mathbf{i} + 1\tfrac{1}{2}t^2\mathbf{j}.$$

Find

(a) the velocity vectors of P and Q at time t seconds,

(b) the *speed* of P when $t = 2$,

(c) The value of t at the instant when the particles are moving parallel to one another.

Show that the particles collide and find the position vector of their point of collision.

[L ADD][14]

Section C: Statistics

11. The midday temperatures, in F°, on ten August days were as follows.

78 83 82 94 73 84 86 75 69 80

Calculate the mean temperature and the standard deviation.

[4]

12. A trial has probability $\tfrac{1}{4}$ of success. The trial is repeated independently 100 times. Use the Normal approximation to find the probability that there are more than 30 successes.

[6]

13. Only 20% of certain silicon chips are satisfactory. In a batch of 10, what is the probability that

(i) 3 will be satisfactory   (ii) at least two will be satisfactory.

How many chips should a batch contain so that the manufacturer can claim that with probability 95% it contains at least one satisfactory chip?

[8]

14. The school record for the 100 m sprint is 12.3 seconds. The time that A takes to run that distance is normally distributed with mean 13 and variance 0.09, and B's time is also normal with mean 13.2 and variance 0.16. If A and B compete in the same race, find the probabilities that:

(i) A beats the school record   (ii) A beats B.

[8]

15. Three envelopes were addressed for three letters. An incompetent secretary put the letters into the envelopes at random. Show that the probability that each letter is in its correct envelope is $\tfrac{1}{6}$.

Let X be the number of letters which are in their correct envelopes. Construct a distribution table for X. Hence or otherwise find the expectation of X.

[10]

16. Suppose X is a random variable whose distribution is normal with mean μ and variance σ^2. An independent sample of size n is taken from X. State the mean and variance of the sample mean $\overline{X}$.

Let X be the total annual rainfall in inches in a town. Give one reason why the normal distribution cannot be an exact model for the distribution of X.

The distribution of X is approximately normal, with standard deviation 10 inches. The annual rainfall was measured over a period of 10 years. The results are below.

$$40 \quad 43 \quad 59 \quad 31 \quad 29 \quad 46 \quad 58 \quad 51 \quad 61 \quad 55$$

Find a 95% confidence for the mean annual rainfall.

[12]

Paper 6

Time 3 hours. *Answer all the questions*

Section (a): Pure Mathematics

1. Solve the simultaneous equations:

$$x + 3y = 6, \quad x^2 - 2y^2 = 4$$

[4]

2. Find the equation of the tangent to the curve $y = e^{3x}$ at the point $(0,1)$.

Find the area between this curve and the x–axis, from $x = 0$ to $x = 2$.

[4]

3. The following figures give the ages of 12 spectators at a soccer match and of 12 spectators at a rugby match.

| Soccer | 17 18 20 16 15 14 23 13 22 18 16 17 |
| Rugby | 16 36 28 18 48 51 29 11 29 39 41 61 |

For each group, draw a box and whisker diagram. [5]

Comment on the differences between the figures, as shown by the diagram. [3]

4. Explain what is meant for two events A and B to be

(i) exclusive   (ii) independent. [2]

A and B are events for which $P(A) = 0.3$ and $P(B) = 0.4$. Find $P(A \mid B)$ in the following cases:

(iii) A and B are independent   (iv) A and B are exclusive

(v) $P(A \text{ or } B) = 0.6$ [6]

Section (b): Mechanics

Throughout take g to be 9.8 m s^{-2}, unless otherwise stated.

5. At time $t = 0$, X starts from the origin with constant speed 5 m s^{-1}. 2 seconds later Y starts from the origin in the same direction, with zero initial speed and acceleration 1 m s^{-2}. Find how long it takes for Y to catch up with X.

[5]

6. A swindler buys and sells diamonds in a lift. When the lift is accelerating down at $2a$ m s^{-2} the diamonds appear to weigh 1.32 grams, and when the lift is accelerating up at a m s^{-2} they appear to weigh 1.41 grams. Calculate the true weight of the diamonds.

[5]

7. A rough wire joins the points (0,0) and (10,0)). A bead is threaded on the wire, and a force of $2\mathbf{i} + 3\mathbf{j}$ is applied to it, where $\mathbf{i}$ and $\mathbf{j}$ are unit vectors in the x and y directions respectively. Ignoring the effects of gravity find the coefficient of friction if the bead moves at a steady speed.

[6]

8. A body of mass 5 kg lies on the floor where the coefficient of friction is $\frac{1}{3}$. It is pulled by a light string making θ with the horizontal. What should θ be if the force needed to shift the body is as small as possible?

[8]

9. A body of mass 2 kg lies on a rough horizontal table. It is attached to a light elastic string of modulus 40 N and natural length 1 m. The other end is attached to a point which is 1.1 m away horizontally and 0.3 m above the table. If the body does not move find the least coefficient of friction.

[8]

Fig 6.1

10. A locomotive of mass M is travelling around a circular bend of radius 1 km. The width of the track is 2 m, and the outer rail is at height h cm above the inner rail. It is found that when the locomotive has speed 20 m s^{-1} there is no sideways pressure on the rails. Show that $h \approx 8$. (Take g as 10 m s^{-2}.)

[SMP][8]

11. A uniform lamina ABCDE consists of a square ABCD of side 4 cm with a right–angled triangle EDA affixed to it. ED = 4 cm. Find the centre of gravity of the lamina. Give your answer in co–ordinates with BA and BC as x–axis and y–axis respectively.

The mass of the lamina is 20 grams. The lamina is placed in a vertical plane with AB on a horizontal plane. Find the greatest weight which can be suspended from E before the lamina topples.

[11]

Fig 6.2

12. Two light elastic strings each have natural length 0.15 m and modulus 75 N. One end of each string is attached to a particle of mass 0.12 kg, and the other ends are attached to points A and B, 0.3 m apart at the same horizontal level. The particle is initially held at rest 0.08 m vertically below D, the mid-point of AB, as shown in the Fig 6.3.

(a) Find the tension in each of the elastic strings.

(b) Show that the energy stored in each of the strings is 0.1 J.

Fig 6.3

The particle is released from rest in this position, and subsequently passes through O with speed v metres per second.

Use the principle of conservation of energy to calculate v, giving your answer to 2 significant figures.

[L][14]

13. Two particles of mass 2 kg and 3 kg are connected by a light inextensible string. The string is slung over a smooth peg and the masses are released. Find the acceleration with which the system moves.

After 1 second the heavier mass strikes the floor and is brought instantaneously to rest. Find the speed with which the heavier mass is jerked into motion when the string next becomes taut.

[11]

14. A boy throws a stone at 20 m s^{-1} at a window which is 5 m above his hand and 20 m away horizontally. Show that there are two angles θ_1 and θ_2 at which he could throw the stone.

If T_1 and T_2 are the times corresponding to the two possible angles of projection, find the ratio $T_1 : T_2$.

[11]

15. ABC is a triangle for which AB = BC = 1 m, and $A\hat{B}C = 90°$. Forces of 5, P and Q newtons act along AB, BC, CA respectively.

(i) If there is no resultant find P and Q.

(ii) If $P = 4$ and $Q = 8$ find the magnitude and direction of the resultant force, and find where this force cuts BC produced.

[12]

16. A particle of mass m starts at the origin. The only force it experiences is a force f(x) directed along the x–axis towards the origin, given by the formula below:

$$f(x) = 2mx^3 \text{ for } x \le a \text{ ; } f(x) = 2.5mx^4 \text{ for } x > a.$$

The particle is projected away from the origin with speed u. Show that if $u \le a^2$ then the particle never reaches the point $x = a$.

If $u = \sqrt{2}a^2$ find the greatest distance that the particle reaches.

[14]

Paper 7

Time 3 Hours *Answer all the questions*

Section (a): Pure Mathematics

1. Solve the following inequalities:
   (a) $x + 7 \le 3x - 9$ [1]
   (b) $x^2 + 7x < 44$ [2]
   (c) $|2x - 1| < 3$ [2]
   (d) $\dfrac{x+1}{x} < 2$ [3]

2. Thirty people at a Disco were asked for their ages. The results are given below.

$$16\ 18\ 19\ 18\ 19\ 23\ 24\ 25\ 19\ 19$$
$$26\ 14\ 13\ 13\ 28\ 29\ 19\ 18\ 17\ 14$$
$$14\ 16\ 19\ 18\ 25\ 22\ 27\ 18\ 19\ 13$$

Construct a stem and leaf diagram to illustrate these figures, using stems of 10, 15, 20 and 25. Comment on the shape of the distribution.

[5]

The Disco was offering a reduced entrance price for people under 20. Does this information alter your interpretation of the diagram?

[3]

3. A chest of drawers has three drawers. The top drawer contains 5 left shoes, the middle drawer contains 3 left and 2 right shoes, the lower drawer contains 3 right shoes. A drawer is selected at random and a shoe taken out.

Find the probabilities that a right shoe is taken. [3]

If a right shoe was selected, find the probability that it came from the middle drawer. [5]

Section (b): Statistics

4. X is a discrete variable with mean 1.55. Its table is given below. Find a and b.

i	0	1	2	3
$P(X=i)$	0.15	a	b	0.3

[3]

5. A poker hand consists of 5 cards, in any order, from the standard pack. How many possible poker hands are there? What is the probability that a poker hand is a flush? (All cards of the same suit).

[6]

6. Show that the correlation coefficient for the following pairs of values (x, y) is 0.

$$(-2, 2) \qquad (-1, 1) \qquad (0, 0) \qquad (1, 1) \qquad (2, 2)$$

By plotting the points or otherwise show that there may be a connection between x and y.

[6]

7. The lifetimes of certain batteries are normally distributed. 90% last less than 20 hours, and 5% last less than 14 hours. Find the mean and variance of the lifetime of a battery. What proportion of the batteries last more than 22 hours?

[6]

8. 40% of a sample of 1000 claimed that they would vote for the Pragmatic Party. Find a 95% confidence interval for the level of support for the Party throughout the country.

How large should the sample be, if the width of a 95% confidence interval is to be less than 2%?

[7]

9. A, B and C are events. By a diagram or otherwise show that:

$$P(A \cup B \cup C) = P(A) + P(B) + P(C) - P(A \cap B) - P(B \cap C) - P(A \cap C) + P(A \cap B \cap C)$$

If $P(A \cap B) = P(A)P(B)$, show that $P(A' \cap B') = P(A')P(B')$

[7]

10. A man takes a bus which leaves a stop at X minutes past 9 a.m., where X is normal with mean 0 and variance 9. The journey time to a station is also normal, with mean 10 and variance 4. The train leaves the station promptly at 9.17. Ignoring change-over time, what is the probability that the connection is made?

Another passenger takes the same train, but he drives to the station, taking a time which is normal with mean 20 and variance 12. When should he leave home to be 99% sure of catching the train?

[10]

11. The probability that a gun hits a target with a single shot is $\frac{1}{8}$. The gun is fired until the target is hit. Assuming that the shots are independent, find the distribution of the number X of shots.

Find $E(X)$. Find the least number of shots that must be fired, so that the target will be hit with 95% probability.

If the target was hit with at most ten shots, what is the probability that the third bullet struck it?

(You may use without proof the identity $1 + 2x + 3x^2 + \ldots \equiv (1 - x)^{-2}$)

[10]

12. The number of appendicitis cases occurring in a year in a town has a Poisson distribution with mean 4. Find the probabilities of:

   (i) 3 cases in a year,

   (ii) 2 cases in 6 months,

   (iii) at least 4 cases in a year, given that there are at least 2,

   (iv) 3 cases in a year, given that there was at least one in the first 6 months of that year.

[12]

13. An athlete runs the mile 7 times. His results in seconds are:

$$250, 245, 253, 260, 248, 251, 257.$$

Find the mean of these figures and the unbiased sample variance.

Assuming that his time to run a mile is normally distributed, and that the variance found above is correct, find a 95% confidence interval for his mean time.

If his time has mean 250 and variance 20, how many times would he have to run a mile before he has a 50% chance of doing so in under 4 mins?

[12]

14. The contingency table below gives the major subject of 200 university science students, and the type of school they had come from. Conduct a test to see whether the subject and the type of school are connected.

	Physics	Chemistry	Biology	Geology
State school	33	29	51	16
Independent school	10	16	33	12

A similar test was conducted in a previous year. There were fewer students in that year, and the expected frequency in the Geology/Independent school box was 4.3. Explain how this would affect the test.

[14]

15. A supermarket sells nectarines in boxes of three. 50 boxes were examined, and in each box the number of rotten fruit was recorded. The results are below.

Number rotten	0	1	2	3
Frequency	23	12	8	7

Give brief reasons why the binomial distribution might or might not be appropriate to model this table.

From the table find the probability p that a nectarine is rotten. Conduct a χ^2 test at 5% significance level to see whether or not a B(3,p) distribution is a good fit for the table.

[15]

16. Z is a random variable with a standard normal distribution. Find, correct to two decimal places, the five numbers y_i ($i = 1, 2, 3, 4, 5$) defined by $P(Z < y_i) = i/6$.

A botanist attempted to measure the heights in centimetres of five wild saplings. Four of his measurements are given below. The fifth sapling was too tall for his measuring instrument.

$$82, 97, 88, 93.$$

Plot a graph of the y_i ($i = 1, 2, 3, 4$) against the members of the above sample arranged in a suitable order, and draw by eye a straight line to fit these points.

Assuming that this is a random sample from a normal distribution with mean μ and variance σ^2, use your graph to estimate μ and σ. Estimate also the height of the fifth sapling.

[O&C] [16]

ULEAC style Examination papers

Paper 8 Modular exam P1

[8]

Time: $1\frac{1}{2}$ hours

Full marks may be obtained for answers to all the questions

Fig 8.1

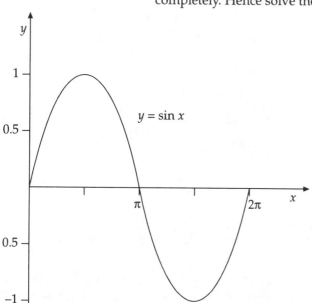

1. Given that $(x - 2)$ is a factor of $f(x) = 2x^3 - 9x^2 + 7x + 6$, factorize $f(x)$ completely. Hence solve the equation $2x^3 - 9x^2 + 7x + 6 = 0$.

[6]

2. The graph of $y = \sin x$ is shown, for $0 \leq x \leq 2\pi$. Make a copy of the graph, and on the same paper sketch the graphs of:

   (a) $y = \sin(x - \frac{1}{3}\pi)$ (b) $y = 2\sin\frac{1}{2}x$

   What single transformation will take the original graph to that of b)?

[12]

3. (a) Express $\dfrac{1}{\sqrt{2}-1} - \dfrac{1}{\sqrt{2}+1}$ as a single fraction, simplifying your answer as far as possible.

   (b) Write $\dfrac{1}{\sqrt{5}-\sqrt{3}}$ in the form $a\sqrt{5} + b\sqrt{3}$, where a and b are fractions.

[10]

Fig 8.2

4. A cardboard sheet is 10 cm by 20 cm. Squares of side x cm are cut from each corner (Fig 8.2). The sides are folded over to form a tray.

   Show that the volume of the tray is $4x^3 - 60x^2 + 200x$. Find the value of x which gives the greatest volume.

[6]

5. The functions f and g are defined by

   f: $x \rightarrow x^2 + 3, x \in \mathbb{R}$

   g: $x \rightarrow 2x + 1, x \in \mathbb{R}$

   (a) Find, in a similar form, the function fg.

(b) Find the range of the function fg.

(c) Solve the equation $f(x) = 12g^{-1}(x)$.

[L][9]

6. (a) Simplify the following expressions

   (i) $\sqrt{(x^{-2})}$ (ii) $\left(\frac{1}{2}\right)^x \times \left(\frac{1}{4}\right)^{-x}$

   (iii) $\ln e^{2x}$

   (b) Solve the equation $e^{2x} - 5e^x + 6 = 0$.

[12]

7. Find the area enclosed by the x–axis, the lines $x = 1$ and $x = 3$, and the curve $y = 2x^3 + 7x - 3$.

[7]

8. A stone is thrown up in the air. After t seconds its height h in metres above the ground is given by: $h = 2 + 40t - 5t^2$

   By completing the square or otherwise find the greatest height which the stone reaches.

   At what times will the stone be 70 m high?

[8]

9. In a certain country, inflation is such that the exchange rate of the Pesta against the £ doubles every 3 months.

   At the beginning of January 1995 there were 250 Pesta to the £. How many were there at the beginning of October 1995?

   Find an expression for the exchange rate n years after January 1995. When will there be 10,000 Pesta to the £?

[8]

10. The functions f and g are defined by: $f(x) = 3x + 2$; $g(x) = 2 - 5x$.

   Find $fg(2)$, $gf(2)$, $fg(x)$.

   Find the value of x for which $f(x) = f^{-1}(x)$.

[10]

11. (a) Show that there is a solution of $x^3 + 2x - 5 = 0$ between $x = 1$ and $x = 2$.

   (b) A quantity x obeys the equation $2.5x - 3.7 = 7.3$, where each of the numbers is given to an accuracy of 1 decimal place. Find the range of values within which x could lie.

[8]

Paper 9 Modular Exam P2

Time: 1 hour 30 minutes

Full marks may be obtained by answers to all the questions

1. It is thought that there is a relationship between y and x of the form $y = ax^2 + bx$, where a and b are unknown constants.

   Several values of y and x are found. How can the relationship be rewritten so that a linear graph can be drawn?

[4]

2. Expand $(1 + x)^{20}$ up to the term in x^2.

   Hence, without a calculator, find an approximation for $1.01^{20} - 0.99^{20}$.

   [8]

3. Let $f(x) = x^3 + 3x^2 - 10x - 24$.

   (a) Show that $(x + 4)$ is a factor of $f(x)$, and find the other factors.

   (b) Sketch a graph of the curve $y = f(x)$, indicating where the curve crosses the axes.

   (c) Find the area enclosed by the loop of the curve above the x-axis.

   [8]

4. A water tank is being replenished at a constant rate of 5 litres per minute. When there is V litres in the tank, water is leaking from the tank at a rate of $0.01V$ litres per minute. At time $t = 0$ minutes, $V = 1000$.

   (a) Find a differential equation in V, and derive the following

   $$\int \frac{100 dV}{V - 500} = -\int dt$$

   (b) Solve this equation, finding V as a function of t.

   (c) What happens in the long run?

   [12]

5. Express $\dfrac{1}{(x + 1)(x + 2)}$ in partial fractions.

   Use your result to find $\displaystyle\sum_{r=1}^{n} \frac{1}{(r + 1)(r + 2)}$

   [9]

6. Sketch the curve defined by the parametric equations

   $$x = 3 \cos \theta, \; y = 2 \sin \theta, \; 0 < \theta < 2\pi.$$

   Show that the equation of the tangent to the curve at the point $P(3 \cos\theta, 2 \sin \theta)$ is $3y \sin \theta + 2x \cos \theta = 6$.

   Describe a transformation which will convert the curve into a circle of radius 3. Hence or otherwise find the area enclosed by the curve.

   Obtain an equation of the curve which does not involve θ.

   [11]

7. Find two integers n and $n + 1$ between which there is a solution of the equation $x^3 + x - 3 = 0$.

   Show that the equation can be written in the following forms

   (a) $x = \sqrt[3]{(3 - x)}$ (b) $x = 3 - x^3$

   (c) $x = 3/(x^2 + 1)$

   Using a starting value $x_0 = n + \frac{1}{2}$, where n is the integer found above, investigate which of the rearrangements gives an iteration which converges to a root of the equation. Hence solve the equation correct to three decimal places.

   [12]

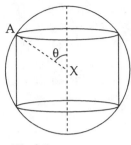

Fig 9.1

8. Figure 9.1 shows a hollow sphere of radius a cm, in which a cylinder has been placed vertically. The centre of the sphere is at X, and A is a point on the rim of the top of the cylinder. The line AX makes an angle θ with the vertical.

(a) Show that the volume, V cm^3, of the cylinder is given by

$$V = 2\pi a^3 \sin^2 \theta \cos \theta$$

(b) Find the values of θ for which V is stationary.

(c) Find the maximum value of V, explaining why your answer is a maximum.

[13]

9. Write down an identity connecting $\cos^2 x$ and $\sin^2 x$. Hence solve the equation $\cos^2 x + 3 \sin x = 2$, giving all the solutions in the range $0° \leq x \leq 360°$.

[11]

10. Evaluate the following integrals:

(i) $\displaystyle\int \sin (3x + 2)\, dx$

(ii) $\displaystyle\int_2^5 \frac{dx}{2x - 3}$

(iii) $\displaystyle\int_0^\infty x e^{-2x}\, dx$

[12]

Paper 10 Modular Exam M1

Time: 1 hour 30 minutes

Full marks may be obtained by answers to all the questions

Where relevant, take g to be 9.8 m s^{-2}

1. The vector position **r** of a particle is given by:

$$\mathbf{r} = (t^2 - 10t)\mathbf{i} + (7 - 3t^2)\mathbf{j}$$

Find expressions for the velocity **v** and the acceleration **a**.

When is **v** perpendicular to **a**?

[6]

2. A ship decelerates constantly from 10 m s^{-1} to 1 m s^{-1}. It travels 2,200 m while decelerating.

By means of a speed–time graph or otherwise find the deceleration and the time taken.

[6]

3. Weights of 3 kg and 4 kg are connected by a light inextensible string, which passes over a smooth peg. The system is released from rest. Find the acceleration of the system.

After two seconds the heavier mass strikes the floor and comes to an instantaneous halt. Find the time before the string is again taut.

[8]

Fig 10.1

4. A solid uniform cylinder has height 6 cm and base radius 2 cm (Fig 10.1). A cone-shaped hole is carved out from the cylinder: the base of the cone coincides with the base circle of the cylinder, and the apex of the cone is in the middle of the top circle of the cylinder.

   Find the centre of mass of the remaining solid. (The centre of mass of a solid cone is a quarter of the distance from the base to the apex.)

   [10]

Fig 10.2

5. The diagram shows a uniform plank AB of mass 20 kg and length 3 m. It rests horizontally on two supports which are 1 m from A and $\frac{1}{2}$ m from B. Find the upthrusts from the supports.

   What is the greatest mass that could be placed at A without disturbing the equilibrium?

   [10]

6. A girl throws a stone at an angle of 45° to the horizontal, at u m s⁻¹. The stone leaves her hand 2 m above the ground, and strikes a bottle on top of a wall which is 3 m high and 20 m away horizontally. Show that u obeys the equation:

$$38 = g\left(\frac{800}{u^2}\right)$$

   Solve this equation to find u.

   The bottle will be knocked off the wall if the speed with which the stone strikes it is greater than 13 m s⁻¹. Will it be knocked off?

   [14]

7. Forces are given by $F_1 = 2i + 3j$ N and $F_2 = i - 4j$ N. Find the resultant R of these two forces.

   Find the magnitude of R and the angle it makes with F_1.

   [8]

8. Suppose a body moves with constant speed v against forces F. Show that the power needed is $P = F \times v$.

   A vehicle of mass 900 kg can develop a power of 5,400 watts. On level ground its maximum speed is 30 m s⁻¹. If the resistances which it experiences are proportional to its speed, find the constant of proportionality.

   The vehicle is driven up a slope of angle α, where $\sin \alpha = \frac{1}{70}$. Find its maximum speed up this slope.

   [14]

9. Particle A, of mass 1, is moving with velocity vector $i + 2j$. Particle B, of mass 3, is moving with vector $-2i - 3j$.

   After they collide, A is moving at $-2i - 4j$. Find the velocity of B. Find the proportion of kinetic energy which has been lost in the collision.

   [12]

10. A particle slides down a slope of angle 30°, where the coefficient of friction μ is $\frac{1}{4}$. Find the distance it has moved when moving from rest to a speed of 3 m s⁻¹.

    [12]

Paper 11 Modular Exam M2

Time $1\frac{1}{2}$ hours

Full marks may be obtained by answers to all the questions

Where relevant take g = 9.8 m s⁻²

1. A uniform stick AB of mass m and length $2a$ rests with A in contact with a rough horizontal floor. The rod is held at an angle θ with the ground by a horizontal string attached to B.

   Find the tension in the string in terms of m, g and θ.

   If the rod is about to slip when $\theta = 60°$, find the coefficient of friction μ.

   [12]

2. A particle of mass 0.2 kg hangs at the end of a light inextensible string of length 1.5 m, the top end of which is held fixed. The mass performs horizontal circles with angular speed 4 rad/s. Find the tension in the string and the angle it makes with the vertical.

   [12]

3. Two small beads A and B, of masses m and $2m$ respectively, are threaded on a fixed smooth vertical wire. The bead A can move freely on the wire, but B is attached to the top end of a light elastic spring whose bottom end is fixed at a point O on the wire, as shown in the diagram. The unstretched length of the spring is a and its modulus of elasticity is $8mg$. Find the length of the spring when B rests in equilibrium.

   Fig 11.1

   With B resting in equilibrium, A is released from rest at a height h above B. When A collides with B, the beads stick together and move as a single particle of mass $3m$. Find an expression for the kinetic energy of the combined particle immediately after impact.

   In the subsequent motion the greatest height above O reached by the combined particle is a. Find h in terms of a.

   [C][14]

4. A uniform lamina occupies the region enclosed by the positive axes and the curve $y = 1 - x^2$. Find the co–ordinates of the centre of gravity of the lamina.

   The lamina is rotated about the x–axis to form a uniform solid of revolution. Find the centre of gravity of this solid.

   If this solid is suspended from the point $(0,1)$ find the angle made with the vertical by the flat surface.

   [12]

5. A football is kicked with speed V from a point O on level ground. Its initial direction of motion makes an angle $\frac{1}{4}\pi$ with the horizontal. Let x and y be the horizontal and vertical displacements respectively of the ball at time t after being kicked. Write down expressions for x and y in terms of t, assuming that air resistance can be neglected. Hence show that

$$y = x - \left(\frac{gx^2}{V^2}\right)$$

Fig 11.2

As the sketch shows, O is 6 m from the foot of a vertical wall AB of height 1.5 m, and 18 m from the foot of a second vertical wall CD also of height 1.5 m. Taking g as 9.8 m s^{-2}, show that the ball clears the nearer wall AB when $V = 9$ m s^{-1}. Find the minimum value of V which ensures that the ball clears both walls.

[MEI] [13]

6. A small smooth sphere moves on a horizontal table and strikes an identical sphere lying at rest on the table at a distance d from a vertical wall, the impact being along the line of centres and perpendicular to the wall. Prove that the next impact between the spheres will take place at a distance

$$\frac{2de^2}{(1 - e^2)}$$

from the wall, where e is the coefficient of restitution for all the impacts involved.

[L] [13]

7. A bead of mass m is threaded on a smooth vertical wire, which is bent into the shape of a circle of radius a. The bead is attached to a light elastic string of natural length a and modulus of elasticity $4mg$. The other end of the string is attached to the lowest point of the wire. The bead is at the lowest point of the wire, and is given a horizontal speed of V.

(i) Show that if $V^2 < ag$ the string never becomes taut.

(ii) Show that the bead will perform complete circles provided that $V^2 > 8ag$.

[12]

8. A particle of mass m kg is projected upwards at 40 m s^{-1}. Ignoring air resistance, find the greatest height it reaches.

Suppose that the air resistance is equal to $m0.098$ N. Show that the motion of the particle obeys the equation

$$100\, v\frac{dv}{ds} = -9.8(100 + v)$$

where v m s^{-1} is its speed and s m the distance it has risen. Use this equation to find the greatest height it reaches.

[12]

Paper 12 Modular Exam T1

Time: 1 hour 30 minutes

Full marks may be obtained for answers to all the questions

1. In a raffle there are 500 tickets, 10 of which will win prizes.

    If I buy 3 tickets, what is the probability that I will win at least one prize?

    [6]

2. Find the mean and the variance for the numbers below.

    2.9 2.7 3.1 3.3 3.2 3.0 2.8 2.9

    3.0, 2.7 3.2 3.7 3.1 2.6 2.9 2.8

    Find the median and quartiles of the numbers, and illustrate them in a box and whisker diagram.

    [10]

3. A video hire firm has two copies of the film "Mad Mathematician III". The daily demand for this film has a Poisson distribution with mean 0.8.

    (a) Find the probability that on a given day no one asks for the film.

    (b) Find the probability that on a given day at least two people ask for the film. (So that both copies are out on loan.)

    (c) Find the mean number of copies which are out on loan.

    [10]

4. The time people take to complete a task testing dexterity follows a normal distribution. 10% of the people completed it in less than 4 minutes, and 25% took over 6 minutes.

    Find the mean and variance of the time taken.

    [10]

5. In a fairground game the customer rolls three dice. If 1 six is obtained, the customer wins £2. If 2 sixes are showing, £3 is won, and if 3 sixes are showing £4 is won.

    Complete the table below to show the amount X won by the customer.

i	£0	£2	£3	£4
$P(X = i)$				

    The customer pays £1 to play this game. What is the percentage profit or loss of the stallholder?

    [10]

6. The continuous random variable X has p.d.f. given by:

    $$\begin{cases} kx^2 & \text{if } 0 \le x \le 2 \\ 0 & \text{otherwise} \end{cases}$$

    (a) Find the value of k.

    (b) Find the mean of X.

    (c) Find the probability that X is greater than the mean.

    [12]

7. My journey to work involves a walk then a bus ride. The times for walking, waiting for the bus and for the bus trip are all normally distributed. Their means are 8 minutes, 10 minutes, 7 minutes respectively. Their variances are 1, 5 and 2 respectively.

    (a) Find the probability that the total journey takes over 30 minutes.

    (b) Find the probability that the time spent waiting at the bus stop is greater than the time spent in the bus.

    [10]

8. Certain computer hard disks are such that the probability that a disk will still be going after x hours of use is

    $$1 - \frac{x^2}{10^8}, \text{ where } 0 \leq x \leq 10^4$$

    Let X be the lifetime of a hard disk. Find the p.d.f. of X.

    (a) Write down and evaluate an integral expression for the mean lifetime of the disk.

    (b) Find the median lifetime of the disk.

    [12]

9. The incomes of 100 employees of a factory are as given in the table below.

Income	Frequency
10,000–14,999	22
15,000–19,999	27
20,000–24,999	21
25,000–29,999	12
30,000–39,999	10
40,000–49,999	6
50,000–90,000	2

    Obtain the cumulative frequencies, and construct a cumulative frequency chart. From your chart obtain the median and the quartiles.

    What do your values for the median and the quartiles tell you about the skewness of the distribution?

    Without any further calculation, state with *brief* reasons whether the mean salary is less or greater than the median salary.

Paper 13 Modular Exam T2

Time $1\frac{1}{2}$ hours

Full marks may be obtained by answers to all the questions

1. The manufacturers of 'Herostratus' matches claim that each box contains 50 matches on average. It is known that the variance of this total is 20.

    A sample of 40 boxes were found to contain an average of 48 matches.

Is this significant at 5% to disprove the manufacturers claim? Show clearly the null and alternative hypotheses you are using.

[10]

2. The lifetime of certain computer components has a standard deviation of $\sqrt{2}$ hours. A sample of 100 of these components found that their mean lifetime was 10 hours. Find a 95% confidence interval for the mean lifetime μ of these components, stating clearly any assumptions that you make.

A batch of 80 similar components had a mean lifetime of 9.6 hours. Is this significant at 5% to show that there is a difference between the batches?

[12]

3. The records of deaths of those aged 70 or above in a town were collected in 1984. The table shows the number of deaths per quarter from a sample of 100.

	Jan–Mar	Apr–Jun	Jul–Sept	Oct–Dec
Number	24	16	22	38

(i) Perform a test to decide whether the sample data indicate that mortality is independent of quarter.

(ii) An accident at a local factory caused atmospheric pollution, during November of that year, and this was thought to increase the number of deaths. Show, by omitting the October–December figure that the data support this belief.

[SUJB] [14]

4. It is thought that the relationship between air resistance and air speed follows a law of the form

$$F = aV + bV^2$$

where F N is the resistance, V m s^{-1} is the speed, and a and b are constants. Experiments gave the following results.

V	5	10	15	20	25	30
F	24	88	192	380	520	750

Define a new variable R by $R = F/V$. Calculate the equation of the line of regression of R on V, and hence estimate a and b.

One of the experimental values of F is suspect. Plot R against V, and identify the suspect value. Predict the correct value.

[14]

5. A group of 100 school students were asked whether they had a computer at home. Their grades in GCSE Mathematics were found. The contingency table below gives the results. Conduct a test at 5% significance to see whether there is a connection.

	With computer	without computer
Grade C or better	35	18
Below grade C	21	26

[10]

6. The crime rate (in offences per 1000 population) and the percentage unemployment rate for ten successive years are given below.

Year	1	2	3	4	5	6	7	8	9	10
Crime	53	61	52	69	72	82	71	66	59	51
Unemployment	5	6	6	7	8	12	10	8	6	5

Find the correlation coefficient between the crime and unemployment rates for these years.

Show that the correlation between these rates is significant at 1%.

A politician claims that the result proves that unemployment causes crime. Is the claim justified? Give *brief* reasons.

[12]

7. Over 100 weeks, a doctor in general practice kept a record of the number of patients he had seen with a particular complaint. The results are below

Number of patients	0	1	2	3	4+
Frequency	16	25	31	15	13

It is suggested that these figures could come from a Poisson distribution with mean 2. Apply a χ^2 test at 5% significance to see whether this is a good fit.

Another doctor made a similar table, and tested whether they could fit a Poisson distribution, with the mean as found from the frequency table. The value obtained was

$$\sum \frac{(f_e - f_o)^2}{f_e} = 8.2$$

What conclusions can the second doctor reach?

[14]

8. A factory makes batteries whose lifetime is normally distributed with mean 30 hours and standard deviation 6 hours.

A new production method is introduced. The method will be tested by finding the average lifetime of a sample of 20 batteries. If the average exceeds a certain value μ, then it will be decided that the method increased the lifetime.

Find μ, given that the probability of a Type I error is to be 0.05.

If in fact the new lifetime is 34 hours, what is the probability of a Type II error?

[14]

NEAB style Examination papers

Paper 14 Methods and Applied 1

Time 3 hours. *Answer as many questions as you can*

1. Solve the equation $\cos(2x - \frac{1}{4}\pi) = \frac{1}{2}$, for $-\pi < x < \pi$.

   [4]

2. Solve the equation $e^{2x} + 3e^x - 10 = 0$, giving your answer to 2 decimal places.

   [4]

3. A balloon of total mass 500 kg is floating at a constant height. 20 kg of ballast is thrown out. Find the acceleration with which the balloon starts to ascend.

   [4]

4. Sketch on the same paper the graphs of $y = \sin x$ and $y = \frac{1}{2}x$, for $-\pi \le x \le \pi$.
   Hence find an approximate positive solution of $x = 2 \sin x$.

   [5]

5. The diagram (Fig 14.1) shows the graph of $y = \sin \sqrt{x}$. Find the area between the curve and the x–axis, from $x = 0$ to $x = 1$, using the trapezium rule with two intervals.

   Is your answer an over or under estimate of the true area? Give *brief* reasons.

   [6]

6. A function f is defined by $f : x \to \dfrac{3}{x - 4}$.

   What is the domain of f? Find f^{-1}, and state its domain. Find $f \circ f$.

   [6]

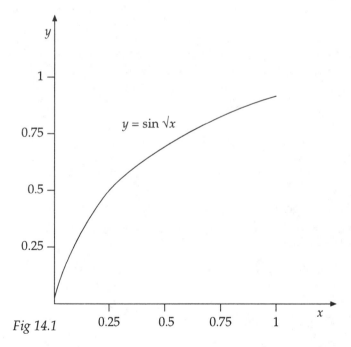

Fig 14.1

7. In a gambling game the player has to guess which of three cups conceals a coin. If the game is played twice, what is the probability that the player wins on both occasions?

   What is the probability that the player wins at least once in five games?

   [7]

8. If I get to work on time, the probability that I shall be late the following day is $\frac{1}{4}$. If I am late, the probability that I shall be late the following day is $\frac{1}{10}$. (See Fig 14.2) Find the probability that I was late on Wednesday, given that I was late on Monday.

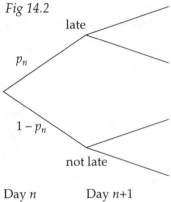

Fig 14.2

late

p_n

$1 - p_n$

not late

Day *n*　　　Day *n+1*

Let p_n be the probability that I am late on day n. Complete the tree diagram shown to find, in terms of p_n, the probability p_{n+1} that I shall be late the following day. Show that $p_{n+1} = 0.25 - 0.15p_n$. Hence find the long-term proportion of days on which I am late.

[7]

9. The table below gives the weights, to the nearest 0.1 kg, of twelve pedigree cats and twelve mongrel cats.

Pedigree cats　　3.1 2.7 3.8 2.5 2.8 3.5 3.7 4.2 4.5 2.6 2.5 4.7

Mongrel cats　　3.7 3.6 3.2 3.1 3.0 4.0 3.5 3.8 2.9 3.0 3.4 3.9

For each set of figures find the median and the quartiles. Plot box and whisker diagrams to illustrate the data.

What do the diagrams tell you about the differences between the groups?

[8]

10. A cylindrical can is to contain 1000 cm³ of liquid. The height of the can is h cm and its base radius is r cm. Find h in terms of r. Find the surface area A of the can in terms of r. Find the ratio of r to h which will ensure that the surface area is as small as possible.

[10]

11. A, B, C, D are four consecutive posts in a row along the side of a railway track. These posts are 200 m apart. A train, which is known to be moving with constant acceleration, takes 60 seconds to go from A to B and 40 seconds to go from B to C. Calculate the acceleration of the train and its velocity at A. Deduce the time the train will take to go from C to D.

[O&C ADD] [11]

12. The growth of a fungus is thought to be such that its weight obeys the law

$$\frac{dW}{dt} = 0.01W$$

where W grams is its weight, and t is time in minutes. When $t = 0$, $W = 0.5$.

(a) By using the approximation $\delta W \approx 0.01W\delta t$, estimate the values of W at $t = \frac{1}{4}$, $t = \frac{1}{2}$, $t = \frac{3}{4}$, and $t = 1$.

(b) Solve the above differential equation, to find the exact value of W when $t = 1$.

[13]

13. Differentiate the function $y = e^x(A \cos x + B \sin x)$.

Find A and B such that $\frac{dy}{dx} = e^x\cos x$. Hence find $\int 5 e^x \cos x \, dx$.

Find constants a, b and c such that:

$$a \frac{d^2y}{dx^2} + b \frac{dy}{dx} + cy = 0.$$

[13]

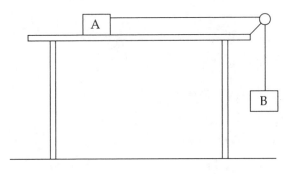

Fig 14.3

14. The diagram shows two particles, A of mass $3m$ and B of mass $2m$, connected by a light inextensible string which passes over a smooth fixed pulley at the edge of a horizontal table. Initially A is held at rest on the table and B is hanging freely at a height h above the floor. The particle A is then released and during its motion along the table experiences a retarding force, due to friction with the table, of magnitude $\frac{1}{3}mg$. The particle B strikes the floor before A reaches the edge of the table.

Find, in terms of m and g, the tension in the string and the acceleration of the particles while they are both moving. Show that the speed of A at the instant when B hits the floor is $\sqrt{\dfrac{2gh}{3}}$.

When B hits the floor, A continues moving along the table but eventually comes to rest before it reaches the edge. Show that the length of the string must be greater than $4h$.

[JMB AS] [12]

Paper 15 Methods and Applied II

Time 3 hours. *Answer as many questions as you can*

1. Solve the inequality $x^2 - 5x + 6 < 0$

[3]

2. Solve the equation $4^x - 3(2^x) - 40 = 0$.

[6]

3. A shell of mass 0.6 kg is fired into the air at 100 m s^{-1} at an angle of elevation of 60°. Find the greatest height reached.

At its greatest height the shell explodes into two fragments of 0.4 kg and 0.2 kg. The heavier fragment flies vertically upwards at 50 m s^{-1}. Find the velocity of the lighter fragment. Find the kinetic energy created by the explosion.

[10]

4. A water trough, 12 metres long, has uniform cross–section in the shape of a semi-circle with horizontal diameter 1 metre. The diagram shows a cross-section of the trough containing water (shaded) to a depth of x metre. The centre of the circle is at O and angle AOB is θ radians.

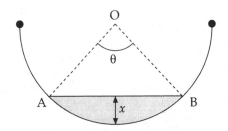

Fig 15.1

(i) Find in terms of θ an expression for the area of the sector AOB.

(ii) Use the fact that the area of triangle AOB is $\frac{1}{8}\sin\theta$ m^2 to obtain an expression for the area of the shaded segment.

(iii) Show that if the volume of water in the trough is V m^3 then

$$V = \tfrac{3}{2}(\theta - \sin\theta).$$

(iv) A formula for x in terms of θ is $x = \frac{1}{2}(1 - \cos \frac{1}{2}\theta)$. Find $\frac{dx}{d\theta}$ and hence express $\frac{dx}{dt}$ in terms of θ and $\frac{d\theta}{dt}$.

(v) It may be shown that $\frac{dV}{dt} = \frac{3}{2}(1 - \cos \theta)\frac{d\theta}{dt}$

When $\theta = \frac{1}{3}\pi$ and $\frac{d\theta}{dt} = 0.04$ rad/min, calculate

(a) the rate in m³ per min at which the volume of water in the trough is increasing,

(b) the rate in metre per min at which the water level is rising.

[SMP ADD] [12]

5. (a) The point A(1,2) lies on the curve C whose equation is $y = \frac{1}{2}x^2 + x + \frac{1}{2}$. Find

(i) the slope of the tangent to C at A,

(ii) the equation of the normal to C at A.

This normal intersects C again at B. Find

(iii) the co–ordinates of B

(iv) the equation of the tangent to C at B.

(b) A rectangular water storage tank, made of material of negligible thickness, is open at the top. The tank is three times as long as it is wide and when it is full it holds 1152 m³ of water. If the width of the tank is x metres

(i) find the length and depth of the tank in terms of x, and

(ii) show that the total internal surface area, A m², is given by

$$A = 3x^2 + \frac{3072}{x}.$$

(iii) Find the dimensions of the tank so that its surface area, A, will be a minimum.

[NI ADD] [14]

6. (a) Obtain an expression for $\cos^2 x$ in terms of $\cos 2x$ and hence evaluate

$$\int_{\frac{\pi}{4}}^{\frac{3\pi}{4}} 4\cos^2 x\, dx.$$

(b) Find the area of the region bounded by the curve $y = \frac{1}{\sqrt{(2x-1)}}$ the x–axis and the lines $x = 1$ and $x = 5$.

Find, to 2 decimal places, the volume obtained when this region is rotated through 360° about the x–axis.

[C ADD] [10]

7. The force a train can exert is 30,000 N. The total mass of the train is 50 tonnes. The total frictional resistance is 12,000 N. Find the maximum acceleration:

(i) along a horizontal track   (ii) down a slope of 1°

(iii) up a slope of $\sin^{-1}(\frac{1}{250})$

Find the steepest slope up which the train can ascend.

[9]

8. Express $\dfrac{1}{r(r+1)}$ in partial fractions.

    Hence show that $\displaystyle\sum_{r=1}^{r=n} \dfrac{1}{r(r+1)} = 1 - \dfrac{1}{n+1}$

    The discrete random variable X has probabilities given by

    $P(X = r) = \dfrac{k}{r(r+1)}$, where k is a constant.

    (i)   Suppose X takes the values 1, 2, 3,..., 10. Find the value of k.

    (ii) Suppose instead that X can take any positive integral value. Find k. If X is greater than 10, find the probability that it is greater than 20.

    [10]

9. A body moves so that its displacement at time t from the origin is given by $\mathbf{r} = \mathbf{i}(2 - \cos t) + \mathbf{j}(3 + \sin t)$, where $\mathbf{i}$ and $\mathbf{j}$ are unit vectors in the x and y directions respectively.

    (i)   Show that the path is a circle, and find its centre and radius.

    (ii) Show that the speed of the body is constant.

    (iii) Find when the velocity is first perpendicular to the displacement, and hence find the greatest distance of the particle from the origin.

    (iv) Show that the acceleration is always perpendicular to the velocity.

    [9]

10. The time T to complete a certain task is a continuous random variable with p.d.f. $f(x) = k(x - 2)^2$ for $2 \le x \le 3$, and $f(x) = 0$ elsewhere.

    (i)   Find k.   (ii) Find the mean time.

    (iii) Find the median time.

    [9]

Fig 15.2

11. In the diagram of the graph of $y = \dfrac{1}{x}$ for $x > 0$,

    the shaded area is equal to half the area of the rectangle. Obtain the equation $2 \ln z = z - 1$, and show that z lies between 3 and 4.

    Use the Newton–Raphson method to calculate an approximation to z, starting at $z = 3$ and continuing the iteration until successive values differ by less than 10^{-2}.

    [SMP] [10]

12. A hot body is immersed into a large tank containing water at $10°$. The rate of temperature loss of the body is proportional to the difference between its temperature T and that of the water, which remains constant throughout.

    Find a differential equation giving the rate of change of T in terms of time t. Find the general solution of this equation.

    Initially the temperature of the body is $100°$. The body cools to $60°$ in 5 minutes. Find the particular solution of the differential equation.

    Find

    (i)   the temperature after 10 minutes   (ii) the time to cool to $40°$.

    [12]

13. The daily demand for petrol at a certain garage has a normal distribution with mean 3000 gallons and standard deviation 150 gallons. If 3200 gallons are stocked at the beginning of the day, what is the probability of the garage running out?

What should the stock be, if the probability of not running out of petrol is to be at least 95%?

The garage is open for 6 days a week. If instead the garage stocks up at the beginning of the week, what should the stocks be if the probability of not running out is to be over 99%? (Assume that the demands on different days are independent of each other).

[12]

Paper 16 Methods and Mechanics

Time 3 hours. *Answer as many questions as you can*

Fig 16.1

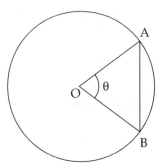

1. Find the equation of the tangent to the curve $y = x^2 + x$ at the point (2,6).

[3]

2. Differentiate:

    (a) $x(1 + x)$ (b) $\sin^2 3x$.

[4]

3. In the circle shown (Fig 16.1) the arc AB subtends θ radians at the centre O. Find the ratio of the area of the sector AOB to the area of the triangle AOB.

[4]

4. The curve $y = e^x$ between $x = 0$ and $x = 1$ is rotated about the x-axis. Find the volume of revolution.

[4]

5. The position vectors of P and Q are $2\mathbf{i} + 2\mathbf{j} + \mathbf{k}$ and $\mathbf{i} - 2\mathbf{j} - 2\mathbf{k}$ respectively.

    (i) Find unit vectors parallel to OP and to OQ, and hence find a vector equation of the bisector of $P\hat{O}Q$.

    (ii) Find a unit vector $\hat{\mathbf{n}}$, perpendicular to OP and OQ. Verify that $\hat{\mathbf{n}}$ is perpendicular to PQ.

[10]

Fig 16.2

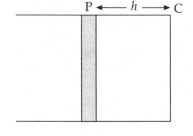

6. A piston P of mass M is in a smooth long horizontal cylinder. In equilibrium, the distance from the piston to the closed end C of the cylinder is h.

    If the piston is displaced x towards C, then the force acting on the piston away from C is

    $$Mg\left(\frac{x}{h}\right)^3 .$$

    Initially the piston is held a distance $\frac{1}{2}h$ away from C and released. Find

    (a) its speed when it passes the equilibrium point

    (b) the greatest value of PC.

[10]

374

7. [Take g to be 10 m s^{-2}.] A particle is projected at 100 m s^{-1}, at an angle of elevation of θ . Show that the equation of its trajectory is

    $$y = xT - \frac{x^2}{2000} (1 + T^2), \text{ where } T = \tan \theta .$$

    Such a particle is projected from the top of a 80 m tower to a horizontal plane below. Write down the equation relating T and the range R. Regarding this equation as a quadratic in T, find the condition on R for there to be real roots. Hence find the greatest possible value of R.

    If a particle is projected at the same speed from the horizontal plane, how close to the base of the tower must the point of projection be if the particle is to reach the top of the tower?

    [16]

8. (a) A curve has parametric coordinates $y = t^2 + 1$, $x = t^3 + 1$. Find the equation of the normal to the curve at the point where $t = 2$.

    (b) A curve is given implicitly by $x^2 + 2xy - y^2 = 1$. Find the equation of the tangent to the curve at the point (1, 2).

    [10]

9. The gravitational attraction exerted by the planet Xurgon is subject to an inverse *cube* law, so that the force experienced by an object is inversely proportional to the cube of its distance from the planet's centre. The radius of Xurgon is 20,000 km, and the acceleration due to gravity on its surface is 50 m s^{-2}.

    Show that the acceleration due to gravity r m from the planet's centre is

    $$\frac{4 \times 10^{23}}{r^3} \text{ m s}^{-2}$$

    Find the speed with which a body must be projected from the surface of the planet if it is to escape completely from its gravitational field.

    [12]

10. (i) Find the range of values of the function $y = x + \frac{1}{x}$. Sketch the graph, and find the equations of its asymptotes.

    (ii) Sketch the graphs of $y = x(1 - x)$ and of $y^2 = x(1 - x)$. Find the volume of revolution when the second graph is rotated about the x-axis.

    [10]

11. From the origin O, the points A, B, C have vector positions given by $a(\mathbf{i} + 2\mathbf{j} - 3\mathbf{k})$, $a(3\mathbf{i} + \mathbf{j} + 2\mathbf{k})$, $a(\mathbf{i} - 3\mathbf{j} + 8\mathbf{k})$ respectively.

    (a) Show that BC is parallel to OA.

    (b) Find the angle between OB and OC.

    [6]

12. (a) Evaluate the following definite integrals:

   (i) $\displaystyle\int_0^1 (1+x^3)^2\, dx$

   (ii) $\displaystyle\int_1^e x^{-\frac{1}{2}} \ln x\, dx$ giving your answer in terms of e.

   (iii) $\displaystyle\int_0^{\frac{\pi}{2}} \frac{\sin 2x}{1+\sin^2 x}\, dx$

   (b) Find the area of the region enclosed between the parabola $y^2 = 4x$ and the line $y = x$.

   [SUJB] [12]

13. On the same diagram sketch the curves with equations

   (i) $y^2 = 9x$, (ii) $y = x^2(1 + x)$,

   clearly labelling each curve.

   Deduce that the equation $x^3(1 + x)^2 - 9 = 0$ has exactly one real root.

   Denoting this root by α, find an integer n such that $n < \alpha < n + 1$, and, taking n as a first approximation, use the Newton–Raphson method to find a second approximation to α, giving two places of decimals in your answer.

   [C] [12]

14. The pyramid VABCD has a square base ABCD of side 4 m. The vertex is at V, and VA = VB = VC = VD = 9 m. Find the height of the pyramid.

   Find the angle between the faces VBA and VCD.

   Let E be the point on VA such that $\hat{AED} = 90°$. Find the length of DE. Hence or otherwise find the angle between the faces VBA and VAD.

   [12]

15. (a) Show that $\tan 4\theta = \dfrac{4\tan\theta(1 - \tan^2\theta)}{\tan^4\theta - 6\tan^2\theta + 1}$.

   Hence show that $\tan 22.5°$ is a root of the equation $t^4 - 6t^2 + 1 = 0$.

   Deduce that $\tan 22.5° = \sqrt{(3 - \sqrt8)}$, and obtain a similar expression for $\tan 67.5°$.

   Use your results to show that $\sec^2 22.5° + \sec^2 67.5° = 8$.

   (b) AB is a chord of a circle centre O which subtends an angle 2θ radians at O ($\theta < \frac{1}{2}\pi$). If AB divides the circle into two regions, one having twice the area of the other, show that θ satisfies the equation

   $$6\theta - 3\sin 2\theta - 2\pi = 0.$$

   Hence show that θ lies between 1.30 and 1.31.

   [W] [14]

Paper 17 Methods and Statistics

Time 3 Hours. *Answer as many questions as you can*

1. Differentiate the following:

   (i) $y = \dfrac{1 + x}{\sqrt{x}}$ (ii) $y = x^2 \cos x$

   (iii) $y = \ln(1 + 3x^2)$

   [6]

2. A vessel is obtained by rotating the curve $y = x^2$, from $y = 0$ to $y = 1$, about the y-axis. Distances are measured in inches.

   (i) Find the volume of the vessel.

   (ii) The vessel is gradually filled with water. At the instant when the depth of water in the vessel is $\frac{1}{2}$ in, 0.05 in^3 is added. Find the approximate increase in the depth of the water.

   [7]

3. (a) a is a positive number for which $\log_a 3 = x$. Express in terms of x

   (i) $\log_a 9$ (ii) $\log_a \frac{1}{3}$

   (b) Solve the equation $5^x = 3$.

   [6]

4. The number of flaws in 2 m lengths of material produced by a factory has a Poisson distribution with mean 0.8. If a length has more than 2 flaws then it is not sent out to the shops.

   (i) Find the proportion of lengths which are sent out to the shops.

   (ii) Find the probability that a length on sale in a shop has no flaws.

   (iii) Find the average number of flaws in the lengths on sale in the shops.

   [11]

5. A continuous random variable X has probability density function given by:

   $$f(x) = k \sin x, \text{ for } 0 \le x \le \pi/2.$$

   (i) Show that $k = 1$.   (ii) find E(X) and Var(X).

   (iii) Find the median value of x.

   (iv) A sample of size 100 is taken from this distribution. Use an appropriate approximation to find the probability that the sample mean is less than 1.05.

   [11]

6. (a) Let $f(x) = x^3 + ax^2 + bx + 12$. $f(x)$ has factors $(x + 2)$ and $(x - 3)$. Find a and b.

   (b) Express the following in partial fractions.

   (i) $\dfrac{5x^2 + x + 3}{x(x^2 + 1)}$ (ii) $\dfrac{x^2 - 6x + 1}{(x + 1)(x - 1)^2}$

   (c) Find the integral of the function in (b) (ii).

   [11]

7. A cone has fixed height h cm and variable semi–vertical angle θ. If θ is increasing at a rate α rads/sec, find the rate of increase of

    (i)   the base radius

    (ii) the volume.

    [8]

8. (i)   Solve the equation $\cos 2\theta + 3 \cos \theta - 1 = 0$, for $0 \leq \theta \leq \pi$.

    (ii) Find the greatest value of the expression $\ln(\cos \theta + 2 \sin \theta)$. Find the range of values between 0 and π for which this function is defined.

    [9]

9. 3 dice are identical in appearance, but though 2 are fair the third is biased so that the probability of it showing 6 is $\frac{1}{4}$. Two of the three are selected at random and rolled.

    (i)   Complete the following to show the distribution of the number X of sixes obtained.

i	0	1	2
$P(X = i)$			

    (ii) If exactly one six was obtained, what is the probability that it was from the biased die?

    (iii) If 2 sixes were obtained, what is the probability that the biased die was one of the two selected?

    [13]

10. A discrete random variable X has the distribution given by:

    $P(X = i) = k(i + 3)$ for $i = -2, -1$

    $P(X = i) = k(4 - i)$ for $i = 0, 1, 2, 3$.

    (i)   Find k.

    (ii) Find the expectation and variance of X.

    (iii) Write down tables showing the distribution of (a) $|X|$ (b) X^2.

    [12]

11. It is suspected that a die is biased towards 6. It is rolled 80 times, and the number of 6's is 20. Test at the 5% level whether or not it is biased.

    Would your conclusion differ if it was not known which number the die might be biased towards? Give your reasons.

    On the basis of the results find a 95% confidence interval for the probability of rolling a 6 with this die.

    [12]

12. Find the equation of the tangent at the point $P(ct, c/t)$ on the rectangular hyperbola $xy = c^2$, and prove that the equation of the normal at P is $ty = t^3x + c(1 - t^4)$.

    The tangent and normal at P ($t \neq \pm 1$) meet the line $y = x$ at T and N respectively and the x-axis at L and M respectively; O is the origin.

    (i)   Prove that OP = PN = PL.

    (ii) Prove that the product of the lengths of OT and ON is independent of t, and determine its value.

    (iii) Find the area S of triangle LMP, showing that $S > \frac{1}{2}c^2$.

    [O&C] [16]

13. A machine produces bolts whose diameters are normally distributed with mean μ and variance 0.001 mm^2. A sample of 10 bolts is found to have mean diameter 5.34 mm. Find a symmetric 95% confidence interval for μ.

How large should the sample be if the width of the confidence interval is to be less than 0.01 mm?

Samples of 40 each were taken from the production of the machine on two successive days. The average diameters of the samples were 5.31 mm and 5.32 mm. Is this significant at 5% to show that the machine was working differently on the two days?

[12]

National Curriculum Consolidation and revision

A1 Errors

The difference between a value and a measurement of it is the *error*. The error divided by the value is the *relative error*. Sometimes relative errors are given in terms of percentages.

Suppose we add or subtract measurements. The maximum error in the sum or difference is the sum of the errors.

Suppose we multiply or divide errors. The maximum relative error in the product or quotient is approximately the sum of the relative errors.

Decimal places and significant figures

When a measurement is given to two decimal places, the maximum error is 0.005.

Exercises A1

1. The true value of a length is 1.357 m. It is mistakenly written down as 1.375. Find the error and the relative error.

2. A weighing machine can be inaccurate by up to 1 kg. Find the maximum relative error when it is used to weigh a 75 kg man.

   This weighing machine records a weight of 58 kg. Between which limits does the true weight lie?

3. A weighing machine can be inaccurate by up to 3%. Find the error when it is used to weigh a 60 kg woman.

   This weighing machine records a weight of 72 kg. Between which limits does the true weight lie?

4. Find the error and the absolute error in approximating π by

   (a) 3.14   (b) $\dfrac{22}{7}$.

5. The fraction $\frac{1}{3}$ is written down as 0.33. Find the error and relative error.

6. Evaluate $\frac{100}{13}$, and write it to

    (a) three decimal places

    (b) three significant figures.

    In each case find the error and the relative error.

7. Two measurements are given as $x = 2.34$ and $y = 4.17$, both being rounded to two decimal places. Find the maximum error in

    (a) x

    (b) $x + y$

    (c) $5x$

    (d) $3x - 2y$

8. A relay race is run by four athletes. The first three take 20.5, 19.3 and 21.7, all times in seconds to the nearest 0.1 s. The total time was 82.1 s, also to the nearest 0.1 s. What are the greatest and least times the fourth athlete could have taken?

9. A square field of side 200 m is to be marked out. Each side is liable to an error of up to 1 m. Find the maximum error in the area of the field.

10. A journey of 150 miles is driven at 50 m.p.h. Both figures could be wrong by up to 2%. What are the greatest and least times the journey could take?

A2 Fractions

Fractions can be simplified by dividing numerator and denominator by a common factor. The fraction $\frac{4}{8}$ is equal to $\frac{1}{2}$.

A fraction in which the numerator is greater than the denominator, such as $\frac{10}{3}$, is an *improper* fraction. It is equal to the *mixed number* $3\frac{1}{3}$.

Multiply fractions by multiplying the numerators and the denominators.

$$\frac{3}{7} \times \frac{4}{5} = \frac{12}{35}$$

Divide one fraction by another by reversing the second fraction and then multiplying.

$$\frac{3}{7} \div \frac{4}{5} = \frac{3}{7} \times \frac{5}{4} = \frac{15}{28}$$

When adding or subtracting fractions, first ensure they have the same denominator.

$$\frac{3}{7} + \frac{4}{5} = \frac{15}{35} + \frac{28}{35} = \frac{43}{35} = 1\frac{8}{35}$$

Exercises A2

1. Simplify the following fractions

    (a) $\frac{2}{8}$

    (b) $\frac{6}{9}$

    (c) $\frac{3}{6}$

    (d) $\frac{12}{15}$

2. Convert the following improper fractions to mixed numbers

   (a) $\dfrac{12}{5}$ (b) $\dfrac{13}{3}$

   (c) $\dfrac{17}{11}$ (d) $\dfrac{18}{8}$

3. Convert the following mixed numbers to improper fractions
   (a) $1\frac{3}{8}$ (b) $2\frac{1}{3}$

   (c) $3\frac{3}{4}$ (d) $3\frac{5}{7}$

4. Evaluate the following, leaving your answers in fractions in their simplest forms.
   (a) $\dfrac{2}{5} \times \dfrac{1}{4}$ (b) $\dfrac{3}{8} \times \dfrac{2}{7}$

   (c) $\dfrac{3}{10} \times \dfrac{2}{3}$ (d) $\dfrac{3}{4} \div \dfrac{1}{3}$

   (e) $\dfrac{2}{5} \div \dfrac{3}{10}$ (f) $\dfrac{5}{6} \div \dfrac{3}{13}$

   (g) $\dfrac{2}{3} + \dfrac{1}{5}$ (h) $\dfrac{3}{4} - \dfrac{1}{8}$

   (i) $\dfrac{5}{6} + \dfrac{2}{15}$ (j) $1\frac{3}{4} \times \dfrac{1}{4}$

   (k) $4\frac{2}{3} \times 1\frac{1}{2}$ (l) $1\frac{2}{3} \div 2\frac{4}{5}$

   (m) $2\frac{2}{3} \div 4\frac{1}{3}$ (n) $1\frac{1}{2} + 2\frac{1}{4}$

   (o) $3\frac{1}{3} - 2\frac{5}{6}$

A3 Powers

A negative power is the reciprocal of the positive power.

$$3^{-2} = \frac{1}{3^2} = \frac{1}{9}$$

The $\dfrac{1}{n}$ th power of a number is its nth root.

$$8^{1/3} = \sqrt[3]{8} = 2$$

Expressions involving the $\sqrt{}$ sign (called *surds*) can sometimes be simplified.

$$\sqrt{2} \times \sqrt{2} = 2; \ 2 \div \sqrt{2} = \sqrt{2}$$

Exercises A3

1. Evaluate the following

    (a) 2^3

    (b) 4^3

    (c) 5^2

    (d) $4^{1/2}$

    (e) $125^{1/3}$

    (f) $16^{1/4}$

    (g) 4^{-1}

    (h) 2^{-3}

    (i) 10^{-2}

    (j) $(\frac{1}{2})^{-1}$

    (k) $(\frac{1}{3})^{-2}$

    (l) $(\frac{3}{4})^{-2}$

2. Simplify the following. Leave your answers in square root form.

    (a) $\sqrt{3} \times \sqrt{3}$

    (b) $(\sqrt{2})^3$

    (c) $\sqrt{10} \times \sqrt{1000}$

    (d) $\sqrt{2} \times \sqrt{8}$

    (e) $3 \div \sqrt{3}$

    (f) $4 \div \sqrt{2}$

    (g) $\sqrt{6} \div \sqrt{3}$

    (h) $\sqrt{10} \div \sqrt{5}$

    (i) $\sqrt{2} + \sqrt{8}$

    (j) $\sqrt{27} \div 3$

    (k) $\sqrt{1000} \div \sqrt{10}$

    (l) $\sqrt{32} \div 4$

    (m) $(1 + \sqrt{2})(2 + \sqrt{2})$

    (n) $(2 - \sqrt{2})(2 + \sqrt{2})$

    (o) $(3 + \sqrt{3})(2 - \sqrt{3})$

    (p) $\sqrt{6}(\sqrt{3} - \sqrt{2})$

    (q) $(1 + \sqrt{3})^2$

    (r) $(3 - \sqrt{2})^2$

    (s) $(\frac{1}{2} + \frac{1}{2}\sqrt{3})^2$

A4 Standard form

Very large or very small numbers can be put in *standard form.*

$$1{,}200{,}000{,}000 = 1.2 \times 10^9; \quad 0.00000075 = 7.5 \times 10^{-7}$$

When multiplying/dividing numbers in standard form, multiply/divide the number parts, and add/subtract the powers of 10.

$$1.2 \times 10^9 \times 2 \times 10^5 = 2.4 \times 10^{14}$$

$$7.5 \times 10^{-7} \div 5 \times 10^6 = 1.5 \times 10^{-13}$$

When adding or subtracting numbers in standard form, first ensure they have the same power of 10.

$$3 \times 10^8 + 2 \times 10^7 = 3 \times 10^8 + 0.2 \times 10^8 = 3.2 \times 10^8$$

Exercises A4

1. Express the following in standard form.

    (a) $320{,}000{,}000$

    (b) five million

    (c) 0.00000000067

    (d) two millionths

    (e) 47×10^8

    (f) 0.21×10^7

    (g) 732×10^{-12}

    (h) 0.03×10^{-9}

2. Evaluate the following, leaving your answers in standard form.

   (a) $4 \times 10^8 \times 2 \times 10^{11}$ (b) $5.2 \times 10^7 \times 2 \times 10^8$

   (c) $4.2 \times 10^{-8} \times 2 \times 10^{-6}$ (d) $4.1 \times 10^{11} \times 3 \times 10^8$

   (e) $8 \times 10^{13} \div 4 \times 10^8$ (f) $1.2 \times 10^{19} \div 4 \times 10^8$

   (g) $3 \times 10^{-12} \div 1.5 \times 10^4$ (h) $4.5 \times 10^{12} \div 9 \times 10^{-4}$

   (i) $3 \times 10^8 + 4 \times 10^7$ (j) $5 \times 10^7 + 3 \times 10^6$

   (k) $4.1 \times 10^9 - 3 \times 10^8$ (l) $5 \times 10^{-10} + 4 \times 10^{-9}$

   (m) $6 \times 10^{-10} - 4 \times 10^{-9}$ (n) $6 \times 10^{10} + 2 \times 10^8$

   (o) $3 \times 10^{-8} - 5 \times 10^{-10}$

A5 Use of calculator

Brackets and memory

A scientific calculator will have brackets and one or more memory. These can be used to evaluate complicated expressions without writing anything down except the final answer.

Suppose you want to evaluate $(1.35 + 3.86) \times (5.23 - 2.81)$.

Using *brackets*, the sequence is:

$$\boxed{(}\;\boxed{1.35}\;\boxed{+}\;\boxed{3.86}\;\boxed{)}\;\boxed{\times}\;\boxed{(}\;\boxed{5.23}\;\boxed{-}\;\boxed{2.81}\;\boxed{)}\;\boxed{=}$$

Using the *memory*, the sequence is

$$\boxed{1.35}\;\boxed{+}\;\boxed{3.86}\;\boxed{=}\;\boxed{\text{Min}}\;\boxed{5.23}\;\boxed{-}\;\boxed{2.81}\;\boxed{=}\;\boxed{\times}\;\boxed{\text{MR}}\;\boxed{=}$$

In either case the value is 12.6082.

Powers

On many calculators, the sequence for finding 3^5 is

$$\boxed{3}\;\boxed{x^y}\;\boxed{5}\;\boxed{=}$$

Fractions

A scientific calculator can operate on fractions. On many calculators the sequence to enter $1\frac{3}{8}$ is

$$\boxed{1}\;\boxed{a\,b/c}\;\boxed{3}\;\boxed{a\,b/c}\;\boxed{8}$$

Standard form

A scientific calculator can perform arithmetic on numbers in standard form. On many calculators, the sequence to enter 3×10^{-8} is as follows:

$$\boxed{3}\;\boxed{\exp}\;\boxed{8}\;\boxed{\pm}$$

Exercises A5

Give your answers to three significant figures

1. Evaluate the following, without writing anything down except the final answer.

    (a) $(2.54 + 3.87) \times (4.29 + 5.23)$

    (b) $(4.39 + 5.78) \times (2.56 - 1.28)$

    (c) $\dfrac{5.493 + 3.197}{2.182 - 1.865}$

    (d) $\dfrac{7.274 - 4.451}{32.01 + 9.57}$

    (e) $\dfrac{32.8 - 24.3}{0.017 + 0.052}$

2. Evaluate the following

    (a) 2^{10}

    (b) 1.3^5

    (c) 0.3^5

    (d) 1.017^{-3}

    (e) $6^{3/4}$

    (f) $3.84^{2/3}$

    (g) $5.17^{-1/2}$

    (h) $12.3^{-1.3}$

    (i) $2^{2.1} \times 3^{2.7}$

    (j) $4^{5.1} \div 5^{3.9}$

    (k) $10^{-3.8} \div 7^{-2.7}$

    (l) $(2.547 + 1.284)^{3.1}$

    (m) $(2.179 + 2.673)^5 \times (72.43 - 43.29)^{-3}$

    (n) $\dfrac{1.234^8}{16.123 - 8.457}$

    (o) $\dfrac{(23.78 + 43.97)^{0.8}}{1.482^9}$

    (p) $\dfrac{0.85^3 - 0.73^2}{6.37^2 + 4.19^3}$

3. Use your calculator to check some of your answers to the fraction problems of Exercises A2.

4. Use your calculator to check some of your answers to the power problems of Exercises A3.

5. Use your calculator to check some of your answers to the standard form problems of Exercises A4.

Section B Algebra

B1. Substitution

Substitution involves putting numbers in place of algebraic letters. Be especially careful when the numbers are fractional or negative.

Exercises B1

Find the values of the following expressions after the substitutions indicated.

1. $2x - 3y$

    (a) $x = 1, y = 3$

    (b) $x = -2, y = -7$

    (c) $x = \frac{1}{3}, y = \frac{1}{4}$

2. $5x + 2y$

    (a) $x = 3, y = 2$ (b) $x = -1, y = -2$

    (c) $x = 1\frac{1}{2}, y = -\frac{1}{2}$

3. $x^2 - 2x - 2$

    (a) $x = 4$ (b) $x = -2$

    (c) $x = \frac{1}{2}$

4. $2x^2 - 3x + 4$

    (a) $x = 5$ (b) $x = -2$

    (c) $x = \frac{3}{4}$

5. $\dfrac{5}{x}$

    (a) $x = 10$ (b) $x = -2$

    (c) $x = \frac{1}{3}$

6. $\dfrac{-2}{x^2}$

    (a) $x = 2$ (b) $x = -4$

    (c) $x = -\frac{1}{4}$

7. $\dfrac{1}{x + 2}$

    (a) $x = 1$ (b) $x = -3$

    (c) $x = -1.5$

8. $\dfrac{3}{4 - x}$

    (a) $x = 1$ (b) $x = -6$

    (c) $x = 3\frac{2}{3}$

9. $\sqrt{x^2 + 3}$

    (a) $x = 1$ (b) $x = -2$

    (c) $x = 5$

10. $\sqrt{5 - 2x}$

    (a) $x = 2$ (b) $x = -2$

    (c) $x = 2\frac{3}{8}$

B2. Expansion of Brackets

When expanding out brackets, make sure to obtain the correct number of terms. Be careful with negative numbers. For example:

$$(2x - 3)(4x - 7) = 8x^2 - 14x - 12x + 21 = 8x^2 - 26x + 21$$

Exercises B2

Expand the following and simplify as far as possible.

1. $(x + y)(a + b)$ 2. $(x + 3)(x - 7)$

3. $(2-x)(4-x)$

4. $(2x-1)(3x+2)$

5. $(2x-5)(3x-1)$

6. $(3-5x)(2-3x)$

7. $(x+y)^2$

8. $(a-b)^2$

9. $(2p-4q)(p+2q)$

10. $(2x+3)^2$

11. $(3x-5y)^2$

12. $\left(2x+\dfrac{3}{x}\right)^2$

13. $(3x)^2$

14. $(4x^2y^3)^2$

15. $(x^2-z)^2$

16. $(ab^2)^3$

17. $(x^2+2x)^2$

18. $\left(x^2-\dfrac{2}{x^3}\right)^2$

B3. Factorization

Factorizing is the opposite operation to expansion. A factorization can therefore be checked by expanding it out again.

When factorizing an expression of the form $x^2 + bx + c$, consider the factors of c whose sum is b. For example:

$$x^2 + 7x + 12 = (x+3)(x+4)$$

When factorizing an expression of the form $ax^2 + bx + c$, consider the factors of ac whose sum is b. For example:

$$6x^2 + 19x + 15 = 6x^2 + 9x + 10x + 15$$
$$= 3x(2x+3) + 5(2x+3)$$
$$= (2x+3)(3x+5)$$

Exercises B3

Factorize the following as far as possible.

1. $x^2y + y^2x$

2. $3x^2y + 9x^3$

3. $x^2 + 4x + 3$

4. $x^2 - 8x + 15$

5. $x^2 - 3x - 28$

6. $x^2 + 5x - 24$

7. $x^2 - 11x - 60$

8. $10 - 3x - x^2$

9. $60 - 17x - x^2$

10. $m^2 - n^2$

11. $4p^2 - 9q^2$

12. $3r^2 - 12s^2$

13. $2x^2 - 3x - 5$

14. $2x^2 - 11x + 12$

15. $3x^2 - 8x - 3$

16. $4x^2 + 20x + 25$

17. $9x^2 - 42x + 49$

18. $4a^2 - 12ab + 9b^2$

19. $4x^2 - 13x + 3$

20. $xp - yq + yp - xq$

21. $6at + bs - 2sa - 3bt$

B4. Equations

The basic rule for solving equation is to do the same to the left as to the right. Once a solution has been found it can be checked by substitution back into the original equation.

Exercises B4

Solve the following equations.

1. $2x - 1 = 3$
2. $7 - 3x = 1$
3. $7 + 2x = 1 - 4x$
4. $3 - x = 9 - 2x$
5. $7 - 2x = 11 - 4x$
6. $\sqrt{(x + 2)} = 3$
7. $\sqrt{x} + 3 = 7$
8. $\sqrt{(\frac{1}{8}x)} = 9$
9. $\sqrt{(2.5x)} = 10$
10. $x^2 - 7 = 9$
11. $\dfrac{x + 8}{x} = 2$
12. $\dfrac{3}{x} = \dfrac{4}{x + 1}$
13. $(x + 3)(x + 2) = x(x - 5)$
14. $\dfrac{x}{x - 3} = \dfrac{x - 2}{x}$
15. $x + 3y = 8$
    $x + 5y = 12$
16. $2x - 3y = 4$
    $5x + 7y = 68$
17. $3x - 2y = 5$
    $7x - 5y = 11$
18. $2x + 3y = -11$
    $4x - 5y = 55$
19. $\frac{1}{2}x + \frac{1}{3}y = 6$
    $\frac{1}{4}x - \frac{2}{3}y = -2$
20. $0.1x - 0.7y = -13.5$
    $0.3x + 0.4y = 9.5$

B5. Changing the subject

The procedure for changing the subject of a formula is the same as for solving an equation. You must get the new subject by itself on one side of the formula.

If the new subject has more than one occurrence, then all the occurrences must be grouped together and factorized.

Exercises B5

Make x the subject of the following formulas.

1. $x + a = b$
2. $3x - a = c$
3. $\sqrt{(x + p)} = q$
4. $q = p + \sqrt{x}$
5. $\dfrac{7}{x} = z$
6. $\dfrac{a}{x + 3} = b$
7. $ax + b = cx$
8. $m - px = n - qx$
9. $x = ax - b$
10. $\dfrac{x + 3}{x} = q$
11. $\dfrac{x + m}{x + n} = p$
12. $\dfrac{x + a}{x + b} = \dfrac{x + c}{x + d}$

13. $a = x^2 + b$

14. $m = \sqrt{(4 - x^2)}$

15. $7x^3 - p = q$

B6. Proportion

A proportionality relationship can be written either as $y \propto x^n$ or as $y = kx^n$, where k is a constant called the *constant of proportionality*. If n is a negative number, then the relationship is one of inverse proportionality.

To find the constant k, we need a pair of values of x and y. To find the power n, we need two pairs of values.

Exercises B6

1) In the following, find the constant of proportionality and the equation giving y in terms of x.

   (a) y is proportional to x. $y = 6$ when $x = 3$.

   (b) y is proportional to x. $y = 1.5$ when $x = 4.5$.

   (c) y is inversely proportional to x. $y = 5$ when $x = 4$

   (d) y is inversely proportional to x. $y = 0.25$ when $x = 0.5$.

   (e) y is proportional to the square of x. $y = 40$ when $x = 2$.

   (f) y is proportional to the square of x. $y = 98$ when $x = 7$.

   (g) y is inversely proportional to the square of x. $y = 15$ when $x = 2$.

   (h) y is inversely proportional to the square of x. $y = 40$ when $x = \frac{1}{2}$.

2) In the following, y is proportional to a power of x. Describe the proportionality relationship, and express y in terms of x.

   (a) $y = 2$ when $x = 5$, and $y = 4$ when $x = 10$.

   (b) $y = 5$ when $x = 2$, and $y = 45$ when $x = 6$.

   (c) $y = 36$ when $x = 3$, and $y = 9$ when $x = 6$.

   (d) $y = 4$ when $x = 2$, and $y = 32$ when $x = 4$.

   (e) $y = \frac{1}{2}$ when $x = \frac{1}{3}$, and $y = 1$ when $x = \frac{1}{6}$.

B7. Algebraic fractions

The rules for algebraic fractions are the same as for numerical fractions.

Fractions are unchanged if both numerator and denominator are multiplied or divided by the same term.

When fractions are multiplied, multiply the numerators and the denominators.

When one fraction is divided by another, turn the second fraction upside down and then multiply.

When fractions are added or subtracted, they must first be put over a common denominator.

Exercises B7

1. Simplify the following fractions:

   (a) $\dfrac{4x^2}{2xy}$

   (b) $\dfrac{x^2 + x}{x^3}$

   (c) $\dfrac{x^2 + 4x + 3}{x^2 + 5x + 4}$

   (d) $\dfrac{p + q}{\dfrac{1}{p} + \dfrac{1}{q}}$

   (e) $\dfrac{a}{\left(\dfrac{1}{b}\right)}$

   (f) $\dfrac{\left(\dfrac{a}{b}\right)}{\left(\dfrac{b}{a}\right)}$

2) Write the following as single fractions, simplifying your answers.

   (a) $\dfrac{1}{x} \times \dfrac{1}{y}$

   (b) $\dfrac{ax}{cy} \times \dfrac{by}{dx}$

   (c) $\dfrac{x^2}{y} \times \dfrac{y^2}{x}$

   (d) $\dfrac{x+1}{x+2} \times \dfrac{x-1}{x-2}$

   (e) $\dfrac{1}{x+3} \times \dfrac{1}{x-4}$

   (f) $\dfrac{1}{x} \times \dfrac{x^2 + x}{x + 3}$

   (g) $\dfrac{a}{b} \div \dfrac{x}{y}$

   (h) $\dfrac{x^2 a}{y^2 b} \div \dfrac{a^2}{b^2}$

   (i) $\dfrac{x+1}{a} \div \dfrac{x^2 - 1}{b}$

   (j) $\dfrac{x}{2} + \dfrac{x}{3}$

   (k) $\dfrac{x+3}{3} + \dfrac{x-7}{4}$

   (l) $\dfrac{1}{x} + \dfrac{1}{y}$

   (m) $\dfrac{1}{ab} - \dfrac{1}{a}$

   (n) $\dfrac{1}{x-1} - \dfrac{1}{x^2 - 1}$

Section C. Shape and space

C1. Lengths, areas and volumes

The areas and volumes of various shapes are as follows.

Triangle of base b and height h. Area $\frac{1}{2}bh$.

Trapezium of height h, parallel sides a and b. Area $\frac{1}{2}h(a + b)$.

Fig C.1

Prism with base area A and height h. Volume Ah.

Pyramid with base area A and height h. Volume $\frac{1}{3}Ah$.

Fig C.2

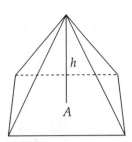

Circle of radius r. Circumference $2\pi r$. Area πr^2

Sphere of radius r. Surface area $4\pi r^2$. Volume $\frac{4}{3}\pi r^3$.

Fig C.3

Cylinder of base radius r and height h. Volume $\pi r^2 h$. Surface area $2\pi r(r + h)$.

Cone of base radius r and height h. Volume $\frac{1}{3}\pi r^2 h$.

If an arc of angle θ is taken from a circle of radius r, then

Length of arc $= 2\pi r \times \dfrac{\theta}{360}$

Area of sector $= \pi r^2 \times \dfrac{\theta}{360}$

Fig C.4

Exercises C1

1. Find the areas or surface areas of the following
   (a) a triangle with base 7 cm and height 4 cm
   (b) a circle with radius 2 m
   (c) a sphere with radius 12 cm
   (d) a cylinder with base radius 4 cm and height 3 cm
   (e) a trapezium with height 4 cm and parallel sides of length 3 cm and 5 cm

2. Find the volumes of the following
   (a) a sphere with radius 6 cm
   (b) a pyramid with height 12 cm and base a square of side 4 cm
   (c) a cone with base radius 8 cm and height 9 cm
   (d) a cylinder with base radius 4 cm and height 3 cm

3. Below are sectors of circles. Lengths are in cm. In each case find the arc length and the area of the sector.

    a)   b)   c)

Fig C.5

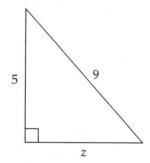

4. A circle has circumference 8 m. Find its radius and its area.

5. A circle has area 12 m². Find its radius and its circumference.

6. A sphere has surface area 25 cm². Find its radius and its volume.

7. A cone with base radius 4 cm has volume 12 cm³. Find its height.

8. A cylinder with height 6 m has volume 15 m². Find its base radius.

9. A sector of area 5 cm² is taken from a circle of radius 4 cm. Find the angle of the sector.

10. An arc of length 8 m is taken from a circle of radius 10 m. Find the angle subtended by the arc at the centre of the circle.

11. A sector of angle 20° has area 30 m². Find the radius of the circle from which it was taken.

C2. Pythagoras

A right-angled triangle is shown. The longest side c is the *hypotenuse*. The theorem of Pythagoras states

$$a^2 + b^2 = c^2$$

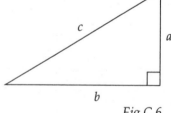

Fig C.6

Exercises C2

1. Find the unknown lengths in the diagrams below. Lengths are in cm.

Fig C.7

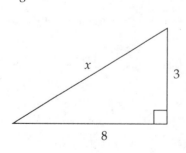

2. In triangle ABC, AB = 8 cm, BC = 7 cm, $\hat{B} = 90°$. Find AC.

3. In triangle DEF, $\hat{D} = 90°$, DE = 12 cm, EF = 17 cm. Find DF.

4. In triangle ABC, AB = BC = 13 cm, AC = 8 cm. By splitting this isosceles triangle into two right–angled triangles, find its height and hence its area.

5. In triangle DEF, DE = DF = 7 cm and EF = 4 cm. Find the area of the triangle.

6. Triangle ABC has AB = AC and BC = 8 cm. The area of ABC is 15 cm². Find AB.

C3. Trigonometry

The *trigonometric* ratios, sine, cosine and tangent, connect together the sides and angles of a right-angled triangle.

Fig C.8

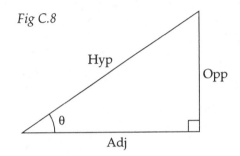

The diagram shows a right-angled triangle. The longest side is the *hypotenuse*. The side next to the angle θ we are dealing with is the *adjacent* side. The side farthest from the angle is the *opposite* side. Three ratios are defined by

$$\sin \theta = \frac{\text{Opp}}{\text{Hyp}} \; ; \; \cos \theta = \frac{\text{Adj}}{\text{Hyp}} \; ; \; \tan \theta = \frac{\text{Opp}}{\text{Adj}}$$

The sin, cos and tan functions go from the angle to the ratio. The inverse functions $\sin^{-1}$, $\cos^{-1}$ and $\tan^{-1}$ go from the ratio to the angle.

$$\theta = \sin^{-1}\left(\frac{\text{Opp}}{\text{Hyp}}\right) = \cos^{-1}\left(\frac{\text{Adj}}{\text{Hyp}}\right) = \tan^{-1}\left(\frac{\text{Opp}}{\text{Adj}}\right)$$

Fig C.9

Fig C.10

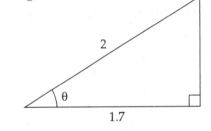

Finding sides

If we know an angle and one of the sides of a right-angled triangle, then we can find the other sides. In the triangle shown (Fig C.9), the angle is 40°and the hypotenuse is 12. The side labelled x is the opposite side. This side will be given by

$$\sin 40° = \frac{x}{12} . \text{ Hence } x = 7.71.$$

Finding angles

If we know two of the sides of a right-angled triangle, then we can find the angles. In the diagram shown (Fig C.10), the hypotenuse is 2 and the adjacent is 1.7. Hence the angle θ is given by

$$\cos \theta = \frac{1.7}{2} = 0.85. \text{ Hence } \theta = \cos^{-1} 0.85 = 31.8°$$

Graphs

The graphs of $y = \sin x$ and $y = \cos x$ are shown, for $0° \le x \le 360°$. The graphs repeat themselves every 360°.

Fig C.11   *Fig C.12*

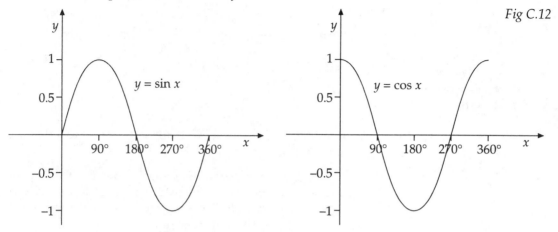

Exercises C3

1. Find the unknown sides in the diagrams below. Distances are in m.

Fig C.13

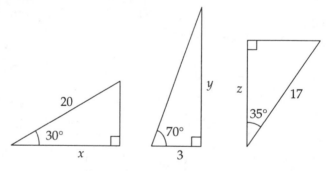

2. Find the unknown angles in the diagrams below.

Fig C.14

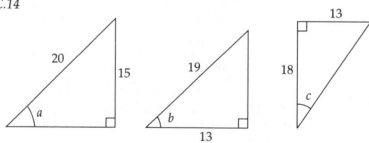

3. In triangle ABC, $\hat{B} = 90°$, $\hat{A} = 35°$ and AC = 12 cm. Find AB and CB.

4. In triangle DEF, $\hat{D} = 90°$, ED = 5 in and FD = 7 in. Find $\hat{E}$ and $\hat{F}$.

5. At 250 m from the base of a tree, the angle of elevation of the top is 27°. Find the height of the tree.

6. A ship is 1500 m out to sea. What is the angle of depression of the ship from the top of a 150 m cliff?

394

7. A ship sails for 10 km on a bearing of 052. How far North is it from its starting place?

8. A kestrel is hovering 30 m above the eye-level of a bird watcher. If it is 70 m from the watcher, what is its angle of elevation?

9. In the diagram shown (Fig C.15) AB = AC = 15 cm, and BC = 8 cm. By splitting this isosceles triangle into two right-angled triangles find B.

10. Find the unknown angles and sides in the diagrams below. Distances are in cm.

Fig C.15

Fig C.16

11. A cone has base radius 2 cm, and height 6 cm. What is the angle at the top of the cone?

12. Refer to the graphs of $y = \sin x$ and $y = \cos x$ above to find approximate solutions of the following

   (a) $\sin x = 0.5$ (b) $\cos x = 0.7$

   (c) $\sin x = -0.3$ (d) $\cos x = -0.4$

Section D. Using and Applying Data

D1. Probability

The *probability* of an event is a measure of our belief that it occurs. The probability of an event A is written P(A).

If A is certain then P(A) = 1.

If A is impossible then P(A) = 0.

Probability of single events

If there are *n* equally likely outcomes of an experiment, then the probability of each is $1/n$.

Suppose a card is drawn from a pack. We might want to know the probability that it is a Heart. There are 52 cards, of which 13 are hearts. Hence the probability that the card is a Heart is:

$$\frac{13}{52} = \frac{1}{4}$$

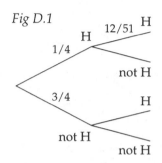

Fig D.1

First card   Second card

Probability of compound events

The results of two successive experiments can be shown on a *tree diagram*. Suppose two cards are drawn from a pack. We might want to know the probability that they are both Hearts.

The tree diagram for the two drawings is shown. Notice that if the first card is a Heart, then the probability that the second is also a Heart is 12/51. Multiply the probabilities along the top branch.

The probability that both are Hearts is $\frac{1}{4} \times \frac{12}{51} = \frac{1}{17}$

Exercises D1

1. A card is drawn from a pack. What is the probability it is an Ace? If two cards are drawn, what is the probability they are both Aces?

2. A bag contains 5 red and 4 blue marbles. If one is drawn, what is the probability it is red? If two are drawn, what is the probability they are both red?

3. In a class there are 10 boys and 12 girls. If one is picked at random, what is the probability that a girl is picked? If two are picked at random, what is the probability they are both girls?

4. On a shelf there are 7 fiction books and 8 non-fiction. If two are picked at random, what is the probability they are both fiction?

5. A fair die is rolled twice. What is the probability that both rolls gave 6?

6. A fair coin was spun twice. What is the probability that Heads came up twice?

7. Two cards are drawn from two separate packs. What is the probability they are both Hearts?

8. A bag contains 5 green and 3 yellow marbles. A marble is drawn, then returned to the bag, then a second marble is drawn. What is the probability that a green marble was drawn on both occasions?

9. A class contains 12 boys and 13 girls. Prizes are awarded at random for Geography and for History. The prizes can be awarded to the same person. What is the probability that boys win both prizes?

10. Two people independently pick a weekday on which to go to the library. What is the probability they both pick Wednesday?

D2. Averages

The *mean* of n numbers is found by adding them up and dividing by n

The *median* is found by arranging them in order and taking the middle number.

The *mode* of a set of numbers is the most common one.

Let us take the following numbers.

$$18\ 17\ 16\ 14\ 17\ 20\ 17\ 21\ 19\ 20$$

There are 10 numbers, and their sum is 179.

The mean is 17.9

Arranged in order, the numbers are 14, 16, 17, 17, 17, 18, 19, 20, 20, 21. Take half way between the fifth and the sixth.

The median is 17.5

The most common number is 17.

The mode is 17

Exercises D2

1. For the following sets of numbers, find the mean, median and where relevant the mode.

   (a) 5, 6, 6, 7, 8, 1, 9, 7, 6, 8

   (b) 121, 130, 140, 128, 139, 129, 125, 135, 142

   (c) −0.3, −1.2, −0.7, 0.1, 0.8, 0.7, 1.1

2. The salaries (in £1,000s) of 10 employees are as below. Find the mean and median salaries. Can you explain why they are different?

   $$18, 17, 19, 20, 21, 23, 49, 19, 18, 20$$

3. Nine people ran a race. Their times to the nearest minute are shown. Find the mean and median times. Why are they different?

   $$42, 41, 40, 45, 59, 43, 41, 43, 42$$

4. The midday temperature in Fahrenheit at a holiday resort in seven days in August are shown below. Find the mean and median temperatures. Which gives a better guide for the average temperature in the resort?

   $$63, 67, 93, 70, 68, 65, 66$$

D3. Frequency diagrams

Discrete and continuous data

Discrete data, like exam marks or numbers or people, take values which are separated from each other.

Continuous data, like mass or temperature, take any values within a range. Numerical data can be shown in a *frequency table*. The labelling of the groups will depend on whether the data is discrete or continuous, as shown below.

Mark	0–9	10–19	Temperature	0–10	10–20
Frequency	5	6	Frequency	5	6

The marks are discrete data. The end of one interval is different from the beginning of the next.

The temperatures are continuous data. The end of one interval is the same as the beginning of the next.

Histograms and frequency polygons

A bar–chart showing the frequencies is a *histogram*. A line joining the midpoints of the tops of the bars is a *frequency polygon*.

Cumulative frequencies

A running total of the frequencies will give the *cumulative frequencies*. These can be illustrated on a *cumulative frequency curve*.

From the cumulative frequency curve we can find the median, which cuts off half the total frequency. The *lower and upper quartiles* cut off the bottom quarter and the top quarter of the frequency.

The difference between the quartiles is the *interquartile range*. It gives a measure of the spread of the data.

Suppose we are given a table showing the midday temperatures in a resort in 40 days of August. The figures are in Fahrenheit rounded to the nearest degree.

Temperature	60 – 69	70 – 79	80 – 89	90 – 99
Frequency	5	13	18	4

Histogram and a frequency polygon

These are shown.

Fig D.2

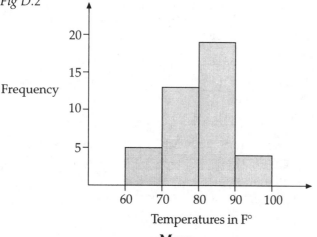

Temperatures in F°

Fig D.3

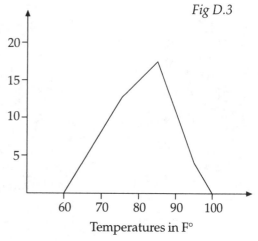

Temperatures in F°

Mean

Take the midpoint of each interval.

$$\text{mean} = \frac{1}{40}(64.5 \times 5 + 74.5 \times 13 + 84.5 \times 18 + 94.5 \times 4) = 79.75$$

The mean is approximately 79.75°

Cumulative frequencies

Obtain these by taking a running total of the frequencies.

Temperature	60 – 69	70 – 79	80 – 89	90 – 99
Cumulative frequency	5	18	36	40

The cumulative frequency graph is shown. Notice that the points are plotted at the right hand ends of each interval, not at the middles.

Fig D.4

Median and quartiles

For the median, find the temperature which corresponds to a cumulative frequency of 20. The lower and upper quartiles correspond to 10 and 30 respectively.

The median temperature is 81° The quartiles are 74° and 86°

Exercises D3

1. The table below gives the marks obtained in a test by 40 pupils. Draw a histogram and a frequency polygon to illustrate the data.

Marks	0 – 9	10 – 19	20 – 29	30 – 40
Frequency	8	17	11	4

2. The table below gives the weights in grams of 100 oranges. Draw a histogram to illustrate the data.

Weights	80 – 90	90 – 100	100 – 110	110 – 120
Frequency	12	35	38	15

3. The time in minutes taken by 80 people to run a race are given below. Draw a histogram and a frequency polygon to illustrate the data.

Time	40 – 45	45 – 50	50 – 55	55 – 60	60 – 65
Frequency	25	28	12	9	6

4. A javelin is thrown by 60 athletes. The results, rounded to the nearest metre, are shown below. Draw a histogram to illustrate the data.

Distance	25 – 29	30 – 34	35 – 39	40 – 44	45 – 49
Frequency	8	19	17	11	5

5., 6., 7., 8. For the data in Questions 1. to 4., estimate the mean.

9., 10., 11., 12. For the data in Questions 1. to 4., find the cumulative frequencies and draw a cumulative frequency curve. Find the median, the quartiles and the interquartile range.

Statistical tables

Table I Cumulative probability of the standard normal distribution

This table gives the values of $\Phi(z) = P(Z < z)$, where Z is normal with mean 0 and variance 1. If z is given to three decimal places, then use linear interpolation.

For example: $\Phi(1.327) - 0.9066 + 0.7 \times 0.0016 \approx 0.9077$.

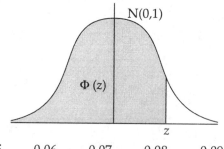

z	0.00	0.01	0.02	0.03	0.04	0.05	0.06	0.07	0.08	0.09
0.0	0.5000	0.5040	0.5080	0.5120	0.5160	0.5199	0.5239	0.5279	0.5139	0.5359
0.1	0.5398	0.5438	0.5478	0.5517	0.5557	0.5596	0.5636	0.5675	0.5714	0.5753
0.2	0.5793	0.5832	0.5871	0.5910	0.5948	0.5987	0.6026	0.6064	0.6103	0.6141
0.3	0.6179	0.6217	0.6255	0.6293	0.6331	0.6368	0.6406	0.6443	0.6480	0.6517
0.4	0.6554	0.6591	0.6628	0.6664	0.6700	0.6736	0.6772	0.6808	0.6844	0.6879
0.5	0.6915	0.6950	0.6985	0.7019	0.7054	0.7088	0.7123	0.7157	0.7190	0.7224
0.6	0.7257	0.7291	0.7324	0.7357	0.7389	0.7422	0.7454	0.7486	0.7517	0.7549
0.7	0.7580	0.7611	0.7642	0.7673	0.7704	0.7734	0.7764	0.7794	0.7823	0.7852
0.8	0.7881	0.7910	0.7939	0.7967	0.7995	0.8023	0.8051	0.8078	0.8106	0.8133
0.9	0.8159	0.8186	0.8212	0.8238	0.8264	0.8289	0.8315	0.8340	0.8365	0.8389
1.0	0.8413	0.8438	0.8461	0.8485	0.8508	0.8531	0.8554	0.8577	0.8599	0.8621
1.1	0.8643	0.8665	0.8686	0.8708	0.8729	0.8749	0.8770	0.8790	0.8810	0.8830
1.2	0.8849	0.8869	0.8888	0.8907	0.8925	0.8944	0.8962	0.8980	0.8997	0.9015
1.3	0.9032	0.9049	0.9066	0.9082	0.9099	0.9115	0.9131	0.9147	0.9162	0.9177
1.4	0.9192	0.9207	0.9222	0.9236	0.9251	0.9265	0.9279	0.9292	0.9306	0.9319
1.5	0.9332	0.9345	0.9357	0.9370	0.9382	0.9394	0.9406	0.9418	0.9429	0.9441
1.6	0.9452	0.9463	0.9474	0.9484	0.9495	0.9505	0.9515	0.9525	0.9535	0.9545
1.7	0.9554	0.9564	0.9573	0.9582	0.9591	0.9599	0.9608	0.9616	0.9625	0.9633
1.8	0.9641	0.9649	0.9656	0.9664	0.9671	0.9678	0.9686	0.9693	0.9699	0.9706
1.9	0.9713	0.9719	0.9726	0.9732	0.9738	0.9744	0.9750	0.9756	0.9761	0.9767
2.0	0.9772	0.9778	0.9783	0.9788	0.9793	0.9798	0.9803	0.9808	0.9812	0.9817
2.1	0.9821	0.9826	0.9830	0.9834	0.9838	0.9842	0.9846	0.9850	0.9854	0.9857
2.2	0.9861	0.9864	0.9868	0.9871	0.9875	0.9878	0.9881	0.9884	0.9887	0.9890
2.3	0.9893	0.9896	0.9898	0.9901	0.9904	0.9906	0.9909	0.9911	0.9913	0.9916
2.4	0.9918	0.9920	0.9922	0.9925	0.9927	0.9929	0.9931	0.9932	0.9934	0.9936
2.5	0.9938	0.9940	0.9941	0.9943	0.9945	0.9946	0.9948	0.9949	0.9951	0.9952
2.6	0.9953	0.9955	0.9956	0.9957	0.9959	0.9960	0.9961	0.9962	0.9963	0.9964
2.7	0.9965	0.9966	0.9967	0.9968	0.9969	0.9970	0.9971	0.9972	0.9973	0.9974
2.8	0.9974	0.9975	0.9976	0.9977	0.9977	0.9978	0.9979	0.9979	0.9980	0.9981
2.9	0.9981	0.9982	0.9982	0.9983	0.9984	0.9984	0.9985	0.9985	0.9986	0.9986
3.0	0.9987									

Table II. Critical Values for the Standard Normal Distribution.

These values cut off percentages of probability from both tails of the normal distribution. If a_i is the critical value for $i\%$, then:

$$P(\, |Z| > a_i) = i\%.$$

Percentage	20%	10%	5%	2%	1%
Critical Value	1.28	1.64	1.96	2.33	2.58

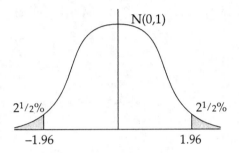

Table III. Critical Values for the *t* distribution.

These values cut off percentages of probability from both tails of the *t* distribution. The number of degrees of freedom is v.

Percentage	10%	5%	2%	1%
$v = 1$	6.31	12.71	31.82	63.66
$v = 2$	2.92	4.30	6.96	9.92
$v = 3$	2.35	3.18	4.54	5.84
$v = 4$	2.13	2.78	3.75	4.60
$v = 5$	2.02	2.57	3.36	4.03
$v = 6$	1.94	2.45	3.14	3.71
$v = 7$	1.89	2.36	3.00	3.50
$v = 8$	1.86	2.31	2.90	3.36
$v = 9$	1.83	2.26	2.82	3.25
$v = 10$	1.81	2.23	2.76	3.17
$v = 12$	1.78	2.18	2.68	3.05
$v = 14$	1.76	2.14	2.62	2.98
$v = 20$	1.72	2.09	2.53	2.85
$v = \infty$	1.64	1.96	2.33	2.58

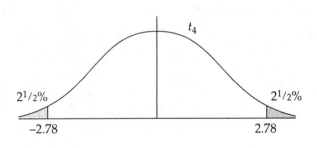

401

Table IV. Critical Values of the χ^2 Distribution.

These values cut off percentages of probability from the top tail of the χ^2 distribution. The number of degrees of freedom is v.

Percentage	10%	5%	1%	0.1%
$v = 1$	2.71	3.84	6.63	10.83
$v = 2$	4.61	5.99	9.21	13.81
$v = 3$	6.25	7.81	11.34	16.27
$v = 4$	7.78	9.49	13.28	18.47
$v = 5$	9.24	11.07	15.09	20.52
$v = 6$	10.64	12.59	16.81	22.46
$v = 7$	12.02	14.07	18.48	24.32
$v = 8$	13.36	15.51	20.09	26.12
$v = 9$	14.68	16.92	21.67	27.88
$v = 10$	15.99	18.31	23.21	29.59
$v = 12$	18.55	21.03	26.22	32.91
$v = 14$	21.06	23.68	29.14	36.12
$v = 20$	28.41	31.41	37.57	45.31

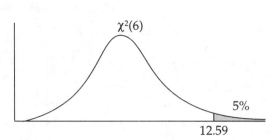

Table V. Critical Values of ρ and r_s

This table gives the critical values of the correlation coefficient ρ and Spearman's rank correlation coefficient r_s.

In each cell the first number is the value of ρ which cuts off the percentage given. The second number is the corresponding value of r_s.

Percentage	5%	2.5%	1%	0.5%
$v = 7$	0.669 0.679	0.755 0.786	0.833 0.857	0.875 0.893
$v = 8$	0.622 0.643	0.707 0.738	0.789 0.810	0.834 0.857
$v = 9$	0.582 0.600	0.666 0.683	0.750 0.767	0.798 0.817
$v = 10$	0.549 0.564	0.632 0.649	0.716 0.733	0.745 0.782
$v = 11$	0.521 0.527	0.602 0.609	0.685 0.700	0.735 0.755
$v = 12$	0.497 0.504	0.576 0.587	0.658 0.671	0.708 0.727
$v = 13$	0.476 0.478	0.553 0.560	0.634 0.648	0.684 0.698
$v = 14$	0.456 0.459	0.532 0.539	0.612 0.622	0.661 0.675

Solutions
(to exercises)

1.1.2 Page 2

1. b, 3, d, 4

2. (a) $4x^3 + x - 3$ (b) $2x^5 + 3x^4 - 2x^2 - 3x$

   (c) $x^3 - x^2 + 2x + 5$ (d) $x^7 - x$

3. (a) $x^2 + 6x + 25, 97$ (b) $x - 4, 18x - 3$

   (c) $x^2 - 4x + 18, -73$ (d) $2x^3 + 3x^2 + 3x + 4.5, 14.5$

4. (a) 38   (b) 29   (c) 7   (d) 18

5. 5   6. $\frac{5}{9}$

7. $a = \frac{1}{3}, b = -\frac{1}{3}$ 8. $a = -\frac{1}{7}, b = 1\frac{6}{7}$

9. 12   10. $\frac{1}{2}$

11. $a = -10, b = 24$ 12. $a = 2\frac{1}{4}, b = -4\frac{3}{4}$

13. $a = -5, b = -4. (x - 5)$

14. (a) $(x-1)(x+1)(x-2)$ (b) $(x-2)(x+2)(x+3)$ (c) $(x-1)(x-3)(x+2)$

    (d) $(2x+1)(x+2)(x+3)$ (e) $(2x+1)(x-2)(x-3)$ (f) $(x-1)(x+2)(x^2 - x + 2)$

    (g) $(x-1)^2(x+1)$ (h) $(x+1)(x+2)^2$

15. (a) $1, -2, -3$ (b) $-1, 2, 3$ (c) $\frac{1}{2}, -1, -2$ (d) $1, \frac{1}{2}, \frac{1}{3}$

1.2.2 Page 5

1. (a) $\dfrac{2x}{(x + 1)(x - 1)}$ (b) $\dfrac{-x + 3}{x(x + 3)}$ (c) $\dfrac{2x^2 - x + 2}{x^2(2 - x)}$

    (d) $\dfrac{2x^2 - x + 2}{x(x^2 + 1)}$ (e) $\dfrac{x + 5}{x + 1}$ (f) $\dfrac{-x^2 + 5x + 3}{(5 - x)}$

2. $\dfrac{1}{x - 1} - \dfrac{1}{x + 1}$ 3. $\dfrac{2}{x - 1} - \dfrac{2}{x + 3}$

4. $\dfrac{4}{x - 1} - \dfrac{3}{x}$ 5. $\dfrac{3}{4(x + 1)} + \dfrac{5}{4(x - 3)}$

6. $\dfrac{-2}{3(x + 1)} + \dfrac{4}{3(2x - 1)}$ 7. $\dfrac{4}{7(x - 2)} + \dfrac{9}{7(3x + 1)}$

8. $\dfrac{-1}{x + 1} + \dfrac{x + 1}{x^2 + 1}$ 9. $\dfrac{3}{x} - \dfrac{3x + 3}{x^2 + x + 1}$

10. $\dfrac{0.6}{x+2} + \dfrac{0.4x - 0.8}{x^2 + 1}$

11. $\dfrac{1}{x+1} - \dfrac{2x}{2x^2 + 3}$

12. $\dfrac{2}{x-1} + \dfrac{2}{(x-2)^2} - \dfrac{2}{x-2}$

13. $-\dfrac{4}{x+1} - \dfrac{1}{x^2} + \dfrac{4}{x}$

14. $\dfrac{1}{9(2x-1)} - \dfrac{1}{3(x+1)^2} + \dfrac{4}{9(x+1)}$

15. $\dfrac{5}{9(x-1)} + \dfrac{10}{3(2x+1)^2} + \dfrac{10}{9(2x+1)}$

16. $1 + \dfrac{1}{x-3} - \dfrac{2}{x+4}$

17. $4 + \dfrac{2}{x-1} - \dfrac{2}{x+1}$

18. $x + \dfrac{1}{x-1} + \dfrac{3}{x+2}$

19. $x^2 + 1 + \dfrac{1}{2(x-1)} - \dfrac{1}{2(x+1)}$

20. $\dfrac{3}{x-1} - \dfrac{6}{x-2} + \dfrac{3}{x-3}$

21. $\dfrac{3}{2x} + \dfrac{1}{3(x-1)} + \dfrac{11}{6(x+2)}$

22. $\dfrac{1}{n} - \dfrac{1}{n+1} \cdot 1 - \dfrac{1}{n+1}$

23. 1

24. (a) $\dfrac{1}{2} - \dfrac{1}{2(2n+1)}$ (b) $\dfrac{1}{4} - \dfrac{1}{4n+4}$

Chapter 2

2.1.2 Page 10

1. (a) 31   (b) 53   (c) 6.2   (d) −19

2. (a) 210   (b) 420   (c) 63.6   (d) −66

3. (a) $3n-2, \tfrac{1}{2}n(3n-1)$ (b) $4n+9, \tfrac{1}{2}n(4n+22)$ (c) $\dfrac{n}{5} + 4, \tfrac{1}{2}n\left(8.2 + \dfrac{n}{5}\right)$

   (d) $14-3n, \tfrac{1}{2}n(25-3n)$

4. (a) $0, 3n-3$ (b) $5, 3n+2$ (c) $1.1, \dfrac{n}{5} + 0.9$ (d) $21, 25-4n$

5. 3, 8

6. (a) 5, 7   (b) 7, 4   (c) $\tfrac{1}{5}, \tfrac{11}{5}$ (d) −2, 1

7. 3, 7, 11, 4

8. (a) 2, 2   (b) 2, −2   (c) 5, 6   (d) $\tfrac{3}{4}, -\tfrac{1}{2}$

9. 103

10. −2, 41

11. $\tfrac{1}{2}n(n+1)$

12. n^2

13. 1365

14. 5

15. $43\tfrac{2}{3}, 34\tfrac{1}{3}$

2.2.2 page 12

1. (a) 128, 62   (b) $\tfrac{1}{16}, 7\tfrac{3}{4}$ (c) 1458, 122

   (d) $-\tfrac{1}{2048}, -1.602$

2. (a) 2^n (b) $4(\tfrac{1}{2})^{n-1}$ (c) $2(-3)^{n-1}$ (d) $-2(-\tfrac{1}{4})^{n-1}$

3. (a) $2(2^n - 1)$ (b) $8(1-\tfrac{1}{2}^n)$ (c) $\tfrac{1}{2}(1-(-3)^n)$ (d) $-\tfrac{8}{5}(1-(-\tfrac{1}{4})^n)$

4. b, 8 d, –1.6

5. (a) $1\frac{1}{2}, 2$ (b) $32, \frac{1}{2}$ (c) $1\frac{1}{4}, -2$ (d) $8, \frac{1}{2}$

6. $\pm 5, \dfrac{\pm 4}{125}$ 7. 6

8. 9   9. 0.706

10. ± 15 11. –4, 2

12. (a) 3, 4   (b) $\frac{1}{4}, 3$

2.4 Page 14

1. $d = \frac{1}{4}(y-x), a = \frac{1}{2}(3x-y)$ 2. $4 \text{ or } -1\frac{1}{2}$

3. 500   4. £709.6

5. £20,850, £168,000   6. £18,616, £150,935

7. 36, 11 bricks high   8. 40.96 mm, 15 times

9. $2^{64} - 1$ 10. 12

11. $\frac{4}{33}$

12. (a) $\frac{8}{11}$ (b) $\frac{6}{11}$ (c) $\frac{1}{27}$ (d) $\frac{5}{37}$

    (e) $\frac{7}{110}$ (f) $\frac{1}{3700}$

13. $1\frac{1}{9}$ seconds.

Chapter 3

3.1.2 Page 18

1. (a) $32 + 80b + 80b^2 + 40b^3 + 10b^4 + b^5$ (b) $1 + 12b + 54b^2 + 108b^3 + 81b^4$

    (c) $16x^4 + 96\,x^3y + 216x^2y^2 + 216xy^3 + 81y^4$ (d) $1 - 12z + 60z^2 - 160z^3 + 240z^4 - 192z^5 + 64z^6$

    (e) $128a^7 - 448a^6b + 672a^5b^2 - 560a^4b^3 + 280a^3b^4 - 84a^2b^5 + 14ab^6 - b^7$

    (f) $128 - 224x + 168x^2 - 70x^3 + 17\frac{1}{2}x^4 - 2\frac{5}{8}x^5 + \frac{7}{32}x^6 - \frac{1}{128}x^7$

2. (a) $56x^3$ (b) $-126y^5$ (c) $180x^8$ (d) $448x^3$

    (e) $720y^3$ (f) $-11250x^2$ (g) $4368x^5y^{11}$ (h) $6048a^5b^2$

    (i) $28x^4$ (j) $-672y^{-3}$ (k) $21x^8$ (l) -84

3. (a) 24310   (b) 672   (c) 20412   (d) 489888

4. 416

5. $1 + 12x + 66x^2 + 220x^3$ (a) 1.26816   (b) 0.61152

6. (a) 1.083   (b) 0.698   (c) 535.5   (d) 227.2

7. $a=3, n=10$ 8. $\dfrac{2}{b}$

9. $\sqrt{224} : \sqrt{5}$ 10. $1 + 10x + 55x^2$

11. (a) $1 - 7x + 28x^2$ (b) $1 + 8x^2 + 28x^4 + 56x^6$

    (c) $1 + 12x + 78x^2$ (d) $128 - 448x + 1568x^2$

    (e) $1 + 8x + 28x^2$ (f) $1 - 9x + 30x^2$

    (g) $1 + 8x + 29x^2 + 64x^3$ (h) $1 - 11x + 56x^2 - 175x^3$

3.2.2 Page 20

1. (a) $1 + \frac{x}{4} - \frac{3x^2}{32}$ (b) $1 + \frac{3x}{2} - \frac{9x^2}{8}$ (c) $1 - \frac{3x}{2} + \frac{3x^2}{8}$ (d) $1 - \frac{8x}{3} + \frac{8x^2}{9}$

    (e) $1 - 2x + 3x^2$ (f) $1 - 2x + 4x^2$ (g) $1 + x^2$ (h) $3 - 3x^2$

2. a, c, e, g, h, $-1 < x < 1$ b, $-\frac{1}{3} < x < \frac{1}{3}$ d, f, $-\frac{1}{2} < x < \frac{1}{2}$

3. (a) 1.00498   (b) 1.02468   (c) 0.98995   (d) 0.9798

4. 1.999975   5. 7.07106

6. (a) 10.0499   (b) 9.8995   (c) 3.0366   (d) 3.97906

7. (a) $1 + 2x + 2x^2$ (b) $1 - 2x + 5x^2$ (c) $1 - x + 2x^2$ (d) $1 + x - x^2$

8. $a = 2, b = -\frac{1}{4}$ 9. $a = -2, b = 1$

10. $1 - \frac{x}{3} - \frac{x^2}{9}$ 11. $1 - \frac{x}{2} - \frac{x^2}{8}$

Chapter 4

4.1.2 Page 24

1. (a) $7, -11$ (b) $5, -1\frac{1}{2}$ (c) $-0.394, -7.61$

    (d) $0.4, -1$ (e) -0.694 or 3.36 (f) -21.4 or 1.40

2. (a) $\pm1.618, \pm0.618$ (b) ±1.377 (c) $-0.837, -1.506$

    (d) ±1.272 (e) $0.427, -2.927$ (f) $3, \frac{1}{2}$

3. 4.437 ft   4. 2.508 cm

5. 1.633 m.p.h.

6. (a) $(2.562, 3.562)$ & $(-1.562, -0.562)$ (b) $(3, 3)$ & $(-0.6, -4.2)$

    (c) $(1\frac{2}{3}, 1\frac{1}{3})$ (d) $(1\frac{1}{2}, \frac{2}{3})$ & $(1, 1)$

    (e) $(-0.926, 1.89)$ & $(1.47, -1.71)$ (f) $(1, 1)$ & $(2, 0)$

7. 22.095 & 0.905 ✓   8. $(-0.593, 1.407)$ & $(0.843, 2.843)$

9. $(2.436, -1.436)$ & $(-1.436, 2.436)$ 10. 12.07 & 4.93

11. $9x - y = 10$. $(1.425, 2.823)$ & $(0.770, -3.067)$

4.2.2 Page 25

1. (a) $(x - 1)^2 + 3. 3$ (b) $(x + 2)^2 - 11. -11$

    (c) $(x - \frac{5}{2})^2 - 3\frac{1}{4}. -3\frac{1}{4}$ (d) $(x + \frac{1}{2})^2 + \frac{3}{4}. \frac{3}{4}$

2. (a) $2(x + 2)^2 - 11$. $x = -2$, least

    (c) $4(x - \frac{1}{4})^2 - \frac{1}{4}$. $x = \frac{1}{4}$, least

    (b) $13 - (x + 3)^2$. $x = -3$, greatest

    (d) $15.5 - 2(x + 2.5)^2$. $x = -2.5$, greatest

3. (a) $(x+1)^2 - 4 = 0$, 1, -3

    (c) $3(x+1)^2 - 2 = 0$, -0.184, -1.816

    (b) $(x - 3.5)^2 - 10.25 = 0$, 6.702, 0.298

    (d) $2(x - 0.75)^2 - 9.125 = 0$, 2.886, -1.386

4. 320 m.

4.3.2 Page 26

1. (a) 0   (b) 1   (c) 2   (d) 2

2. (a) $\lambda \leq \frac{1}{3}$ (b) $\lambda \geq -2\frac{1}{4}$ (c) $\lambda \geq 4$ or $\lambda \leq -4$ (d) $-\sqrt{\frac{1}{8}} \leq \lambda \leq \sqrt{\frac{1}{8}}$

4. $k = -2 \pm \sqrt{8}$ 6. $\lambda \leq -\sqrt{\frac{1}{3}}$ or $\lambda \geq \sqrt{\frac{1}{3}}$

7. $\pm\sqrt{8}$ 8. $\pm\sqrt{12}$

9. $\pm\sqrt{15}$ 10. $\pm\sqrt{15}$

Chapter 5

5.1.2 Page 30

1. $x > 1$

2. $x \leq -\frac{1}{2}$

3. $x < \frac{5}{3}$

4. $x \leq -\frac{9}{4}$

5. $-6 < x < -2$

6. $x < -3$ or $x > 6$

7. all x

8. $-2.3 \leq x \leq 1.3$

9. $-2 < x < 1$

10. $x < -5$ or $x > 7$

11. $x < -3$ or $-2 < x < -1$

12. $x < \frac{1}{2}$ or $1\frac{1}{2} < x < 3$

13. $x \leq 1$

14. $x > -\frac{1}{2}$, $x \neq 0$

15. $x < -3$ or $-2 < x < 1$

16. $-3 < x < -2$, $-2 < x < \frac{1}{2}$

17. $x < -5$ or $0 < x < 2$

18. $\frac{1}{2} < x < 2$

19. $x < -6$ or $0 < x < 6$

20. $x < 0$

5.2.2 Page 31

1. $-5 < x < 5$

2. $x \leq -4$ or $x \geq 4$

3. $-\frac{1}{2} < x < \frac{1}{2}$

4. $-2 < x < 6$

5. $x < -5$ or $x > -1$

6. $x < 0$

7. $x > 0$

8. $-\frac{1}{3} \leq x \leq 1$

9. $x \geq 2$ or $x \leq -2$

5.3.2 Page 32

4. (a) 6   (b) 4

5. (a) $3\frac{1}{9}$ (b) 4

6. (a) 4   (b) $-1\frac{1}{2}$

7. (a) -1.75 to 3.2   (b) -1.4 to 3

Chapter 6

6.1.2 Page 35

1. (a) 4   (b) 1000   (c) 16   (d) 16

   (e) 25   (f) 3

2. (a) x^{-4} (b) y^3 (c) 5^{9x} (d) 2^{20n}

3. (a) $4 = \log_2 16$ (b) $3 = \log_{10} 1000$ (c) $\frac{3}{2} = \log_9 27$ (d) $-\frac{1}{2} = \log_{25} \frac{1}{5}$

   (e) $\ln 7.34 = 2$ (f) $\ln 10 = 2.0258$

4. (a) $2^3 = 8$ (b) $9^{1/2} = 3$ (c) $10^{-1} = 0.1$ (d) $16^{3/4} = 8$

   (e) $e^{1.792} = 6$ (f) $e^{2.5} = 12.18$

5. (a) 4   (b) 3   (c) $\frac{1}{2}$ (d) -3

   (e) -3 (f) 1   (g) 2   (h) $-\frac{1}{2}$

6. (a) 1.585   (b) 1.585   (c) 0.431   (d) -5.657

7. (a) $\log 2x$ (b) $\log_2 \frac{1}{3}$ (c) $\log_2 x^4$ (d) $\log 9x^3$

   (e) $\log 10x$ (f) $\log_2 4x$

8. (a) 1.585   (b) 0.778   (c) 0.262   (d) $\frac{3}{8}$

   (e) 1 or 1.585   (f) 3.15   (g) 0.672   (h) 0.898

   (i) 1.609 or 0.693   (j) ± 1.317

9. (a) $y = \dfrac{1000}{x}$ (b) $y = \sqrt[3]{x}$

10. (a) 128   (b) 2   (c) $\frac{200}{99}$ (d) 15.59

    (e) 81   (f) 1.3195   (g) 20.09   (h) 0.135

11. 22.5 years   12. 5.93 years

13. 3.1 years   14. 0.083, 26.6 years

Chapter 7

7.1.2 Page 40

1. (a) 6.32   (b) 5.39   (c) 3.61   (d) 11.7

   (e) 5   (f) 7.62

3. 6.5

4. (a) $(3, 4)$ (b) $(1, 2\frac{1}{2})$ (c) $(3, 7\frac{1}{2})$ (d) $(0, 2\frac{1}{2})$

   (e) $(-1, -3\frac{1}{2})$ (f) $(-1\frac{1}{2}, -4\frac{1}{2})$

6. No.

7.2.2 Page 42

1. (a) $y = 4x - 3$ (b) $3y = x + 10$ (c) $y = -2x + 7$ (d) $4y + 3x = 30$

    (e) $y = 2x - 2$ (f) $2y = x$ (g) $y = -3x + 8$ (h) $4y + 3x = -9$

    (i) $y = 4x - 5$ (j) $y = 3 - x$ (k) $y = 12 - x$ (l) $2y + x = -4$

2. (a) 1.66   (b) 7.07   (c) 1.34   (d) 0.277

5. No   6. $(2,2)$, $\sqrt{5}$

7. $y = 4x - 5$, $3y = 4x - 7$, $y = 3$: $4y + x = 16$, $4y + 3x = 18$, $x = 1$. Meet at $(1, 3\frac{3}{4})$

7.3.2 Page 44

1. (a) $(x-1)^2 + (y-2)^2 = 25$ (b) $(x-1)^2 + (y+3)^2 = 64$

2. (a) $(-2,1)$, $\sqrt{8}$ (b) $(1\frac{1}{2}, \frac{1}{2})$, $\sqrt{\frac{3}{2}}$ (c) $(0,3)$, $\sqrt{7}$ (d) $(-1\frac{1}{2}, 0)$, $1\frac{1}{2}$

3. $(x-1)^2 + (y-3)^2 = 17$ 4. $(x+1)^2 + (y-5)^2 = 5$

5. 0.6, $(x-1)^2 + (y+1)^2 = 0.6^2$ 6. $(x-2)^2 + (y-3)^2 = 0.4$

7. $y = x$ 8. $(1,0)$ & $(2,0)$. $2y = x-1$, $2y = 2-x$

9. $(-1, -1)$ & $(-\frac{1}{2}, -\frac{1}{2})$. $2y = x-1$, $y = 2x + \frac{1}{2}$ 10. $(4, -12)$, $\sqrt{40}$

11. $(x-3)^2 + (y-3)^2 = 9$ 12. $(3,1)$, $\sqrt{17}$

13. $(3,1)$, $\sqrt{33}$ 14. 5, outside, 4.

15. $m = 0.0811$ or -3.0811 16. $k = -2 \pm \sqrt{14}$

7.4.2 Page 45

1. (a) $x^3 = y^2$ (b) $xy = 5$ (c) $y = 3x - 5$ (d) $y+1 = (\frac{1}{2}x)^2$

    (e) $xy^3 = 1$ (f) $x = (\frac{1}{y} - 1)^2$ (g) $x^2 - y^2 = 1$ (h) $x + 2y = 1$

2. $pqy + 3x = 3(p+q)$ 3. $4y = (p+2)x - 8p$, $y = x - 4$ 4. $(\frac{1}{2}, 0)$, $\frac{1}{2}$

7.5.2 Page 46

1. (a) $45°$ (b) $71.6°$ (c) $-63.4°$ (d) $56.6°$

    (e) $-36.9°$ (f) $33.7°$

2. $26.6°$ $11.3°$ $135°$ $26.6°$

Chapter 8

8.1.2 Page 50

1. (a) 52   (b) 50   (c) $7 - 15x$ (d) $\dfrac{2 - x}{5}$

2. (a) -17 (b) -7 (c) $6x - 5$ (d) $6x + 5$

    (e) $\dfrac{x-3}{2}$ (f) $\dfrac{x+4}{3}$ (g) $\dfrac{x+5}{6}$ (h) $\dfrac{x-5}{6}$

    (i) $\dfrac{x-5}{6}$ (j) $\dfrac{x+5}{6}$

4. $\{y: y \geq 7\}$

5. $\dfrac{x-2}{5}$. Dom. $\{x:x \geq 7\}$, Range $\{y:y \geq 1\}$

6. (a) $\{-1 \leq x \leq 1\}$ (b) $\{x:x \geq 0)$ (c) $\{2 \leq x \leq 4\}$ (d) $\{x > 0\}$

     (e) $\{-3 \leq x \leq 1\}$ (f) $\{5 \leq x\}$ (g) $\{-3 \leq x\}$ (h) all x.

7. (a) No. restrict to $\{x \geq 0\}$ (b) yes. $\dfrac{x+4}{3}$ (c) yes. $\sqrt[3]{x}$

     (d) no. $\{-90° \leq x \leq 90°\}$ (e) no. $\{x \geq 1\}$ (f) yes. $\sqrt[3]{x} - 1$.

8.2.2 Page 55

3. (a) $x=0, y=0$ (b) $x=1, y=0$ (c) $x=1, y=0$ (d) $x=0, y=3$

     (e) $x=-3, y=2$ (f) $x=-2, y=1$

4. inverses of each other.

6. (a) $x=0$ (b) $x=0$ (c) $x=2$ (d) $x=-2$

     (e) $x=1\frac{1}{2}$ (f) $x=-\frac{1}{6}$

7. (a) $b=0, c=1$ (b) $b=-2, c=0$ (c) $b=2, c=1$

8. (a) $b=2, c=1$ (b) $b=0, c=-1$ (c) $b=-2, c=0$

9. (a) $b=0, a=1$ (b) $a=0, b=-2$ (c) $a=-1, b=1$

11. (a) $x=0, y=1$ (b) $y=0, x=2$ (c) $x=-1, y=-1$

12. 0.47

13. -0.39

14. 90°, 270°, 30°, 150°

15. 51°

16. (a) 27°, 207°   (b) 0.44   (c) 66°, 204°   (d) 0°, 60°, 180°, 300°

17. (a) even   (b) odd   (c) odd, periodic, period 360°.

     (d) even, periodic, 360° (e) odd   (f) even, periodic, 180°   (h) odd, periodic, 180°

     (j) odd, periodic, 60°   (k) odd, periodic, 720° (l) periodic, 180°

Chapter 9

9.1.2 Page 61

1. (a) 11.3   (b) 9.43

2. (a) 50.5   (b) 4.85

3. (a) 136.5°   (b) 129°

4. (a) 44.4° or 135.6°   (b) 124.5° or 5.47°

5. 4.22 & 3.60

6. $\hat{A} = 70.7°$ or 109.3°, $\hat{B} = 55.3°$ or 16.7°

7. 2807 m

8. 29.8 km

9. 54 m

10. 075° or 175°. 3.03 km or 0.25 km

11. (a) 3.88   (b) 7.30

12. (a) 46.6°   (b) 134.6°

13. 65.6°, 63.0°, 51.3°

14. 25.1

15. 81.8 miles

16. 5.35 km

17. 12.6 cm

18. 126.6°, 6.89

19. 6.4°

20. (a) 76°   (b) 92.8°

21. (a) 3.86   (b) 80.3

22. 33.8°

23. 36.9°

24. 4.25

25. 27.9 or 7.29

26. 45.5

28. 14.4 cm

9.2.2 Page 65

1. (a) 45°   (b) 90°   (c) 60°   (d) 54.7°

2. (a) 45°   (b) 45°   (c) 35.3°   (d) 0°

3. (a) 45°   (b) 54.7°   (c) 35.3°   (d) 90°

4. (a) 71°   (b) 61.5°   (c) 34.9°   (d) 81.2°

5. (a) 38.9°   (b) 70.5°   (c) 61.9°   (d) 69.3°

6. (a) 45°   (b) 47.1°   (c) 15.8°   (d) 21.8°

7. (a) 54.7°   (b) 70.5°

8. 70.3°

9. 31.2 m^2

10. 195 m

11. 52.2°

Chapter 10

10.1.2 Page 68

2. $\dfrac{5}{3}, \dfrac{4}{5}, \dfrac{3}{4}$

3. $\sqrt{5}, \dfrac{1}{\sqrt{5}}, \dfrac{2}{\sqrt{5}}$

4. $\dfrac{1-t^2}{1+t^2}, \dfrac{2t}{1-t^2}$

5. (a) $\sin^2 x$ (b) $2\sec^2 x$ (c) $\cos x \sin x$ (d) $\sin x \cos x$

7. (a) $x^2 + y^2 = 9$ (b) $\dfrac{x^2}{4} + \dfrac{y^2}{9} = 1$ (c) $y^2 - x^2 = 1$ (d) $\dfrac{y^2}{4} - 4x^2 = 1$

(e) $(x-1)^2 + (y-2)^2 = 1$ (f) $\left(\dfrac{x-3}{2}\right)^2 + \left(\dfrac{y-2}{3}\right)^2 = 1$

(g) $x^2 + y^2 = 2$ (h) $xy = 1$

10.2.2 Page 70

1. (a) $\sin 24°$ (b) $-\cos 40°$ (c) $-\tan 35°$ (d) $-\cot 50°$

(e) $\sec 10°$ (f) $\operatorname{cosec} 64°$

2. (a) 35°, 325°   (b) 36°, 126°, 216°, 306° (c) 103°, 317°   (d) 86°, 314°

(e) 76°, 284°   (f) 92°, 188°   (g) 44°   (h) 215°

(i) 24°, 216°   (j) 168°, 348°

3. 143°

4. 247°

5. $-\frac{15}{17}$ 6. $\frac{25}{7}$

7.   (a) $45°, 135°$ (b) $60°, 120°$ (c) $55°, 125°$ (d) $55°, 125°$

(e) $79°$ (f) $0°, 180°$ (g) $60°, 71°$ (h) $60°$

(i) $45°$

10.3.2 Page 72

1.   (a) $\sin 40°$ (b) $\cos 20°$ (c) $-\sin A$ (d) $\cos 4A$

2.   (a) $\frac{1}{2}\sin 80°$ (b) $\tan 40°$

3.   (a) $\sin(\theta + \alpha)$ (b) $\cos(\theta - \alpha)$

4.   (a) $\frac{1}{\sqrt{2}}\left(\frac{1}{2}\sqrt{3}+\frac{1}{2}\right)$ (b) $\frac{1}{\sqrt{2}}\left(\frac{1}{2}\sqrt{3}-\frac{1}{2}\right)$ (c) $\frac{1}{\sqrt{2}}\left(\frac{1}{2}\sqrt{3}-\frac{1}{2}\right)$ (d) $\frac{\sqrt{3}-1}{\sqrt{3}+1}$

(e) $\sqrt{\left(\frac{1}{2}\left(\frac{1}{\sqrt{2}}+1\right)\right)}$ (f) $\sqrt{2}-1$

5. $\frac{1}{2}$

6.   (a) $\frac{56}{65}$ (b) $\frac{16}{65}$ (c) $\frac{63}{65}$ (d) $\frac{56}{33}$

7.   (a) $0°, 180°, 32°$ (b) $39°$ (c) all angles   (d) $45°$

(e) $0°, 180°, 30°, 150°$ (f) no solutions

10. (a) $65°, 175°$ (b) $90°, 45°, 135°$ (c) $45°, 135°, 10°, 50°, 130°, 170°$ (d) $75°$

(e) $60°, 120°$ (f) $90°, 22\frac{1}{2}°, 112\frac{1}{2}°$

11. $4\cos^3 A - 3\cos A$ 12. $3\sin A - 4\sin^3 A$

10.4.2 Page 74

1.   (a) $5, 53.1°$ (b) $\sqrt{41}, -51°$ (c) $\sqrt{45}, 117°$ (d) $\sqrt{2}, -45°$

(e) $\sqrt{\left(\frac{5}{16}\right)}, 27°$ (f) $\sqrt{\left(\frac{145}{64}\right)}, -5°$

2.   (a) $5, 37°$ (b) $\sqrt{41}, 141°$ (c) $\sqrt{45}, -27°$ (d) $\sqrt{2}, 135°$

(e) $\sqrt{\left(\frac{5}{16}\right)}, 63°$ (f) $\sqrt{\left(\frac{145}{64}\right)}, 95°$

3.   (a) $-5 < f < 5$ (b) $-\sqrt{41} < f < \sqrt{41}$ (c) $-\sqrt{45} < f < \sqrt{45}$ (d) $-\sqrt{2} < f < \sqrt{2}$

(e) $-0.559 < f < 0.559$ (f) $-1.5052 < f < 1.5052$

4.   (a) $-40°, 108°$ (b) $79°, -157°$ (c) $9°, 73°$ (d) $96°, 170°$

5. $r=5, \alpha = 53.1°.\ s = 5, \beta = 36.9°.\ x = -23°, 97°.$

Chapter 11

11.1.2 Page 77

1.   (a) π (b) $\frac{\pi}{3}$ (c) $\frac{4\pi}{3}$ (d) $\frac{\pi}{6}$

(e) $\frac{\pi}{18}$

2. (a) 60°   (b) 74.5°   (c) 212°   (d) 720°

    (e) 45°

3. 5.24   4. 191

5. 1.75×10^{-3}, 1.45×10^{-4} 6. 70 m/s

7. 8.9

8. (a) 7.27×10^{-5} (b) 1.99×10^{-7}

9. 2 cm, 5 cm²   10. $\frac{1}{5}$

11. 4.55 cm   12. 13.1, 439

13. 45.3   14. $\frac{1}{2}ra$

15. (a) 0.201, 2.940   (b) 1.982, 4.301   (c) 1.107, 4.249   (d) 2.034, 5.176

    (e) 0, π, $\frac{3\pi}{4}$, $\frac{7\pi}{4}$ (f) 0.685, 2.457, 3.826, 5.598   (g) 1.994, 5.336

    (h) 0.507, 3.649   (i) $\frac{1}{2}\pi$, 6.12, 3.31

17. (a) $-\frac{\pi}{6}$ (b) π (c) $-\frac{\pi}{4}$ (d) 0

    (e) $\frac{\pi}{6}$ (f) $2 - \pi$

18. $\frac{1}{2}\pi$

11.2.2 Page 79

1. (a) 1   (b) 2   (c) $\frac{1}{2}$ (d) $\frac{1}{2}$

    (e) $\frac{4}{9}$ (f) $\frac{1+\theta}{1-\theta}$ (g) $\frac{1+2\theta}{1-2\theta}$

2. 2   3. $\frac{1}{2} + \frac{1}{2}\sqrt{3}\theta$

4. $-\frac{1}{2}\sqrt{3}$ 5. $1 - \frac{1}{2}\left(\frac{\pi}{90}\right)^2$

6. ± 0.45 7. 0.051

Chapter 12

12.1.2 Page 83

1. a, c

2. (a) 5   (b) $\sqrt{54}$ (c) $\sqrt{10}$ (d) $\sqrt{19.25}$

3. (a) (1,2)   (b) (−1, −5, −1)   (c) $(p-x, q-y)$ (d) $(1-x, 2y-3, z)$

4. $\frac{1}{2}(\mathbf{b} - \mathbf{a})$ 6. $\mathbf{a+c}$, $\frac{1}{2}(\mathbf{a} + \mathbf{c})$

7. $\frac{1}{2}(\mathbf{a+b})$, $\frac{1}{2}(\mathbf{b+c})$, $\frac{1}{2}(\mathbf{c+d})$, $\frac{1}{2}(\mathbf{d+a})$. $\frac{1}{2}(\mathbf{c-a})$, $\frac{1}{2}(\mathbf{d-b})$, $\frac{1}{2}(\mathbf{c-a})$, $\frac{1}{2}(\mathbf{d-b})$

Parallelogram.

8. $\frac{1}{2}(\mathbf{b} + \mathbf{c})$ 9. $2\mathbf{a} - \mathbf{b}$

10. 0.6   11. $\mathbf{b}$, $\mathbf{a} - \mathbf{b}$, $-\mathbf{b}$, $2\mathbf{a} - 2\mathbf{b}$

12.2.2 Page 84

1. (a) 11   (b) 18   (c) 9   (d) −7

2. (a) 10.3°   (b) 55.3°   (c) 47.9°   (d) 112.4°

3. −1   4. $(7, -2)$

5. $\left(\frac{24}{25}, -\frac{7}{25}\right)$ 6. $x = -1.8, y = -5.1$

7. $(3, -4, -1)$ 8. $\left(\frac{1}{\sqrt{2}}, -\frac{1}{\sqrt{2}}, 0\right)$

9. $\sqrt{10}$ 10. $\dfrac{3}{\sqrt{10}}$

16. $(-0.72, 0.96)$, 1.2   17. $(-2.8, -0.6)$, 8.

12.3.2 Page 86

1. (a) $(1,1,2)+ \lambda(2,1,7)$ (b) $(1,0,3)+ \lambda(4,2,0)$ (c) $(1,3,1)+ \lambda(1,2,1)$ (d) $(1,2,-1)+ (0,-4,2)$

2. (a) $\dfrac{x-1}{2} = \dfrac{y-1}{1} = \dfrac{z-2}{7}$ (b) $\dfrac{x-1}{4} = \dfrac{y}{2} = \dfrac{z-3}{0}$

   (c) $\dfrac{x-1}{1} = \dfrac{y-3}{2} = \dfrac{z-1}{1}$ (d) $\dfrac{x-1}{0} = \dfrac{y-2}{-4} = \dfrac{z+1}{2}$

3. (a) $t = 3$ (b) $t = -2$

4. (a) 40.5°   (b) 98°

5. (a) $(1,2,3)+ \lambda(1,1,1)+ \mu(1,0,1)$ (b) $(1,2,1)+ (1,-1,2)+ \mu(0,3,0)$

6. (a) $\mathbf{r}.(2,1,-1)= 3$ (b) $\mathbf{r}.(0,0,1)= 4$ (c) $\mathbf{r}.(1,-1,0)= 0$ (d) $\mathbf{r}.(1,1,1)= 5$

7. (a) 25°   (b) 14°   (c) 17°

8. (a) 60°   (b) 50°   (c) 60°

9. (a) 0.816   (b) 1.67

10. $(3,1,-1)$. 79°   11. $\left(\frac{1}{2},1,-1\right)$. 47°

Chapter 13

13.1.2 Page 92

1. (a) $3x^2$ (b) $35x^4$ (c) $6x+2$ (d) $-2+20x^4$

   (e) $-6x^{-4}$ (f) $2+12x^{-5}$ (g) $2x^{-1/2}$ (h) $-9x^{-4}-x^{-3/2}$

   (i) $-21x^{-4}$ (j) $-2x^{-2}+24x^{-4}$ (k) $\frac{1}{2}x^{-1/2}$ (l) $\frac{3}{2}x^{-1/2}+\frac{7}{2}x^{-3/2}$

   (m) $10x^4+30x^{-7}-\frac{7}{4}x^{-5/4}$ (n) $-x^{-3/2}+9x^{-2}$

2. (a) $2x-3$ (b) $2x-5$ (c) $-15x^4+6x^2-24x$ (d) $2-6x^{-3}-9x^{-4}$

   (e) $2x+4$ (f) $24x+16x^3$ (g) $-12x^{-2}-18x^{-3}$ (h) $18x-32x^{-3}$

   (i) $\frac{3}{2}x^{1/2}-2x^{-1/2}$ (j) $1-\frac{1}{2}x^{-1/2}$ (k) $-3x^{-4}-68x^{-5}$ (l) $2-x^{-2}$

   (m) $\frac{1}{2}x^{-1/2}-4x^{-3/2}$ (n) $-\frac{1}{6}x^{-7/6}+\frac{1}{4}x^{-5/4}-\frac{3}{2}x^{-3/2}$

3. (a) $6x$ (b) 4   (c) $12x^2-24x$ (d) $-\frac{3}{4}x^{-3/2}-12x^{-4}$

13.2.2 Page 94

1. (a) $y = 4x - 4$ (b) $y = x - 2$ (c) $y = -13x - 1$ (d) $y = \frac{1}{8}x$

2. (a) $y = -\frac{1}{4}x + 4\frac{1}{2}$ (b) $y = -x$ (c) $13y = x + 157$ (d) $y = -8x + 32\frac{1}{2}$

3. $x = -\frac{2}{3}$ 4. $\pm \sqrt{\frac{1}{3}}$

6. $7\frac{1}{4}$

13.3.2 Page 96

1. (a) (1,–1)min (b) (2,6)max (c) (1,–2)min, (–1,2)max

   (d) (2,24)max,(3,23)min (e) (1,2)min, (–1,–2)max (f) (2,3)min

2. (a) none (b) none (c) (0,0) (d) (2.5,23.5)

   (e) none (f) none

3. 6 4. $a = -\frac{3}{4}$, $b = 3$

5. 11.7 cm 6. 12.6 cm

7. 10 cm 8. 4.3 cm

9. 7.69 cm 10. 25 m by 50 m

12. 7 cm 13. $(0, 2-m)$, $(1 - 2/m, 0)$, $m=\pm 2$

14. 5 (a) £2.89 (b) £3.63

Chapter 14

14.1.2 Page 100

1. (a) $(x^2+7x-3)+ x(2x+7)$ (b) $(2x^3+6x)+ (x+3)(6x^2+6)$

   (c) $2x(3x^5 -3x^2+x)+ x^2(15x^4 -6x+1)$ (d) $2x(x^2+1)+ 2x(x^2-1)$

2. (a) $\dfrac{(x + 3) - x}{(x + 3)^2}$ (b) $\dfrac{(2x + 7)(x^2 + 3) - 2x(x^2 + 7x - 2)}{(x^2 + 3)^2}$

   (c) $\dfrac{6x(x - 17) - 3x^2}{(x - 17)^2}$ (d) $\dfrac{-1}{(x + 3)^2}$

3. $y = 4. 3y + 4x = 27$

4. (a) (0,0)max, (2,4)min (b) (0.414,0.828)min, (–2.414,–4.828)max (c) (0,1)max

   (d) $(-2, \frac{1}{5})$max

14.2.2 Page 102

1. (a) $1\frac{1}{2}(3x+7)^{-1/2}$ (b) $-10x(2-x^2)^4$ (c) $2x(1+2x^2)^{-1/2}$ (d) $-\frac{1}{2}(1+x)^{-3/2}$

   (e) $\frac{1}{2}(2x+1)(1+x+x^2)^{-1/2}$ (f) $200x(1+x^2)^{99}$

2. (a) $(1+2x)^{1/2} + x(1+2x)^{-1/2}$ (b) $(x-17)^{21}+ 21(x+3)(x-17)^{20}$

   (c) $\dfrac{\sqrt{(x^2 + 1)} - x(x + 4)(x^2 + 1)^{-1/2}}{x^2 + 1}$ (d) $\dfrac{x^{-1/2} (\sqrt{x} + 1) - 1}{2(\sqrt{x} + 1)^2}$

3. $y = \frac{1}{2}x + 1\frac{1}{2}. y + 2x = 4$

14.3.2 Page 103

1. (a) $3\cos 3x$ (b) $-4\sin 4x$ (c) $2e^{2x-1}$ (d) $5\sec^2(5x-3)$

   (e) $-15\cos 3x - 8\cos 4x$ (f) $-\sin x\, e^{\cos x}$ (g) $\dfrac{2}{2x-3}$

   (h) $-\tan x$ (i) $\cos x - x\sin x$ (j) $2x\sin x + x^2\cos x$ (k) $e^x(\tan x + \sec^2 x)$

   (l) $\ln x + 1$ (m) $e^x\ln x + \dfrac{e^x}{x}$ (n) $-e^{-x}\sin 2x + 2e^{-x}\cos 2x$

   (o) $-3\sin 3x\sin 2x + 2\cos 3x\cos 2x$ (p) $-2x\sin(1+x^2)$

   (q) $\sin(1+3x^2) + 6x^2\cos(1+3x^2)$ (r) $-2\cos x\sin x$

   (s) $9\cos 3x\sin^2 3x$ (t) $\dfrac{\cos x + x\sin x}{\cos^2 x}$

   (u) $\dfrac{2x(\cos x + \sin x) - x^2(\cos x - \sin x)}{(\cos x + \sin x)^2}$ (v) $\dfrac{-2\cos x\sin x\ln x - \dfrac{\cos^2 x}{x}}{(\ln x)^2}$

   (w) $-x(x^2+3)^{-1/2}\sin\sqrt{(x^2+x)}$ (x) $-2e^x\sin x$

   (y) 0 (z) 1

3. $-\text{cosec}^2 x,\ \sec x\tan x,\ -\cot x\,\text{cosec}\,x$

4. $(\ln 10)10^x$ 5. $\dfrac{1}{x\ln 10}$

6. $(\ln a)\,a^x,\ \dfrac{1}{x\ln a}$

7. (a) $(0,0)$min. $(-2, 4e^{-2})$ max. (b) $(-\tfrac{1}{2}, \ln\tfrac{3}{4})$min.

14.4.2 Page 105

1. (a) $-\tfrac{1}{2}$ (b) $\tfrac{1}{2}$ (c) $-\tfrac{1}{4}$ (d) ∞

   (e) 3 (f) $-1\tfrac{1}{3}$ (g) $-\tfrac{1}{2}$ (h) -10

2. (a) $-\dfrac{x}{y}$ (b) $\dfrac{3-2x}{3y^2+1}$ (c) $\dfrac{2x+4y}{2y-4x}$ (d) $\dfrac{-(2x+9yx^2)}{3x^2+4}$

4. $y = 1\tfrac{1}{4}x - \tfrac{1}{4}$ 5. $\pm\dfrac{2}{\sqrt 3}$

6. $\pm\dfrac{2}{\sqrt 3}$

7. (a) $3t$ (b) $-2t(1+t)^2$ (c) $\dfrac{2t-3t^2}{1-4t}$ (d) $\dfrac{2t(1+t)^2}{(1+t^2)^2}$

   (e) $\dfrac{1}{t}$ (f) $-\dfrac{1}{t^2}$ (g) $-\cot t$ (h) $-\tfrac{2}{3}\cot t$

   (i) $\dfrac{e^t + e^{-t}}{e^t - e^{-t}}$ (j) $1\tfrac{1}{2}\sin t$

8. $3y + 4x = 12\sqrt 2$ 9. $3y + x = 26$

10. $0.4\ \text{cm}^2$ 11. $0.27\ \text{cm}^3$

12. 3.2×10^{-4}

13. 95 cm^3

14. 8.6×10^{-3}, 0.58

15. 2%

16. 2%

17. $15 \text{ cm}^2/\text{s}$

18. $3 \text{ cm}^2 \text{ s}^{-1}$, $9 \text{ cm}^3 \text{ s}^{-1}$

19. 0.07 cm s^{-1}

20. 0.014 cm s^{-1}

21. $\frac{1}{16} \text{ cm s}^{-1}$, $3 \text{ cm}^2 \text{ s}^{-1}$

22. 0.293 m s^{-1}

Chapter 15

15.1.2 Page 111

1. (a) $y = x^2 + 1$
   (b) $y = x^3 + \frac{1}{2}x^2 - \frac{1}{2}$
   (c) $y = \frac{1}{3}x^3 + \frac{1}{2}x^2 + x + \frac{7}{6}$
   (d) $y = 2 - \frac{1}{x}$

   (e) $y = \frac{2}{5}x^{5/2} - 11.8$
   (f) $y = 6\sqrt{x} - 20$
   (g) $y = \frac{1}{4}x^4 + \frac{1}{2}x^2 - \frac{3}{4}$
   (h) $y = \frac{2}{5}x^{5/2} + 6\sqrt{x} - 21.8$

2. (a) $x^2 + c$
   (b) $x^3 + x^2 + x + c$
   (c) $\frac{1}{3}x^3 + \frac{1}{2}x^4 + 5x + c$
   (d) $\frac{1}{3}x^6 - \frac{5}{16}x^8 + c$

   (e) $\frac{2}{5}x^{5/2} + c$
   (f) $3x - \frac{2}{3}x^{3/2} + c$
   (g) $c - \frac{1}{2}x^{-2}$
   (h) $-\frac{2}{x} - \frac{7}{2x^2} + 2x + c$

   (i) $\frac{3}{4}x^4 + \frac{7}{2}x^2 + c$
   (j) $\frac{1}{4}x^4 - \frac{1}{3}x^3 - 3x^2 + c$
   (k) $x^4 - \frac{2}{5}x^5 + c$

   (l) $\frac{x^{5.5}}{5.5} + \frac{x^{4.5}}{4.5} - 2x^{1.5} - 6x^{0.5} + c$

15.2.2 Page 112

1. (a) 36
   (b) 0.283
   (c) $14\frac{2}{3}$
   (d) $43\frac{1}{2}$

   (e) 10.4
   (f) 45.43

2. (a) $8\frac{2}{3}$
   (b) 0.95
   (c) 6
   (d) $-\frac{1}{4}$

3. $10\frac{2}{3}$

4. (a) $\frac{1}{4}$
   (b) $-\frac{1}{4}$

5. (a) $\frac{1}{6}$
   (b) $\frac{7}{6}$

6. 12

7. 0.15625, -32.15625

8. (a) 64
   (b) 1.5
   (c) $5\frac{1}{3}$
   (d) 4

9. $\frac{4}{15}$

10. $\frac{37}{24}$

15.3.2 Page 114

1. (a) 175.3
   (b) 14.1
   (c) 2.83
   (d) 64.9

   (e) 490
   (f) 37.7

2. $4, 12, 603$

4. Sphere. 4.189

5. $y = x + 1$, 27.2

6. $2\frac{2}{3}a^2$, $2\pi a^3$

Chapter 16

16.1.2 Page 118

1. (a) $-\frac{1}{2}\cos 2x + c$ (b) $2\sin\frac{1}{2}x + c$ (c) $-\frac{1}{3}\cos(3x-1) + c$ (d) $2\sin(2x+3) + c$

    (e) $\frac{1}{3}e^{3x} + c$ (f) $\frac{1}{2}e^{2x+1} + c$ (g) $\ln(x+3) + c$ (h) $\frac{1}{2}\ln(2x-5) + c$

2. $\frac{1}{5}$ 3. 23

4. 3.37   5. 25.9

6. 0.649   7. $\frac{1}{2}\ln(1+a)$

8. 0.693   9. 0.847

10. $\frac{2}{9}(x^3+4)^{3/2} + c$ 11. $2\sin\sqrt{x} + c$

12. $\frac{1}{4}\tan^4 x + c$ 13. $\ln(\ln x) + c$

14. $0.4(x+3)^{5/2} - 2(x+3)^{3/2} + c$ 15. $\frac{4}{27}(1+3x)^{3/2} - \frac{4}{9}(1+3x)^{1/2} + c$

16. $\frac{2}{7}(1+x)^{7/2} - 0.8(1+x)^{5/2} + c$ 17. $-\frac{1}{6}(3x-1)^2 + c$

18. $\frac{1}{256}(1+4x)^{16} - \frac{1}{240}(1+4x)^{15} + c$ 19. $\frac{1}{14}(x+2)^{14} - \frac{5}{13}(x+2)^{13} + c$

20. $\sin x - \frac{1}{3}\sin^3 x + c$ 21. $-\cos x + \frac{2}{3}\cos^3 x - 0.2\cos^5 x + c$

22. $\ln(1 - e^{-x}) + c$ 23. $\frac{1}{2}x + \frac{1}{4}\sin 2x + c$

24. $\frac{1}{2}x - \frac{1}{12}\sin 6x + c$ 25. $\dfrac{1}{1+x} - \dfrac{1}{2+x} \cdot \ln(1+x) - \ln(2+x) + c$

26. (a) $\ln(2+x) - \ln(3+x) + c$ (b) $2\ln(2+x) - 2\ln(1+x) - \dfrac{3}{1+x} + c$

    (c) $\frac{1}{2}\ln(1+2x) - \frac{1}{3}\ln(1-3x) + c$

16.2.2 Page 120

1. $-xe^{-x} - e^{-x} + c$ 2. $x\sin x + \cos x + c$

3. $-x\cos x + \sin x + c$ 4. $\frac{1}{2}x^2 \ln x - \frac{1}{4}x^2 + c$

5. $\frac{1}{3}x^3 \ln x - \frac{1}{9}x^3 + c$ 6. $\dfrac{x^{n+1}}{n+1}\ln x - \dfrac{x^{n+1}}{(n+1)^2} + c$

7. $x\sin^{-1}x + \sqrt{(1-x^2)} + c$ 8. $x\tan^{-1}x - \frac{1}{2}\ln(1+x^2) + c$

9. $x^2 e^x - 2xe^x + 2e^x + c$ 10. $\dfrac{x^2 e^{ax}}{a} - \dfrac{2xe^{ax}}{a^2} + \dfrac{2e^{ax}}{a^3} + c$

11. $\frac{1}{3}x^2 \sin 3x + \frac{2}{9}x\cos 3x - \frac{2}{27}\sin 3x + c$ 12. $xe^x - 4e^x + c$

13. $-\dfrac{x^2}{a}\cos ax + \dfrac{2x}{a^2}\sin ax + \dfrac{2}{a^3}\cos ax + c$ 14. $-\dfrac{1}{x}\ln(x) - \dfrac{1}{x} + c$

Chapter 17

17.1.2 Page 124

1. -0.2 2. -0.166796

3. $2, 3, 2\frac{1}{3}$ 4. 2.48558

5. 0.442854

6. 0.510973

7. 1.132268

8. 0.739

9. 0.682

10. 2.058

11. 0.443

12. 0.382

17.2.2 Page 126

1. 2.135

2. 0.6295

3. 10.6875

4. (a) 1   (b) 0.987

5. 316

6. 0.806

7. 28.65, 74.625

Chapter 18

18.1.2 Page 131

1. (a) $1 - 2x^2 + \frac{2}{3}x^4$ (b) $3x - 4\frac{1}{2}x^3 + \frac{81}{40}x^5$ (c) $1 + 3x + 4\frac{1}{2}x^2$ (d) $1 - 2x + 2x^2$

   (e) $x + x^2 + \frac{1}{3}x^3$ (f) $1 - x + \frac{1}{3}x^3$ (g) $2x - 2x^2 + \frac{8}{3}x^3$ (h) $-x^2 - \frac{1}{2}x^4 - \frac{1}{3}x^6$

2. (a) 1.646   (b) 0.969   (c) 0.0998   (d) 0.366

   (e) 0.0954   (f) −0.223

3. $x - \frac{2}{3}x^3$

4. $1 - x^2 + \frac{1}{3}x^4$

5. $x - \frac{1}{2}x^2 + \frac{1}{3}x^3 - ...$

6. $\ln 2 + \frac{1}{2}x - \frac{1}{8}x^2 + \frac{1}{24}x^3 - ...$

7. $\frac{1}{2}$

8. (a) $\frac{1}{2}$ (b) 0   (c) 1   (d) 2

9. $1 + x\ln 2 + \frac{(x\ln 2)^2}{2!} + \frac{(x\ln 2)^3}{3!} + ...$

10. $\frac{\ln 2}{\ln 3}$

11. $1 - x + \frac{1}{2}x^2.\ x = 0.59$

12. (a) 0.32   (b) 0.

13. $\frac{1}{1-x} + \frac{1}{1+x} \cdot 2 + 2x^2$

14. (a) $2 - 5x + 13x^2. -\frac{1}{3} < x < \frac{1}{3}$ (b) $4 - 3.5x + 3.25x^2. -1 < x < 1$

    (c) $2 - x + 4x^2. -1 < x < 1$ (d) $-1 + 2x - x^2. -1 < x < 1$

18.2.2 Page 133

3. (a) $x + \frac{x^3}{6}$ (b) $\frac{1}{2}\pi - x - \frac{x^3}{6}$ (c) $1 + \frac{1}{2}x^2$ (d) $1 + x + \frac{1}{2}x^2 + \frac{1}{2}x^3$

5. $\frac{1}{2} - \frac{1}{2}\sqrt{3}x - \frac{1}{4}x^2$

6. $2 + 2x + 2x^2 + 2x^3$

Chapter 19

19.1.2 Page 136

1. (a) $y = Ae^{x^2}$

   (b) $y = \sqrt{(x^2 + c)}$

   (c) $y = Ae^{-\frac{1}{2}x^2} - 1$

   (d) $y = \cos^{-1}(c - \sin x)$

   (e) $y = \dfrac{Ax}{1 - Ax}$

   (f) $y = -\ln(-\ln Ax)$

2. (a) $y = e^{\frac{1}{2}(x^2 - 1)}$

   (b) $y = \frac{4}{3} x$

   (c) $y = \dfrac{-1}{\ln e(1 + x)}$

   (d) $y = e^{-\cos x}$

   (e) $y = -\ln\left(-\ln\dfrac{x}{e}\right)$

3. $y = Ax^2.$

   (a) $y = 2x^2$

   (b) $y = -x^2$

   (c) $y = 0$

4. $y = \dfrac{x}{cx + 1}$

   (a) $y = x$

   (b) $y = \dfrac{x}{x + 1}$

   (c) $y = \dfrac{x}{1 - 0.5\,x}$

5. $y = Ae^x - 1 - x$

6. (a) $y = \tan(x+c) - x$

   (b) $y = Ae^{0.5x} - x$

7. (a) $y = 1 - Ae^{-x} - x$

   (b) $y = Ae^{2x} - \frac{3}{4} - 1\frac{1}{2}x$

8. (a) $y = x \ln x + cx$

   (b) $y = x \tan(\ln x + c)$

   (c) $y = x \sin(\ln x + c)$

10. (a) $\dfrac{dy}{dx} = 2y$

    (b) $\dfrac{dy}{dx} = -3y$

    (c) $\dfrac{dy}{dx} = \dfrac{4y}{x}$

    (d) $\dfrac{d^2y}{dx^2} = -y$

    (e) $\dfrac{d^2y}{dx^2} = -4y$

    (f) $\dfrac{d^2y}{dx^2} = -y$

19.2.2 Page 138

1. $\dfrac{dP}{dt} = 0.03P.$ $P = P_0 e^{0.03t}.$ $t = 23.1$

2. $A = 2^{t/10}$

3. $h = 6 \times 2^{-t/12}$

4. $M = M_0 e^{-t/1000}.$ 693

5. $p = \dfrac{1}{1 + 9e^{-t/10}}.$ $t = 22$

6. Amount $= \dfrac{1}{1 + 9 \times 2.25^{-t/100}}.$ $t = 317$ s.

7. $\dfrac{dM}{dt} = kM(10 - M).$ $M = \dfrac{10}{1 + 4 \times 4^{-t}}.$ 2.58 hours.

19.3.2 Page 139

1. (a) 2.86

   (b) 1.742

   (c) 0.3995

2. (a) 8

   (b) 6. 25%

3. 2.88. 3.09

Chapter 20

20.1.2 Page 142

1. (a) $\frac{1}{36}$

   (b) $\frac{1}{36}$

   (c) $\frac{1}{6}$

   (d) $\frac{5}{12}$

   (e) $\frac{1}{6}$

   (f) $\frac{11}{36}$

2. (a) $\frac{1}{4}$ (b) $\frac{1}{17}$ (c) $\frac{13}{204}$ (d) $\frac{4}{663}$

3. (a) $\frac{5}{18}$ (b) $\frac{4}{9}$ (c) $\frac{5}{6}$ (d) $\frac{4}{9}$

4. (a) $\frac{20}{171}$ (b) $\frac{31}{57}$ (c) $\frac{91}{171}$

5. (a) $\frac{1}{36}$ (b) $\frac{11}{36}$

6. (a) $\frac{1}{9}$ (b) $\frac{4}{9}$

7. (a) $\frac{1}{6}$ (b) $\frac{5}{36}$ (c) $\frac{25}{216}$ (d) $\frac{125}{216}$

8. (a) $\frac{1}{80}$ (b) $\frac{567}{6400}$

9. (a) $\frac{1}{32}$ (b) $\frac{31}{32}$

10. (a) $\frac{1}{81}$ (b) $\frac{65}{81}$

11. (a) $\frac{32}{243}$ (b) $\frac{211}{243}$

20.2.2 Page 145

1. A & C, A & D, B & C, B & D indep. None exc.

2. A & C, A & D indep. B & C, C & D excl.

3. A & B indep. C & D exclusive   4. A & D indep. B & C excl.

5. (a) $\frac{4}{51}$ (b) $\frac{13}{51}$

6. (a) $\frac{1}{5}$ (b) $\frac{1}{6}$

7. (a) $\frac{1}{6}$ (b) 0

8. (a) $\frac{1}{4}$ (b) $\frac{3}{4}$

9. $\frac{6}{10}$

10. (a) $\frac{35}{68}$ (b) $\frac{5}{8}$ (c) $\frac{1}{2}$

11. (a) $\frac{1}{100}$ (b) $\frac{612}{625}$ (c) $\frac{25}{52}$

12. (a) 0.9712   (b) 0.3125   (c) 0.999

13. $\frac{7}{8}$ 14. $\frac{4}{9}$

15. $\frac{5}{6}$ 16. 0.1, $\frac{1}{2}$

17. 0.15, 0.55. 0.375

18. (a) 0.8, 0   (b) 0.65, 0.15

Chapter 21

21.1.2 Page 152

1. (a) 15.1   (b) 1.36   (c) $63\frac{2}{3}$ (d) 118.5

2. (a) 14   (b) 1.3   (c) $63\frac{1}{2}$ (d) 117

3. (a) 14.7   (b) 1.32   (c) 63.5   (d) 117.9

4. (a) 12.1, 3.48   (b) 0.0984, 0.314   (c) 20.6, 4.53   (d) 138, 11.74

5. (a) 153, 1210   (b) 15.6, 9.84   (c) 639, 2060   (d) 1187, 13800

6. 6.2, 0.96   7. 3.633, 0.875

8. 21.1, 8.8, 21.6

9. 1.55, 1.52, 0.63

10. 14.2

11. (a) 50   (b) 60   (c) 20   (d) 40, 50

12. $38 + 0.2x$

21.2.2 Page 154

8. 61.5, 51 & 67.5. 93 an outlier

9. 13, 11.5 & 15. 1 and 28 outliers

Chapter 22

22.1.2 Page 159

1. 4 m s^{-1}, 10 m

2. 1.5 m s^{-1}, 75 m

3. 10 s

4. 0.02 s

5. $\frac{5}{9} \text{ m s}^{-2}$, $6\frac{2}{3} \text{ m s}^{-1}$

6. 11.4 s

7. 75 m

8. 4 s

9. 0.8 m s^{-2}, 5 s

10. 3.194 s, 31.3 m s^{-1}

11. 2.33 s, 32.86 m s^{-1}

12. 11.48 m, 5.35 s, 37.43 m s^{-1}

13. 15 s, $6\frac{2}{3} \text{ m s}^{-1}$

14. 40.65 m

15. $1\frac{1}{3} \text{ m s}^{-2}$

16. $13\frac{1}{8}$ s

17. 30 s, 1.5 m s^{-2}.

22.2.2 Page 161

1. 6, –126

2. (a) 4   (b) 4   (c) 0.71 s   (d) 1.09

3. 4, 5, 4.5 m

4. 3, 22.5

5. $4, 5\frac{1}{3}$, 6 s, $10\frac{2}{3}$

6. 164 m s^{-1}, 95 m

7. (a) 121 m s^{-1} (b) 1764 m   (c) 32 s, 362 m s^{-1}

8. (a) 2.73 s, 6.13 m   (b) 4.37 s, 8.37 m s^{-1}

9. 6 s, 21 m s^{-1}.

22.3.2 Page 163

1. (a) $3\mathbf{i} + 14t\mathbf{j}$ (b) $3t^2\mathbf{i} - 4t\mathbf{j}$ (c) $-\sin t\, \mathbf{i} + \cos t\, \mathbf{j}$ (d) $2\cos 2t\, \mathbf{i} - 6\sin 2t\, \mathbf{j} + \mathbf{k}$

2. (a) $\sqrt{(9 + 196t^2)}$ (b) $\sqrt{(9t^4 + 16t^2)}$ (c) 1   (d) $\sqrt{(4\cos^2 2t + 36\sin^2 2t + 1)}$

3. (a) $14\mathbf{j}$ (b) $6t\mathbf{i} - 4\mathbf{j}$ (c) $-\cos t\, \mathbf{i} - \sin t\, \mathbf{j}$ (d) $-4\sin 2t\, \mathbf{i} - 12\cos 2t\, \mathbf{j}$

4. (a) $3t\mathbf{i} + 5t\mathbf{j}$ (b) $\frac{1}{2}t^2\mathbf{i} + 1\frac{1}{2}t^2\mathbf{j} - 2\frac{1}{2}t^2\mathbf{k}$

     (c) $\frac{1}{2}\sin 2t\, \mathbf{i} + (\frac{1}{3}\cos 3t - \frac{1}{3})\mathbf{j}$ (d) $(e^t - 1)\mathbf{i} - (1\frac{1}{2}e^{2t} - 1\frac{1}{2})\mathbf{j}$

6. (a) $t = \frac{1}{2}$ (b) $t = 2$

7. $-\mathbf{i} + \mathbf{j}$. $t = 3$

8. $\mathbf{i} + (2t+1)\mathbf{j}$. $t = 2$

Chapter 23

23.1.2 Page 167

1. 49 N

2. 30 N

3. 24 N

4. $\frac{1}{3}$ kg

5. 3 m s^{-2}

6. 4000 N

7. 950 N

8. 100.8 N

9. 10000 N

10. 50000N

11. 980 N

12. 2.95 N

13. 0.3 m s^{-2}

14. 0.976 kg

15. 4.8 m s^{-2}

16. 653 N. 3.27 m s^{-2}

17. 78.93 kg

18. 0.588 m s^{-2}

19. 69.87 kg

20. 1.25 kg

21. 2.45 m s^{-2}

22. 8.93 kg

23. $1\frac{1}{2}\mathbf{i} + \mathbf{j}$

24. $(4 + 4t)\mathbf{i} + 48\mathbf{j}$

25. $4t\mathbf{i} + 10t^2\mathbf{j}$. $\mathbf{v} = 2t^2\mathbf{i} + 3\frac{1}{3}t^3\mathbf{j}$. $\mathbf{s} = \frac{2}{3}t^3\mathbf{i} + \frac{5}{6}t^4\mathbf{j}$

26. $2\frac{1}{2}\cos t\,\mathbf{i} + 2\frac{1}{2}\sin t\,\mathbf{j}$. $v = 2\frac{1}{2}\sin t\,\mathbf{i} + (2\frac{1}{2} - 2\frac{1}{2}\cos t)\mathbf{j}$ $\mathbf{s} = (-2\frac{1}{2}\cos t + 3\frac{1}{2})\mathbf{i} + (2\frac{1}{2}t - 2\frac{1}{2}\sin t)\mathbf{j}$

23.2.2 Page 169

1. 3250 N, 1150 N

2. 24000 N & 12000 N

3. 20000 N & 40000 N

4. 2.45 m s^{-2}, 36.75 N, 73.5 N

5. 3.27 m s^{-2}, $65\frac{1}{3}$ N, $130\frac{2}{3}$ N

7. 3.675 m s^{-2}, 18.375 N

8. 3.267 m s^{-2}, $32\frac{2}{3}$ N

10. 1.4 m s^{-2}, 42 N, 33.6 N

11. 31 N

12. 9.6 N

Chapter 24

24.1.2 Page 174

1. 6.2 N, 23.2 N

2. (a) 9.8 N   (b) 0   (c) 0.018   (d) −25.4

3. 7.3 N, 227°

4. (a) 24.8 N, 133.4°   (b) 5N, 336.9°   (c) 69.3 N, 181.4°   (d) 17 N, 186.6°

5. 15 N, 225°

6. (a) 34.2 N, 2.2°   (b) 2.1 N, 141.3°   (c) 48.3 N,162.5°

7. 1 m s^{-2}, 24°

8. 2 m s^{-2}, 346.6°

9. 20.7 N

10. 144.9 N

11. 0.35 m s^{-2}

12. 195 N

13. 0.19 m s^{-2}

24.2.2 Page 176

1. 5.62 m s^{-2}

3. 92.1 N, 35.67 N

4. 82.8 N

5. 1.45 m s^{-1}

6. 0.38 m s^{-2}

7. 1.63 m s^{-2}, 32.7 N

8. 8 kg

9. 2.9 kg

10. 2.1 kg

11. 2.67 m s^{-2}

12. 3.54 kg

13. 14.3 kg

14. 63 N, 21.4°

15. 12.5 N

16. 27.7 N

17. 46.5 N, 38°

18. 32 N, 49.3 N

19. 46.9 N & 36.5 N

20. 29.4°

21. 46.4 N, 26°

22. 45°, 37.4°

Chapter 25

25.1.2 Page 180

1. 29.4 N

2. 0.57

3. 2.55 m

4. 24 N

5. 0.46

6. 1.57 m s^{-2}

7. 34.4 N

8. 0.235

9. 26.6°

12. 8.33 N, 21.1 N

13. (a) 3.4 s   (b) 4.5 s   (c) 3.1 s

14. (a) 112.7 N   (b) 100.8 N   (c) 103.6 N

15. (a) 183.75 N   (b) 198.4 N   (c) 215.1 N

16. 6.85 N, 13.42 N

17. 5.39 m s^{-2}

18. 0.184

19. 4.1 m s^{-2}

Chapter 26

26.1.2 Page 183

1. (a) 16 N   (b) 300 N   (c) 14 N

2. (a) $1\frac{1}{3}$ m   (b) $3\frac{1}{3}$ m   (c) 10.8 m

3. $1\frac{1}{3}$ m from centre

4. 50 kg

5. 0.7 m from one end

6. 2.5 kg

7. 12.5 kg

8. 8 kg

9. 58.8 N

10. 1.6 m from pivot

11. 23.5g N, 26.5g N

12. $1\frac{1}{8}$ m from end

13. 280g N, 210g N,

14. 0.3g N, 0.35g N

26.2.2 Page 186

1. (a) 10 N   (b) 9.4 N   (c) 13.5 N

2. (a) 3.62 m   (b) 0.23 m   (c) 1.47 m

3. (a) 50.3°   (b) 53.1°   (c) 81.8°

4. 2.31 N

5. 22.6 N

6. 5 N

7. 17°

8. 6.1g N

9. 45.6°

10. 0.182

11. 170 N

12. 44 N

13. 26.6°

14. 29.2 N, 0.6

Chapter 27

27.1.2 Page 190

1. $x=5$

2. $(\frac{2}{3}, 0)$

3. $\frac{2}{3}$ kg

4. $(-8\frac{1}{2}, 0)$

5. 18.53 cm from base

6. 1.23 m from base

7. $4\frac{1}{3}$ cm from top of head

8. $\frac{1}{11}$ m from centre

9. $\frac{2}{11}$ m from centre

10. $11\frac{2}{3}$ from bottom

11. 3.35 cm from base

12. 7.71 cm from base

13. 3.37 cm from base

14. $\frac{1}{33}$ cm from centre

15. $\frac{1}{333}$ from centre

27.2.2 Page 192

1. (1.3, 0.4)

2. 5 kg

3. $(8, 11\frac{3}{4})$

4. (a) (5, 3)   (b) (2.86, 3.82)   (c) (2.93, 3.91)

5. $(1\frac{1}{4}, 1\frac{1}{4})$

6. (2.042, 1.042)

7. (4.73, 1.13)

8. $(2\frac{1}{2}, \frac{3}{4}, 2\frac{11}{12})$

9. (29, 65, 85)

27.3.2 Page 194

1. $(\frac{3}{4}, 0.3)$

2. $(\frac{5}{6}, 0)$

3. (0.4, 0.43)

4. (1.39, 0.29)

5. $(1.29, 0)$

6. $(1\frac{1}{8}, 3.6)$

7. $(0, 3)$

8. $(\frac{15}{16}, 0)$

11. $(0, \frac{4a}{3\pi})$

12. $(0, \frac{3}{8}a)$

27.4.2 Page 196

1. $36.9°$

2. 4.2 cm

3. $51.7°$

4. $60.2°$

5. $10.8°$

6. $45°$

7. 11 cm

8. 4.2 cm

Chapter 28

28.1.2 Page 199

1. (a) 1 Nm

    (b) 2 Nm

    (c) 1.126 Nm

2. (a) 3, 1 Nm

    (b) $2\sqrt{2}$, 1.6 Nm

    (c) 3, 5.2 Nm

3. 4.12 N, 7.12 N, 6 Nm

4. 15 Nm

5. 1.2 Nm

6. 3.73 Nm

7. 4.22 N

8. 17.9 N

28.2.2 Page 201

1. (a) 7.21 N, $56.3°$ to AB, $\frac{1}{6}$ m from A along BA produced

    (b) 8.32 N, $70°$ to AB, 0.74 from A along AB

2. 9.97 N, $49°$ to AB, 1.06 m from A

3. $5\mathbf{i} + 4\mathbf{j}$, $(3, 0)$

4. 9.79 N, $41°$ to BC, 2.29 from B

5. 8.06 N, $83°$ to AB, 3 cm from A, 0.24 Nm

6. $3\mathbf{i} + \mathbf{j}$, $(0, -2\frac{2}{3})$, 8

28.3.2 Page 202

1. 1.17 m from one end

2. $30°$

3. $70°$ to vertical

4. $\sqrt{3}$

5. $16°$ to vert.

6. $18.4°$ to vert

7. $30°$

8. 0.166

9. 0.83 m from one end

10. $15°$

11. 0.42

12. $45°$

13. 69% of way up.

28.4.2 Page 204

1. BC: $W\sqrt{2}$, tension CD: W thrust BD: $W\sqrt{2}$ thrust AB: 2W tension

2. AB: $W\sqrt{2}$, tension DB: W thrust BC: W tension DC: 0

3. AC & BC: $W/\sqrt{2}$, thrust AB: $\frac{1}{2}$W, tension

4.　CA: $\frac{1}{2}\sqrt{3}W$, thrust　　CB: $\frac{1}{2}W$, thrust　　AB: $\frac{1}{4}\sqrt{3}W$, tension

5.　CA: $\dfrac{5}{2\sqrt{3}}$ W, thrust　　DB: $\dfrac{7}{2\sqrt{3}}$ W, thrust　　AE: $\dfrac{5}{4\sqrt{3}}$ W tension　　BE: $\dfrac{7}{4\sqrt{3}}$ W tension

　　CE: $\dfrac{1}{2\sqrt{3}}$ W tension　　DE: $\dfrac{1}{2\sqrt{3}}$ W thrust　　CD: $\frac{1}{2}\sqrt{3}$ thrust

Chapter 29

29.1.2 Page 208

1.　60 J

2.　10 m

3.　3 N

4.　(a) 196 J　　(b) 24.5 J　　(c) 0.00353 J　　(d) −98 J

5.　(a) 9 J　　(b) 225,000 J

6.　1.6875 N

7.　6.125 m

8.　312.5 N

9.　1500 N

10.　25 m s^{-1}

11.　14 m s^{-1}

12.　3.66 m s^{-1}

13.　6.53 m

14.　11.9 m s^{-1}

15.　0.41 m

16.　7.25 m

17.　16.1 m s^{-1}

18.　6.26 m s^{-1}

19.　1.19 m s^{-1}

20.　0.013 m, 9.2°

21.　19 J

22.　13 J

23.　3.74 m s^{-1}

29.2.2 Page 210

1.　400 W

2.　2 m s^{-1}

3.　58.8 W

4.　343 W

5.　980 W

6.　245 W

7.　14.1 m s^{-1}

8.　596 W

9.　5.9 m s^{-1}

10.　16 m s^{-1}. 0.625 m s^{-2}

11.　7.64 m s^{-1}

12.　6.1°

13.　8000 W

14.　13.2 m s^{-1}

15.　35.2 m s^{-1}

16.　1.5 m s^{-2}

17.　3 m s^{-2}

18.　$4\frac{2}{3}$ W

19.　6.26 W

Chapter 30

30.1.2 Page 214

1. 2.24, 26.6°

2. 5.1, 78.7°

3. $-\mathbf{i} - 9\mathbf{j}$, 9.1, 84° with $\mathbf{i}$

4. 8.6 km hr^{-1}, 122°

5. 782 km hr^{-1}, 118°

6. 2.3 km hr^{-1}, 352°

7. 14.1 km hr^{-1}, from 89°

8. 1430 km hr^{-1}, from 094°

9. 60 m

10. 20.5 km hr^{-1}, 293°

11. 11.1 km hr^{-1}, 331°

12. 42° to line across. 89 secs.

13. 010°, 1.86 hr

14. 81.2°, 3.58 hr

30.2.2 Page 215

1. 222°, 1.34 min

2. 258°, 0.67 hr

3. 42° with $-$ve x–axis, $3.09\mathbf{i} + 6.18\mathbf{j}$

4. 30° with y–axis, $7.52\mathbf{i} + 10.03\mathbf{j}$

5. 300.1

6. 72° with touch line. 2.62 s (or 5°, and 29.1 s.)

30.3.2 Page 216

1. 12.8 m, after 72 s

2. 5.55 m, 4.6 m

3. 2.77

4. $1, -\frac{1}{3}\mathbf{i} + \mathbf{j}$

5. 212 km, after 20.5 min

6. 34 km

Chapter 31

31.1.2 Page 221

1. 44.1 m, 60 m

2. 3.78 s, 56.7 m

3. 0.553 s, 0.553 m

4. 0.11 m

5. 1.225 m

6. 1980 m s^{-1}

7. 1.24 m

8. 40.1 m s^{-1}, 38.6° to vert

9. 13.7 m s^{-1} at 18.8° to horiz

10. 7423 m, 386 m s^{-1}, 39° to horiz.

31.2.2 Page 222

1. 161 m, 5.25 s, 33.7 m

2. 34.4 m, 2.65 s

3. 17,720 m

4. 23.78 m, 24.7° to horiz

5. 17.59 m, 2.05 m

6. 18 m s^{-1}, 16.4 to horiz, after 0.38 s

7. 43° to horiz, 1.74 s

8. 5.05 s, 77.4 m, 67.3° to horiz

9. 10.6 m, at 47° to wall

10. 105 m

11. 1676 m

31.3.2 Page 223

1. 18.9° & 71.1°

2. 23.7° & 66.3°

3. 80° & 17.6°

4. 75° & 14.7°

5. 85.89° & 25.9

6. 28.3°, 38°

7. 67.5° or −9.5°

8. 8.85 m s^{-1}

9. 155 m s^{-1}

Chapter 32

32.1.2 Page 229

1. (a) 10000 Ns   (b) 0.5 Ns

2. 4 m s^{-1}

3. 8 m s^{-1}

4. 2.4 Ns

5. 9 Ns

6. 5.4 Ns

7. $5\frac{5}{9}$ m s^{-1}, 11111J

8. 17.3 m s^{-1}

9. 400 kg

10. 0.494 m s^{-1}, 39.5 J, 1317 N

11. 10 m s^{-1}, 150 N

12. 10 m s^{-1}, 7794 N

13. 1 m s^{-1}, 6 J

14. 1.25 m s^{-2}, $10\frac{1}{2}$ Ns

15. 29.1 Ns

16. $4\mathbf{i} + 6\frac{1}{2}\mathbf{j}$, $45\frac{1}{4}$ J

17. $\frac{1}{7}\mathbf{i} + \frac{4}{7}\mathbf{j}$, $\pm(4\frac{2}{7}\mathbf{i} + 7\frac{1}{7}\mathbf{j})$

18. 1.59 m s^{-1}, at 9° to original line of motion

19. 0.84, at 27° to original line of motion

20. 2 m s^{-1}, 3208 J

21. 400 m s^{-1}, 400000J

22. 4.33 Ns, at 56.3° to line of wickets

23. 1.45 Ns at 25° to line of wickets

24. 6.16 Ns

25. 32 m s^{-1} at 51.3 to line of wickets

26. 25.1 m s^{-1}

27. 20 N

28. 30 N

29. 200 N

30. 40 N

32.2.2 Page 232

1. 1.914 m

2. $\frac{1}{2}$

3. 2 m s^{-1} & 3 m s^{-1}

4. 0.6 m s^{-1}, 0.4 m s^{-1}

5. $\frac{1}{5}$

6. $\frac{1}{4}$

7. $\frac{7}{16}$

8. 0

9. $\frac{1}{2}$

10. $\frac{1}{4}$

11. $\frac{49}{32}$. yes

12. $2\frac{1}{24}$. yes

13. 2.45. no

14. $\frac{49}{60}$. no

32.3.2 Page 233

1. 50.5°   2. 0.834

3. 8.83 Ns. 7.07 Ns

4. A: 5 m s^{-1} perpendicular to loc. B: 8.7 m s^{-1} along loc

5. 0.647   6. 18.4°

8. $(2 - \sqrt{3})m$ kg

Chapter 33

33.1.2 Page 239

1. 196 m s^{-1} 2. 7.67 m s^{-1}

3. 25 m s^{-1} 4. 42.5 m s^{-1}

5. 1.96   6. 0.383

7. 171   8. 0.05

9. 1   10. 2.4

11. 2, 0.693. 0.386   12. 1.52

13. 3   14. 2.565

15. 10. 6.93/g   16. 19.3/g

17. 1.83 s   18. 26.2 m

19. 40 m s^{-1}. 30.9 s   20. 436 m

21. 25 m s^{-1}. 5.45 s. 37 m.

33.2.2 Page 241

1. 17.32   2. 1.45 m s^{-1}

3. 0.284 m   4. 17 m

5. 1.63 m s^{-1}

6. (a) 2 m s^{-1} (b) $1\frac{1}{6}$ s

8. 495000 m   9. 11200 m s^{-1}

Chapter 34

34.1.2 Page 246

1. (a) 151   (b) 8.06   (c) 0.262   (d) 0.0048

2. (a) 1.45×10^{-4} (b) 1.75×10^{-3} (c) 7.27×10^{-5} (d) 1.99×10^{-7}

3. 8 m s^{-1} 4. 1.68 m s^{-1}

5. 0.524 m s^{-1} 6. 360 m s^{-1}, 1080 N

7. 4.44 m   8. 2.63

9. 1.225 m

10. 0.215

11. 8.57

12. (a) 21 m s^{-1} (b) 45.4 m

13. 1.42

14. 4.43 m s^{-1}

15. 0.98

34.2.2 Page 247

1. 25°

2. 3.07

3. 16.3 m

4. 2.86

5. 5.875 N

6. 4.95

7. 5.43

8. 16.8 m s^{-1}

9. 35.4 m s^{-1}

10. 0.932

11. 99.2 m

12. 20°

13. 1.21 m s^{-1}

14. 0.92 m

34.3.2 Page 249

1. 5.42 m s^{-1}

2. 0.735

3. 3.13 m s^{-1}

4. 22.1 m s^{-1}

5. (a) 17.9 m s^{-1},   (b) 302 N

6. 19 m s^{-1}, 361 N

7. (a) 15.5°   (b) 10.25 N

8. 2.32 m s^{-1}, 0.05 N

9. 0.204 m, 0.59 N

Chapter 35

35.1.2 Page 253

1. 1.47 m

2. 6.125 N

3. $32\frac{2}{3}$ N

4. 0.75 m

5. 19.6 N

6. 4900 N

7. 0.8 m, 78.4 N

8. 1.95 m

9. 0.4875

10. 1.375 m

11. 0.098 J

12. 17.64 J

13. 11.1 m s^{-1}

14. 51 m s^{-1}

15. 0.226 m

16. 3.43 m

17. 0.8 m, 0.29 m

18. (a) 29.6 m   (b) 18 m s^{-1} (c) 18.6 m

19. 0.08 m, 0.22 m s^{-1}

35.2.2 Page 255

1. (a) $3, \pi, 1$ (b) $4, 4\pi, -2$ (c) $5, 2\pi, 0.64$ (d) $13, \frac{2}{3}\pi, -1.18$

    (e) $2, \frac{2}{3}\pi, \frac{1}{4}\pi$ (f) $\sqrt{5}, 4\pi, 0.987$

2. $1\frac{1}{2}$

3. $10 \sin 6t$

4. $\frac{2}{3}\pi$

5. 0.212

6. 0.262

7. 6.97 cm

8. 36 s

9. 9.978 cm

10. 10 cm s^{-1}, 0.823 s

35.3.2 Page 257

1. 2.84 s

2. 6.2 m

3. 6.58 m s^{-2}

4. $\frac{1}{2}\%$

5. 0.16 cm

6. 0.065 m s^{-1}

7. 0.705

8. $0.562, 0.0018$

9. $0.281, 0.224$ m s^{-1}

10. $\dfrac{\sqrt{g}}{2\pi\sqrt{a}}$

11. $\dfrac{2\pi\sqrt{(\rho a)}}{\sqrt{g}}$

Chapter 36

36.1.2 Page 262

1. (a) 720 (b) 3628800 (c) 39916800 (d) 20

    (e) 11880 (f) 1860480 (g) 15 (h) 792

2. (a) 120 (b) 94109400 (c) 1 (d) 500500

    (e) 500500

5. No

6. 120

7. 210

8. $15!$

9. 60

10. 840

11. 2184

12. 13800

13. 40320

14. 330

15. 220

16. 36

17. 3003

18. $3003, 360360$

19. 6.35×10^{11}

20. 210

21. 126

36.2.2 Page 264

1. (a) 60   (b) 5040   (c) 120   (d) 60
   (e) 5.28×10^{13}

2. 120   3. 240

4. 240   5. 72

6. 6885   7. 1800

8. 203212800

9. (a) 362880   (b) 5760   (c) 14400   (d) 2880

10. 2401   11. 729

12. 50   13. 225

14. 132

15. (a) 78624000   (b) 175760000

16. 33   17. 6

18. (a) $\dfrac{365!}{338! \times 365^{27}} = 0.373$ (b) 0.627

19. 5.364×10^{28}

20. (a) 0.0088   (b) 0.035

21. 0.68

22. (a) 5760   (b) 31680

23. (a) 35   (b) $\frac{1}{2}n(n-3)$

24. 40

Chapter 37

37.1.2 Page 269

1. 0.4   2. $\frac{7}{60}$

3. 0.1   4. 0.05

5. 0.175

6.

i	1	2	3	4	5	6
$P(X=i)$	$\frac{1}{6}$	$\frac{1}{6}$	$\frac{1}{6}$	$\frac{1}{6}$	$\frac{1}{6}$	$\frac{1}{6}$

7.

i	2	3	4	5	6	7	8	9	10	11	12
$P(X=i)$	$\frac{1}{36}$	$\frac{2}{36}$	$\frac{3}{36}$	$\frac{4}{36}$	$\frac{5}{36}$	$\frac{6}{36}$	$\frac{5}{36}$	$\frac{4}{36}$	$\frac{3}{36}$	$\frac{2}{36}$	$\frac{1}{36}$

8.

i	1	2	3	4	5	6
$P(X=i)$	$\frac{1}{36}$	$\frac{3}{36}$	$\frac{5}{36}$	$\frac{7}{36}$	$\frac{9}{36}$	$\frac{11}{36}$

9.

i	1	2	3	4
P(X=i)	$\frac{1}{10}$	$\frac{2}{10}$	$\frac{3}{10}$	$\frac{4}{10}$

10.

i	0	1	2
P(X=i)	$\frac{1}{7}$	$\frac{4}{7}$	$\frac{2}{7}$

37.2.2 Page 270

1. $2\frac{7}{8}$
2. 12.2
3. 2.7
4. $1\frac{1}{2}$
5. 1.3
6. 4
7. 2
8. 3.5
9. 2.75
10. $3\frac{1}{2}$
11. 7
12. $\frac{161}{36}$
13. 3
14. $\frac{8}{7}$
15. $3\frac{1}{3}$
16. $a = 0.4, b = 0.3$
17. $\frac{37}{13}$
18. $\frac{7}{6}$
19. £20, £100
20. £17

37.3.2 Page 272

1. 1.243
2. 1.45
3. 0.81
4. 0.75
5. $a = 4, b = 6$
6. $\frac{4}{5}, \frac{32}{75}$
7. $3\frac{1}{2}, 2\frac{11}{12}, 7, 5\frac{5}{6}$
8. $0, 5\frac{5}{6}$

Chapter 38

38.1.2 Page 277

1. (a) 0.297 (b) 0.0044 (c) 0.822 (d) 0.995
2. (a) 0.238 (b) 0.191 (c) 0.181 (d) 0.946
3. (a) 0.190 (b) 0.122 (c) 0.878 (d) 0.392
4. (a) 0.056 (b) 0.282 (c) 0.244
5. (a) 0.0115 (b) 1×10^{-14} (c) 0.218 (d) 0.931
6. (a) 0.354 (b) 0.114
7. 2, 1.8
8. $7\frac{1}{2}, 1\frac{7}{8}$
9. 4, 3.2
10. 0.6, 0.54
11. 18
12. 9
13. $\frac{4}{5}$
14. $\frac{1}{10}$

38.2.2 Page 279

1. (a) 0.126   (b) 0.223   (c) 0.809   (d) 0.442
2. (a) 0.14   (b) 0.260   (c) 0.125   (d) 0.960
3. (a) 0.168   (b) 0.161
4. (a) 0.076   (b) 0.779
5. (a) 0.104   (b) 0.092   (c) 0.865
6. (a) 0.224   (b) 0.223
7. (a) 0.195   (b) 0.122   (c) 0.368   (d) 0.865
8. (a) 0.693   (b) 0.120
9. 1.386, 0.085
10. 0.168
11. 0.0164
12. 0.271
13. 0.037
14. (a) 0.219   (b) 0.217

Chapter 39

39.1.2 Page 284

1. (b) $\frac{15}{16}$ (c) $\frac{5}{16}$ (d) $\frac{1}{4096}$
2. (c) $\frac{1}{16}$ (d) 0.5525
3. (c) 0.75   (d) $\frac{1}{9}$
4. 2
5. 2
6. 2
7. $^3\sqrt{3}$
8. 1.56
9. (a) $\frac{4}{5}$ (b) 0.0267   (c) 0.841
10. (a) $\frac{2}{3}$ (b) $\frac{2}{9}$ (c) 0.586
11. 2, $\sqrt{2}$
12. $\frac{1}{3}$, for $2 \leq x \leq 5$
13. $\frac{1}{b-a}$, for $a \leq x \leq b$
14. 9
15. (b) $\frac{1}{3}$ (c) 0.854   (d) $\frac{2}{3}$ (e) 0.722

39.2.2 Page 287

1. (a) x^5 for $0 \leq x \leq 1$ (b) $\frac{1}{4}x + \frac{1}{8}x^2$ for $0 \leq x \leq 2$ (c) $1 - \cos x$ for $0 \leq x \leq \frac{1}{2}\pi$

    (d) $1 - \frac{1}{x}$ for $x \leq 1$

2. (a) $\frac{1}{2} + x$ for $0 \leq x \leq 1$ (b) $\frac{8}{x^3}$ for $x \geq 2$ (c) $2 \cos 2x$ for $0 \leq x \leq \frac{1}{4}\pi$ (d) $3e^{-3x}$ for $x \leq 0$

3. x^4 for $0 \leq x \leq 1$ 4. $x - \frac{1}{4}x^2$ for $0 \leq x \leq 2$

5. $1 - \dfrac{1}{x^2}$ for $x \geq 1$

6. 0.732

7. $\frac{1}{4}$

8. $\frac{1}{6}$

9. $\frac{2}{5}$

10. (a) $\frac{1}{15}e^{-x/15}$ (b) 15 min   (c) 10.4 min   (d) 0.368

11. $\dfrac{x-a}{b-a}$ for $a \leq x \leq b$. $\frac{1}{2}(a+b)$. $\dfrac{(b-a)^2}{12}$

Chapter 40

40.1.2 Page 292

1. (a) 6   (b) 45   (c) 14   (d) −4
       (e) 20   (f) 21

2. (a) 8   (b) 5   (c) 45   (d) 5
       (e) 35   (f) 25   (g) 69   (h) 9

3. $a=2, b=3$

4. $\frac{1}{8}, -1$

5. $\dfrac{1}{\sigma}, -\dfrac{\mu}{\sigma},$

6. $a=3, b=-3$

7. 210, 18. 170, 38

8. 73 kg, 5 kg^2

9. 53.4 s, 5.6 s^2

10. −1.4, 7.9

40.2.2 page 294

1. 23, 1.49

2. 3.07, 0.038

3. 72

4. 94g

5. 0.03

6. $\frac{1}{7}$

7. 0.26

8. 0.8

9. 0.64

10. 1.2

11. (ii) $a = \frac{4}{5}, b = \frac{1}{5}$

12. (i) $0.0075\sigma^2, 0.0067\sigma^2$. W   (ii) $a = \frac{1}{7}, b = \frac{6}{7}$

13. $0.000417\pi(1-\pi), 0.0004\pi(1-\pi)$. W

40.3.2 Page 296

1. (a) $2\frac{2}{9}$, 2.5   (b) 90.2, 103.1   (c) $1.18 \times 10^{-5}, 1.38 \times 10^{-5}$ (d) 0.519, 0.577

2. (a) 1.157, 1.197   (b) 0.950, 0.969   (c) 1.002, 1.013

3. $\frac{7}{30}$

4. (a) 1250   (b) $1\frac{23}{30}$

Chapter 41

41.1.2 Page 300

1. (a) 0.994   (b) 0.067   (c) 0.081   (d) 0.9965
   (e) 0.301   (f) 0.464

2. (a) 0.842   (b) 0.524   (c) −0.1   (d) −1.175

3. (a) 0.6915   (b) 0.106   (c) 0.599   (d) 0.266

4. 4.022 & −0.022

5. 6.24

6. (a) 87.82   (b) 82.39   (c) 65.46   (d) 54.46

7. 15.6

8. 60

9. 3.75

10. 81.8

11. 1001.6 cc, 26.3

12. 1.9975 cm

13. 31 m

41.2.2 Page 302

1. (a) 0.5   (b) 0.6915   (c) 0.909   (d) 0.553
   (e) 0.47   (f) 0.159   (g) 0.32   (h) 0.37

2. (a) 43.9   (b) 5.51   (c) 112   (d) 35
   (e) 48.7   (f) 100.2

3. 0.0295

4. 0.29

5. 0.987

6. 0.69

7. (a) 0.76   (b) 0.998   (c) 0.52   (d) 0.455
   (e) 0.223   (f) 0.135

8. (a) 49.5   (b) 45.9   (c) 3.41   (d) 2.71
   (e) 0.41   (f) 0.35

9. (a) 0.057   (b) 0.376

10. (a) 0.02   (b) 0.02

41.3.2 Page 305

1. 0.103

2. 0.94

3. 0.9

4. 0.05

5. 0.214

6. 0.904

7. 0.028

8. 0.18

9. 0.014

10. 0.085

11. 0.896

12. 0.08

13. 0.07

14. 0.19

15. 0.12

16. 0.26

17. 0.088

18. 0.206

Chapter 42

42.1.2 Page 311

1. $z = 2.01$ sig.
2. not sig.
3. $z = 2.5$ sig.
4. $z = 3.36$ no
5. $z = 1.5$ not sig.
6. $z = 4.07$ yes
7. $z = 2.12$ no
8. $z = 3.1$ yes.
9. 0.921
10. 0.132

42.2.2 Page 313

1. $z = 1.17$ no
2. $z = 2.12$ yes
3. $z = 1.69$ no
4. $z = 1.94$ yes (1 tail)
5. $z = 0.78$ no
6. $z = 1.18$ no
7. $z = 0.5$ no
8. $z = 3.6$ yes

42.3.2 Page 315

1. $z = 0.56$ no
2. $z = 1.875$ yes
3. $z = 4$ yes
4. $z = 1.59$ no
5. $z = 1.9$ (a) no   (b) no
6. $z = 1.3$ no
7. $z = 3.3$ yes
8. $z = 1.16$ no
9. $z = 1.22$ no
10. $z = 0.95$ no.
11. 0.822
12. 0.194

42.4.2 Page 317

1. $11.9 < \mu < 14.1$
2. $989 < \mu < 1001$
3. $11.7 < \mu < 12.3$
4. $21.2 < \mu < 25.4$
5. $245.5 < \mu < 256$
6. $3.19 < \mu < 3.22$
7. $1170 < \mu < 1390$
8. $12\% < p < 23\%$
9. $27\% < p < 33\%$
10. $75\% < p < 85\%$

Chapter 43

43.1.2 Page 321

1. not sig.
2. not sig
3. sig
4. sig
5. not sig
6. not sig
7. sig

43.2.2 Page 322

1. (a) 1.26 ± 0.037 (b) 55.2 ± 4.09 (c) 0.21 ± 0.36 (d) 160.2 ± 11.8

2. (a) 1.26 ± 0.056 (b) 55.2 ± 5.81 (c) 0.21 ± 0.53 (d) 160.2 ± 18.5

3. $t_7 = 3.67$. Sig.   4. $t_8 = 2.31$. (Just)sig at 5%

5. $t_{10} = 4.03$. sig.   6. $t_7 = 1.97$. sig at 5%

7. $t_6 = 2.98$. sig at 5%

43.3.2 Page 324

1. $\chi^2(9) = 15$. Not sig.   2. $\chi^2(3) = 4$. Good fit

3. $\chi^2(2) = 3.125$. Good fit   4. $p = 0.287$. $\chi^2(1) = 5.7$. Not good fit

5. $\chi^2(2) = 9.5$. Not good fit   6. $\chi^2(3) = 2.9$. Good fit

7. $\chi^2(3) = 3.3$. Good fit   8. $\chi^2(3) = 1.9$. Good fit

9. $\hat{\mu} = 26$. $\chi^2(1) = 40$. Not good fit   10. $10.8, 33$. $\chi^2(2) = 24$. Not good fit.

43.4.2 Page 327

1. $\chi^2(1) = 10.7$ (Yates, 9.375). Sig   2. $\chi^2(1) = 1$ (Yates, 0.6). Not sig.

3. $\chi^2(2) = 0.74$. Not sig.   4. $\chi^2(1) = 1$ (Yates, 0.6). Not sig.

5. $\chi^2(4) = 15.7$. Sig.

Chapter 44

44.1.2 Page 332

1. $3, -1$ 2. $-13, 50$

3. $3, -6.5$ 4. $0.01, 0.05$

5. $4, 2.5$ 6. $0.3, 1.4$

7. $(5, 2300)$

8. (a) $X = x^3, Y = y$ (b) $X = x, Y = y^2$ (c) $X = \dfrac{1}{\sqrt{x}}, Y = y$ (d) $X = x^2, Y = yx$

    (e) $X = x, Y = y\sqrt{x}$ (f) $X = x, Y = yx^2$ (g) $X = \ln x, Y = \ln y$ (h) $X = x^2, Y = \ln y$

    (i) $X = \ln x, Y = \ln y$ (j) $X = \dfrac{1}{x}, Y = \ln y$

44.2.2 Page 334

1. (a) $y = 1.41x - 0.2$ (b) $y = 0.25x + 0.44$ (c) $y = 0.75x + 0.74$ (d) $y = -5.4x + 31.6$

2. (a) 13.9 (b) 2.95 (c) 8.24 (d) -22.4

3. (a) $x = 0.7y + 0.16$ (b) $x = 3.6y - 1.3$ (c) $x = 1.28y - 0.8$ (d) $x = -0.17y + 5.6$

4. $y = 2.25x + 0.44$

5. (a) $y = 1.78x + 1.96$ (b) $x = 0.52y - 0.58$

6. $y = 2.08x^2 - 1.86$

7. $\dfrac{y}{x} = 2.9x + 5.7$

8. $r = 2.7s^{0.22}$

9. 48.8. Outlier (4,51). 0.743

10. $y = 2.2x^2 + 3.9.$ $y = 2.2x^2 + 3.6$

44.3.2 Page 337

1. (a) 0.1   (b) 0.87   (c) −0.998

2. (a) 0.956. yes   (b) −0.957. yes   (c) −0.297. no

5. (a) $\frac{2}{3}$ (b) −0.85   (c) 0.18

6. 0.9. yes

7. (a) 0.98. yes   (b) −0.97. yes   (c) −0.36. no

Solutions
(to end of chapter examination questions)

These solutions are the responsibility of the author, and have neither been supplied nor approved by the examination boards.

If a method is suggested for the solution of a question, then that method is not necessarily the best or the only way to answer the question.

Edexcel acknowledgements
Edexcel Foundation, London Examinations accepts no responsibility whatsoever for the accuracy or method of working in the answers given.

1.3 Page 6

1. (i) $x + 4$ is a factor. The factors are $(x + 4)$, $(x + 3)$, $(x + 2)$. The coefficient of x^2 is 9.

   (ii) $a=3$, $b=2$, $r=7$. (By long division)

2. (a) 6 (Put $x=1$)   (b) 0

   (c) $x(x-3)(2x+1)(3x-4)$ (Divide by $x(x-3)$)   (d) $x = 0, 3, -\frac{1}{2}, 1\frac{1}{3}$.

3. (a) $a = -21$, $b = -54$ (Put $x=3$ and -2)   (b) $x = 2$ or $\frac{1}{2}$ or 1 (First solve $2u^2 - 9u + 10 = 0$)

4. A = 6, B = 1, C = -2

2.5 Page 15

1. $-\frac{1}{3}$ or $-\frac{2}{3}$ (Use the equation $1+r+r^2=\frac{7}{9}$)

2. (i) 25 (Use the formula for the sum of an AP)

   (ii) $a = \pm12$, $r = \pm\frac{1}{6}$. Series is 12, 2, $\frac{1}{3}$, $\frac{1}{18}$ or -12, 2, $-\frac{1}{3}$, $\frac{1}{18}$.

   (iii) 12. (Must have $4^n > 6000001$)

3. (i) By 1.12. 1.76. 76%.

   (ii) £$(25n - 5)$. £$\frac{1}{2}n(15 + 25n)$ 9 years. (When $\frac{1}{2}n(15+25n) > 1000$)

4. $S_{n-1} = \frac{1}{4}(5(n-1)^2 + 11(n-1))$; $u_n = 2.5n + 1.5$. (Take $S_n - S_{n-1}$); $a = 4$, $d = 2.5$.

5. (Common ratio is $1 - \dfrac{x}{10}$. This is between -1 and 1.) (The sum is $\dfrac{100}{x}$)

   n is at least 44. ($x = 1$. Sum is $100(1 - 0.9^n)$)

3.3 Page 21

1. (i) $1 - 15x + 90x^2$ (ii) $16 + 32x + 24x^2$.   Coeff. = 984

2. (i) $1 - 5x + 10x^2 - 10x^3 + 5x^4 - x^5$. x^3 term is $-40x^3$.(Multiply together).

   (ii) 0.9225. The x^3 term is 0.00004, which does not affect the answer.

3. $1 - 8x + 28x^2 - 56x^3 + 70x^4 - 56x^5 + 28x^6 - 8x^7 + x^8$. 0.663. 6.63 m. (Height = 10 x $(0.95)^8$)

4. (a) 495 $\left({}^{12}C_4 x^8 \left(\frac{1}{x^2} \right)^4 \right)$ (b) $1 - x - \frac{3x^2}{2} + \frac{5x^3}{2}$. Valid for $-\frac{1}{2} < x < \frac{1}{2}$.

5. $q = 0.45$, $p = 0.55$. (Expand both series, and equate coeffs.)

   (Write $33^{0.1} = (32+1)^{0.1}$. Put $x = \frac{1}{32}$ in the result above.)

6. (a) $\frac{1}{1+x} - \frac{1}{2+x}$ (Refer to 1.2) (Write $\frac{1}{2+x}$ as $\frac{1}{2\left(1 + \frac{x}{2}\right)}$)

   (b) Next term = $\frac{1}{6}\left(\frac{1}{n^4} \right)$ 0.98952. (Put $n = 10$)

7. $1 - \frac{x}{4} - \frac{3x^2}{32} - \frac{7x^3}{128}$. 1.49535. x^3 term $\approx 10^{-7}$, hence need not be included.

4.4 Page 27

1. $3(x+2)^2 + 5$.

   (a) Both terms are positive.   (b) Least value is 5.

   (c) −1.2 and −2.8.   (d) See Fig E.1.

2. (a) 3 and $-\frac{3}{4}$. (The discriminant must be 0.)

   (b) $m > 4$ or $m < -4$. (Discriminant must be positive.)

3. $(a\beta^2 + b\beta + c = 0$ and $an^2\beta^2 + bn\beta + c = 0$. Eliminate β)

(−2,5)

Fig E.1

5.4 Page 32

1. (a) $-4 < x < 1\frac{1}{2}$ (b) $x < -1$ or $x > 2$ (Subtract 1 from both sides.)

2. (a) $(x-3)(x^2 + 4x + 4)$ (b) $(x + 2)^2$

   (c) $x > 3$. (As $g(x)$ is positive, it does not affect the answer.)

3. $2y - 3x$ is greatest at (0,3) Area = 3 (The triangle is right–angled)

4. (a) (i) $x < 2$ or $x > 4$ (ii) $\frac{2}{5} \le x < 1$ (Subtract 2 from both sides)   (b) (5,3)

5. (a) $0 \le x \le 4, 3 \le y \le 12$.   (b) $x < 2$ or $3 < x < 5$ (Collect both terms on one side.)

6. $x < 0$ or $x > 1$.

6.2 Page 37

1. (i) $2^{2/3} \cdot 8$ (ii) $\dfrac{z}{x^2}$.   (iii) 2.

2. (i) $\log_{10}\left(\frac{4}{5}\right)$.   (ii) 1 or –1.585 (Consider it as a quadratic in 2^x)

3. (a) $2^{-4}, 2^{6a}, 2^{3b-2c}$ (b) $\sqrt{30}$, 27000.   (c) 0.774.

4. (a) $x=6$ (and –9). (Regard 1 as $\log_3 3$)   (b) (i) $k-1$ (ii) $\dfrac{1}{2\left(1+\frac{1}{k}\right)}$

    (Note: $\log_9 x = \frac{1}{2}\log_3 x$. Also $\log_a b = \dfrac{1}{\log_b a}$)

5. (i) $\dfrac{1}{\ln a - 2}$ (ii) $\sqrt{\dfrac{ea}{4}}$

6. (i) $5050 \ln 2$ (Refer to 2.1)   (ii) $\dfrac{\ln 2}{1 - \ln 2}$ (Refer to 2.2)

7.6 Page 47

1. Gradient $\frac{2}{3}$ E(2,3) $2y + 3x = 12$. B(0,6) $4y = 7x - 28$. D(4,0).

2. (a) $y = 1\frac{1}{2}x - 1\frac{1}{2}$ (b) C(3, 3)   (c) Both $\sqrt{65}$. (P is at (–3, 7).

3. (a) $\sqrt{884}$ (b) $11x - 10y + 19 = 0$

4. $x = \pm \dfrac{3}{\sqrt{2}}, y = 2 \pm \dfrac{3}{\sqrt{2}}$. (Centre is (0,2), radius is 3)

    (Find the radii and the distance apart of the centres.)

5. (a) $C_1(-1,2)$. $C_2(1,3)$. Radii $\sqrt{10}$ and $\sqrt{5}$. A(0,5), B(2,1). (Gradient AB = –2, Gradient $C_1C_2 = \frac{1}{2}$)

    (b) (Gradient of PQ is $\dfrac{2}{q + p}$)

    $R\left(\dfrac{a}{2}\left(p^2 + \dfrac{1}{p^2}\right), a\left(p - \dfrac{1}{p}\right)\right)$. (Put $x = \dfrac{a}{2}\left(p^2 + \dfrac{1}{p^2}\right), y = a\left(p - \dfrac{1}{p}\right)$).

8.3 page 57

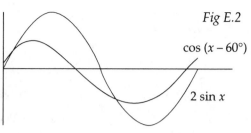

Fig E.2

cos (x − 60°)

2 sin x

1. (i) (a) $x^2 + 3$, (b) $(x + 3)^2$.

   (ii) $\{x : x \geq 3\}$ (iii) No. gf(1) = gf(−1).

2. (a) (i) $f^{-1} : x \to \dfrac{x + 3}{2 - x}$ for $x \neq 2$

   $ff : x \to \dfrac{x - 9}{3x - 2}$ for $x \neq \frac{2}{3}$.   (ii) $x^2 - x + 3$ has no roots.

   (b) $a = 5$.(Use the discriminant. Refer to 4.2)

3. (a) $24°, 204°$ (b) $0 \leq x \leq 24°, 204° \leq x \leq 360°$. See Fig E.2

4. See Fig E.3

5. $2[(x–3)^2 – 4.5]$.

   (a) Shift 3 to right.   (b) Shift down by 4.5.

   (c) Stretch by 2, parallel to y–axis.

   $f^{-1} : x \to \sqrt{\dfrac{x}{2} + \dfrac{9}{2}} + 3$.   Range $\{x : x \geq 3\}$ Domain $\{x : x \geq -9\}$

(a)

1

Fig E.3

Fig E.4

6. See Fig E.4. $a = \frac{3}{2}$.

7. See Fig E.5

Fig E.5   (a)

(b)

(c)

(d)

9.3 Page 66

1. 3.386 knots. 003°.   (Find the distances out to sea, and use the cos rule.)

2. (a)   (Use the cos rule)   (b) 10.4 cm²

    (c) 71.5°($\tan^{-1} \frac{PA}{AB}$)   (d) 74°(Find the distance from A to BC).

3. 48.2°, 21.7 m².

4. AF = 2.08 m   (First find AD, then find DF.) 60°.(Find the distance from F to AC.)

10.5 Page 74

1. (Put over a common denominator.)

2. (i) 35°, 145°, 215°, 325°

    (ii) 76°, 256°, 135°, 315°(Regard as a quadratic in tan x)

    (iii) 90°, 37°, 143°(Use $\cos^2 x = 1 - \sin^2 x$)

3. (i) See Fig E.6   (ii) 49°, 90°, 131°, 270°.

    (iii) 49° ≤ x ≤ 90°, 131° ≤ x ≤ 270°.

4. (i) (a) $\frac{1}{2}$ (sin 30°) (b) $\frac{1}{2}$ (sin 30°) (c) $\frac{1}{\sqrt{3}}$ (tan 30°)

    (ii) 23.8°, 203.8°   (Use the cos(A–B) formula)

Fig E.6

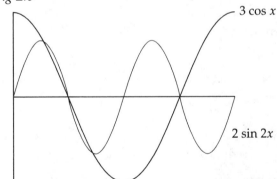

3 cos x

2 sin 2x

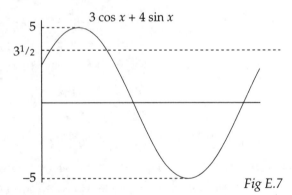

3 cos x + 4 sin x

5

3¹/₂

−5

Fig E.7

5. 0°, 45°, 90°, 135°, 180°, 60°, 120°.

    (Either sin 4x = 0 or cos 4x = cos x cos 3x. Write RHS as $\frac{1}{2}$(cos 4x + cos 2x).)

6. 15°, 75°, 90°, 135°.(Use the factor formulae.)

7. 5 cos (x – 53.1°) Max. 5, at x = 53.1°. Min. –5, at x = 233.1°. See Fig E.7

    (i) 98.7°, 7.6°.   (ii) 0≤x<7.6 & 98.7<x≤360°.

11.3 Page 79

1. (i) $60\frac{1}{2}\theta^2$ (ii) $37\frac{1}{2}\theta^2$ (iii) 0.894   (iv) 28.4 cm.

2. (a) See Fig E.8

   (d) 0, 0.848, 2.29, 3.14, 4,71.

   (e) 27%(Between 0 & 0.848, and between 2.29 & 3.14)

3. (i) $-\frac{1}{2}\pi$ (ii) $\frac{1}{3}\pi$ (iii) $\frac{1}{2}\pi$

4. (a) (i) $r = 25$, $\theta = 1.287$.
   (ii) 25, for $\theta = 2.858$.
   (iii) Least Positive value $\frac{1}{30}$, for $\theta = 2.858$.

   (b) (ii)
   (Let the radius be r. Express the angles in terms of r and x.)

5. 0.27

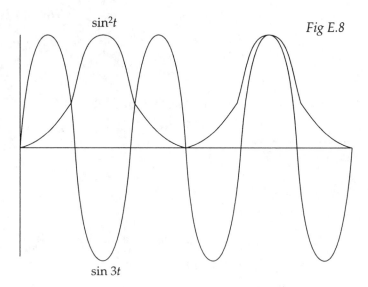

sin²t

sin 3t

Fig E.8

12.4 Page 87

1. $2i - j$, $5i - 5j$, $2i - 2j$, $5i - j$. $-i - 2j$.

   (a) $5\lambda i - \lambda j$ (b) $(3 - \mu)i + (1-2\mu)j$.

   $\lambda = \frac{5}{11}$, $\mu = \frac{8}{11}$. (Equate i and j coefficients).

2. (i) $m = 19$, $n = -3$ (ii) 0. Hence they are perpendicular.   (iii) 33.7°.

3. (BN = AB) $(2-q{:}1 = q{:}p)$ LM:LN = 1:4 $\frac{6}{7}i + \frac{9}{7}j + \frac{18}{7}k$.

4. (i) $r = 2i - \frac{1}{3}j + 2k + t(i - \frac{2}{3}j + 2k)$ (ii) $3i - j + 4k$.

5. (i) $4i + 18j - 12k$ and $4i + 6j$.   (ii) $4i + 6j + t(j - k)$

   (iii) $4i + 2j + 4k$.   (iv) 88°.

6. (0.6, 0.8) and (0.8, –0.6). $r = t(1.4, 0.2)$ (The line goes through (0,0).)

   $r = (13, 13) + t(1.4, 0.2)$ (The line goes through (13,13).)

7. (i) (Put $s = -2$, $t = 4$) (ii) B(5, 8, –6) (For $s = 2$) (iii) (No value of t) (iv) 0.529, 32°

8. (a) $a(-4,4,-1) + \lambda(3,-2,4)$ (b) $r = \lambda(5,-1,-3) + \mu(-4,4,-1)$

   (c) 0.618   (d) $r.(3,-2,4) = 5a$

   $3x - 2y + 4z = 5a.$ $\dfrac{x + 4a}{3} = \dfrac{y - 4a}{-2} = \dfrac{z + a}{4}$

9. (Show that $(0,-1,1)+ \lambda(1,0,1)$ cannot equal $(2,1,3) + \mu(1,-1,2)$)

   (i) (1,–1,–1)   (ii) 19.5° (AB = (2,2,2))   (iii) $x - y - z = 0$

   (iv) $|AB| = 2\sqrt{3}$. From B to $\pi = \frac{2}{\sqrt{3}} = \frac{1}{3}|AB|$. $((ii) = \sin^{-1}\frac{1}{3})$

13.4 Page 97

1. (i) $3x^2 - 3x^{-4}$ (ii) $3x^2 - 4x + 1$ (iii) $-\frac{1}{162}$ (iv) $\frac{3}{4}$

2. (a) $y = x + 10\frac{2}{3}$ (b) $x = 6$ (c) (The equation $x^2 - 8x + 16$ has only one root)

3. $6\frac{2}{3}$

4. (i) $h = \dfrac{1000}{\pi r^2}$ (ii) Area $= \dfrac{2000}{r} + \dfrac{8}{r^2}$ $r = 5, h = 12.7$, cost = 6p.

5. At $(4a, 4a)$ $y = 2x - 4a, x = 2y - 4a$.

   (Gradients are 2 and $\frac{1}{2}$. Use the tan(A–B) formula of 10.3)

6. (a) $(AC = \dfrac{y}{t}$. $AB = 2(x + \dfrac{y}{t})$. Height $= tx + y)$ (Differentiate with respect to t)

   (b) $(tx + y = l \sin \theta)$ $(S = 2xy)$ (Differentiate with respect to x)

14.5 page 106

1. (a) (i) $\dfrac{3}{3x + 1}$ (ii) $\cos 2x - 2x \sin 2x$

   (b) $7y = x - 11$ (c) $\dfrac{-2xy}{x^2 + 2y}$

2. (a) See Fig E.9

   (b) $\dfrac{1}{e}$ (The curve goes through $(e-3, 0)$)

3. (a) 0.19 cm/s $(r = 3.385, \dfrac{dA}{dr} = 8\pi r)$

   (b) 27 $(\dfrac{dV}{dr} = 4\pi r^2)$ 3.4 cm³ (First find δr)

4. $\dfrac{5}{x - 3} - \dfrac{2}{3x + 2}$ (Refer to 1.2) -4.90625

5. (a) $\dfrac{y - 3x^2}{3y^2 - x}$ (Put $x = 3y^2$. Show original equation has no root).

   (b) (For $x = 0, y = 1$. The derivative is > 0.)

6. (a) $5y - 2x = 7\frac{1}{4}a$ (b) $\dfrac{a + y - x}{y - x - a}$ (c) 0.33

7. 0.02 $(\dfrac{d(\tan x)}{dx} = \sec^2 x$. Put $x = \frac{1}{4}\pi)$

8. Gradient $\dfrac{-b \cos \theta}{a \sin \theta}$ $U((0, \dfrac{b}{\sin \theta})$, $T(\dfrac{a}{\cos \theta}, 0)$, $M(\dfrac{(a^2 - b^2) \cos \theta}{a}, 0)$, $N(0, \dfrac{(b^2 - a^2) \sin \theta}{b})$

   Product of gradients $= -1$. (See Fig E.10).

   $Q(\dfrac{a}{2 \cos \theta}, \dfrac{b}{2 \sin \theta})$ $\left(\dfrac{a}{2x}\right)^2 + \left(\dfrac{b}{2y}\right)^2 = 1$ (Put $x = \dfrac{a}{2 \cos \theta}, y = \dfrac{b}{2 \sin \theta}$, eliminate θ)

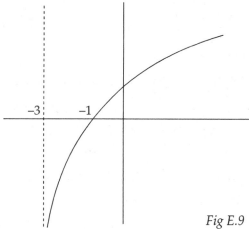

Fig E.9

Fig E.10

15.4 Page 114

1. (a) (i) $\frac{1}{3}x^3 - \frac{2}{5}x^{5/2} + c$ (ii) $\frac{1}{5}x^5 - \frac{2}{3}x^3 + x + c$ (b) $y = \frac{2}{3}x^{3/2} + 3x - 43$, $y = 6x - 52$

2. $\frac{16}{15}\pi$ (Crosses at $x = 0$ and $x = 2$)

3. (a) See Fig E.11. (b) See Fig E.11. (c) 95 m³ (Integrate $20\left(3 - \dfrac{5}{t^2}\right)$ from 2 to 4)

Fig E.11

Fig E.12

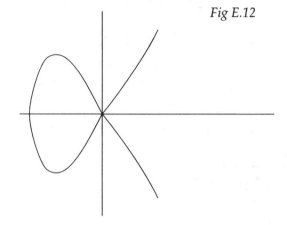

4. (Integrate πx^2 with respect to y, from 3 to $3 + h$)

   (a) 6.28 secs (Put $h = 6$: divide V by 30)

   (b) (i) 0.354 cm/s (Use $\dfrac{dV}{dt} = \dfrac{dV}{dh} \times \dfrac{dh}{dt}$)

   (ii) 10 cm²/sec. (Use $A = \pi x^2$)

5. See Fig E.12

   $\frac{8}{15}$ (Integrate between $t = 0$ and $t = 1$)

6. See Fig E.13.

   $\frac{5}{6}$

Fig E.13

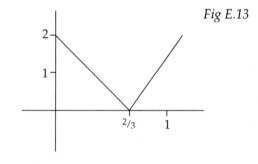

16.3 Page 120

1. (a) (i) $-\frac{1}{4}\cos 4x + c$ (ii) $\sin(\frac{1}{2}x + \frac{1}{2}) + c$

   (b) $\frac{1}{9}\ln 10$

2. See Fig E.14.

   $2(e^2 - e)$

3. (a) (i) $\ln x - \ln(x + 1) + c$ (partial fractions)

   (ii) $x - \ln(e^x + 1) + c$

   (b) $-x^2 \cos x + 2x \sin x + 2 \cos x + c$

4. (i) $e^{2x}(1\frac{1}{2}x + 1\frac{1}{4}) + c$ (By parts)

   (ii) 0.0803 (Use $\cos 2A = 2\cos^2 A - 1$)

Fig E.14

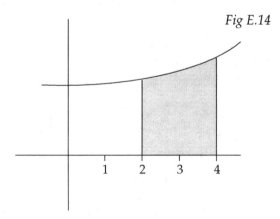

5. $\frac{1}{2}\pi$ (Use cos 2A = 2 cos²A − 1)

6. See Fig E.15

Domain {x: −a ≤ x ≤ a}, Range {x: −$\frac{1}{2}$π ≤ x ≤ $\frac{1}{2}$π}
(Substitute u = x + 1)

17.3 Page 127

1. (i) 18 See Fig E.16.

   (ii) (The trapezia enclose the area)

2. (a) a = 6, b = 2 (divide by x)

   (b) 2.602 (x₃ and x₄ agree)

3. ($\frac{dy}{dx}$ = 3x² + 2 > 0 for all x) (ii) Converges to 1.926

4. (Refer to 17.1) 0.33

5. (Use parts, twice. Refer to 16.3) Trapezium rule gives 0.7454. (The trapezia enclose the area.)

6. (b) −1.9659, −1.9647, −1.9646, −1.9646. Solution −1.9646

   (c) x₃ does not exist

18.3 Page 133

1. (i) $x^3 - \frac{1}{2}x^5$ (ii) $\frac{1}{2}x^3 - \frac{1}{24}x^5$; 2

2. $a = -\frac{1}{2}$, $b = \frac{1}{2}$ (Expand and equate coefficients)

3. $x - \frac{1}{2}x^2 + \frac{1}{3}x^3 - \frac{1}{4}x^4 + \frac{1}{5}x^5$ (log $\frac{a}{b}$ = log a − log b) Valid for −1 < x < 1 Put x = $\frac{1}{2n-1}$

   ln $\frac{n}{n-1}$ = $\frac{2}{2n-1}$ + $\frac{2}{3(2n-1)^2}$ + $\frac{2}{5(2n-1)^5}$ Valid for n > 1 or n < 0

   k = 2 (Put n = 9 and n = 6) $\log_e 1.62 \approx 0.48243$

4. $y = 1 + x + \frac{1}{2}x^2 - \frac{1}{6}x^3 - \frac{7}{24}x^4$

   (Differentiate (1+x²) $\frac{dy}{dx}$ = y, and put x = 0)

Fig E.15

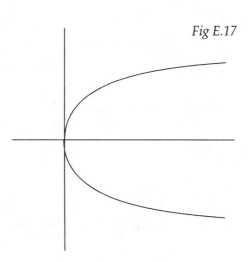

Fig E.16

Fig E.17

19.4 Page 140

1. $x = \tan(\frac{1}{2}y^2 + y + \frac{1}{4}\pi)$ (Separate the variables)

2. (i) $y = (1 + x)^2 e^{-x}$ (Separate the variables)

   (ii) $y^2 = 2x$ See Fig E.17

3. $y = (\frac{1}{2}e^{-x} + c)^2$

4. $y = kx^2$ See Fig E.18

5. $y = e^{2x^2-2}$ ($\frac{dy}{dx} = 4xy$)

Fig E.18

20.3 Page 146

(1) (a) True   (b) True   (c) False

    (d) False (If B ∩ C, then A)

    (e) False (LHS = $\frac{1}{4}$, RHS = $\frac{1}{8}$)

2. (i) (a) $\frac{2}{15}$ (b) $\frac{1}{5}$ (c) $\frac{2}{15}$ (d) $\frac{2}{5}$ (e) $\frac{3}{5}$

    (Write out a 6 by 6 table)

    (ii) (a) $\frac{1}{75}$ (X must draw 12 then 13, or 13 then 12, or 13 then 13)   (b) $\frac{74}{75^2}$

3. (a) (i) 0.855   (ii) 0.145 [(ii) = 1 – (i)] (iii) 0.14

    (b) (i) 0.266 (WWL or WLW or LWW) (ii) 0.578 (1 – P(WWW)

    Most likely WWW, least likely LWL

4. (i) P(A ∪ B) ≠ P(A) + P(B) P(A ∩ B) = 0.17 ≠ P(A) × P(B)   (ii) 0.138, 0.19

5. (i) $\frac{1}{50}$ (ii) $\frac{9}{50}$ (P(Both red) – P(Both red and maggot–free))

    (iii) $\frac{27}{95}$ ((ii) ÷ P(Both red))   (iv) 0.655

(6) (a) (i) $\frac{9}{100}$ ((X,Y) could be (1,0), (2,1),... (9,8)) (ii) $\frac{1}{100}$ (Must be (1,0))

    (iii) $\frac{3}{25}$ (All the R cases, and (0,0), (0,1), (1,1)) (iv) 0.25 ((ii) ÷ P(S))

    (b) (i) 0.074   (ii) 0.0811   (iii) 0.0093

21.3 Page 155

1. (i) 14   (ii) 12   (iii) 5.5
    (iv) 41   (v) 12.6

2. $p = 3$ and $q = -40$

    (50 = 30p + q and 15 = 5p) 38

3. For Smith: 111.3. For Jones: 110.92 116
    and 106

    (Let the values be x and y.
    Find two simultaneous equations).

4. (a) (i) 2.6

      (ii) 46%   100.4 to 106.4

    (b) (i) See Fig E.20

      (ii) 68.4 (By linear interpolation)

Fig E.19

Fig E.20

5. (i)

240	0 2
245	6 8 9
250	0 2 2 2 3 4
255	7 9
260	1
265	5

(ii) Some (a third) underweight.　　　　(iii) 252 grammes, 6.52 grammes

(iv) 1. raise the mean　　2. lower the standard deviation

22.4 Page 164

1. (a) 38 m s^{-1}　　(b) 16 s　　(c) 230 m　　(d) 380 m

2. (a) $t = 1.2 \text{ s}$　　(b) $10\frac{2}{3} \text{ m}$

3. 30 m s^{-1}. $3\mathbf{i} - 14\mathbf{j}$　1 second later. (Put the $\mathbf{i}$ velocity equal to 0)　1 second. $54\mathbf{i} - 108\mathbf{j}$

4. (a) $3\frac{1}{3} \text{ m s}^{-2}$ (Find time at constant velocity)

   (b) $t = 8$ and $t = 14$ (Find the distances at time t.)　72, 210

5. (i) (a) $t = \frac{1}{4}\pi$ (When the velocity vectors are parallel)　　(b) $t = \frac{3}{4}\pi$

   (ii) $(t + 1)e^{-t} - 2\cos t + 1$ (Integrate twice)

6. $\mathbf{v} = -\omega a \sin \omega t\, \mathbf{i} + \omega a \cos \omega t\, \mathbf{j} + b\mathbf{k}$　$\mathbf{a} = -\omega^2 a \cos \omega t\, \mathbf{i} - \omega^2 a \sin \omega t\, \mathbf{j}$

   speed $= \sqrt{(\omega^2 a^2 + b^2)}$　$|\mathbf{a}| = \omega^2 a$　Particle moves in a spiral with constant speed.

23.3 Page 170

1. 6000 N & 3800 N　10500 N & 4500 N

2. $p = -6$ (Net force must be (k,k))　(Acceleration = $(-30, -30)$)　$-58\mathbf{i} - 52\mathbf{j}$

3. (a) 1.4 m s^{-2}　　(b) 3.36 N

4. $R = 200 \text{ N}$　$T_1 = 40 \text{ N}$

5. 10M　(Acc. down is 1 m s^{-2})　(Find the new mass; the upthrust is unchanged)

   (a) $p = 0.2$ (Use $0 = u^2 - 2as$)

   (b) 30 secs　(Find the acceleration of the balloon).

6. 　　(Forces are $16\mathbf{i} - 2\mathbf{j} + 8\mathbf{k}$ and $(6-t)(-2\mathbf{i} + 2\mathbf{j} - \mathbf{k})$)　(Integrate the acceleration)

   At $t = 6$, $\mathbf{v} = 32\mathbf{i} + 12\mathbf{j} + 15\mathbf{k}$

24.3 Page 177

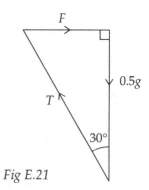

Fig E.21

1. (a) 5.66 N, 2.83 N   (b) 49°   (See Fig E.21)

2. $T_1 = 1.47$ N $T_2 = 2.55$ N $x = 0.79$ N (Along AB the T's cancel out)

3. $T = 10.4$ N (Resolve at A and and B) $a = 4.606$ m s^{-2}

   Distance = 81.4 m (Find the speed when B hits the floor)

4. 310 N   0.33 m s^{-2}

5. $\sqrt{7}$ (Draw a triangle of forces: use the cos rule)

25.2 Page 181

1. $P = 55, Q = 27.5$ (Resolve horiz. and vert.)

2. (a) 2 m s^{-2}, 36 N, 40 N (Resolve at A, B and C) (b) 1 m s^{-2}, 33 N, 45 N

3. (i) (Show that the force down the plane is greater than friction)

   (ii) (Resolve along and perp. to the plane. Write $\mu = \tan \lambda = \dfrac{\sin \lambda}{\cos \lambda}$)

   Least P = $W \sin (\alpha - \lambda)$, when $\beta = \frac{1}{2}\pi + \lambda - \alpha$

   (iii) Least = $W \sin (\alpha + \lambda)$, when $\beta = \frac{1}{2}\pi - \lambda - \alpha$

   (Repeat part (ii), with friction acting down the plane)

26.3 Page 187

1. (a) 3 kg (Moments about D)   (b) C: 10g N, D:5g N

2. 3.6 m up the ladder (Resolve and take moments about the base)

3. (Resolve and take moments about the base)

4. (a) (Note that $\triangle$APB is isosceles) $F = Mg \cot \theta$ (Resolve at B) (b) (Resolve at B)

   $S = 1\frac{1}{3} Mg \cot \theta$ (Take moments about A)   (c) 3M (T is now $\dfrac{Mg}{\sin \theta}$. Resolve at B)

5. (i) $\dfrac{W}{\sqrt{3}}$, $\dfrac{2W}{\sqrt{3}}$ (Resolve horiz. and vert. for the disc)

   (ii) $1\frac{1}{3} W$ (Take moments about A for the rod)

   (iii) 2.4 W, 14° to vertical (Resolve horiz. and vert. for rod)

27.5 Page 196

1. (a) (Moments about AB and BC)   (b) 23°   2. $\frac{1}{4}h(1 + k)$ $k = \frac{1}{3}$

3. $((0.385a, \dfrac{a}{6})$ $1\frac{5}{6} mg$

   (Take moments about C: split the weight into x and y components)

4. (Split the shell up into rings subtending $d\theta$ at the centre. Integrate from $\theta = 0$ to $\theta = \tfrac{1}{2}\pi$)

   (Take moments about base)

5. (Write y in terms of x)   (Use $\cos 2A = 2\cos^2 A - 1$) $y = \dfrac{4b}{3\pi}$ (By symmetry) $\tan \theta = \dfrac{b}{a}$

28.5 Page 205

1. 0.49 Nm (Moments about A)

2. (a) 8.22 N, 18° to OA   (b) $y = -\tfrac{1}{3}x$ (Gradient of line = $-\tan 18°$)   (c) 13.4 Nm, anticlockwise

3. 2 N, 60° to AC, 2 from C   2 N, 60° to AC, 6.93 Nm, anticlockwise (if ABC is lettered clockwise).

4. (i) $P = 5$ (Moments about midpoint)   (ii) 8.94 N   (iii) $\tfrac{1}{2}a$

   $2\tfrac{2}{3}a$ (Moments about A)   8a Nm, anticlockwise (if ABCD is lettered clockwise).

29.3 Page 211

1. 4650 J

2. (a) 3.265, 8 m s^{-1} (b) 10000 N   (i) 3.39 m s^{-2} (ii) 12.1 m s^{-1}

3. (i) 1000 N (Convert to m s^{-1})   (ii) 1.21 m s^{-2} (iii) 300 kg

4. (Use scalar product)   14 $\mathbf{F}_1 = 6\mathbf{i} + 4\mathbf{j} - 12\mathbf{k}$ (Find a unit vector parallel to AB)

   $\mathbf{F}_2 = -4\mathbf{i} - 12\mathbf{j} - 6\mathbf{k}$ (Subtract $\mathbf{F}_1$ from $\mathbf{F}$) $\mathbf{R} = \mathbf{F}_2$

5. (Obtain two expressions for P, and eliminate $\sin \alpha$) $3.8gk$ m s^{-2} (Find the net force at this speed)

6. (a) (Resolve horiz. and vert. for the ring)   (b) (T must be positive)

   Work done = $\dfrac{15 \sin \theta}{2(\sin \theta - 0.3 \cos \theta)}$

   (Distance travelled = $2\tfrac{1}{2}$ m. Use 'work = force x distance')

30.4 Page 217

1. (a) (i) 93.8° (ii) 36 mins   (b) 26 km hr^{-1}, 067.3°

2. 187 km hr^{-1}, at 202°   4.96 secs   375 m   (See Fig E.22)

3. (i) 43.3 km hr^{-1}, 050°   (ii) 25.7 km, 42.8 min   200°

4. $u_1 = 1$ (Let the wind velocity be $x\mathbf{i} + y\mathbf{j}$) $u_2 = 4\sqrt{3}$ $\sqrt{3}\mathbf{i} + 3\mathbf{j}$

5. $\sin \beta = \dfrac{W}{V} \sin \alpha$ (The resultant velocity is $u_1\mathbf{i}$)

   (Use $\cos^2 A = 1 - \sin^2 A$) $U_2 = -W \cos \alpha + \sqrt{(V^2 - W^2 \sin^2 \alpha)}$ (Time is $\dfrac{a}{U_2} - \dfrac{a}{U_1}$)

6. (i) $t = 4$ hr, dist. = 20 km (Find the position vectors of A and C)

   (ii) $\lambda = 3$ (Find $_B\mathbf{v}_A$: the $\mathbf{i}$ component is 0.) $\mu = 6$ ($_C\mathbf{v}_A$ is parallel to $\mathbf{i} + \mathbf{j}$) $\dfrac{10}{\sqrt{2}}$

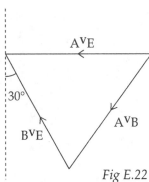

Fig E.22

31.4 Page 224

1. (i) 11.6 m   (ii) 37 m s^{-1}, 20.8° above horizontal   (iii) 4.08 s
   (iv) 20.4 m   (v) 141.4 m

2. (a) 80 m (Put $t = 0$)   (b) 5.8 s (Put $h = 0$)   (c) $5[18.25 - (1\frac{1}{2} - t)^2]$ (Refer to 4.1)
   (d) at $t = 1\frac{1}{2}$ s, 91.25 m   (e) 88.8 m, 1.4 s

3. (i) (Find horiz. and vert. speeds)   (ii) 6.4 m
   (iii) 48 m (Use the range formula)

4. $H = \dfrac{V^2}{2g}$

   (a) $\theta = 15°$ or 75°. 0.0034 V^2, 0.048 V^2 (Use $R = \dfrac{V^2 \sin 2\theta}{g}$)   (b) $\theta = 45°$, $R = \dfrac{V^2}{9.8}$

5. (a) 11 cm   (b) 16.6 m s^{-1} (Horiz. speed = 16. Find the vert. speed)
   (i) 15.2°   (ii) 4.1°

6. (a) $x = (u \cos \alpha)t$, $y = (u \sin \alpha)t - \frac{1}{2}gt^2$

   (b) (i) (Write $\tan \beta = \dfrac{\sin \beta}{\cos \beta}$)

   (ii) $R = \dfrac{2u^2 \cos \alpha \sin (\alpha - \beta)}{g \cos^2 \beta}$. ($R \cos \beta = x$)   (iii) ($\dfrac{y\text{-speed}}{x\text{-speed}} = -\cot \beta$)

32.4 Page 234

1. 5.89 m s^{-1}, 45390 J   1.12 m s^{-1}, 627.2

2. 7 m s^{-1}, 6 m s^{-1} $R - 3500g$ $R = 160300$ N

3. (a) 250 m s^{-1} and 4 m s^{-1} (b) 1000 N   (c) 4 m

4. (a) 4.33 Ns, 26.6° to new line   (b) 7.6 x 10^6, at 19° to new line

5. 1.5 m s^{-1} 20°   8.2 Ns (Change of momentum of arrow and target)

6. $\sqrt{(\dfrac{d}{g})}(\sqrt{5} - \sqrt{3})$ sec. (Speed at floor = $\sqrt{(5gd)}$) $e = \sqrt{0.8}$ $1\frac{1}{2}d$ high, speed = $\sqrt{(gd)}$

7. After first collision: A at $\dfrac{u}{5}$, B at $\dfrac{6u}{5}$ After second collision: B at $\dfrac{2u}{5}$, C at $\dfrac{8u}{5}$.
   B is faster than A.

8. A's speed = $\dfrac{u}{6}$ in other direction.

   (i) Both move at $\frac{1}{3}u$ (ii) Impulse = $\frac{1}{2}mu$ Ns   (iii) Time = $\dfrac{4a}{3u}$ (iv) $\frac{1}{3}mu^2$ lost

9. (a) (i) $\frac{1}{2}u$ (ii) $\frac{1}{3}$ (iii) $\frac{5}{6}mu^2$
   (b) (i) $\frac{3}{8}v$ (ii) $1\frac{7}{8}mv$ (iii) $0.9375mv^2$

33.3 Page 242

1. 6.93 m (First find the constant of proportionality to be 10)

2. $\dfrac{u}{9}$ (Find v in terms of x and u) (Find the constant of proportionality)

3. (i) (Write $\dfrac{d(0.5v^2)}{dx} = \dfrac{-4}{x^3}$, and integrate) (ii) (Write $\dfrac{dx}{dt} = \dfrac{2}{x}$, and integrate)

   Loss = 0.17778 (Work done = $\displaystyle\int F\,dx$)

4. $F = 8000$ N, $b = 5$ (Power = force x velocity)

   (i) 832 secs ($M\dfrac{dv}{dt} = F - 40(100 + bv)$) 4636 m ($Mv\dfrac{dv}{ds} = F - 40(100 + bv)$)

5. (a) 0.231 (Integrate $\dfrac{dv}{dt} = 6e^{-3t}$) 3 (b) (Use $v\dfrac{dv}{dx} = -n^2x$, and integrate)

   $\sqrt{3\tfrac{1}{2}}\,na$ (Use $v\dfrac{dv}{dx} = \dfrac{-n^2x^3}{a^2}$, and integrate)

6. (Use $Mv\dfrac{dv}{ds} = T - kv^2$)

34.4 Page 250

1. (a) 6.13 N, 2.87 N (Radius of circle is 0.4 m. Resolve at B)

   (b) 5.72 (Lower tension = 0)

2. $\dfrac{v^2}{r}$ speed $= \sqrt{\dfrac{GM}{R+h}}$ (Length of orbit = $2\pi(R + h)$)

3. (a) (Tension = mg. Resolve at P) (b) (Resolve at P)

4. $mg(2 + 3\cos\theta)$ (Initial speed = $2\sqrt{(ag)}$) (Find the speed at θ. Resolve perpendicular to the wire)

   $\dfrac{d\theta}{dt} = 2\sqrt{\dfrac{g}{a}}\cos\tfrac{1}{2}\theta$ (Use $v = a\dfrac{d\theta}{dt}$, and $\cos 2A = 2\cos^2 A - 1$)

   (Integrate from $\theta = 0$ to $\theta = \tfrac{1}{2}\pi$. $\displaystyle\int \sec x\,dx = \ln(\sec x + \tan x) + c$)

5. $v^2 = u^2 - 2ag\cos\theta$ (By energy) $T = \dfrac{mu^2}{a} - 3mg\cos\theta$ (Resolve along the string) (Put $T = 0$)

   (Find the velocity when $\theta = 30°$. Show that the trajectory goes through $(1\tfrac{1}{2}a, -\tfrac{1}{2}\sqrt{3}a)$. Refer to 31.3)

35.4 Page 258

1. (a) $\tfrac{1}{3}$m (Refer to 34.1. The string provides the centripetal force)

   (b) $\theta = 60°$, $v = 1.732$ m s^{-1}. (Find the tension, and resolve at the particle. Refer to 34.2)

2. (Take moments about A) $\tan \theta = \frac{3}{4}$

    (Resolve horiz. and vert. Normal force = weight, frictional force = tension in string))

3. (ABC is equilateral)

    (i)   (Find the tension T. Take moments about A)

    (ii) (Resolve horiz. and vert.)
          $3\sqrt{3}\lambda$, at 30° to vertical

Fig E.23

4. (i)   2.1 m s⁻¹ (First find ω)
    (ii) 0.87 m

    (iii) 0.022 N   3 secs
          (Power = force x velocity)

5. $A = -3$, $B = 4$, $c = 2$, $n = 3$
    (Refer to 20.3)   (Refer to 10.4)

    (i)   −1, 7   (ii) 12, 15   (See Fig E.23)

6. (i)   (Use $\dfrac{dv}{dt} = v\,\dfrac{dv}{dx}$. Refer to 33.1)   (ii) (Substitute) $a = 5$, $\omega = 2$ (Use (i))

    Time = 0.142 sec   (Use (ii))   Slides.   (Greatest acceleration = 20 m s⁻² > μg)

7. $\lambda = 140$ newtons   Speed = 1.67 m s⁻¹ ($\omega = \sqrt{70}$)

    Height = 0.413 m.   (elastic energy lost = potential energy gained)

36.3 Page 265

1. (a) 5040 ($^{10}P_4$)   (b) 10000 (10^4)   (c) 0.496 ($1 - \dfrac{(a)}{(b)}$)   (d) 0.9 ($^{10}P_2 \times \dfrac{10^2}{(b)}$)

2. 720 (6!)   72 ($2 \times 3! \times 3!$)   144 ($^4P_3 \times 3!$)

3. (a) $2 \times 9!$ (b) (i) 56 ($^8C_3$)

    (ii) 252 ($2 \times {}^9C_4$)   (iii) 196 ($^{10}C_5 - {}^8C_5$)

4. (i) (a) 302400 ($\dfrac{10!}{3!\,2!}$)   (b) 5040 (7!)

    (ii) (a) $\frac{1}{12}$ $\left(\dfrac{^5C_3}{^{10}C_3}\right)$ (b) $\frac{1}{40}$ (2E's and 1 L must be taken)

5. 50400 ($\dfrac{10!}{3!\,3!\,2!}$) 98

    (2 ways in which all are the same, 36 ways with 2 the same, $^5P_3$ ways with all different)

    0.295

    (Consider the cases for the first draw:

        (i) 2S's or 2 T's (ii) 1 S or 1 T, and one A, I or C (iii) 2 A, I or C's)

37.4 Page 272

1.

x	0	1	2	3
0	0	0	0	0
1	0	1	2	3
2	0	2	4	6
3	0	3	6	9

i	0	1	2	3	4	6	9
$P(X=i)$	$\frac{7}{16}$	$\frac{1}{16}$	$\frac{1}{8}$	$\frac{1}{8}$	$\frac{1}{16}$	$\frac{1}{8}$	$\frac{1}{16}$

$E(X) = 2.25$. Loss of 75 p.

2.

(i)

n	1	2	3	4
$P(X=n)$	$\frac{2}{5}$	$\frac{3}{10}$	$\frac{2}{10}$	$\frac{1}{10}$

m	1	2	3
$P(Y=m)$	$\frac{7}{15}$	$\frac{4}{15}$	$\frac{4}{15}$

$E(Y) = 1\frac{4}{5}$

3. (i) $\frac{5}{8}$ (Score 5, 4 or 3)   (ii) $\frac{15}{64}$ (Score 1, then 5, 4 or 3)

(iii) $\frac{9}{64}$ (Score 1, then 1)

$E(X) = 1\frac{33}{64}$, $E(X^2) = 2\frac{53}{64}$, $Var(X) = 0.531$

(iv) $\frac{3}{4}$ (v) $\frac{3}{16}$ (vi) $\frac{1}{16}$

$E(Y) = 1\frac{5}{16}$, $E(Y^2) = 2\frac{1}{16}$, $Var(Y) = 0.34$

B better and more consistent.

4. (i) (a) A,A   (b) A,not A,A or not A,A,A

(c) ABC (in any order) then A)

(ii) (a) $\frac{1}{16}$,   (b) $\frac{3}{32}$,   (c) $\frac{3}{64}$

(iii) $P(X=2) = \frac{3}{8}$, $P(X=3) = \frac{7}{16}$, $P(X=4) = \frac{3}{16}$ ($P(X=2) = \frac{1}{4} + \frac{1}{16} + \frac{1}{16}$ etc)

Most likely is 3. $E(X) = 2\frac{13}{16}$

5. 0.619 (Find the ways in which A could win. Use the sum of a G.P. Refer to 2.2)

B, with probability 0.52.

(P(A wins the first non–drawn game) = 0.692. A wins the series if A wins the first two non–drawn games, with probability $0.692^2 < \frac{1}{2}$)

38.3 Page 280

1. (X = number right. $X \sim B(5, \frac{1}{3})$) 0.373 (Y = number who pass. $Y \sim B(4, \frac{131}{243})$)

2. (i) 0.165 ($X \sim B(5, \frac{1}{3})$) (ii) 0.79

    0.738 ($Y \sim B(4, \frac{3}{4})$. Find $P(Y = 4 \text{ or } 3)$)

3. (i) 0.346 ($X \sim B(4, 0.4)$) (ii) 0.04

    ($0.8 \times 0.6 + 0.4 \times 0.9 \times 0.3$) 0.4736 (Wins either 3 or 2 of his good first serves)

4. (Use the series for e^a. Refer to 18.1) 2 (Let X = demand. Find $P(X=1)$ & $P(X=2)$ & $P(X=3)$)

    (i) 45.6% ($P(X > 2)$) (ii) 0.191

    (Either 1 refusal on both days, or 2 refusals on one day and none on the other)

    (iii) 0.185 ($P(X=0) + \frac{1}{2}P(X=1)$)

5. (i) (a) (X is Poisson, mean $\frac{1}{4}$) (b) $1\frac{1}{2}$ (X is Poisson, mean $1\frac{1}{2}$)

    (ii) 0.577 (X is Poisson, mean 3) (iii) 0.0249

6. (i) 0.11 ($P(X = 0)$) (ii) 0.181 (iii) 5 days (If n days, $(i)^n < 0.0001$)

    0.369 (Y = number of days. $Y \sim B(7, 0.181)$)

39.3 Page 288

1. (i) (ii) 1.75, 0.5375

2. $\frac{11}{128}$ $E(X) =$, $\text{Var}(X) = \frac{19}{80}$

3. $P(X \le t) = 2kt - \frac{1}{2}kt^2$ (Integrate) $\frac{1}{2}$

4. (i) $A = 3$ (ii) $1\frac{1}{2}, \frac{3}{4}$ (iii) $\frac{1}{125}$ (Find $P(X < n+1 \mid X > n)$)

5. (i) $\frac{2}{3}$ (ii) $\frac{2}{3}$ (iii) $\frac{1}{3}x$ (iv) $\frac{x}{3} + \frac{1}{3}$

    (Consider the areas of rectangles)

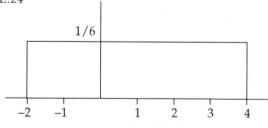

Fig E.24

Fig E.25

(v) 1 $f(t) = \frac{1}{3}$ for $0 \le t \le 2$; $\frac{1}{6}$ for $2 \le t \le 4$; 0 elsewhere (Find the c.d.f.) $E(|X|) = 1\frac{2}{3}$

6. (By integration) $a = 92.2$, $A = 1/92.2$

    (i) 0.114 (Use the c.d.f.) (ii) 0.338 ($P(T > 300 \mid T > 200)$)

    (iii) 0.202 ($2 \times P(T > 200) \times P(T < 200)$)

40.4 Page 297

1. $V(X) = \int x^2 f(x)\,dx - \left(\int x f(x)\,dx\right)^2$ $V(X)$ is also $\int (x - \mu)^2 f(x)\,dx$

   $\text{Var}(Y) = \frac{7}{9}$ $(E(X_1) = E(X_2) = \frac{1}{6},\ \text{Var}(X_1) = \text{Var}(X_2) = \frac{7}{180})$ Y goes from –2 to 4

2. $np,\ np(1-p)$ (Refer to 40.1) $(X \sim B(20,\theta))$ $(Y \sim B(10, 2\theta))$

   $\text{Var}(P_1) = \dfrac{\theta(1-\theta)}{20}$ $\text{Var}(P_2) = \dfrac{\theta(1-2\theta)}{20}$ Choose Method 2. (Variance is smaller)

3. (i) 7.55, 7.95 7.55, 8.37   (ii) 2.75, 2.3125 (a) 0.5, 9.25 (b) 0, 4.625

4. $\text{Var}(X) = 0.8$

i	0	$\frac{1}{2}$	2
$P(T=i)$	0.36	0.32	0.32

   $((X_1 - X_2)^2$ can only be 0, 1 or 4) $E(T) = 0.8$

41.4 Page 306

1. (i) 0.2   (ii) 0.6   (iii) 0.3 424.4 grams

2. (a) 1.881 $(\Phi(1.881) = 0.97)$ (b) 0.496 $(\Phi(0.496) = 0.69)$

   (c) 15.5 $\left(\dfrac{25-13}{1.881+0.496} = 5\right)$ (d) (i) 7% (ii) 7% $(\mu = 15.5)$

3. (a) 44   (b) 4.954

   54.5%, 683 (Assuming that it is normal)

4. (i) 0.159   (ii) (B's prob. = 0.19)   (iii) 0.584 (B–A $\sim$ N(0.2, 0.89))

5. (i) (a) $\frac{1}{2}$ (b) 0.759 (B(100, 0.025))   (c) 0.071 (B(100, 0.375))

   (ii) 158 (Sample proportion – N(0.6, $\dfrac{0.24}{n}$). Require $1.282 \times \sqrt{(0.24/n)} < 0.05$

6. $Y \sim N(n\mu, n\sigma^2)$ (If $n = 9$, $P(Y > 725 = 1 - \Phi(5.5))$

   (i) 0.011   (ii) 0.739 By above, $N = 9$ 0.132 $(0.8^9 \times 0.9798)$

7. (i) (By symmetry) 0.1 (Area of rectangle)   (ii) 4, $\dfrac{3}{100}$ 0.92(X $\sim$ N(4, $\dfrac{3}{100}$)

   (iii) $1 \le x \le 2.2$ or $5.8 \le x \le 7$ Prob. = 0.4

42.5 Page 318

1. (a) $0.44 < p < 0.5$ (b) $53 < \mu < 54.4$ (Find the unbiased sample variance)

2. (a) 6.122, 0.0175   (b) $6.091 < \mu < 6.153$ (Using the figures in (a))

   $z = 1.74$. No sig. difference at 5%. (two–tailed test)

   (The variance of the difference of the sample means is 4.7×10^{-4})

   It is assumed that the populations are normal.

3. For A: $z = 1.77$. Significantly better. (A 1–tailed test)   For B: $z = 1.49$. Not significant.

   Total mean $= 45.9$ $z = 2.29$. Significantly better.

   Variance $= 223$ (Find $\sum X^2$ for A and B. Combine these)

43.5 Page 328

1. (a) (i) $0.02, 0.012$ (ii) $-0.08 < \mu < 0.12$ (Using a t_4 distribution)

(b) £$85.3 < \mu <$ £87.5 $-$£$0.1 < D <$ £2.5

   £0 is included in the interval. Hence the claim is not disproved.

2. For a paired sample test, there must be a natural association between the members of each pair.

   H_0: no difference H_1: old tyres wear more $t_7 = 2.65$. Reject H_0 at 5% $0.044 < D < 0.24$

3. The differences might be due to chance.

   $\chi^2(4) = 4.42$. Not significant. $\chi^2(4) = 9.94$. Significant at 5%. (Combine the figures)

4. (a) $\chi^2(2) = 7.6$. Significant at 5%. Not a good fit.   (b) The odd group is 35–39

   It would be fairer to combine this group with the 40–49 group.

5. (a) $\chi^2(2) = 32.5$. Significant.   (b) $\upsilon = (4–1)(2–1) = 3$ 8.12 is significant at 5%.

   There is a difference.

   (c) $\upsilon = 6$. 9.32 is not significant. No proved difference.

44.4 Page 338

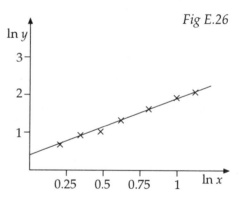

Fig E.26

1. $\ln y = \ln A + B \ln x$. Plot $\ln y$ against $\ln x$. (Fig E.26)

$\ln x$	.182	.322	.457	.615	.806	.997	1.128
$\ln y$	.621	.829	.967	1.267	1.556	1.842	2.037

   $A = 1.4$, $B = 1.5$ 3rd term should be (1.58, 2.81)

2. (a) $\frac{y}{\sqrt{x}} = ax + b$ $a = -1.25, b = 1.8$

   (b) (i) $\ln y$ against x $\ln Y$ against $\ln(X+1)$

   (ii) gradient $= -k$. Intercept $= \ln h$.   gradient $= q$.
   Intercept $= \ln p$.

3. (i) $-1 \le r \le 1$ (ii) How closely the order match.

   (iii) The populations may not necessarily be correlated.
   (10.5, 11.8) is far from the line.

   Spearman's coefficient $= 0.85$. (See Fig E.28)
   (For tied ranks, at 9 say, allot $9\frac{1}{2}$ each)

   This is significant at 1% to show that there is a correlation.

Fig E.27

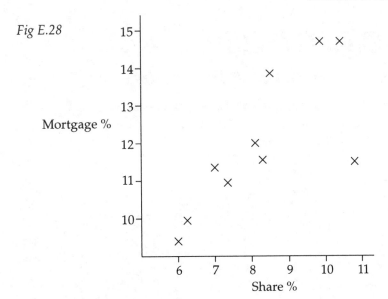

Fig E.28

Solutions
(to examination papers)

Paper 1

1. $x = 32, y = 43$

2. $(x + 1\frac{1}{2})^2 - 1\frac{1}{4}. \ k < -1\frac{1}{4}$

3. (i) $\frac{2}{3}p$ (ii) 4π (iii) 2π

4. $\dfrac{1}{x-1} - \dfrac{1}{x+1}. \ \ln 3 - \ln 2$

5. (i) $\dfrac{2\cos 2x}{\sin 2x}$ (ii) $\dfrac{\cos x}{\sin x} - \dfrac{\sin x}{\cos x}$

6. (i) $1 + 8x + 24x^2 + 32x^3 + 16x^4$ (ii) -160 (iii) 2.16

7. $y = -2x + 3. \ (0,3)$ and $(1\frac{1}{2},0). \ 2\frac{1}{4}$

8. $\tan \frac{1}{2}x + c$

9. $(x-1)(x+3)(2x+1). \ -3 < x$ and $-\frac{1}{2} < x < 1$

10. common difference = log(common ratio)

11. $n = 2. \ 2.35. \ 2.4418$

12. (i) $2r\cos\theta$ (ii) $4\theta r^2 \cos^2\theta$ (iii) $r^2\sin\theta\cos\theta$ (iv) $\frac{1}{2}r^2(\pi - 2\theta - \sin 2\theta)$

13. $k = 1$ or 3

14. $\dfrac{dy}{dx} = 3y. \ Y = Ae^{3x}. \ y = e^{3x-3}. \ 0.317$

15. $\frac{4}{27}$ (a) $\frac{1}{8}$ (b) $\frac{41}{72}$ (c) $\frac{8}{31}$

Paper 2

1.

Prize	£5	£3	£1	£0	
Prob.	$\frac{1}{20}$	$\frac{19}{20^2}$	$\frac{19^2}{20^3}$	$\frac{19^3}{20^3}$	54p

2. -0.455. Not sig.

3. $z = 2.57$. sig. $0.55 < p < 0.75$

4. $\chi^2(2) = 5.015$. Not sig.

5. 54 tins. $z = 1.6$, not sig. 0.03

6. (i) Method I: 0.086. Method II: 0.104

   (ii) Method I: 0.149. Method II: 0.178. Method I better in both cases.

7. (ii) (166, 73)   (iv) 171 cm, 76.6 kg.   (v) Spearman = 0.786

8. 0.61. Average = 11.6.   Unbiased sample variance 0.14. $z = 1.69$, sig.

Paper 3

1. (a) 2525 J.   (b) $\mathbf{R} = -3\mathbf{i} - 12.9\mathbf{j}$. $\mu = 0.23$

2. (i) 17.89 m s^{-1}

3. $s = 36ge^{-t/6} + 6gt - 36g$. $s = -6v - 36g\ln\left(1 - \dfrac{v}{6g}\right)$

4. 0.397

5. AB:th, 30$\sqrt{2}$ N. CD:th, 10$\sqrt{2}$ N. AE: te, 30 N. DE: te, 10 N. BE:th, 10$\sqrt{2}$ N. CE: te, 10$\sqrt{2}$ N. BC:th, 20 N

6. $\dfrac{h^2 + 8h + 220}{4h + 176}$ cm. $h < 11.5$ cm

7. (i) $\frac{1}{3}u(1 - 2e)$, $\frac{1}{3}u(1 + e)$ (ii) $(1 - 2e)^2 : 2(1 + e)^2$ (iii) $\dfrac{2\pi a}{eu}$

    Ultimately both have speed u.

8. $\omega = \sqrt{\dfrac{g}{\rho L}}$. Speed $= \delta\sqrt{\dfrac{g}{\rho L}}$. Time $= \frac{1}{2}\pi\sqrt{\dfrac{\rho L}{g}}$

Paper 4

1. 16:1   2. $y = 3x$, $y = -3x + \pi$. $(\frac{\pi}{6}, \frac{\pi}{2})$
3. $a = \frac{3}{4}$, $b = \frac{1}{4}$ 4.   10.2°, 102.4°
5. $y = e^{x^2} - 1$
7. (a) $\frac{1}{7}$ (b) −1.19
8. (a) −9   (b) 0. $(x - 2)(2x + 1)^2$. $x = -\frac{1}{2}$ or $x \geq 2$
9. 0.786
10. (a) none   (b) $(1, e^{-1})$, max.   (c)   (0,0) min, $(2, 4e^{-2})$ max
11. (ii) $\sqrt{48}$, $\sqrt{32}$
12. (a) 71.73   (b) $\sin x - \frac{1}{3}\sin^3 x + c$ (c) $\frac{1}{3}\pi$
13. $2\mathbf{i} + \mathbf{k}$. $\mathbf{r} = a(\mathbf{i} + \mathbf{j} + 2\mathbf{k}) + \lambda(2\mathbf{i} + \mathbf{k})$
14. (i) 1.25   (ii) 5.48   (iii) $\lambda = \ln 3$. $\dfrac{6}{\ln 3}$

Paper 5

1. 123°   2.   (i) 0.011 cm s^{-1} (ii) $3\frac{1}{3}$ cm^2 s^{-1}
3. (i)   52, 15.8   (ii) 20
4. (a) (i) 0.1   (ii) 0.2   (b) 0.324
5. 0.7   6.   2.87 m s^{-2}
7. (i)   4000 N   (ii) 4060 N   (iii) 0.018 m s^{-2}
8. 1.63 m s^{-2} $\frac{2}{3}$ sec.   1.361 m

9. (a) (i) 30 m s^{-1} (ii) 0.4 m s^{-2} (iii) 15 m (b) 75 secs.

10. (a) $\mathbf{v}_P = 6t\mathbf{i} + 2\mathbf{j}$, $\mathbf{v}_Q = \mathbf{i} + 3t\mathbf{j}$ (b) $\sqrt{148}$

     (c) $t = \frac{2}{3}\text{s}$. At $t = 1$, $7\mathbf{i} + 1\frac{1}{2}\mathbf{j}$

11. 80.4^2, 6.77^0 12. 0.102

13. (i) 0.201 (ii) $0.624. 14$

14. (i) 0.01 (ii) 0.61

15.

i	0	1	2	3	
$P(X = i)$	$\frac{1}{3}$	$\frac{1}{2}$	0	$\frac{1}{6}$	$E(X) = 1$

16. μ, $\dfrac{\overline{\sigma}^2}{n}$. $41.1 < \mu < 53.5$

Paper 6

1. $x = -6, y = 4$, or $x = 2\frac{4}{7}, y = 1\frac{1}{7}$ 2. $y = 3x + 1. 134.1$

4. (iii) 0.3 (iv) 0 (v) $\frac{1}{4}$

5. 11.7 secs   6. 1.38 grams

7. $\frac{2}{3}$ 8. $18.4°$

9. 0.3 11. $(3\frac{1}{9}, 2\frac{2}{9})$. $4\frac{4}{9}$ grams

12. (a) 10N (c) 1.3 m/s

13. 1.96 m s^{-2}. 0.784 m s^{-1}

14. $1 : 0.32$

15. (i) $P = 5, Q = 5\sqrt{2}$ (ii) 1.78 N, $22°$ to BC. 7.6 m from C

16. $^5\sqrt{(a^4 + a^5)}$

Paper 7

1. (a) $x \geq 8$ (b) $-11 < x < 4$ (c) $-1 < x < 2$ (d) $x < 0$ or $x > 1$

3. $\frac{7}{15}$. $\frac{2}{7}$

4. $a = 0.45, b = 0.1$ 5. $2,598,960. 0.002$

6. e.g. $y = |x|$

7. $17.4, 4.21, 0.012$

8. 37% to 43%. 9220   10. 0.974. 11 mins to 9.

11. $P(X = i) = \frac{1}{8} \times \left(\frac{7}{8}\right)^{i-1}$. $E(X) = 8$. 23 shots

12. (i) 0.195 (ii) 0.271 (iii) 0.624 (iv) 0.198

13. $252, 26\frac{2}{3}$. $248 < \mu < 256$. 55 times

14. Not significant. $\chi^2(3) = 4$

15. $p = 0.327$. $\chi^2(1) = 8.79$, not good fit.

16. −0.97, −0.43, 0, 0.43, 0.97. 91 cm, 8 cm. 99 cm.

Paper 8

1. $(x - 2)(x - 3)(2x + 1)$. $x = 2, 3, -\frac{1}{2}$

2. enlargement scale factor 2, centre O

3. (a) 2   (b) $\frac{1}{2}\sqrt{5} + \frac{1}{2}\sqrt{3}$

4. 2.11

5. (a) fg: $x \to (2x + 1)^2 + 3$ (b) fg$(x) \geq 3$ (c) $x = 3$

6. (a) (i) x^{-1} (ii) 2^x (iii) $2x$ (b) 0.693, 1.099

7. 62

8. 82 m. 2.45 secs, 5.55 secs

9. 2000. 250×2^{4n}. After 1.33 years

10. −22, −38, $8 - 15x$. $x = -1$

11. (b) between 4.27 and 4.53

Paper 9

1. $\frac{y}{x} = ax + b$

2. $1 + 20x + 190x^2$. 0.4

3. (a) $(x - 3), (x + 2)$ (c) 8

4. (b) $V = 500 + 500e^{-0.01t}$ (c) tends to 500 litres

5. $\frac{1}{x + 1} - \frac{1}{x + 2}$. $\frac{1}{2} - \frac{1}{n + 2}$

6. 6π. $\frac{x^2}{9} + \frac{y^2}{4} = 1$

7. $n = 1$. (i) converges to 1.213. Others diverge.

8. (b) $\theta = 0, 0.9553, -0.9553$ (c) $2.418a^3$ cm^3

9. $\cos^2 x + \sin^2 x = 1$. $22.5°, 157.5^0$

10. (i) $-\frac{1}{3}\cos(3x + 2) + c$ (ii) $\frac{1}{2}\ln 7$ (iii) $\frac{1}{4}$

Paper 10

1. $\mathbf{v} = (2t - 10)\mathbf{i} - 6t\mathbf{j}$. $\mathbf{a} = 2\mathbf{i} - 6\mathbf{j}$. $t = \frac{1}{2}$

2. 0.0225 m s^{-2}, 400 s.

3. 1.4 m s^{-2}. $\frac{4}{7}$ s

4. 3.75 m from base.

5. $6\frac{2}{3}$ g N, $13\frac{1}{3}$ g N. 10 kg

6. 14.4 m s^{-1}. yes

7. $3\mathbf{i} - \mathbf{j}$ N. $\sqrt{10}$ N. 74.7°

8. $k = 6$. 21.3 m s^{-1}

9. $-\mathbf{i} - \mathbf{j}$. $\frac{9}{22}$

10. 1.62 m

Paper 11

1. $\frac{1}{2}mg \cot \theta$. 0.289

2. 4.8 N, 66°

3. $\frac{3}{4}a$. $\frac{1}{3}mgh$. $h = 1\frac{1}{2}a$

4. $(\frac{3}{8}, \frac{2}{5})$. $(\frac{5}{16}, 0)$. 17.4°

5. $x = V\frac{t}{\sqrt{2}}$, $y = V\frac{t}{\sqrt{2}} - \frac{1}{2}gt^2$. 13.9 m s⁻¹

8. 81.6 m. 64.8 m

Paper 12

1. 0.059

2. 2.994, 0.0753. 2.95, 2.8, 3.15

3. (a) 0.449   (b) 0.191   (c) 0.742

4. $\mu = 5.31$, $\sigma^2 = 1.05$

5.

i	£0	£2	£3	£4	
P($X = i$)	$\frac{125}{216}$	$\frac{25}{72}$	$\frac{5}{72}$	$\frac{1}{216}$	8%

6. (a) $\frac{3}{8}$ (b) $1\frac{1}{2}$ (c) $\frac{37}{64}$

7. (a) 0.04   (b) 0.87

8. $f(x) = \frac{2x}{10^8}$, for $0 \le x \le 10^4$ (a) 6667 hours   (b) 7071 hours

9. £20,200. £15,500 and £27,100

Paper 13

1. $z = 2.83$. Yes

2. $9.7 < \mu < 10.3$. $z = 1.88$, not sig.

3. $\chi^2(3) = 10.4$. Sig. $\chi^2(2) = 1.69$. Not sig.

4. $a = 0.88$, $b = 0.818$. $F = 380$ suspect. Predict 345.

5. Not significant. ($\chi^2(1) = 3.79$, with Yates' correction.)

6. 0.917

7. $\chi^2(4) = 1.86$. Good fit. $v = 3$, not good fit

8. 32.2 hours. 0.09

Paper 14

1. $\frac{7\pi}{24}$, $-\frac{\pi}{24}$, $\frac{23\pi}{24}$, $-\frac{17\pi}{24}$

2. 0.693

3. 0.41 m s⁻²

4. $x = 1.9$

5. 0.573. Under

6. $\{x:x \ne 4\}$. $f^{-1}:x \to \frac{3}{x} + 4$. $\{x: x \ne 0\}$. $f^0f:x \to \frac{12 - 3x}{4x - 19}$

7. $\frac{1}{9}$. $\frac{211}{243}$

8. $\frac{47}{200}$. $p_{n+1} = \frac{1}{10}p_n + \frac{1}{4}(1-p_n)$. 0.217

9. Pedigree: 3.4, 2.65, 4.0.   Mongrel: 3.45, 3.05, 3.75

10. $h = \dfrac{1000}{\pi r^2}$. $A = 2\pi r^2 + \dfrac{2000}{r}$. 1:2   11. $\frac{1}{30}$ m s^{-2}, $2\frac{1}{3}$ m s^{-1}. 32 secs.

12. a) 0.50125, 0.5025, 0.50376, 0.505018 kg   b) $W = 0.5e^{0.01t}$. 0.505025 kg

13. $\dfrac{dy}{dx} = e^x((A + B)\cos x + (B - A)\sin x)$. $A = B = \frac{1}{2}$. $2\frac{1}{2}e^x(\cos x + \sin x)$. $a = 1$, $b = -2$, $c = 2$

14. $T = 1\frac{1}{3}\,mg$, $a = \frac{1}{3}g$.

Paper 15

1. $2 < x < 3$ 2.   3

3.   383 m. 180 m s^{-1}, 33.7° below horiz. 3000 J

4.   (i) $\frac{1}{8}\theta\,\text{m}^2$ (ii) $\frac{1}{8}(\theta - \sin\theta)\,\text{m}^2$ (iv) $\frac{1}{4}\sin\frac{1}{2}\theta$. $\dfrac{dx}{dt} = \frac{1}{4}\sin\frac{1}{2}\theta\,\dfrac{d\theta}{dt}$

     (v) a) 0.03 m^3 per min   (b) 0.005 metre per min

5.   (a) (i) 2   (ii) $y = -\frac{1}{2}x + 2\frac{1}{2}$ (iii) $(-4, 4\frac{1}{2})$ (iv) $y = -3x + 7\frac{1}{2}$

     (b) (i) $3x$ m, $\dfrac{384}{x^2}$ m.   (iii) 8 by 24 by 6

6.   (a) $\cos^2 x = \frac{1}{2}(1 + \cos 2x)$. $\pi - 2$ (b) 2. 3.45

7.   (i) 0.36 m s^{-2} (ii) 0.53 m s^{-2} (iii) 0.32 m s^{-2}. 2.1°

8. $\dfrac{1}{r} - \dfrac{1}{r+1}$.   (i) $\frac{11}{10}$ (ii) 1. $\frac{11}{21}$

9.   (i) (2, 3), 1.   (iii) 2.16. 4.61

10. (i) $k = 3$.   (ii) $2\frac{3}{4}$ (iii) 2.79

11. 3.513

12. $\dfrac{dT}{dt} = -k(T - 10)$. $T = Ae^{-kt} + 10$. $T = 90 \times e^{-0.118t} + 10$. (i) 37.8°   (ii) 9.35 mins

13. 0.091. 3247 gallons. 18,855 gallons

Paper 16

1. $y = 5x - 4$ 2.   (a) $1 + 2x$ (b) $6\sin 3x \cos 3x$

3. $\theta : \sin\theta$ 4.   10.03

5.   (i) $\frac{1}{3}(2\mathbf{i} + 2\mathbf{j} - \mathbf{k})$, $\frac{1}{3}(\mathbf{i} - 2\mathbf{j} - 2\mathbf{k})$. $\mathbf{r} = \lambda(\mathbf{i} - \mathbf{k})$ (ii) $\hat{\mathbf{n}} = \frac{1}{3}(2\mathbf{i} - \mathbf{j} + 2\mathbf{k})$

6.   (a) $\sqrt{\dfrac{gh}{32}}$ (b) $1\frac{1}{2}h$

7. $-80 = RT - \dfrac{R^2}{2000}(1 + T^2)$. $R^2 > 4\dfrac{R^2}{2000}\left(\dfrac{R^2}{2000} - 20\right)$. 1077 m. 917 m.

8.   (a) $y + 3x = 32$ (b) $y = 3x - 1$

9.   31,600 m s^{-1}

10. (i) $\{y \geq 2 \text{ or } y \leq 2\}$. $y = x$, $x = 0$.   (ii) $\frac{\pi}{6}$

11. (b) $60.2°$

12. (a) $\frac{23}{14}$ (b) $4 - 2\sqrt{e}$ (c) $\ln 2$. (b) $2\frac{2}{3}$

13. $n = 1.1.31$ 14. 8.54 m. $26.3°$. 3.90 m. $93°$

15. (a) $\sqrt{(3 + \sqrt{8})}$

Paper 17

1. (i) $\frac{1}{2}x^{-1/2} - \frac{1}{2}x^{-3/2}$ (ii) $2x\cos x - x^2\sin x$ (iii) $\dfrac{6x}{1 + 3x^2}$

2. (i) $\frac{1}{2}\pi$ cu. in. (ii) 0.032 in

3. (a) (i) $2x$ (ii) $-x$ (b) 0.683

4. (i) 0.953 (ii) 0.472 (iii) 0.679

5. (ii) $1, \pi - 3$ (iii) $\frac{1}{3}\pi$ (iv) 0.092

6. (a) $a = -3, b = -4$

   (b) (i) $\dfrac{3}{x} + \dfrac{2x + 1}{x^2 + 1}$ (i) $-\dfrac{1}{x - 1} - \dfrac{2}{(x - 1)^2} + \dfrac{2}{x + 1}$

   (c) $-\ln(x - 1) + \dfrac{2}{x - 1} + 2\ln(x + 1) + c$

7. (i) $h\alpha\sec^2\theta\,\mathrm{cm\,s^{-1}}$ (ii) $\frac{2}{3}\pi h^3\tan\theta\sec^2\theta\,\mathrm{cm^2\,s^{-1}}$

8. (i) $\frac{1}{3}\pi$ (ii) $\ln\sqrt{5}$. $0 < \theta < 2.68$

9. (i) $\frac{35}{54}, \frac{17}{54}, \frac{1}{27}$ (ii) $\frac{15}{34}$ (iii) $\frac{3}{4}$

10. (i) $k = \frac{1}{13}$ (ii) $\frac{6}{13}, \frac{302}{169}$

i	0	1	2	3
$P(|X| = i)$	$\frac{4}{13}$	$\frac{5}{13}$	$\frac{3}{13}$	$\frac{1}{13}$
i	0	1	4	9
$P(X^2 = i)$	$\frac{4}{13}$	$\frac{5}{13}$	$\frac{3}{13}$	$\frac{1}{13}$

11. $z = 1.85$. Sig. Yes. $0.155 < p < 0.345$

12. $y = \dfrac{-x}{t^2} + 2\dfrac{c}{t}$ (ii) $4c^2$ (iii) $S = \frac{1}{2}c^2(1 + t^{-4})$

13. $5.32 < \mu < 5.36$. At least 154. $z = 1.41$. Not sig.

Solutions
(to GCSE revision & consolidation questions)

A1

1. 0.018 m, 0.013

2. 0.013. 57–59 kg

3. 1.8 kg.70–74 kg

4. (a) 0.0016, 0.0005.

(b) 0.0013, 0.0004

5. 0.0033, 0.01

6. (a) 7.692. 0.0003, 0.00004

(b) 7.69. 0.002, 0.0003

7. (a) 0.005 (b) 0.01 (c) 0.025 (d) 0.025

8. 20.8 s, 20.4 s

9. 400 m²

10. 3.12 hours, 2.88 hours

A2

1. (a) $\frac{1}{4}$ (b) $\frac{2}{3}$ (c) $\frac{1}{2}$ (d) $\frac{4}{5}$

2. (a) $2\frac{2}{5}$ (b) $4\frac{1}{3}$ (c) $1\frac{6}{11}$ (d) $2\frac{1}{4}$

3. (a) $\frac{11}{8}$ (b) $\frac{7}{3}$ (c) $\frac{15}{4}$ (d) $\frac{26}{7}$

4. (a) $\frac{1}{10}$ (b) $\frac{3}{28}$ (c) $\frac{1}{5}$ (d) $2\frac{1}{4}$

(e) $1\frac{1}{3}$ (f) $3\frac{11}{18}$ (g) $\frac{13}{15}$ (h) $\frac{5}{8}$

(i) $\frac{29}{30}$ (j) $\frac{7}{16}$ (k) 7 (l) $\frac{25}{42}$

(m) $\frac{8}{13}$ (n) $3\frac{3}{4}$ (o) $\frac{1}{2}$

A3

1. (a) 8 (b) 64 (c) 25 (d) 2

(e) 5 (f) 2 (g) $\frac{1}{4}$ (h) $\frac{1}{8}$

(i) $\frac{1}{100}$ (j) 2 (k) 9 (l) $\frac{16}{9}$

2. (a) 3 (b) $2\sqrt{2}$ (c) 100 (d) 4

(e) $\sqrt{3}$ (f) $2\sqrt{2}$ (g) $\sqrt{2}$ (h) $\sqrt{2}$

(i) $3\sqrt{2}$ (j) $\sqrt{3}$ (k) 10   (l) $\sqrt{2}$

(m) $4 + 3\sqrt{2}$ (n) 2   (o) $3 - \sqrt{3}$ (p) $3\sqrt{2} - 2\sqrt{3}$

(q) $4 + 2\sqrt{3}$ (r) $11 - 6\sqrt{2}$ (s) $1 + \frac{1}{2}\sqrt{3}$

A4

1. (a) 3.2×10^8 (b) 5×10^6 (c) 6.7×10^{-10} (d) 2×10^{-6}

    (e) 4.7×10^9 (f) 2.1×10^6 (g) 7.32×10^{-10} (h) 3×10^{-11}

2. (a) 8×10^{19} (b) 1.04×10^{16} (c) 8.4×10^{-14} (d) 1.23×10^{20}

    (e) 2×10^5 (f) 3×10^{10} (g) 2×10^{-16} (h) 5×10^{15}

    (i) 3.4×10^8 (j) 5.3×10^7 (k) 3.8×10^9 (l) 4.5×10^{-9}

    (m) -3.4×10^{-9} (n) 6.02×10^{10} (o) 2.95×10^{-8}

A5

1. (a) 61.0   (b) 13.0   (c) 27.4   (d) 0.0679

    (e) 123

2. (a) 1024   (b) 3.71   (c) 0.00243   (d) 0.951

    (e) 3.83   (f) 2.45   (g) 0.440   (h) 0.0383

    (i) 83.3   (j) 2.21   (k) 0.0303   (l) 64.3

    (m) 0.109   (n) 0.701   (o) 0.845   (p) 0.000712

B1

1. (a) -7 (b) 17   (c) $-\frac{1}{12}$

2. (a) 19   (b) -9 (c) $6\frac{1}{2}$

3. (a) 6   (b) 6   (c) $-2\frac{3}{4}$

4. (a) 39   (b) 18   (c) $2\frac{7}{8}$

5. (a) $\frac{1}{2}$ (b) $-2\frac{1}{2}$ (c) 15

6. (a) $-\frac{1}{2}$ (b) $-\frac{1}{8}$ (c) -32

7. (a) $\frac{1}{3}$ (b) -1 (c) 2

8. (a) 1   (b 0.3   (c) 9

9. (a) 2   (b) 2.65   (c) 5.29

10. (a) 1   (b) 3   (c) $\frac{1}{2}$

B2

1. $xa + xb + ya + yb$
2. $x^2 - 4x - 21$
3. $x^2 - 6x + 8$
4. $6x^2 + x - 2$
5. $6x^2 - 17x + 5$
6. $15x^2 - 19x + 6$
7. $x^2 + 2xy + y^2$
8. $a^2 - 2ab + b^2$
9. $2p^2 - 8q^2$
10. $4x^2 + 12x + 9$
11. $9x^2 - 30xy + 25y^2$
12. $4x^2 + 12 + \dfrac{9}{x^2}$
13. $9x^2$
14. $16x^4y^6$
15. $x^4 - 2x^2z + z^2$
16. a^3b^6
17. $x^4 + 4x^3 + 4x^2$
18. $x^4 - \dfrac{4}{x} + \dfrac{4}{x^6}$

B3

1. $xy(x + y)$
2. $3x^2(y + 3x)$
3. $(x + 3)(x + 1)$
4. $(x - 5)(x - 3)$
5. $(x - 7)(x + 4)$
6. $(x + 8)(x - 3)$
7. $(x + 4)(x - 15)$
8. $(2 - x)(5 + x)$
9. $(3 - x)(20 + x)$
10. $(m - n)(m + n)$
11. $(2p - 3q)(2p + 3q)$
12. $3(r - 2s)(r + 2s)$
13. $(2x - 5)(x + 1)$
14. $(2x - 3)(x - 4)$
15. $(3x + 1)(x - 3)$
16. $(2x + 5)^2$
17. $(3x - 7)^2$
18. $(2a - 3b)^2$
19. $(4x - 1)(x - 3)$
20. $(x + y)(p - q)$
21. $(2a - b)(3t - s)$

B4

1. 2
2. 2
3. −1
4. 6
5. 2
6. 7
7. 16
8. 648
9. 40
10. ±4
11. 8
12. 3
13. −0.6
14. 1.2

15. $x = 2, y = 2$

16. $x = 8, y = 4$

17. $x = 3, y = 2$

18. $x = 5, y = -7$

19. $x = 8, y = 6$

20. $x = 5, y = 20$

B5

1. $b - a$

2. $\frac{1}{3}(c + a)$

3. $q^2 - p$

4. $(q - p)^2$

5. $\dfrac{7}{z}$

6. $\dfrac{a - 3b}{b}$

7. $\dfrac{b}{c - a}$

8. $\dfrac{m - n}{p - q}$

9. $\dfrac{b}{a - 1}$

10. $\dfrac{3}{q - 1}$

11. $\dfrac{m - pn}{p - 1}$

12. $\dfrac{ad - bc}{b + c - a - d}$

13. $\sqrt{(a - b)}$

14. $\sqrt{(4 - m^2)}$

15. $\sqrt[3]{\dfrac{q + p}{7}}$

B6

1. (a) $2, y = 2x$
    (b) $\frac{1}{3}, y = \frac{1}{3}x$
    (c) $20, y = \dfrac{20}{x}$
    (d) $\frac{1}{8}, y = \dfrac{1}{8x}$

    (e) $10, y = 10x^2$
    (f) $2, y = 2x^2$
    (g) $60, y = \dfrac{60}{x^2}$
    (h) $10, y = \dfrac{10}{x^2}$

2. (a) direct, $y = 2.5x$
    (b) square, $y = 1.25x^2$

    (c) inverse square, $y = \dfrac{324}{x^2}$
    (d) cube, $y = \frac{1}{2}x^3$

    (e) inverse, $y = \dfrac{1}{6x}$

B7

1. (a) $\dfrac{2x}{y}$
    (b) $\dfrac{x + 1}{x^2}$
    (c) $\dfrac{x + 3}{x + 4}$
    (d) pq

    (e) ba
    (f) $\dfrac{a^2}{b^2}$

2. (a) $\dfrac{1}{xy}$
    (b) $\dfrac{ab}{cd}$
    (c) xy
    (d) $\dfrac{x^2 - 1}{x^2 - 4}$

    (e) $\dfrac{1}{(x + 3)(x - 4)}$
    (f) $\dfrac{x + 1}{x + 3}$
    (g) $\dfrac{ay}{bx}$
    (h) $\dfrac{x^2 b}{y^2 a}$

(i) $\dfrac{b}{a(x-1)}$ (j) $\dfrac{5x}{6}$ (k) $\dfrac{7x-9}{12}$ (l) $\dfrac{y+x}{xy}$

(m) $\dfrac{1-b}{ab}$ (n) $\dfrac{x}{x^2-1}$

C1

1. (a) 14 cm^2 (b) 12.6 m^2 (c) 1810 cm^2 (d) 176 cm^2
   (e) 16 cm^2
2. (a) 905 cm^3 (b) 64 cm^3 (c) 603 cm^3 (d) 151 cm^3
3. (a) $6.28 \text{ cm}, 25.1 \text{cm}^2$ (c) $12.6 \text{ cm}, 75.4 \text{ cm}^2$ (e) $0.628 \text{ cm}, 0.0942 \text{ cm}^2$
4. $1.27 \text{ m}, 5.09 \text{ m}^2$ 5. $1.95 \text{ m}, 12.3 \text{ m}$
6. $1.41 \text{ cm}, 11.8 \text{ cm}^3$ 7. 0.716 cm
8. 0.892 m 9. $35.8°$
10. $45.8°$ 11. 13.1 m

C2

1. (a) $x = 8.54 \text{ cm}$ (b) $y = 9.80 \text{ cm}$ (c) $z = 7.48 \text{ cm}$
2. 10.6 cm 3. 12.04 cm
4. $12.4 \text{ cm}, 49.5 \text{ cm}^2$ 5. 13.4 cm2
6. 5.48 cm

C3

1. (a) $x = 17.3 \text{ m}$ (b) $y = 8.24 \text{ m}$ (c) $z = 13.9 \text{ m}$
2. (a) $48.6°$ (b) $46.8°$ (c) $35.8°$
3. $9.83 \text{ cm}, 6.88 \text{ cm}$ 4. $54.5°, 35.5°$
5. 127 m 6. $5.7°$
7. 6.16 km 8. $25.4°$
9. $74.5°$
10. (a) $71.8°$ (b) $29.0°$ (c) 8.21 cm (d) 7.36 cm
11. $36.9°$
12. (a) $30°, 150°$ (b) $45° \ 315°$ (c) $200° \ 340°$ (d) $115°, 245°$

D1

1. $\frac{1}{13}$, $\frac{1}{221}$

2. $\frac{5}{9}$, $\frac{5}{18}$

3. $\frac{6}{11}$, $\frac{2}{7}$

4. $\frac{1}{5}$

5. $\frac{1}{36}$

6. $\frac{1}{4}$

7. $\frac{1}{16}$

8. $\frac{25}{64}$

9. $\frac{144}{625}$

10. $\frac{1}{25}$

D2

1. (a) 6.3, 6.5, 6   (b) 132.1, 130   (c) 0.0714, 0.1

2. £22,400. £19,500

3. 44 min. 42 min.

4. 70.3°. 67°

D3

5. 17.3

6. 100.6 g

7. 48.9 min.

8. 35.8 m

9. 8, 25, 36, 40. 17.4, 11.5, 25, 13.5

10. 12, 47, 85, 100. 101 g, 94 g, 107 g, 13 g

11. 25, 53, 65, 74, 80. 48 m, 44 m, 53 m, 9 m

12. 8, 27, 44, 55, 60. 36 m, 32 m, 40 m, 8 m

Index